the **illustrated**
Atlas of the Human Body

BEVERLY MCMILLAN

Illustrations
ARGOSY PUBLISHING

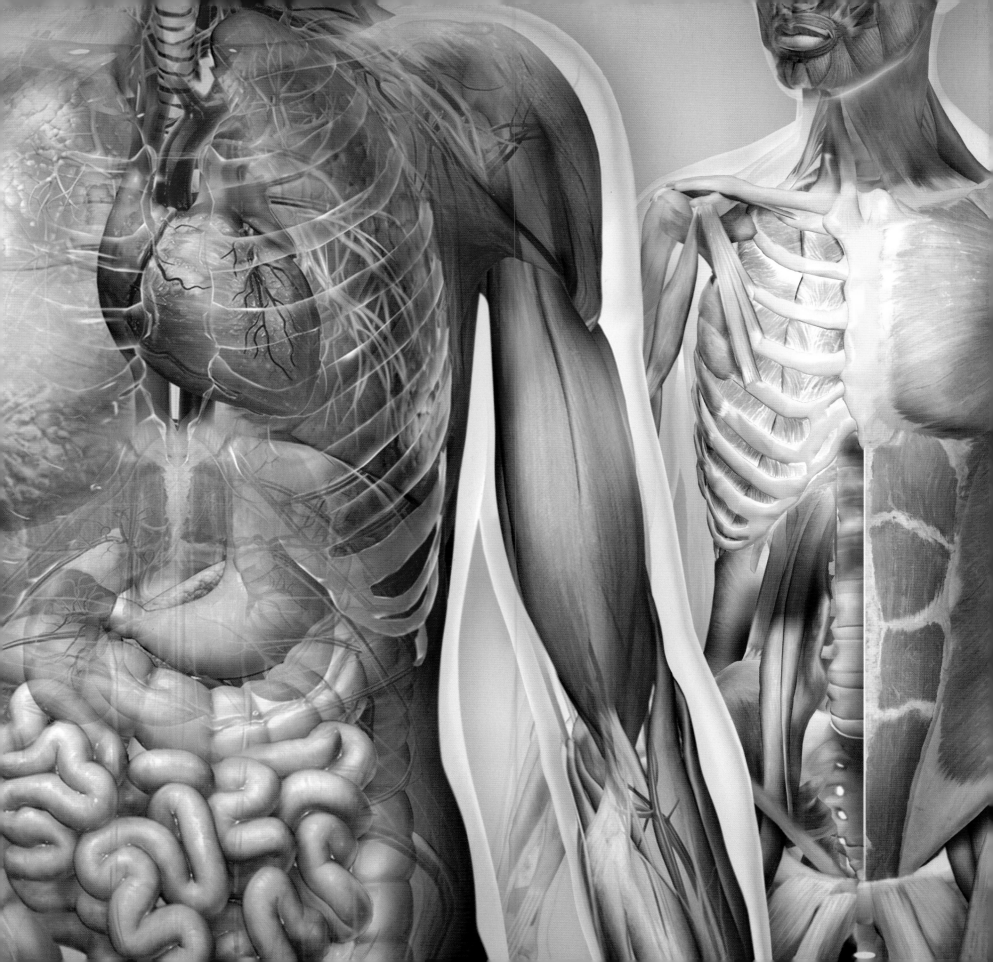

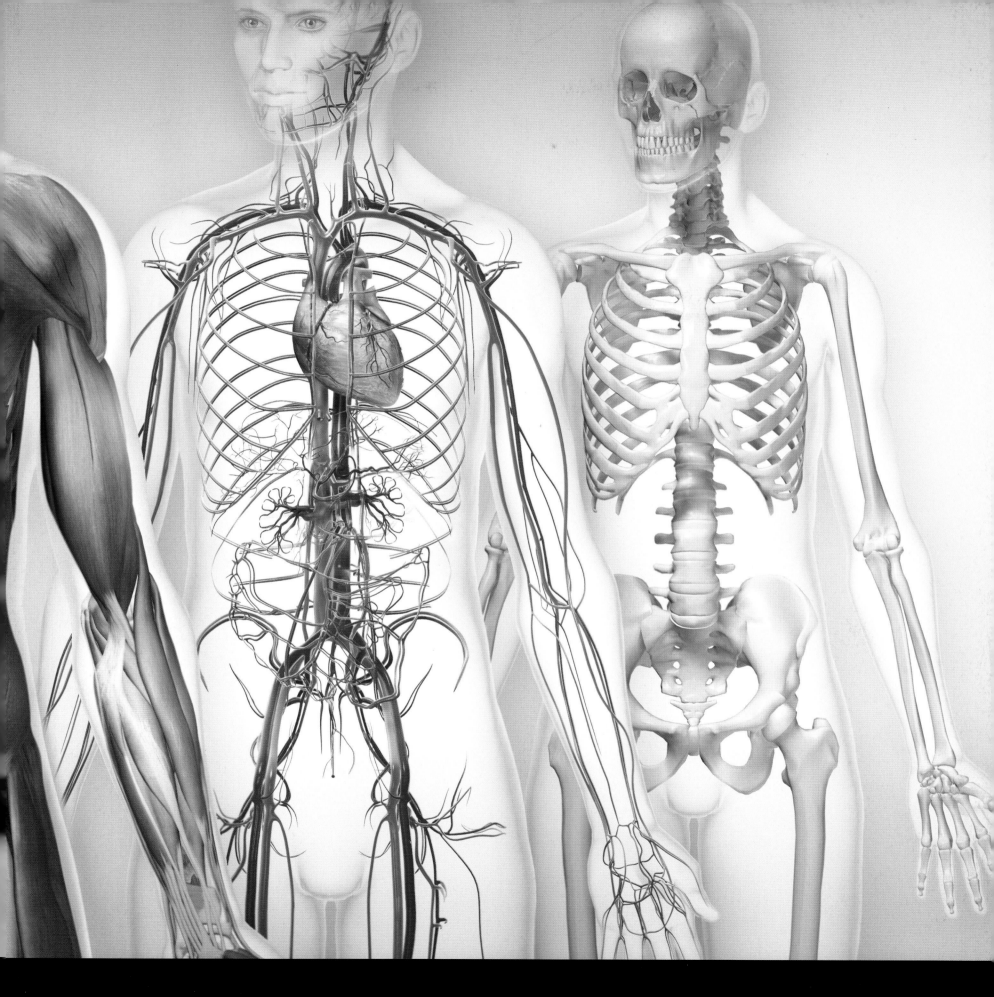

the illustrated
ATLAS OF THE HUMAN BODY

Conceived and produced by Weldon Owen Pty Ltd
59–61 Victoria Street, McMahons Point
Sydney NSW 2060, Australia
Copyright © 2008 Weldon Owen Pty Ltd
Reprinted in 2012

WELDON OWEN PTY LTD
Managing Director Kay Scarlett
Publisher Corinne Roberts
Creative Director Sue Burk
Senior Vice President, International Sales Stuart Laurence
Sales Manager, USA Ellen Towell
Administration Manager, International Sales Kristine Ravn
Production Director Todd Rechner
Production and Prepress Controller Mike Crowton
Production Controller Lisa Conway
Production Coordinator Nathan Grice

Managing Editor Jennifer Taylor
Art Manager Trucie Henderson
Consultant Dr. Robin Arnold
Jacket Design John Bull, The Book Design Company
Picture Research Joanna Collard

ARGOSY PUBLISHING
Director, Content Development Maite Suarez-Rivas
Development Editors Patty Mahtani, Lisa Benjamin
Project Managers Roy Small, Yael Rubinstein
Manager, Desktop Publishing Andrea Nix
Senior Desktop Publishers Misty Horten, Dunja Hein
Director, Medical Art Bert Oppenheim
Senior Medical Illustrators Joe Gorman, Chris Scalici
Medical Illustrators Kevin Brennan, Maya Chaphalkar, Anne Matuskowitz
Manager, Editorial Services Stacey Kim
Copy Editors Artemis Hionides, Martha Holmes, Grace Jeromski, Jack Meditz, Steve Thompson
Picture Research Brindey Weber

ISBN 978-1-74089-648-1

Color reproduction by Chroma Graphics (Overseas) Pte Ltd
Printed by 1010
Manufactured in China

A WELDON OWEN PRODUCTION

Golgi apparatus (right)
This colored electron micrograph shows a Golgi apparatus in orange.
The Golgi apparatus is one of several organelles, or "little organs,"
within a cell. It functions as a central delivery system for the cell—
modifying and transporting proteins and lipids to other locations in
the cell or "exporting" them outside the cell. The Golgi apparatus is
named after Camillo Golgi, an Italian physician and histologist who
first identified it in 1898.

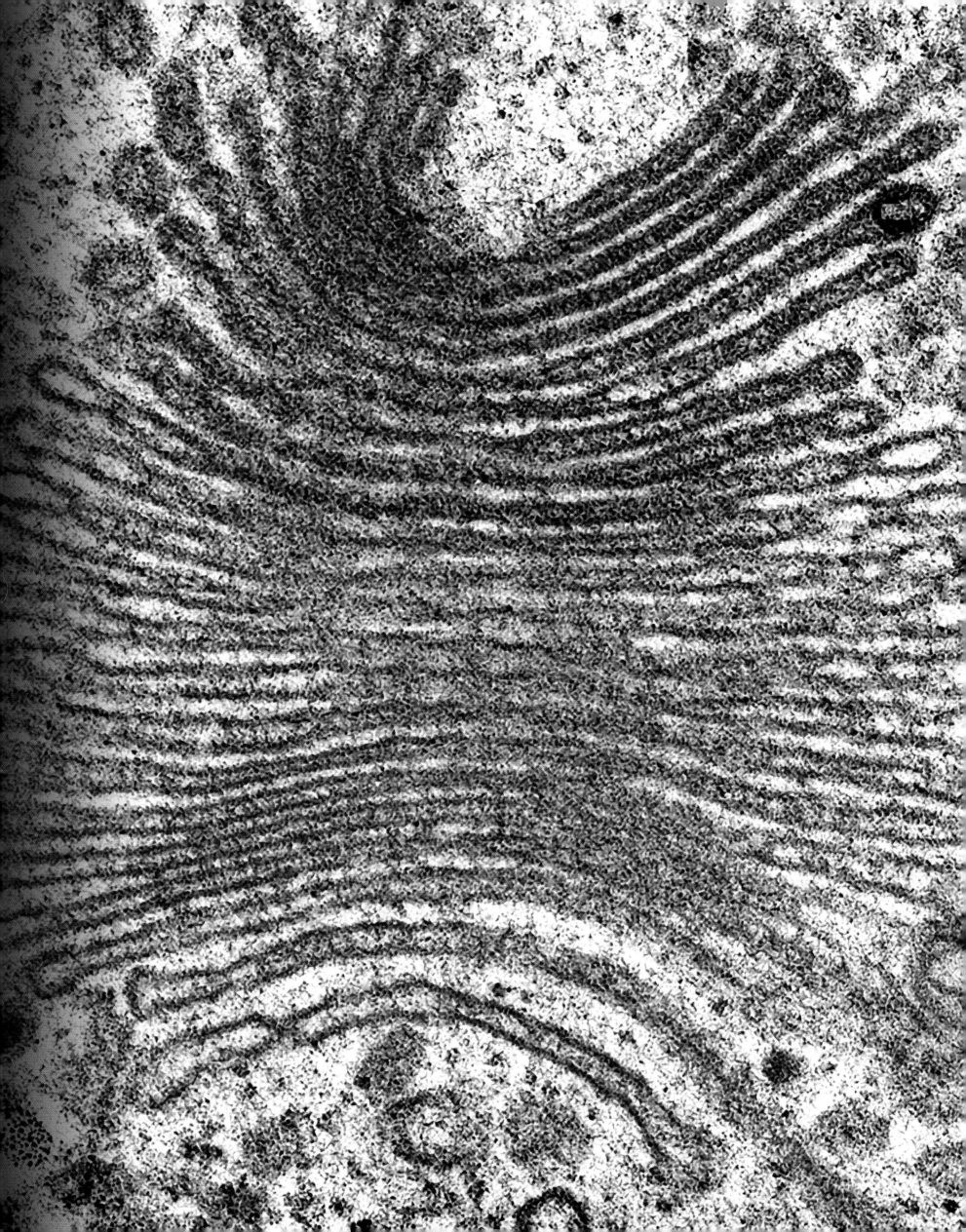

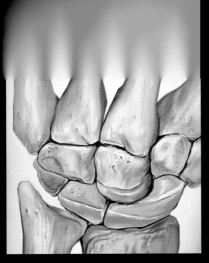
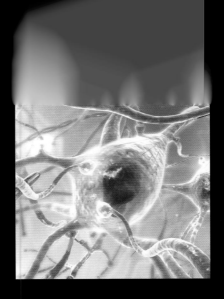
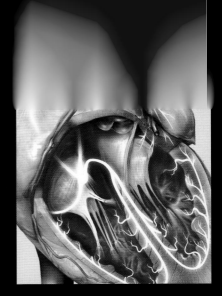

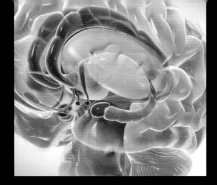
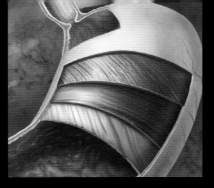
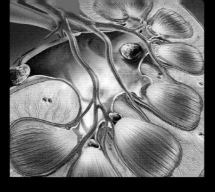
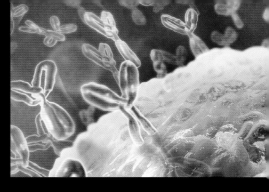

Nephrons (below left)
This colored electron micrograph shows the interior of a curving nephron tubule, where urine forms. A steady drip of urine flows into collecting ducts that carry it to the kidney's central cavity, the renal pelvis.

Neuron support (below)
This is a colored electron micrograph of an oligodendrocyte, a cell that supports axons of nerve cells. Its main function is to produce the insulating myelin sheath around axons.

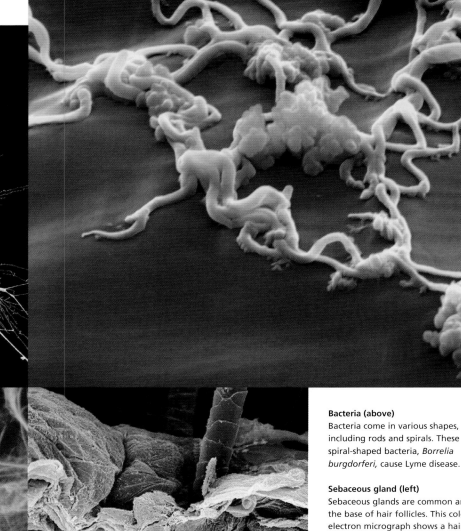

Bacteria (above)
Bacteria come in various shapes, including rods and spirals. These spiral-shaped bacteria, *Borrelia burgdorferi,* cause Lyme disease.

Sebaceous gland (left)
Sebaceous glands are common around the base of hair follicles. This colored electron micrograph shows a hair protruding above the skin's surface and a sebaceous gland (light blue, lower center) secretes oily sebum onto the hair and the skin.

Nervous tissue (far left)
This colored electron micrograph highlights star-shaped astrocytes, which form part of the nervous tissue in the brain. They belong to a class of cells called neuroglia that provide structural and nutritional support to neurons.

FOREWORD

Regardless of age or nationality, gender or ethnicity, Earth's billions of people all have something in common—all are human. Despite years of research and progress in medicine, many aspects of body functioning are still the subject of research. How does the brain generate thoughts? Why and how does the body age? How does the body defend itself against disease threats? Today, remarkable scientific and technological advances are helping to answer these and other questions about the body's inner workings. More than ever before, a profound new understanding is emerging of the intricate events underlying both the body's structure and the functioning of all its parts.

The Illustrated Atlas of the Human Body is an indispensable family reference for understanding how the body is built and how it operates. In a single volume, it assembles knowledge gleaned from research laboratories and medical sources around the world. In addition to multichapter sections on each of the body's eleven organ systems, this volume delves into major diseases and disorders, ever-expanding options for diagnosis and treatment and timely topics, such as stem cell research, eating disorders, tissue engineering and organ transplantation.

The book begins with a look at powerful imaging technologies that allow physicians and researchers to see and work inside the living body. The next section presents the fundamentals of body structure and functioning, including chapters on cells and tissues, DNA and basic genetics and a survey of infectious disease threats. Next are informative sections devoted to each of the body's major organ systems, subdivided into chapters that describe each system's key components and related health issues. Throughout, clear explanations describe the ebb and flow of physiological processes, from breathing, digestion and the heart's rhythmic pumping to the moment-to-moment coordination of thousands of biological events by the nervous and endocrine systems. Other sections explore the life-sustaining contributions of human skin, muscles and bones, the urinary system, immune system and the reproductive organs that produce each new generation. This wealth of information is enhanced by more than 700 striking photographs and beautifully rendered illustrations of body systems and their components.

Conceived and developed by an international team of subject experts, science educators and biological illustrators, *The Illustrated Atlas of the Human Body* takes readers on an enlightening and visually stunning tour of the natural wonder that is the human body.

HOW TO USE THIS ATLAS

The atlas is organized into two major sections. The first, Fundamentals, includes an introductory survey of the most basic components of human life and a presentation of the diseases and cell mutations that compromise them. The second and larger section, Body Systems, presents the anatomy and physiology of the systems that work together to sustain life. A reference section completes the atlas. It includes a visual timeline of medical history, a glossary of anatomical and physiological terms and a comprehensive index.

Body system overview
Each subsection begins with an overview of the body system that is being profiled. These opening pages include illustrations that reveal the position and structure of the organs that form each system and explanations of how the parts work together.

Illustration detail
"Zoomed in" illustrations provide necessary detail on intricate areas of anatomy.

Placement figure
"Glass" body images show the relative position of systems or organs within the body, providing greater understanding of how everything fits together.

Label with description
Informative labels include additional factual information and provide a deeper understanding of illustrations and photographs.

Introduction
This text gives a clear, concise overview of the most salient facts about the featured anatomical or physiological content.

Data chart
Charts concisely explain physiology and function.

Medical image
Images taken by technology ranging from microscope to positron emission tomography (PET) provide views of what cannot be seen with the naked eye.

Information box
Important information on medical issues around the world is discussed in greater detail within these informative text boxes.

Locator icon
These icons visually position each system within the body.

Photograph
Current photographs provide behind-the-scenes looks at medical events and give a realistic picture of diseases and issues around the world.

Fundamentals

This section provides an overview of the structure of the human body. From the breathtaking complexity housed within a single cell to the organs that form the body's 12 main systems, this section reveals how the body is put together. Threats from infectious agents and cell mutation are also profiled.

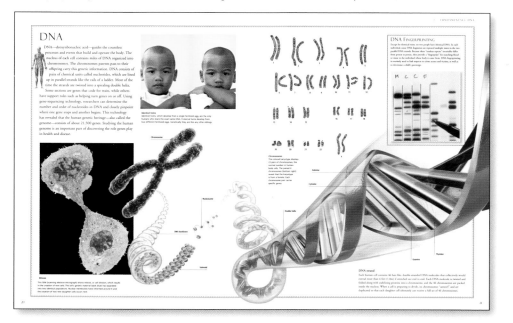

Organs

Following the system overview, each body system is presented component by component, allowing for great depth in both the written and visual treatments. Explanations are provided of how the healthy organ functions and its role within its system and the body as a whole. Descriptions are clear and accessible while providing a wealth of technical information.

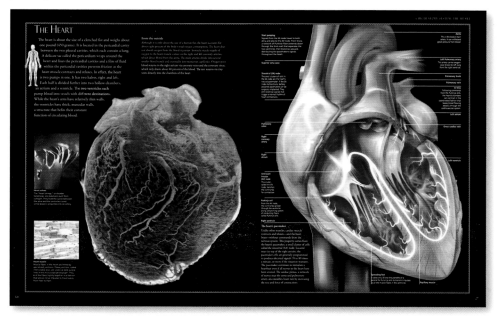

Disease

Each subsection concludes with a presentation of threats to the healthy function of the system being presented. From the common cold to rare genetic disorders, these pages explain how and why the body comes under attack and what can be done to prevent it. Information about the most up-to-date diagnosis and treatment techniques is also included.

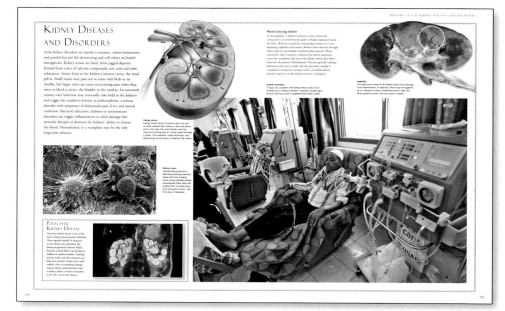

VISUAL AIDS

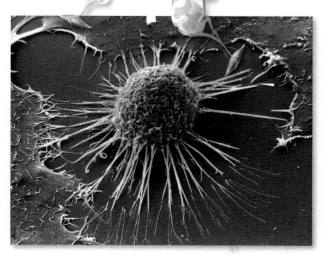

Illustrations

Beautiful and technically accurate illustrations are the focus of most of the pages in this atlas. Cutaways, segments and zoomed-in illustrations allow even the most remote areas of the body to be presented in detail and with clarity.

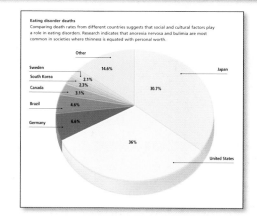

Photographs

Photographs range from the microscopic to the larger-than-life and represent subjects and disease threats from around the world. Selected for their accuracy and beauty, photographs give a realistic view of the body's structure and ailments.

INFECTIOUS DISEASES		
PATHOGENS	MODE OF ATTACK	EXAMPLES
Bacteria	Use poisonous toxins to change cells or launch dangerous immune responses	Lyme disease, gonorrhea, botulism, syphilis, septic shock, tooth decay
Fungi	Use enzymes to break down, then consume living and dead material	Yeast infections, athlete's foot, histoplasmosis, thrush
Parasites	Use host cells and tissues as a source of nourishment; can launch dangerous immune responses	Giardiasis, liver flukes, malaria, other worms
Viruses	Use living cells to replicate, then attack other cells; can cause cells to become cancerous	SARS, influenza, pneumonia, encephalitis, meningitis

Eating disorder deaths
Comparing death rates from different countries suggests that social and cultural factors play a role in eating disorders. Research indicates that anorexia nervosa and bulimia are most common in societies where thinness is equated with personal worth.

Other 14.6%
Japan 30.7%
Sweden 2.1%
South Korea 2.3%
Canada 3.1%
Brazil 4.6%
Germany 6.6%
United States 36%

Charts, tables and graphs

Complex information about the body, disease and public health is succinctly presented in charts, tables and graphs. Graphic treatments unlock intricate data, outline the steps in physiological processes and clarify issues that can be difficult to explain in words.

IMAGING THE BODY

Imaging technologies are revolutionizing the diagnosis and treatment of disease and deepening understanding of the functioning of the body. X-rays provide a general view of dense structures, such as bones and tumors. In nuclear medicine, radioactive materials called radioisotopes are used to track the movement or destination of substances in the body, while ultrasonography utilizes sound waves to generate low-resolution images of tissues and organs. Many sophisticated technologies combine images from X-rays, radioisotopes or magnetic interactions with computer analysis and color enhancement. This includes computed tomography (CT), positron emission tomography (PET) and magnetic resonance imaging (MRI). Each provides a particular type of image, such as the high-contrast views of soft tissues provided by MRI. In endoscopy, a flexible tube containing a fiber optic device is inserted through a body opening or a small incision, allowing physicians to see and work directly inside the body.

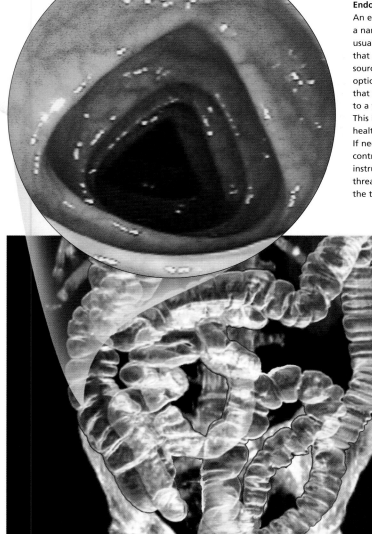

Endoscopy
An endoscope is a narrow, hollow, usually flexible tube that contains a light source and a fiber-optic viewing device that may be connected to a video monitor. This image shows a healthy human colon. If need be, remotely controlled surgical instruments can be threaded through the tube.

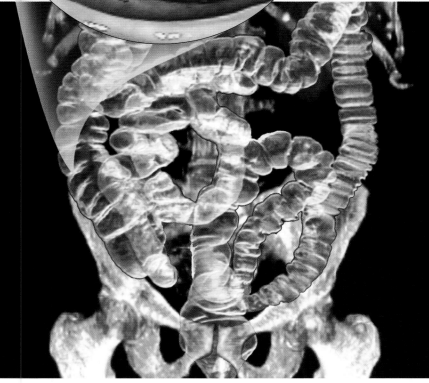

3-D computed tomography (CT) scan
With 3-D CT scanning (formerly CAT), X-rays are beamed into the body from a device that rotates around the patient. The computer-generated images give extremely clear, three-dimensional views of the area of interest—here, the intestines. The subject's ribs and pelvis appear blue-green.

3-D ultrasonography
In ultrasound, the echoes of pulsed sound waves generate images. Obstetricians routinely use this relatively simple, noninvasive procedure to periodically monitor the growth and position of a fetus before birth. In 3-D scanning, a computer manipulates the sound wave data to provide more detailed images, such as this image of a second-trimester fetus.

Scanning electron microscopy (SEM)
A scanning electron microscope sweeps an electron beam across the surface of a specimen that has in some cases been thinly coated with gold or some other metallic material. The electrons are converted via computer into a three-dimensional image. This SEM reveals the layered structure of a small blood vessel.

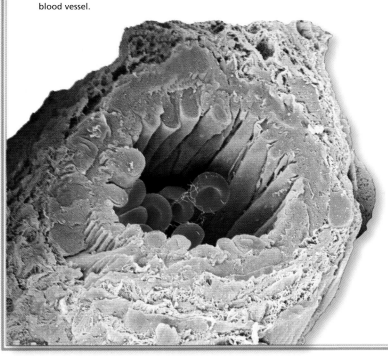

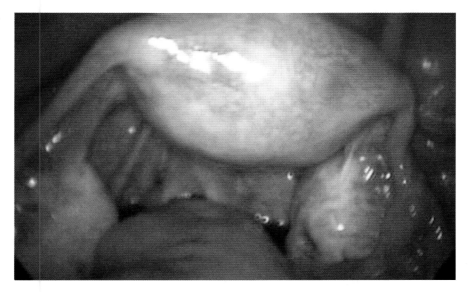

Endoscopic diagnosis and treatment

Various types of endoscopy are mainstays of minimally invasive diagnostic and surgical procedures. Laparoscopy employs a tube inserted through a small incision in the abdomen and is commonly used in operations involving organs such as the gallbladder, stomach and uterus. The laparoscopic examination seen above of a woman's uterus and ovaries reveals healthy organs. In arthroscopy, the tube is inserted into joints, such as the shoulder and knee. Other procedures take advantage of natural openings, such as the mouth, nose and anus.

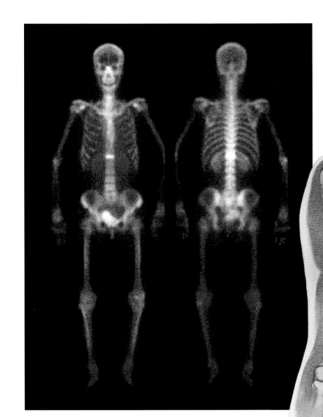

Nuclear scan
In nuclear medicine, a mildly radioactive substance is used to generate images. A radioisotope is administered, then a detection device tracks the path or destination of the isotope. This nuclear bone scan reveals a compression fracture of a patient's vertebra. The injury shows up as a glowing spot in the spinal column.

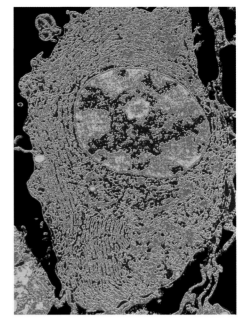

Transmission electron microscopy (TEM)
In TEM, electrons beamed through a specimen produce a detailed image of its internal parts. This colored micrograph shows the large, oval nucleus, internal membrane system and other components of a healthy human cell. Red particles are ribosomes, structures that assemble proteins manufactured in a cell.

Magnetic resonance imaging (MRI)
MRI uses a combination of magnetism and radio waves to map the presence of chemical elements in soft tissues. MRI produces detailed, high-contrast images of organs and their parts. Functional MRI (fMRI) provides real-time images of oxygen use in tissues, an indicator of cell activity. This colored image was assembled from several scans.

Positron emission tomography (PET)
PET tracks the uptake by cells of radioactively labeled substances. Colors show which areas of a tissue or organ are more or less metabolically active. PET is widely used to pinpoint areas of the brain that are active when subjects are reading, speaking or performing other cognitive tasks. This image shows reduced brain activity in an Alzheimer's patient.

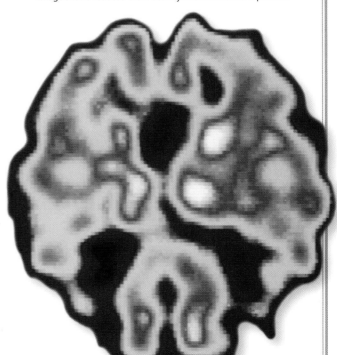

Colored X-ray
X-rays are shortwave electromagnetic waves that are absorbed well by dense masses. As a result, structures such as bones or tumors show up as clearly outlined light areas. Fat and hollow organs appear dark and fuzzy. This image shows part of a woman's skeleton and those of two full-term fetuses, but the mother's uterus is shadowy.

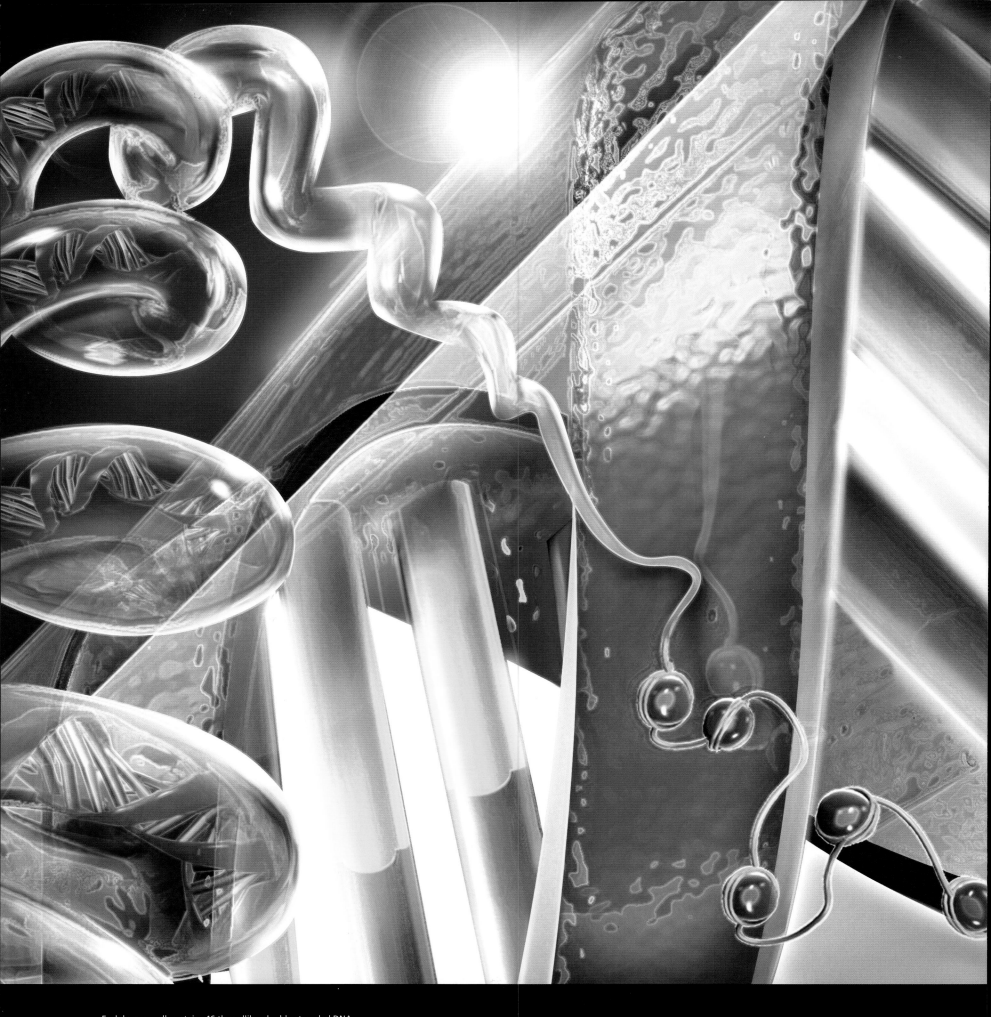

Each human cell contains 46 threadlike, double-stranded DNA molecules that collectively would extend more than 6 feet (1.8m) if stretched out end to end. Each DNA molecule is twisted and folded along with stabilizing proteins into a chromosome, and

FUNDAMENTALS

FUNDAMENTALS

In the human body, a remarkable assortment of structures form a complex living unit—a whole that is far more than the sum of its parts. This feat of biological engineering depends on the organization of body parts into integrated functional units. To begin with, the multitude of tasks required for normal operations are divided among eleven organ systems. Within each one, two or more organs cooperate to perform a given role, such as extracting oxygen from air or nutrients from food. Each organ in turn is a blend of a number of tissues—nervous tissue that conveys and processes information; sturdy, contractile muscle tissue; connective tissue such as bone, cartilage, collagen and elastin; and epithelial tissue that forms the skin and internal linings. The building blocks of tissues, an estimated 60 trillion cells, are the body's smallest living units. Moment to moment, all these parts interact to keep the whole body alive and thriving.

Organ systems

As with other animals, each human organ system solves one or more basic problems of survival. For example, the skeleton provides firm support for soft flesh and manufactures blood cells, and as the circulatory system moves blood, it transports a wide array of substances, including oxygen, nutrients from food and wastes generated by metabolically active cells. Organ systems are also interdependent. None can function properly without the contributions of others.

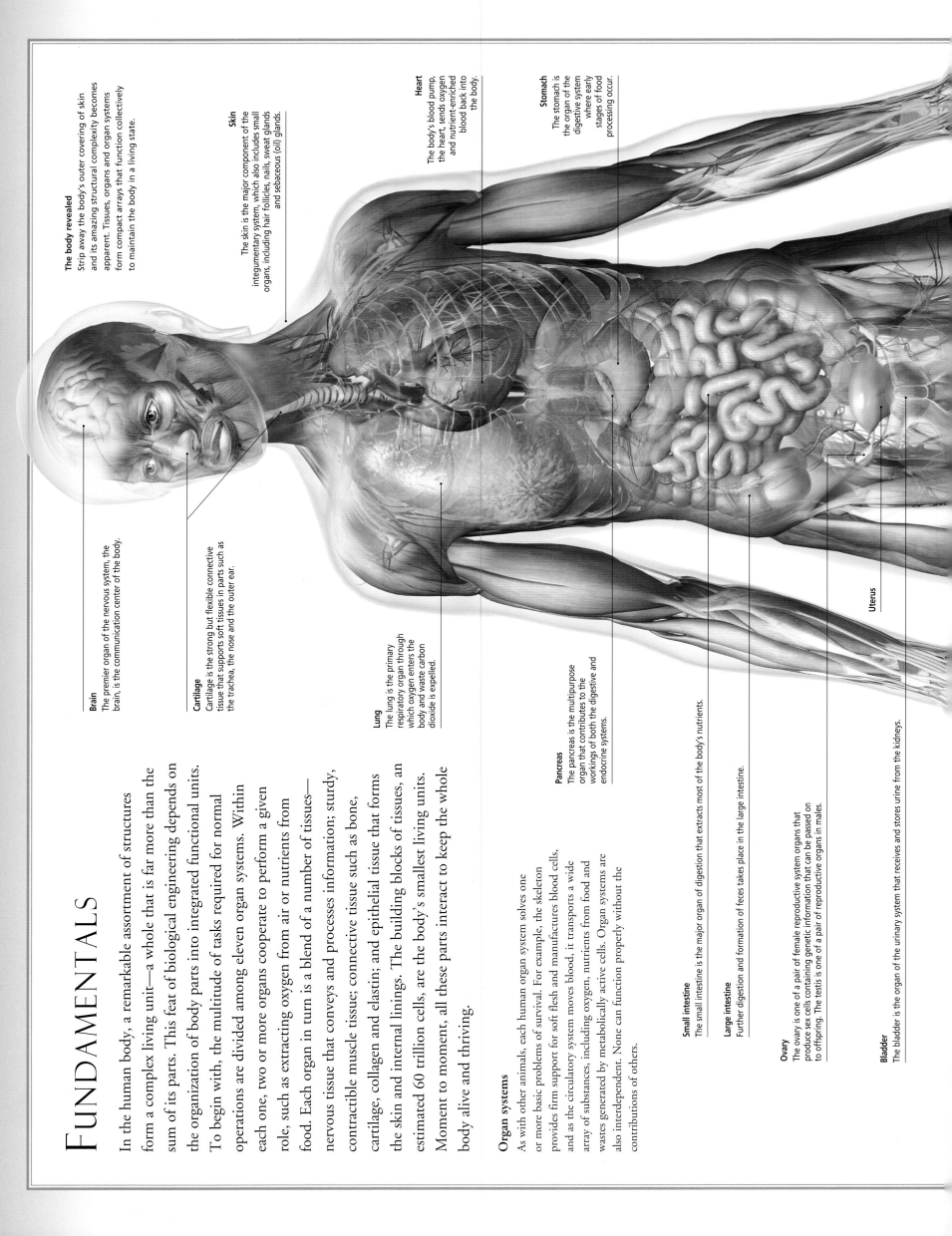

The body revealed
Strip away the body's outer covering of skin and its amazing structural complexity becomes apparent. Tissues, organs and organ systems form compact arrays that function collectively to maintain the body in a living state.

Skin
The skin is the major component of the integumentary system, which also includes small organs, including hair follicles, nails, sweat glands and sebaceous (oil) glands.

Heart
The body's blood pump, the heart, sends oxygen and nutrient-enriched blood back into the body.

Stomach
The stomach is the organ of the digestive system where early stages of food processing occur.

Brain
The premier organ of the nervous system, the brain, is the communication center of the body.

Cartilage
Cartilage is the strong but flexible connective tissue that supports soft tissues in parts such as the trachea, the nose and the outer ear.

Lung
The lung is the primary respiratory organ through which oxygen enters the body and waste carbon dioxide is expelled.

Pancreas
The pancreas is the multipurpose organ that contributes to the workings of both the digestive and endocrine systems.

Small intestine
The small intestine is the major organ of digestion that extracts most of the body's nutrients.

Large intestine
Further digestion and formation of feces takes place in the large intestine.

Ovary
The ovary is one of a pair of female reproductive system organs that produce sex cells containing genetic information that can be passed on to offspring. The testis is one of a pair of reproductive organs in males.

Uterus

Bladder
The bladder is the organ of the urinary system that receives and stores urine from the kidneys.

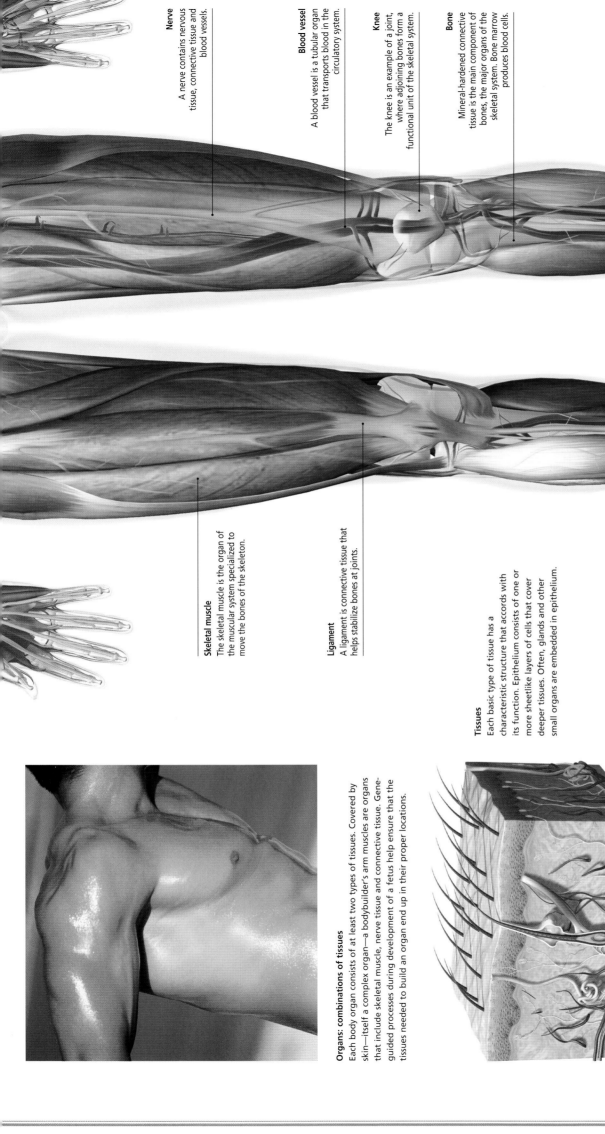

Nerve
A nerve contains nervous tissue, connective tissue and blood vessels.

Blood vessel
A blood vessel is a tubular organ that transports blood in the circulatory system.

Knee
The knee is an example of a joint, where adjoining bones form a functional unit of the skeletal system.

Bone
Mineral-hardened connective tissue is the main component of bones, the major organs of the skeletal system. Bone marrow produces blood cells.

Skeletal muscle
The skeletal muscle is the organ of the muscular system specialized to move the bones of the skeleton.

Ligament
A ligament is connective tissue that helps stabilize bones at joints.

Tissues
Each basic type of tissue has a characteristic structure that accords with its function. Epithelium consists of one or more sheetlike layers of cells that cover deeper tissues. Often, glands and other small organs are embedded in epithelium.

Cells
There are at least 200 different types of cells in the human body. Most are specialized to perform a particular function such as connecting body parts, fighting disease, storing nutrients or controlling body functions. For example, muscle cells are specialized to move organs including the heart, stomach and bones.

Organs: combinations of tissues
Each body organ consists of at least two types of tissues. Covered by skin—itself a complex organ—a bodybuilder's arm muscles are organs that include skeletal muscle, nerve tissue and connective tissue. Gene-guided processes during development of a fetus help ensure that the tissues needed to build an organ end up in their proper locations.

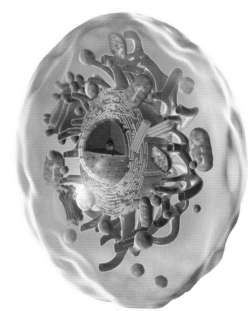

CELLS

Cells are the smallest units of life, most so tiny that they are only visible under a microscope. The cell's plasma membrane encloses its internal parts and permits ceaseless movement of substances into and out of the cell. In all organisms except bacteria, a special compartment called the nucleus houses the genetic material DNA. The nucleus is one of many organelles, or "little organs," within the cell. Guided by instructions in DNA, these components perform the myriad specialized operations that help keep cells alive and allow each one to play its particular biological role—as a muscle cell, a nerve cell in the brain and so forth. Gelatinous cytoplasm surrounds the organelles. Within it, a framework of fibers and filaments called the cytoskeleton provides structural support and helps physically organize and move internal cell parts.

The plasma membrane

Far from being a solid barrier, the plasma membrane that surrounds each cell is actually an oily, double-layered mosaic of proteins and lipids, molecules that are the chemical building blocks of fats and oils. This composite structure is crucial to the membrane's function. The lipids, including cholesterol, can bend and move, making the plasma membrane flexible. Different proteins embedded in the membrane identify chemicals, bind substances such as hormones and help move substances into and out of the cell.

SPECIALIZED CELLS

Most body cells mature into a specialized role—as a blood cell, neuron or some other cell type. By contrast, stem cells, especially from embryos, retain the potential to give rise to a variety of more specialized types. This property makes embryonic stem cells appealing in terms of potential use in treating cell-destroying disorders such as Parkinson's and Alzheimer's disease. Controversy surrounding the use of embryonic cells has spurred a search for ways to obtain them from other sources.

Ribosomes
Assemble proteins

Plasma membrane
Encloses the cell and helps substances move in and out

Nucleus
Contains a cell's DNA, keeping it separate from organelles

Cytoplasm
Refers to the jellylike fluid, organelles and everything else between the plasma membrane and the nucleus

Cytoskeleton
Provides the structural framework and helps move cell parts

Golgi apparatus
Processes and releases proteins and lipids for use in the cell or packaged for export

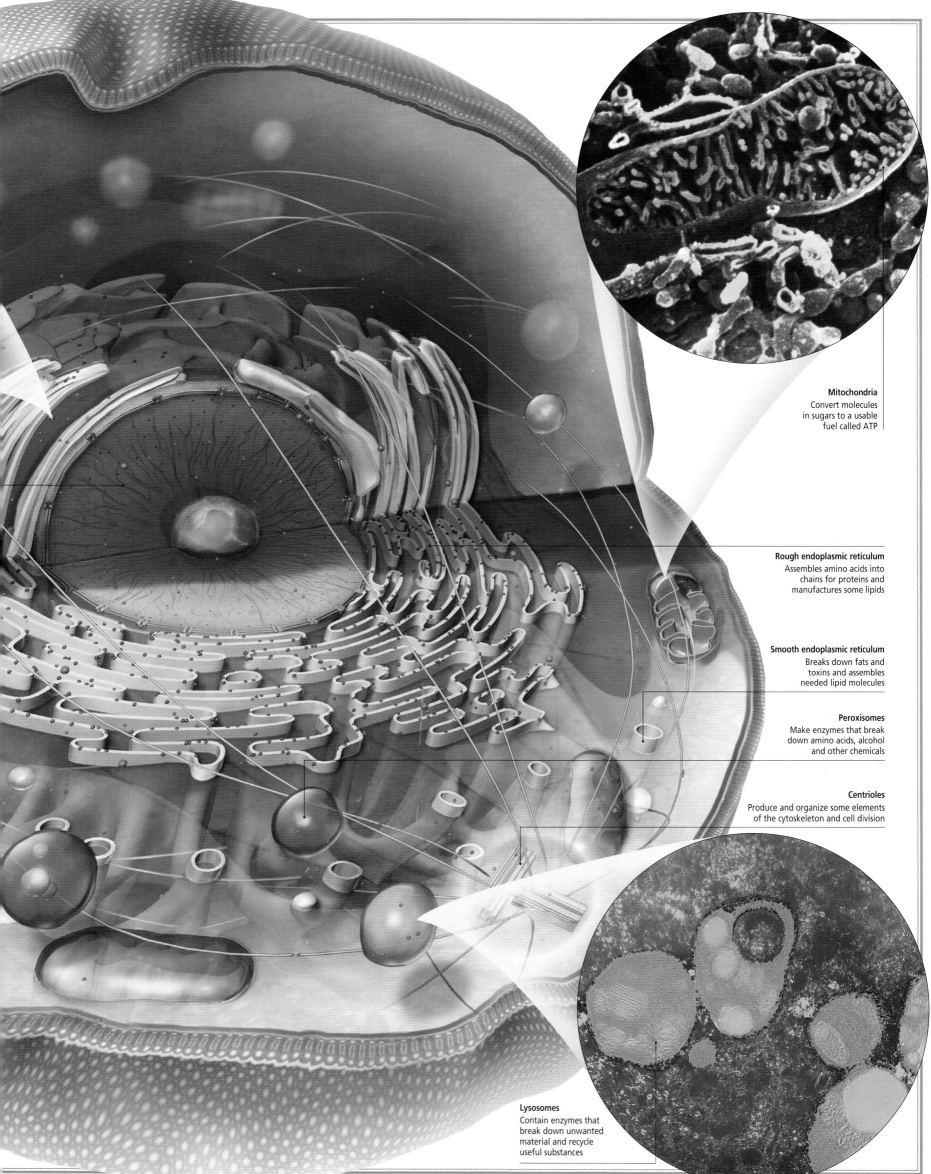

Mitochondria
Convert molecules
in sugars to a usable
fuel called ATP

Rough endoplasmic reticulum
Assembles amino acids into
chains for proteins and
manufactures some lipids

Smooth endoplasmic reticulum
Breaks down fats and
toxins and assembles
needed lipid molecules

Peroxisomes
Make enzymes that break
down amino acids, alcohol
and other chemicals

Centrioles
Produce and organize some elements
of the cytoskeleton and cell division

Lysosomes
Contain enzymes that
break down unwanted
material and recycle
useful substances

DNA

DNA—deoxyribonucleic acid—guides the countless processes and events that build and operate the body. The nucleus of each cell contains miles of DNA organized into chromosomes. The chromosomes parents pass to their offspring carry this genetic information. DNA consists of pairs of chemical units called nucleotides, which are lined up in parallel strands like the rails of a ladder. Most of the time the strands are twisted into a spiraling double helix.

Some sections are genes that code for traits, while others have support roles such as helping turn genes on or off. Using gene-sequencing technology, researchers can determine the number and order of nucleotides in DNA and closely pinpoint where one gene stops and another begins. This technology has revealed that the human genetic heritage—also called the genome—consists of about 21,500 genes. Studying the human genome is an important part of discovering the role genes play in health and disease.

Identical twins
Identical twins, which develop from a single fertilized egg, are the only humans who share the exact same DNA. Fraternal twins develop from two different fertilized eggs. Genetically they are like any other siblings.

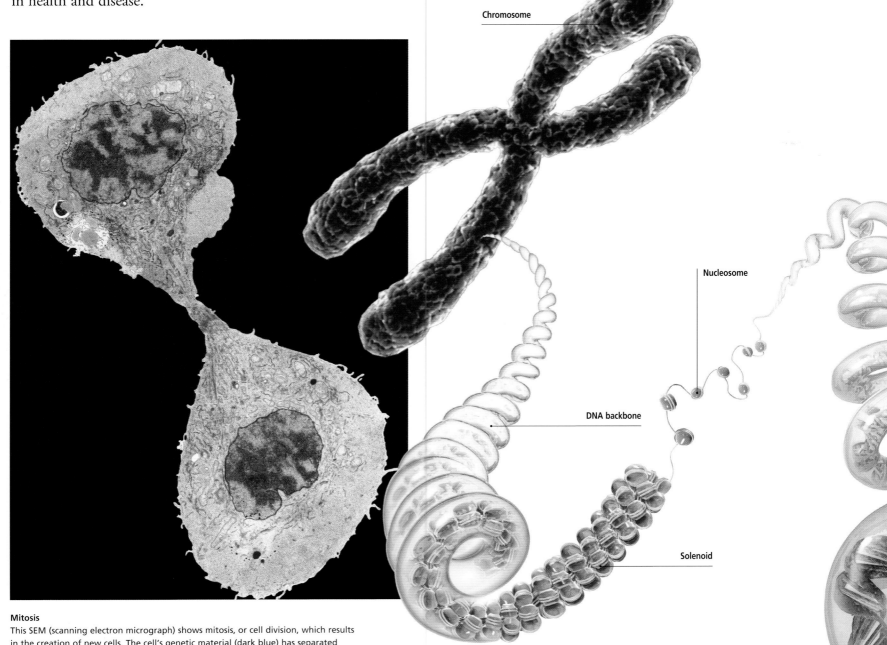

Chromosome

Nucleosome

DNA backbone

Solenoid

Mitosis
This SEM (scanning electron micrograph) shows mitosis, or cell division, which results in the creation of new cells. The cell's genetic material (dark blue) has separated into two identical populations. Nuclear membranes have reformed around it and the creation of two new daughter cells occurs next.

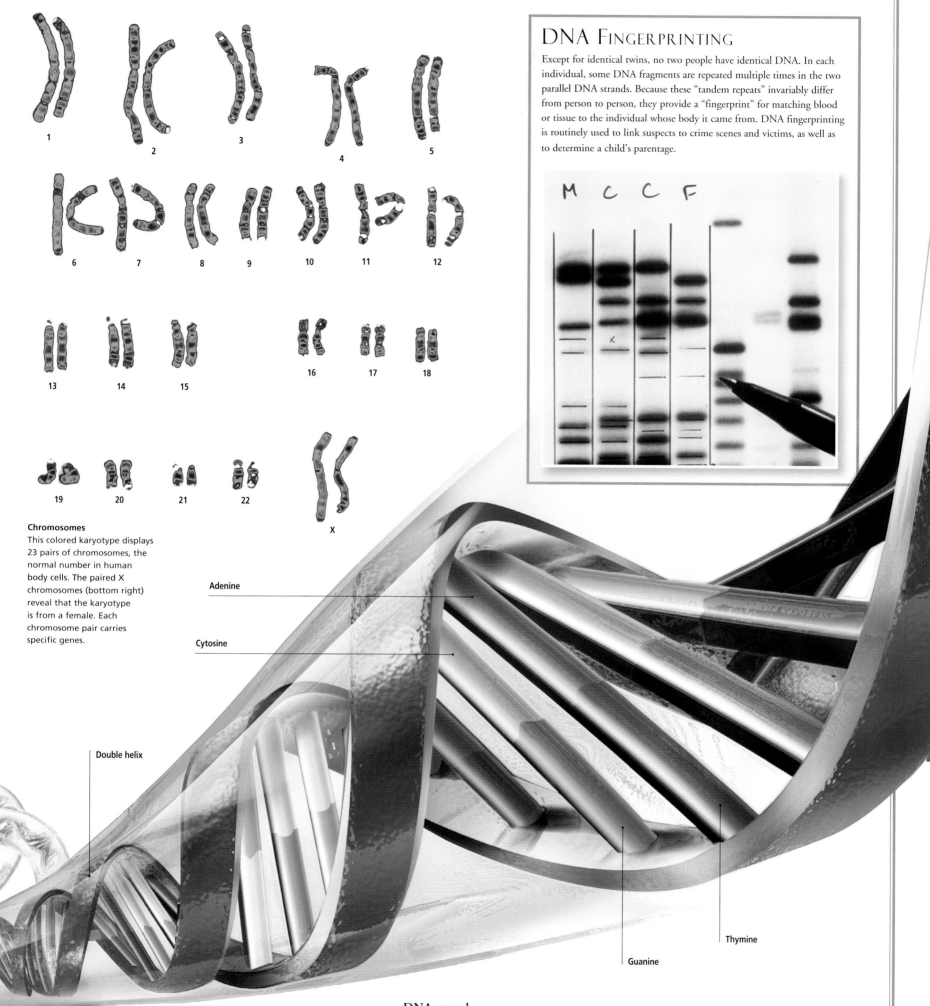

1 2 3 4 5

6 7 8 9 10 11 12

13 14 15 16 17 18

19 20 21 22

X

DNA Fingerprinting

Except for identical twins, no two people have identical DNA. In each individual, some DNA fragments are repeated multiple times in the two parallel DNA strands. Because these "tandem repeats" invariably differ from person to person, they provide a "fingerprint" for matching blood or tissue to the individual whose body it came from. DNA fingerprinting is routinely used to link suspects to crime scenes and victims, as well as to determine a child's parentage.

M C C F

Chromosomes
This colored karyotype displays 23 pairs of chromosomes, the normal number in human body cells. The paired X chromosomes (bottom right) reveal that the karyotype is from a female. Each chromosome pair carries specific genes.

Adenine

Cytosine

Double helix

Guanine

Thymine

DNA strand

Each human cell contains 46 hair-like, double-stranded DNA molecules that collectively would extend more than 6 feet (1.8m) if stretched out end to end. Each DNA molecule is twisted and folded along with stabilizing proteins into a chromosome, and the 46 chromosomes are packed inside the nucleus. When a cell is preparing to divide, its chromosomes "unravel" and are duplicated so that each daughter cell ultimately can receive a full set of 46 chromosomes.

TISSUES

The body contains four basic types of tissues, each one a group of similar cells that perform a particular function. Epithelial tissue is a major component of body coverings, most notably the skin and the linings of body cavities or tubes. The body also contains three types of muscle tissue: skeletal muscle, smooth muscle and cardiac muscle, all specialized to generate movement. Nervous tissue consists of nerve cells or neurons, involved in the body's communication, and cells that support their operations. By sheer volume, most of the body is connective tissue, a wide-ranging category that encompasses bone, cartilage, adipose (fat) tissue and even blood. As the name suggests, connective tissues physically bind or anchor body parts or provide metabolic support. Most connective tissues are a blend of proteins and a surrounding matrix, which can be solid as in bone, liquid as with blood plasma or somewhere in between.

Cartilage under the microscope

Cartilage (green) consists of collagen and sometimes elastin fibers in a rubbery matrix, resulting in a dense, pliable tissue that resists compression. Hyaline cartilage at the ends of bones reduces friction in movable joints, such as the hips, shoulders and fingers. It also forms parts of the ribs, trachea and nose. Elastic cartilage is found where flexibility is important, as in the external ear. Pressure-resistant fibrocartilage is especially rich in collagen. It provides padding in the knees and between the spinal vertebrae.

BODY FAT

The body stores fat in adipose tissue, which consists mostly of cells containing fat droplets that have been manufactured from carbohydrates and proteins not used for metabolism. Most adipose tissue occurs immediately below the skin, where it serves as a cushion and provides insulation. Some people store excess fat mainly in the hips, buttocks and thighs, while others store extra fat in the abdomen. Some studies correlate abdominal fat with increased risk of certain disorders, including heart disease.

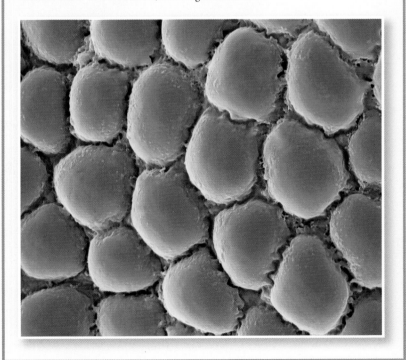

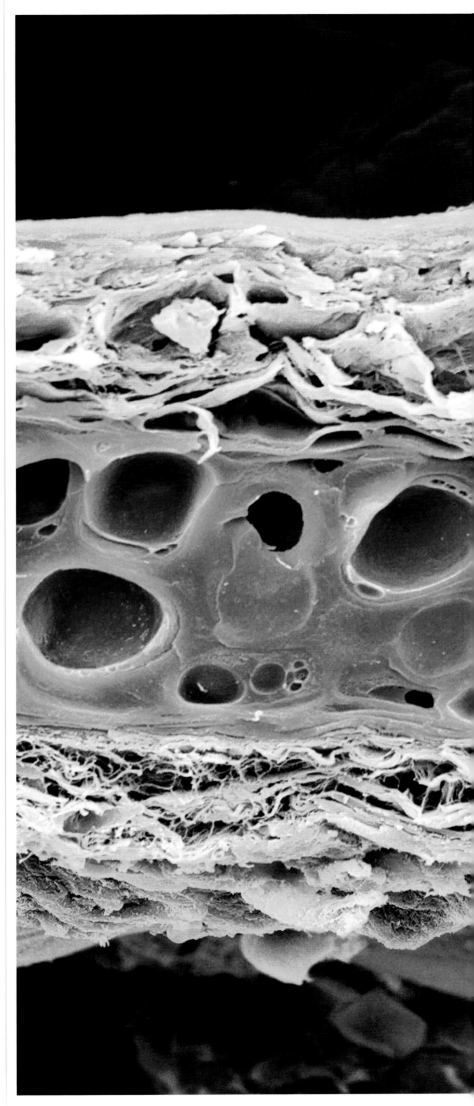

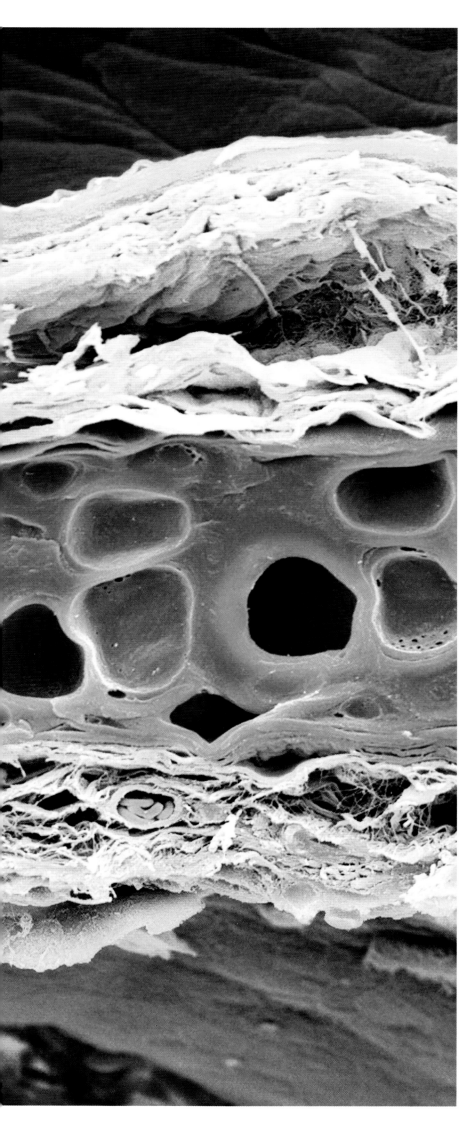

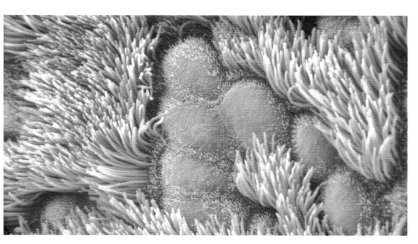

Epithelium

This image shows the ciliated epithelium that lines the upper bronchial passages. The tissue includes gland cells that secrete debris-trapping mucus and epithelial cells with hair-like cilia (pink) that move the mucus upward toward the throat to keep it moist and protected.

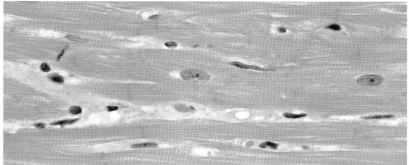

Muscle

Cardiac muscle is one of the three types of muscle tissue in the body. The individual muscle cells are long cylinders. Special junctions fuse the cells (vertical pink lines), giving them the appearance of continous tissue and enabling them to contract as a unit.

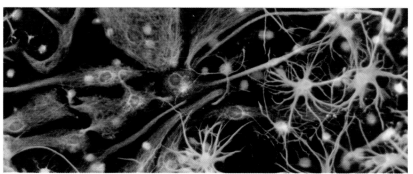

Nervous tissue

This image highlights star-shaped astrocytes, which form part of the nervous tissue in the brain. They belong to a class of cells called neuroglia that provide structural and nutritional support to neurons. Astrocytes are the most abundant type of neuroglial cell.

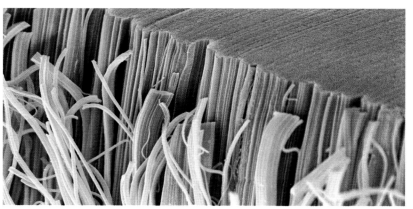

Connective tissue

Tendons, which attach muscles to bones, must be strong and flexible. Made up of connective tissue consisting of bundles of collagen fibers as shown here, tendons (pink) align parallel to one another to resist tearing. Tendons transfer the force of skeletal muscles to bone.

TISSUE REPAIR

Tissue damage, especially a cut or tear in the skin where infectious microbes can enter, presents a potentially serious challenge to health. Accordingly, when tissues are injured a series of mechanisms almost immediately begins repair operations. In a badly skinned knee, for example, an inflammation response mobilizes defensive blood cells and proteins to form a blood clot that stops bleeding and walls off healthy tissue from microbes. Next, the damaged tissue begins to regenerate as signaling chemicals called growth factors spur healthy cells to divide and produce replacements for dead or dying ones. New blood vessels gradually establish a blood supply to cells in the healing wound. Certain cells and tissues of internal organs also can regenerate. The most dramatic example occurs in the liver, which can fully regenerate from as little as a third of its original tissue.

Steps to healing

A wound that draws blood unleashes a flood of chemicals that attract infection-fighting cells and trigger the formation of a clot. As blood vessels infiltrate the area, fibroblasts migrate to the wound to generate collagen and a collagen-rich layer called granulation tissue develops. After a scab forms, growth factors stimulate the development of new tissue to fill the wound. Within a week or two, the scab sloughs off, revealing pale pink regenerated skin at the wound site. Collagen remaining from the granulation tissue may gradually form a visible scar.

HEALING, INTERRUPTED

Most wounds heal without incident, but some become chronic or problematic. Chronic wounds fail to close because some factor, such as an impaired blood supply or high blood sugar in a diabetic patient, interferes with the normal sequence of healing. Surgery involving the heart, abdominal organs or pelvic organs often results in adhesions—bands of scar tissue that bind normally separate body parts. A wound that is reinjured or infected may be slow to heal due to persistent inflammation.

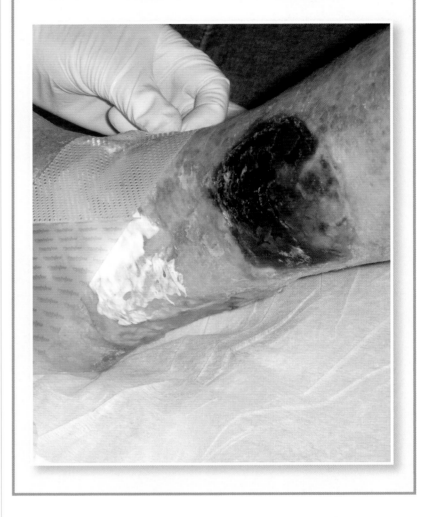

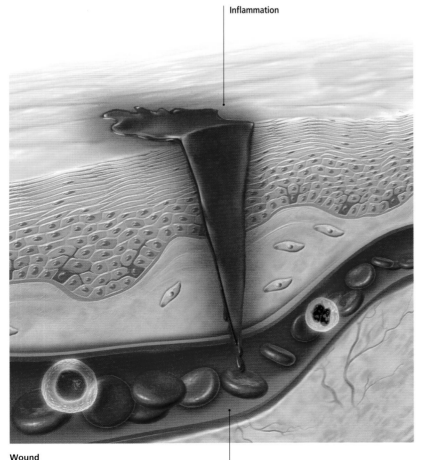

Inflammation

Wound

Blood vessel

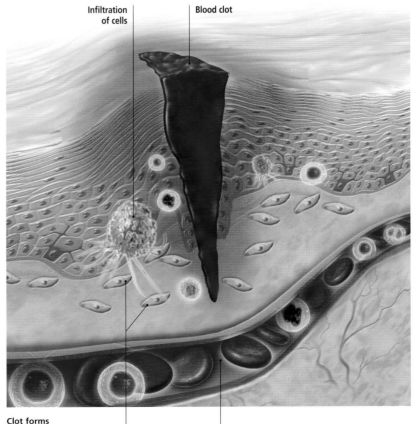

Infiltration of cells

Blood clot

Clot forms

Fibroblasts

Constricted blood vessel

Inflammation
During an inflammation, blood capillaries dilate and narrow spaces open in their walls. More blood flows to the site of the inflammation, so the tissue reddens. Defensive cells exit the vessels into the injured area, along with water that causes swelling.

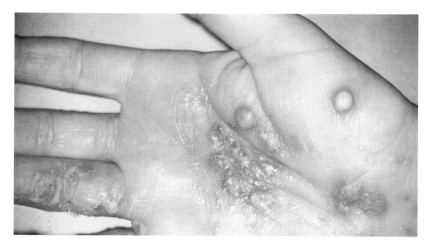

Granulation
Tissue regeneration includes a granulation stage in which cells multiply and slowly fill in the injured area. This photograph shows a case of dermatitis vegetans, in which a secondary infection has triggered excessive granulation.

Ritual scarring
Among the Mursi people of Ethiopia, decorative scarring of the skin, or scarification, marks a warrior who has slain an enemy. The scars are healed cuts incised into a fighter's shoulders in a spiral pattern.

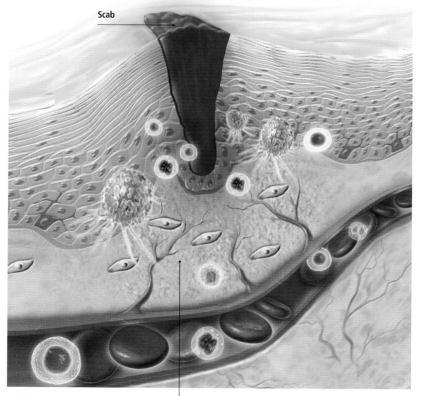

Scab

Scab forms

Granulation tissue

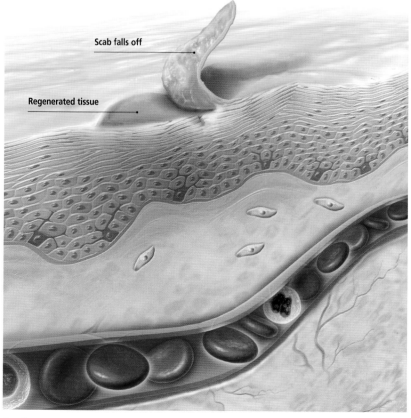

Scab falls off

Regenerated tissue

Scar forms

MEMBRANES AND GLANDS

Membranes play major roles in protecting or lining body surfaces and cavities, and most consist in part of epithelium—a tissue that also forms glands. Epithelial membranes combine epithelium with connective tissue to form a thin sheet. This category includes most body membranes. One type, the moist, pink mucous membranes, lines the tubes and channels of the digestive, urinary, respiratory and reproductive systems. Another type, serous membranes, occurs in paired sheets with two layers. Fluid in the space between them prevents friction when one or both sheets move. Serous membranes enclose organs that expand and contract, such as the heart and lungs, and also line chambers in which these organs are located. The skin, technically a cutaneous membrane, is a third type of epithelial membrane. Synovial membranes, consisting only of connective tissue, are a fourth group. They line movable parts, such as the shoulder and hip joints, and contain cells that release lubricating fluid.

MUCOUS MEMBRANES

Mucous membranes line the airways, the passages and organs of the digestive tract, reproductive passages, such as the vagina, and much of the urinary tract. All have a top layer of epithelium many containing cells specialized to make and secrete slippery, viscous mucus. A blend mainly of water and proteins called mucins, mucus lubricates surfaces and helps moisten chewed food. In the nose and bronchial passages it also traps dust, small pathogens, such as bacteria, and other foreign material that might otherwise enter the lungs.

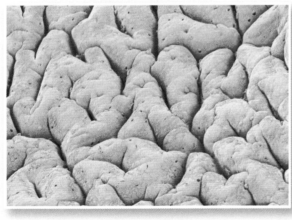

Synovial membranes
This close-up view is the synovial membrane of a human knee joint. The synovial fluid its cells produce flows into the joint, lubricating its movements and nourishing its cartilage components.

Serous pericardium
This image shows an electron micrograph of a section of serous pericardium, a sac that wraps around and lubricates the heart (blue). It consists of two layers: the parietal layer (top) and the epicardium layer (bottom). The pericardial cavity is in between the two.

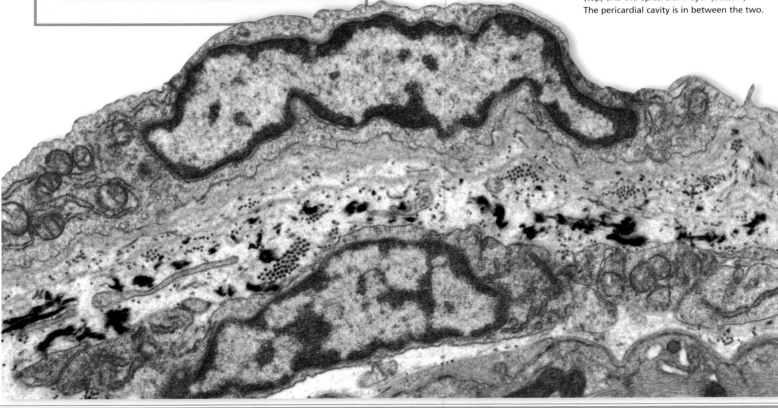

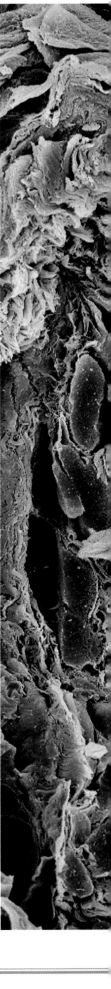

Glands

Glands are structures that secrete substances and they fall into two overall categories. Endocrine glands, such as the pituitary, release hormones into the bloodstream. By contrast, exocrine glands secrete substances onto the skin or the internal lining of an organ. Exocrine glands range from sweat and sebaceous glands in the skin and salivary glands in the mouth to glands that secrete mucus, digestive enzymes and earwax. Mammary glands in a female's breasts are modified sweat glands that instead lactate, or produce milk.

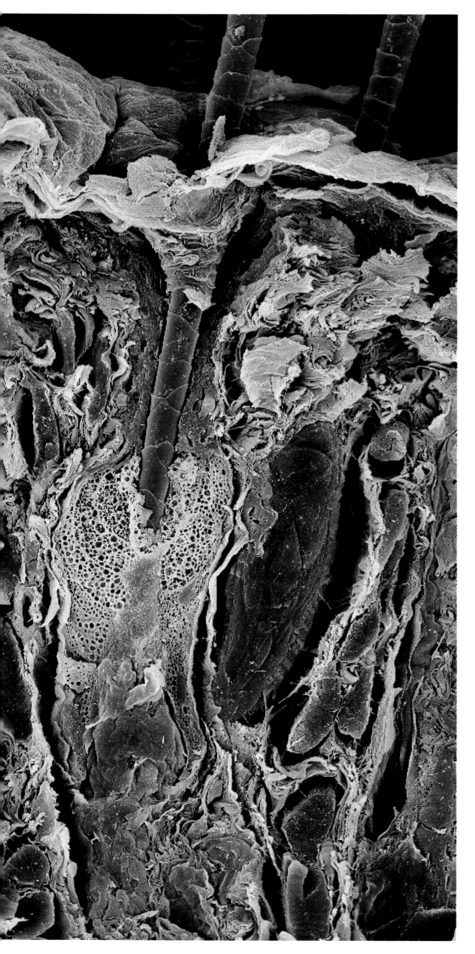

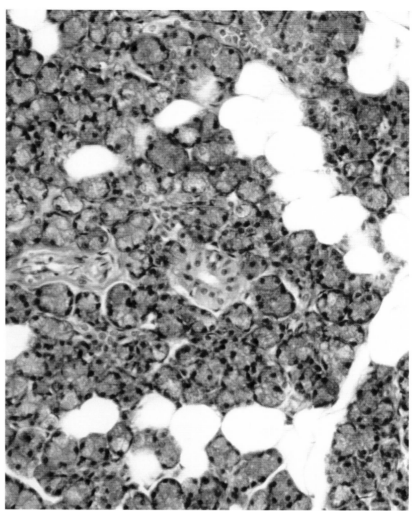

Salivary glands
Salivary glands, such as this paratoid gland near the ear, secrete saliva, which is a blend of water, mucus, enzymes and other substances. Like other exocrine glands, salivary glands release substances through ducts or tubes.

Sweat glands
The body's millions of sweat glands, also called sudoriferous glands, release transparent, acidic perspiration onto the skin or into hair follicles. Sweat contains a great deal of water, which helps dissipate excess body heat when it evaporates.

Sebaceous glands
Sebaceous glands are common around the base of hair follicles. This colored electron micrograph is of a section through a hair follicle in the dermis of the skin. A hair protrudes above the skin's surface and a sebaceous gland (light blue, lower center) secretes oily sebum onto the hair and the skin.

Organs and Body Cavities

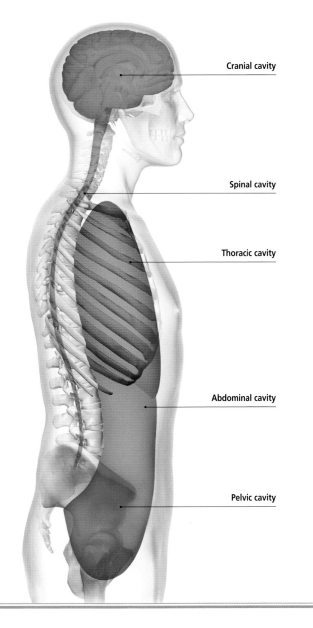

An organ is a combination of two or more types of tissue that jointly perform one or more body functions. Structures such as the brain, liver, stomach and lungs fit the familiar concept of organs, but whole muscles and bones are also organs because they include nerves, blood vessels and various types of connective tissue. Every organ is part of one or more of the body's eleven organ systems. Of the eleven, only the reproductive system does not contribute to the body's day-to-day survival; functional reproductive organs are needed solely to produce offspring. Organs are suspended inside or attached to the walls of the major body cavities. These cavities protect and organize the body's soft vital parts and prevent access to outside pathogens. Two cavities, the abdominal cavity and the pelvic cavity, form a single chamber with two distinct areas.

Small Body Cavities

Numerous small body cavities are formed by the arrangement of bony parts. In the skull alone are four pairs of sinus cavities, orbital cavities that enclose all but the front of the eyeballs, the oral cavity (mouth), and nasal and ear cavities. The brain and spinal cord contain cavities that are filled with cerebrospinal fluid, and synovial joints such as the knees, hips and shoulders have chambers filled with synovial fluid.

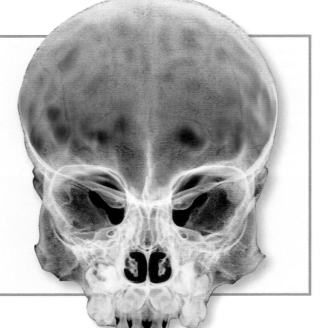

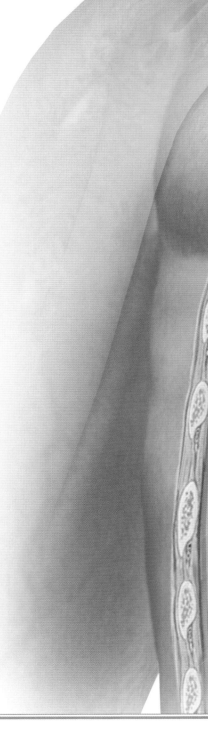

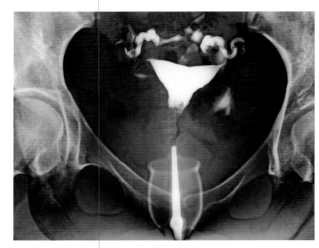

Pelvic cavity
A color-enhanced X-ray of a woman's pelvic cavity reveals her reproductive organs, including the fallopian tubes on top of the uterus. Injecting an opaque material via a catheter (white tube) makes the organs more visible.

Cranial cavity

Spinal cavity

Thoracic cavity

Abdominal cavity

Pelvic cavity

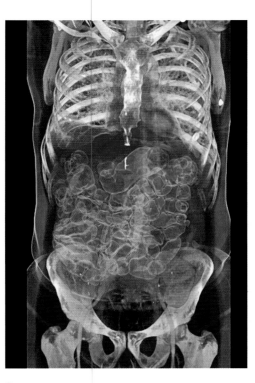

Organs
A color scan shows organs in the abdominal cavity of a kidney transplant patient. The donor kidney (orange, lower right) has been grafted to blood vessels in the lower abdomen. Coiled intestines are visible above.

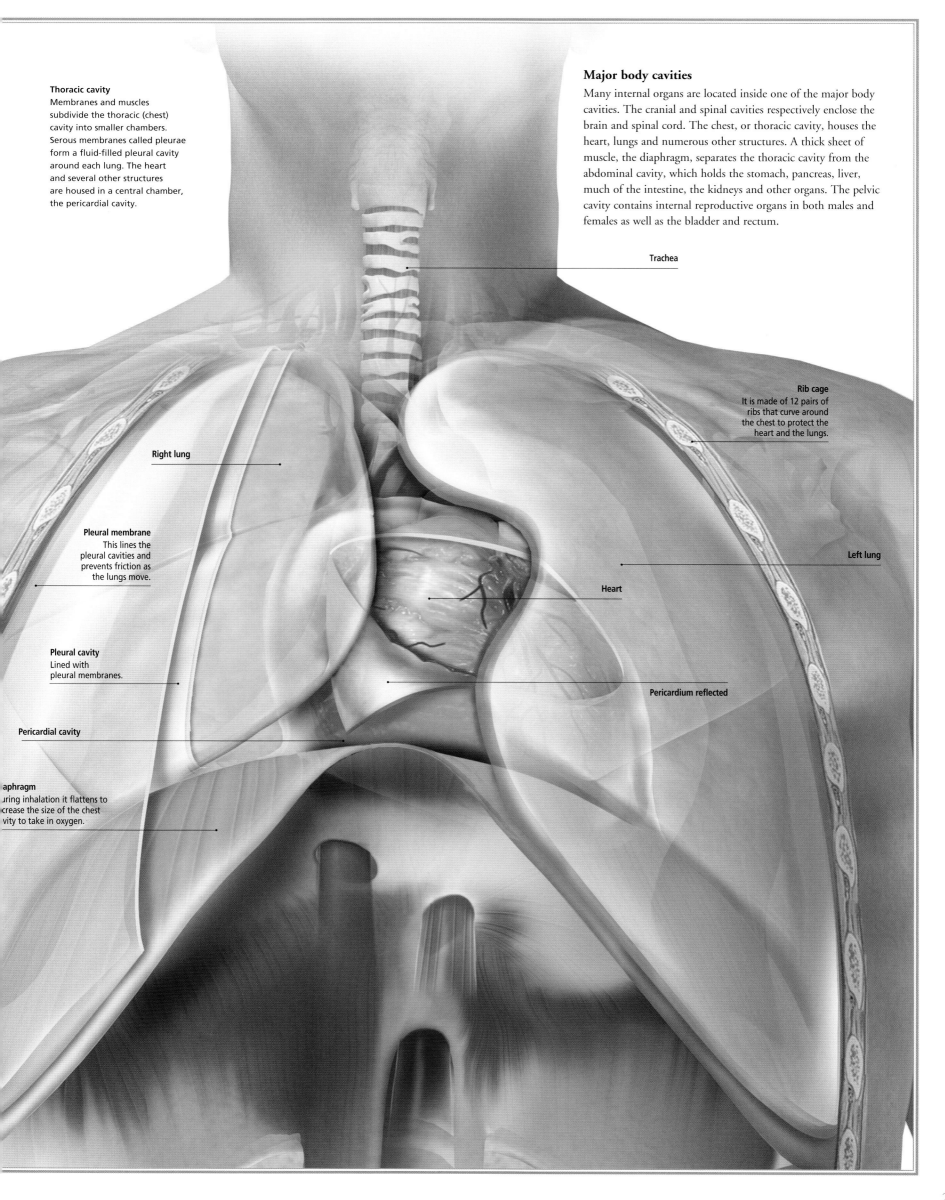

Thoracic cavity
Membranes and muscles subdivide the thoracic (chest) cavity into smaller chambers. Serous membranes called pleurae form a fluid-filled pleural cavity around each lung. The heart and several other structures are housed in a central chamber, the pericardial cavity.

Major body cavities

Many internal organs are located inside one of the major body cavities. The cranial and spinal cavities respectively enclose the brain and spinal cord. The chest, or thoracic cavity, houses the heart, lungs and numerous other structures. A thick sheet of muscle, the diaphragm, separates the thoracic cavity from the abdominal cavity, which holds the stomach, pancreas, liver, much of the intestine, the kidneys and other organs. The pelvic cavity contains internal reproductive organs in both males and females as well as the bladder and rectum.

Trachea

Rib cage
It is made of 12 pairs of ribs that curve around the chest to protect the heart and the lungs.

Right lung

Pleural membrane
This lines the pleural cavities and prevents friction as the lungs move.

Left lung

Heart

Pleural cavity
Lined with pleural membranes.

Pericardium reflected

Pericardial cavity

Diaphragm
During inhalation it flattens to increase the size of the chest cavity to take in oxygen.

29

Infectious Diseases

Disease-causing agents, or pathogens, are inescapable. They are in the air, on most things, in water, soil and food. Some infectious diseases are communicable, spreading from one host to another. This group includes common, highly contagious ailments, such as colds and influenza. Other infectious diseases are neither communicable nor contagious, such as foodborne illnesses which occur when a person consumes contaminated food. Pathogens attack the body using different methods. Viruses directly invade and destroy cells. Bacteria produce toxins that poison or damage cells. Some of these are endotoxins, which are released from dying cells, while others are exotoxins secreted by bacteria. Fungi and parasites feed on body tissues and may trigger immune responses, such as dangerous inflammation, that exacerbate the harm.

Antibiotics and Resistance

Antibiotics can kill or inhibit the growth of bacteria and some other microorganisms but do not work against viruses. The misuse of these potent drugs to treat viral diseases, and in other ways, has been a major factor in the rise of antibiotic-resistant microbes. With ailments ranging from strep throat to tuberculosis, the most susceptible pathogens are rapidly disappearing, leaving behind strains such as the strep bacterium *Staphylococcus aureus*, which is genetically resistant to most available antibiotics.

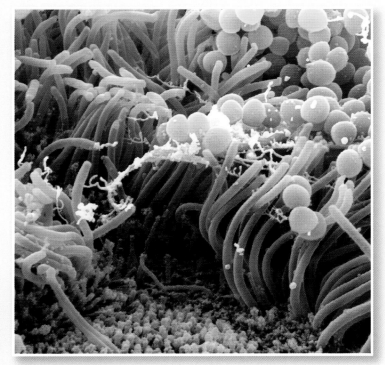

Staphylococcus bacteria
Bacteria (yellow) stick to hair-like cilia (brown) protruding from epithelial cells inside the nose. This kind of bacterium can cause abscesses and infection.

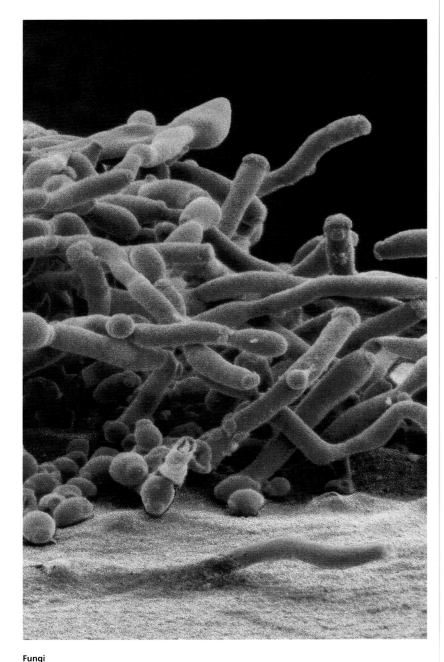

Fungi
This fungus, *Candida albicans,* causes yeast infections.
It produces enzymes that digest a host's tissues.

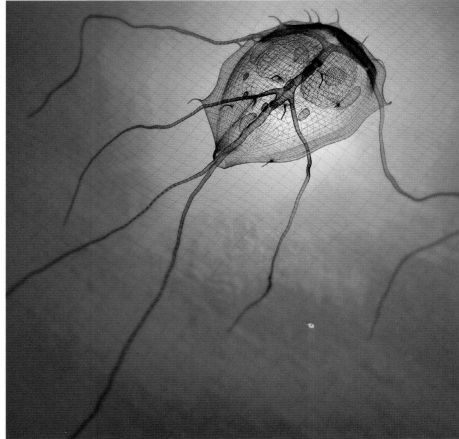

Parasites
This parasite, *Giardia intestinalis,* occurs in feces-contaminated water and causes the serious intestinal inflammation called giardiasis.

INFECTIOUS DISEASES

PATHOGENS	MODE OF ATTACK	EXAMPLES
Bacteria	Use poisonous toxins to change cells or launch dangerous immune responses	Lyme disease, gonorrhea, botulism, syphilis, septic shock, tooth decay
Fungi	Use enzymes to break down, then consume living and dead material	Yeast infections, athlete's foot, histoplasmosis, thrush
Parasites	Use host cells and tissues as a source of nourishment; can launch dangerous immune responses	Giardiasis, liver flukes, malaria, other worms
Viruses	Use living cells to replicate, then attack other cells; can cause cells to become cancerous	SARS, influenza, pneumonia, encephalitis, meningitis

A world of pathogens
Common pathogens run the gamut of bacteria, viruses, fungi, parasitic worms and microscopic protozoa. More rare but often highly virulent are prions, infectious proteins that cause mad cow disease and some other disorders. Unusual bacteria called mycoplasmas cause the mild respiratory disease walking pneumonia.

Virulence

Infectious organisms are ranked according to their virulence, or capacity to endanger health. Virulence factors include the nature and biological role of the infected tissue or organ and the speed with which the pathogen takes hold. Bacteria and viruses that target major organs, such as the brain, liver and lungs, pose a much greater danger than does a common cold virus. Highly virulent human pathogens include bacteria that cause blood poisoning (sepsis), an infection that can kill a person within a few days.

Clostridium perfrigens is one of several types of bacteria that can cause blood poisoning.

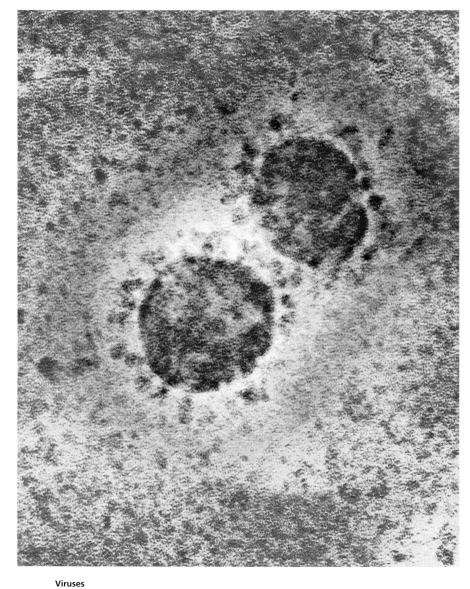

Viruses
Viruses, like the SARS viruses pictured here, usurp a cell's metabolic machinery to make copies of themselves.

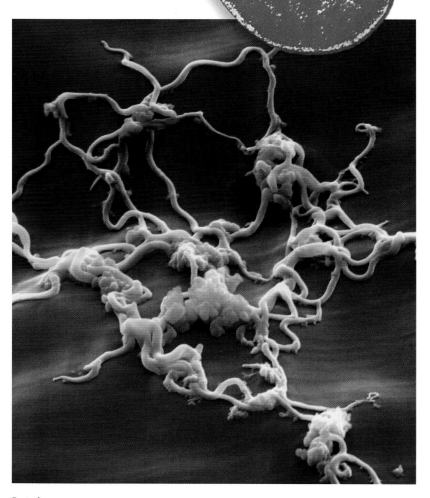

Bacteria
Bacteria come in various shapes, including rods and spirals. These spiral-shaped bacteria, *Borrelia burgdorferi,* cause Lyme disease.

Disease Spread and Prevention

Infectious diseases are contagious or communicable; they can be spread from person to person in various ways. Direct contact involves one-on-one routes such as touching an open sore. Many diseases are spread indirectly, as when a healthy person touches a used tissue or drinks sewage-contaminated water. Lyme disease spread by ticks and malaria spread by mosquitoes are examples of vector-transmitted diseases. But by far the most common source of infection is airborne microbes, such as a flu virus, which are inhaled from what an infected person coughs or sneezes. Understanding how disease organisms spread and where they are located is a powerful disease preventative. The World Heath Organization cites several practical measures proven to limit the incidence of infectious disease, ranging from simple hand washing to governmental efforts to ensure access to uncontaminated food, water and blood supplies.

Emerging and re-emerging diseases

An emerging disease is one that suddenly appears in a host species it formerly did not infect or that has begun to spread beyond its historical range. Examples include Lyme disease, which was first recognized in humans in the mid-1900s, and respiratory infections caused by the SARS virus. Tuberculosis is re-emerging as a major threat due to growing antibiotic resistance of the TB bacterium, as well as increased international travel and crowded living conditions in urban areas worldwide.

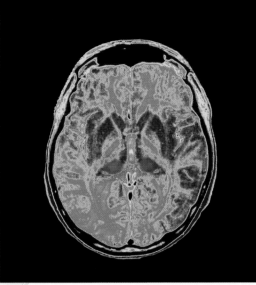

Mad cow disease
This scan shows diseased areas (red) in the brain of a teenager who died from CJD (Creutzfeld-Jakob), which destroys nerve cells. A form of CJD has appeared in people who ate beef from cattle infected with mad cow disease.

Disease hot spots
Many emerging infectious threats are zoonoses—diseases in which nonhuman animals are the main reservoirs. This map indicates disease hotspots, most of which are in developing nations in equatorial regions.

KEY
▪ = Higher levels
▪ = Middle levels
□ = Lower levels

Disease Reservoirs

Soil, water, infected animals and the human body itself can all serve as disease reservoirs—places where a pathogen can survive until the opportunity arises for it to infect a host. Reservoirs include carriers, which are organisms such as the mosquito seen below or people in which the pathogen resides without causing symptoms. Humans are the only known reservoirs for some ailments, for example the common cold and gonorrhea.

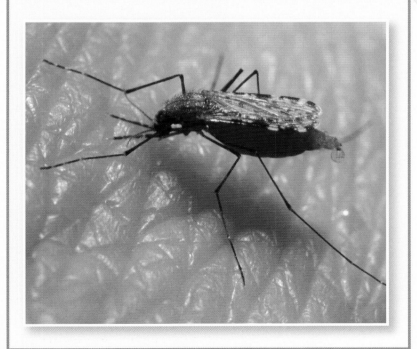

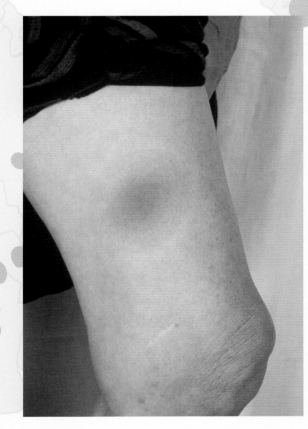

Lyme disease
Transmitted by ticks, Lyme disease is a major emerging disease in the United States. A bull's-eye rash around the site where the tick injected its bacteria-laden saliva is a classic sign of the disease.

Patterns of disease

The science of epidemiology tracks the patterns in which diseases occur. An endemic disease such as Lyme is always present in a population, while a sporadic disease such as avian (bird) flu turns up only now and then. In an epidemic, a large number of people in the same community develop a given disease relatively suddenly. In a disease pandemic, epidemics of the same disease break out in various parts of the world. The spread of HIV infections and AIDS has become one of the most challenging modern pandemic diseases.

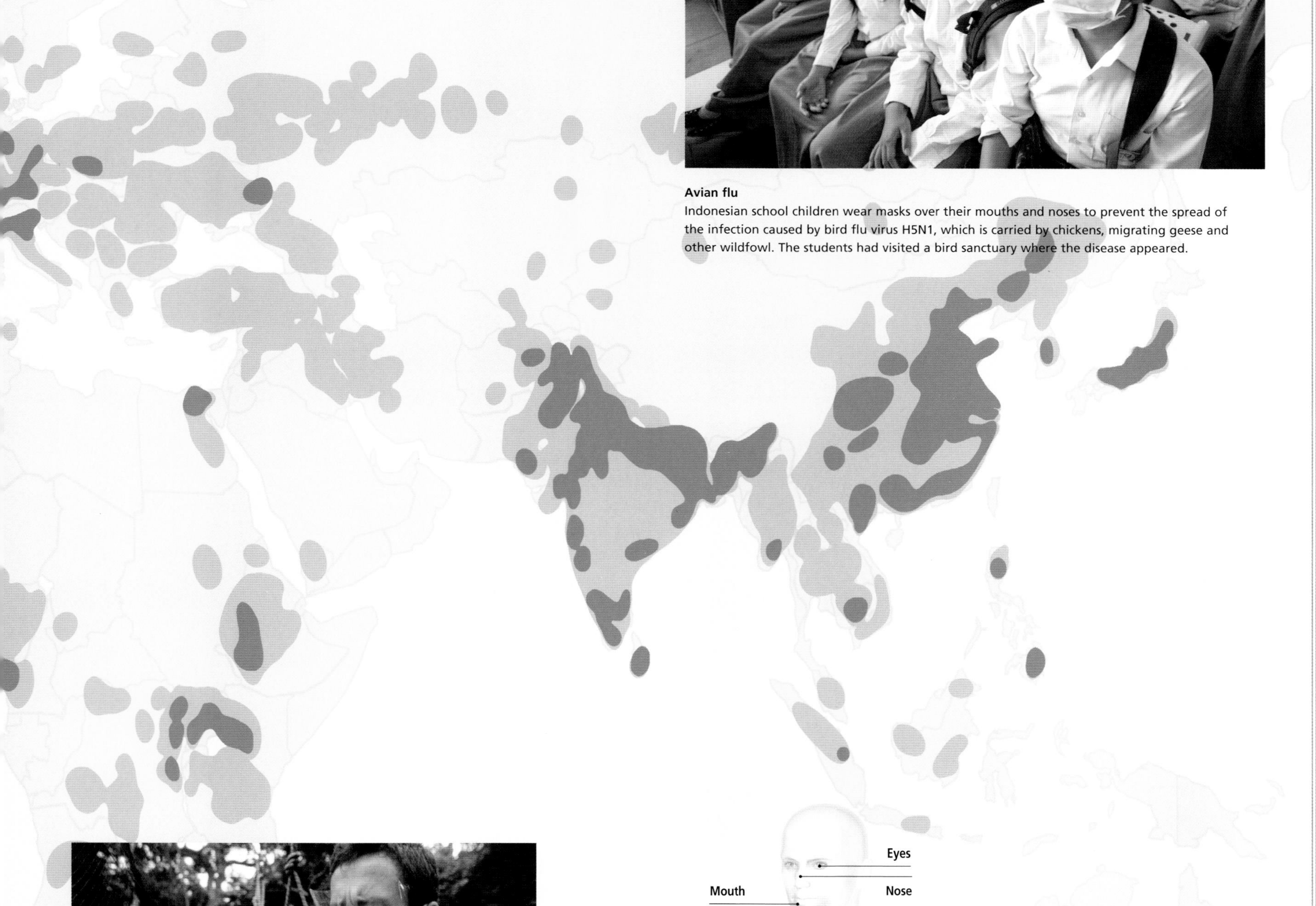

Avian flu
Indonesian school children wear masks over their mouths and noses to prevent the spread of the infection caused by bird flu virus H5N1, which is carried by chickens, migrating geese and other wildfowl. The students had visited a bird sanctuary where the disease appeared.

Eyes

Mouth   Nose

Digestive tract

Cuts or scrapes on skin

Urinary tract

Genitals

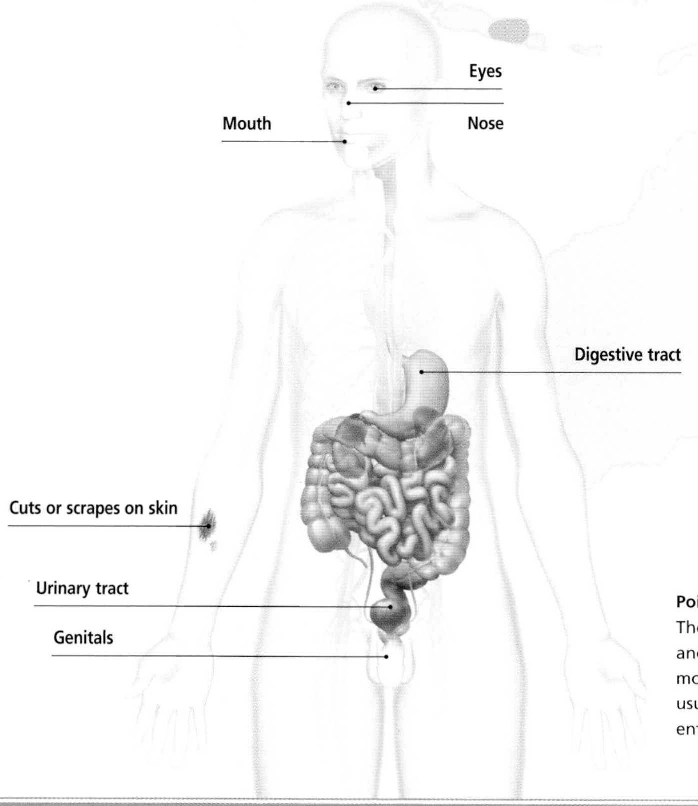

Points of entry
The skin, outer surfaces of the eyes and body openings, such as the nose, mouth and urogenital openings, are usual sites where pathogens gain entry to the body.

Ebola virus
The Ebola virus causes a sporadic hemorrhagic fever that triggers massive bleeding. Years of research have identified a possible infection source—the droppings of Ebola-infected bats. This bat was captured and tested for the virus.

CANCER

Cancer is a constellation of diseases that share one basic feature: the loss of genetic controls preventing normal cells from dividing more often than normal. In a cancer cell, a series of gene mutations instigates an abnormally frequent division of cells that causes the cell's highly organized internal structure to go awry. If the immune system does not quickly detect and kill the defective cells, their steadily multiplying descendants may invade the surrounding tissue and form a cancerous tumor. The most dangerous cancers are invasive, spreading beyond the primary site by the process of metastasis. Carcinogenesis, the development of cancer, usually involves several steps, including the activation of oncogenes and the deactivation of one or more suppressor genes that normally prevent unbridled cell division. Cancer may arise by unlucky chance, but an inherited predisposition, viral infection, ionizing radiation and chemical carcinogens can cause the onset of carcinogenesis.

Asbestos fibers

DETECTING CANCER

The definitive test for any cancer is a biopsy of the suspect tissue that allows a pathologist to examine cells for signs of cancerous changes. Prior to biopsy, blood tests such as the Prostate Specific Antigen test (PSA) for prostate cancer can detect tumor markers—substances that are produced either by malignant cells or by normal cells responding to the presence of a cancer. Medical imaging using MRIs, CTs, specialized X-rays and ultrasound has virtually eliminated the need for exploratory surgery to determine the location of cancerous tumors.

Triggering cancer

In virtually all cases of cancer, normal genetic controls over cell division break down. The change may begin with a mutation that converts a proto-oncogene (precancer gene) into a cancer-causing oncogene. Usually a second step also is required, in which at least one tumor suppressor gene also is disabled. A viral infection, carcinogens such as asbestos fibers in building materials and radiation from sunlight and medical X-rays can mutate genes. Inherited mutations are responsible for an estimated five percent of cancers.

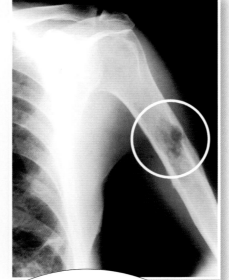

Normal tissue

Cancerous tumor forms

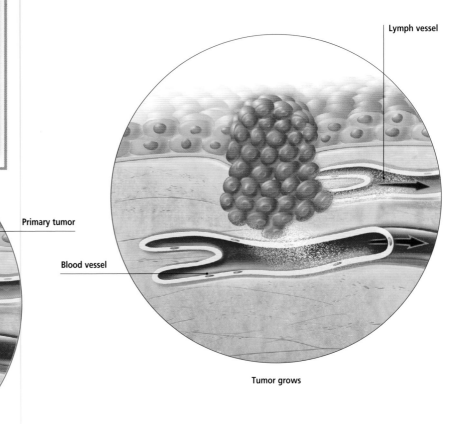

Lymph vessel

Primary tumor

Blood vessel

Tumor grows

How cancer metastasizes

Cancer spreads (metastasizes) in three steps. First, malignant cells break away from the parent tumor; next, they release enzymes that allow them to enter blood or lymph vessels; finally, they move through the bloodstream to a new location and reenter that tissue in the same way.

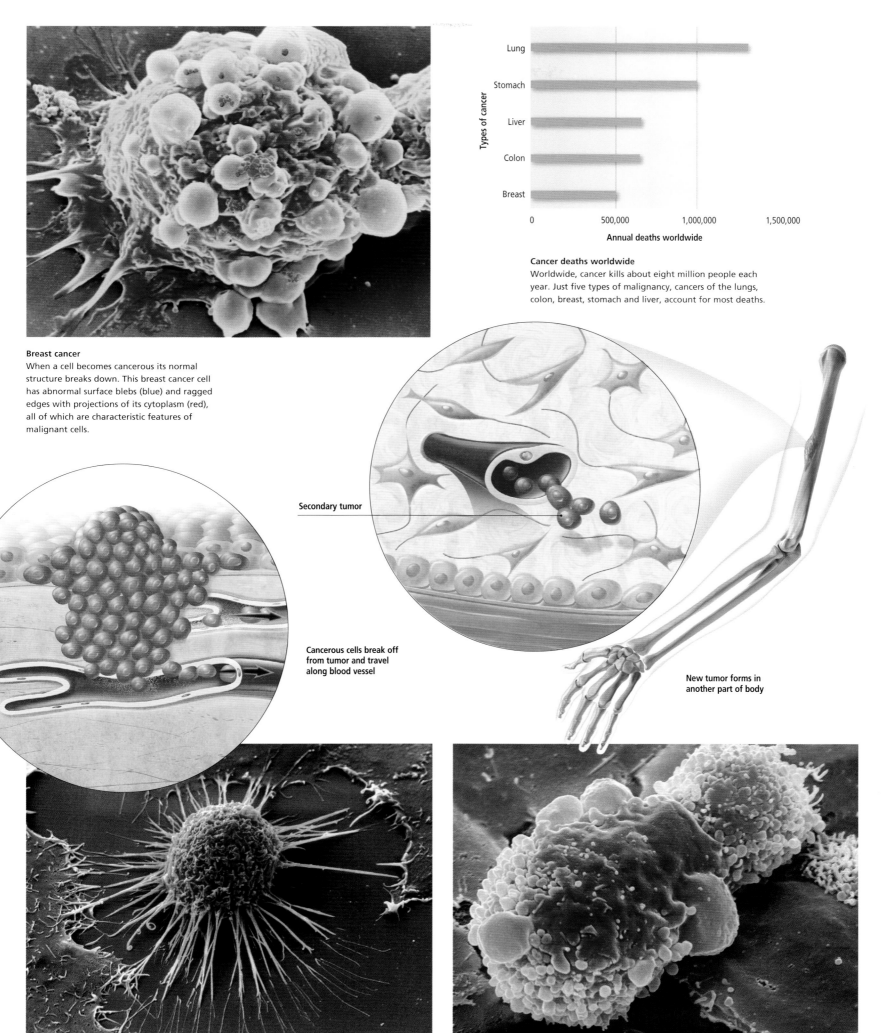

Breast cancer
When a cell becomes cancerous its normal structure breaks down. This breast cancer cell has abnormal surface blebs (blue) and ragged edges with projections of its cytoplasm (red), all of which are characteristic features of malignant cells.

Cancer deaths worldwide
Worldwide, cancer kills about eight million people each year. Just five types of malignancy, cancers of the lungs, colon, breast, stomach and liver, account for most deaths.

Secondary tumor

Cancerous cells break off from tumor and travel along blood vessel

New tumor forms in another part of body

Cervical cancer
This cell from a cancerous tumor of the cervix is abnormally large—another cancer characteristic. Although cervical cancer is relatively common in women, it is easily cured if detected early as part of a regular gynecological exam.

Lung cancer
The irregular surface of this lung cancer cell is a sign of its diseased state. The overwhelming majority of lung cancers develop as a result of exposure to tobacco smoke, industrial pollutants and asbestos.

This illustration shows the immune system at work. Antibodies first appear like antennae at a B cell's surface, positioned to bind with an invader. The encounter spurs the B cell to multiply and produce the antibody "factories" called plasma cells. Antibodies attach to targets and label them for destruction.

BODY
SYSTEMS

BODY SYSTEMS ILLUSTRATED

The human body is a collection of 12 organ systems, each organized to perform a particular function. The skin, or integument, is a multipurpose outer cover, while bones of the skeletal system provide a supportive physical framework. The body's hundreds of skeletal muscles interact with bones to move the body and its parts. It is nourished by a digestive system that brings in and processes food, releasing nutrients to the blood and eliminating indigestible residues. Systems for blood circulation and respiration move oxygen, nutrients and other vital supplies to the trillions of body cells, and carry away the potentially toxic wastes of the metabolic activity that maintains life. Closely aligned with the circulatory system is a system of lymphatic organs and vessels that provides a staging ground for immune responses. The urinary system cleanses the blood of impurities and manages the body's "internal sea" of water, salts and other substances. Reproductive systems provide the biological means for producing offspring. Controlling and regulating every aspect of body functioning are the hormones of the endocrine system and the unparalleled human nervous system.

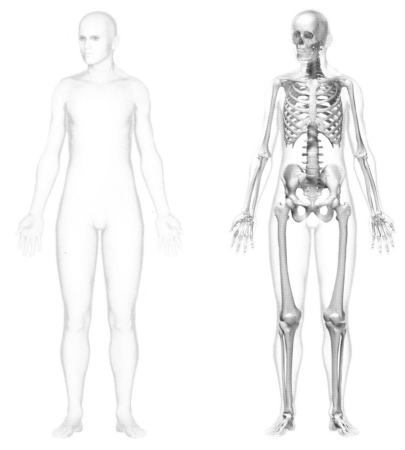

Integumentary system
The integument (from Latin, "to cover") consists of the skin and structures such as hair and nails that are derived from it. Skin is a barrier against water loss and microbes. It also protects deeper tissues against physical damage, helps control body temperature and contains sensory receptors. Glands embedded in the skin excrete certain body wastes.

Skeletal system
The skeleton supports the body's soft tissues and protects vital organs, such as the brain, spinal cord, heart and lungs. Bones provide rigid attachment sites for skeletal muscles, serving as levers in body movements. Bones also store the minerals calcium and phosphorus while bone marrow produces red blood cells.

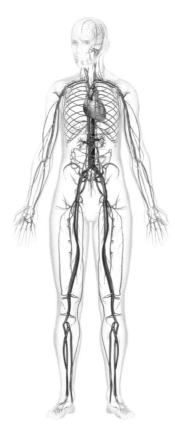
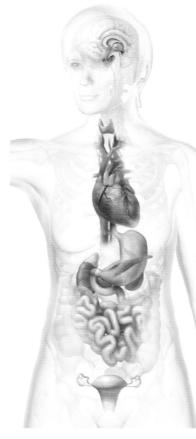
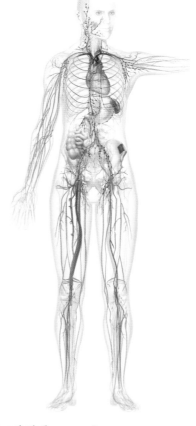

Circulatory system
The blood-pumping heart and blood-transporting vessels rapidly move oxygen, nutrients and many other materials to and from cells. The system also helps stabilize body temperature and internal chemical conditions.

Endocrine system
Endocrine organs produce hormones with major roles in controlling body functions both short-term and long-term. System operations are closely coordinated with activities of the nervous system.

Respiratory system
This system extracts oxygen from air and delivers it to the bloodstream for circulation throughout the body. It also removes waste carbon dioxide and helps manage the body's acid-base balance.

Lymphatic /immune system
This network of filtering organs and vessels collects and returns tissue fluid to the bloodstream. It also produces cells and substances that defend the body against tissue damage and infection.

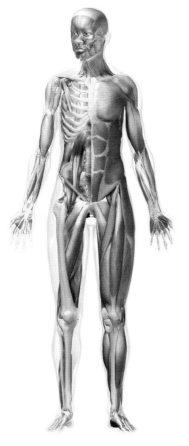

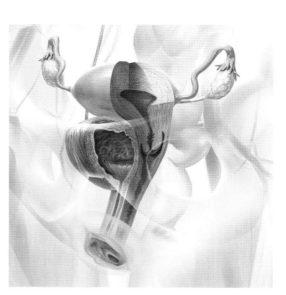

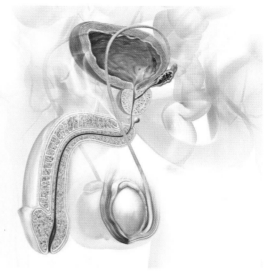

Muscular system

The body's hundreds of skeletal muscles—classified as voluntary because they are under conscious control—work with bones to move the body and its parts. Skeletal muscles also produce body heat and some maintain upright human posture. The body's smooth and cardiac muscles are not controllable at will and are thus classified as involuntary.

Nervous system

This system integrates the activities of all other organ systems. In tandem with sensory organs, it detects stimuli from outside and inside the body and organizes and controls bodily and behavioral responses. The central nervous system includes the brain and spinal cord; the peripheral nervous system comprises all other nervous structures.

Reproductive system

The female reproductive system produces eggs, the female sex cells, and nurtures developing young. The male reproductive system forms sperm, the male sex cells, and transfers sperm to the female. Both systems produce hormones with widespread effects in the body.

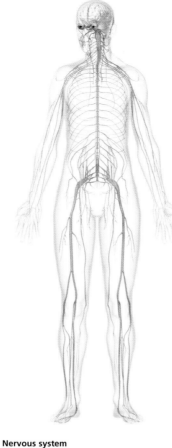

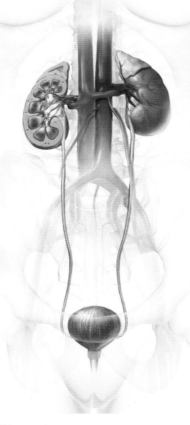

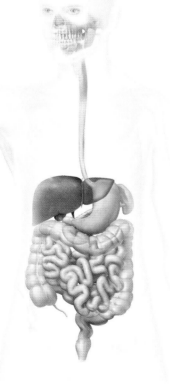

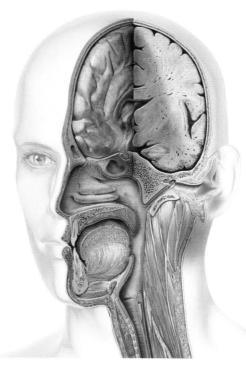

Digestive system

This system takes in bulk food and breaks it down mechanically and chemically to extract nutrients for body cells. Parts of the system are specialized to realize digestive enzymes, absorb nutrients and eliminate undigested food residues.

Urinary system

This is the body's filtering system, which has primary responsibility for maintaining the proper chemical balance of the blood and tissue fluid. It removes bloodborne wastes and excess water and excretes them in urine.

Sensory system

This system brings information to the body allowing it to receive, manage and respond to changes both within and outside the body. There are two groups of human senses—general senses, such as touch, pressure and pain, and the special senses of vision, hearing, smell, taste and balance.

INTEGUMENTARY SYSTEM

Skin makes up most of the body's outer covering, the integument. Except where it is thickened by regular abrasion, such as on the soles of the feet, human skin is only about as thick as wrapping paper. Even so, it provides an array of essential functions, from barring microbes and preventing excessive loss of body water to absorbing harmful solar radiation and dissipating metabolic heat. The skin makes cholecalciferol, the key ingredient in vitamin D, and its sensory receptors convey information about touch, temperature, pain and other conditions. Skin has two layers: the waterproof upper epidermis with cells containing keratin and the dermis below. Required to withstand a lifetime of washing, stretching, bumps and scrapes, the epidermis is constantly regenerating. As dead outer cells flake or rub off, living cells below replace them—a process that helps cuts heal.

SKIN CHANGES

Human skin changes over time. A newborn has delicate, soft skin with a thin, translucent epidermis, few functional sweat glands and a substantial layer of insulating fat. Although hormonal changes of adolescence increase the size and output of sebaceous (oil) glands—contributing to pimples and acne—youthful skin also contains enough collagen and elastin to make it supple and resilient. With advancing age and exposure to sun over time, the epidermis and dermis thin and changes in the structure of collagen and elastin result in sagging and wrinkles.

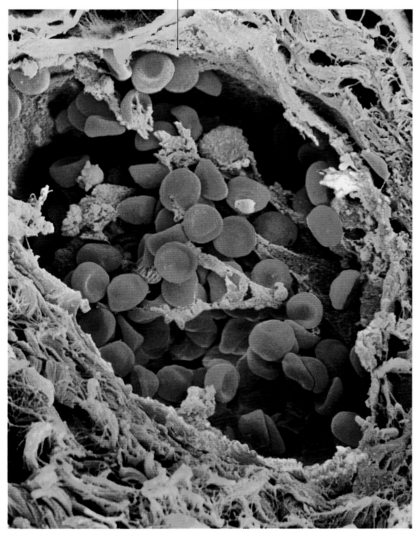

Blood vessel in dermis

Lymphatic system/Immunity
Skin is a barrier against invaders; immune responses help heal wounds.

Respiratory system
Hairs in nasal cavity help filter inhaled air; respiratory system supplies oxygen and removes carbon dioxide.

Reproductive system
Skin nerve endings in external genitalia and glands contribute to reproductive functions.

Muscular system
Skin makes an active form of vitamin D, which helps keep muscles strong; active muscles increase blood flow to the skin.

Nervous system
Skin nerve endings provide sensory information to the brain; nervous system regulates many skin functions.

Endocrine system
Androgens produced by the endocrine system activate sebaceous glands and regulate hair growth.

Digestive system
Skin helps convert vitamin D to its active hormonal form, calcitriol, which aids in the absorption of calcium and phosphate.

Urinary system
Skin excretes some wastes in sweat; the urinary system disposes of wastes of skin metabolism.

Circulatory system
Skin prevents fluid loss and dissipates blood-borne heat; the circulatory system brings nutrients to skin.

Skeletal system
Skin helps activate vitamin D required for absorption of calcium and phosphate used to form bone; the skeletal system provides structural support.

Skin and body temperature

Blood-monitoring sensors in a brain region called the hypothalamus can detect changes in core body temperature. For most people, the optimum temperature is 98.2 °F (36.8 °C). When the core temperature rises to an unhealthy level, the hypothalamus signals blood vessels in the skin to dilate. More blood flows and excess heat dissipates. When the core temperature drops too low, the vessels contract to reduce heat loss.

Interrelationships with other body systems
The integumentary system helps support the operations of other body systems, and all systems except the reproductive organs contribute in some way to the healthy functioning of skin and structures derived from it.

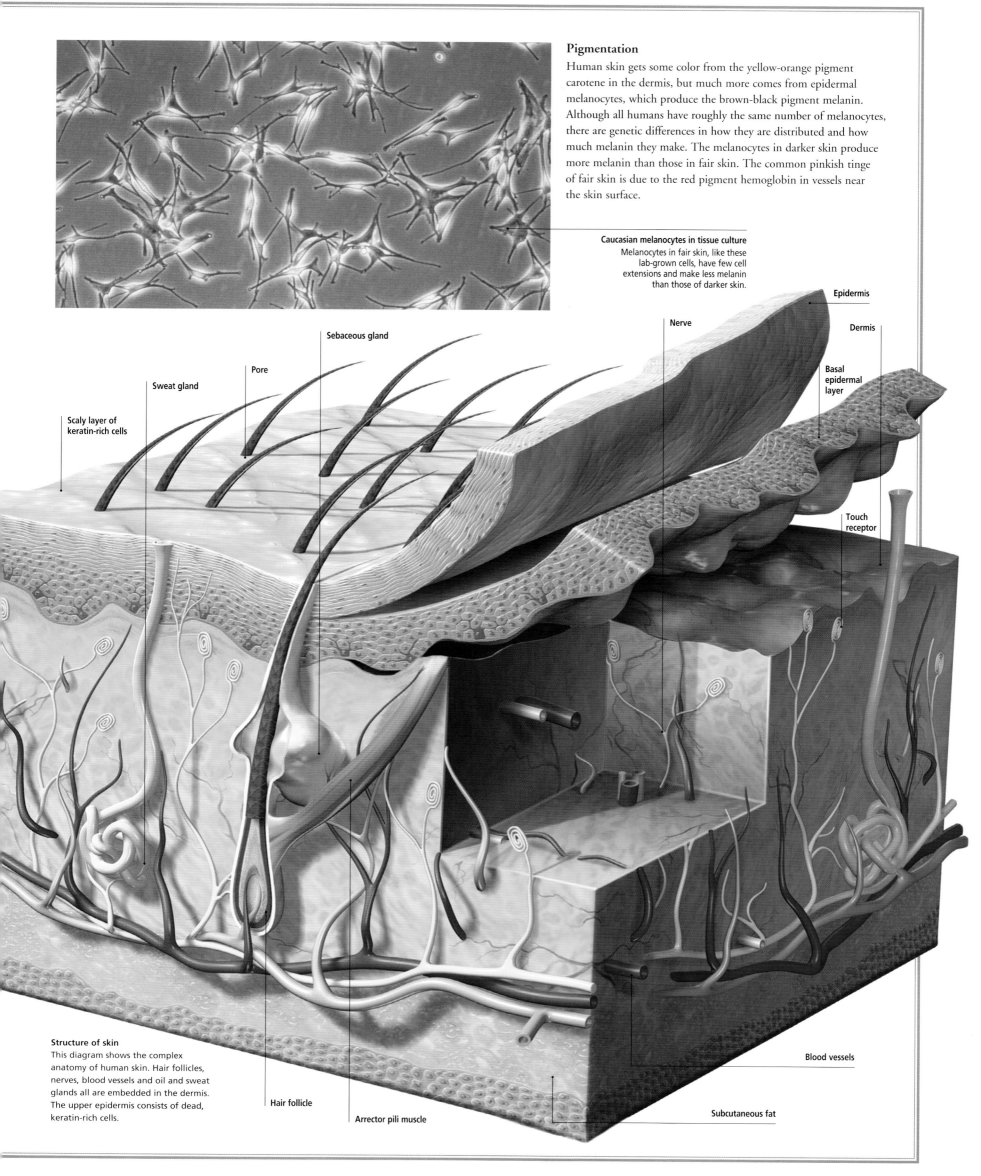

Pigmentation

Human skin gets some color from the yellow-orange pigment carotene in the dermis, but much more comes from epidermal melanocytes, which produce the brown-black pigment melanin. Although all humans have roughly the same number of melanocytes, there are genetic differences in how they are distributed and how much melanin they make. The melanocytes in darker skin produce more melanin than those in fair skin. The common pinkish tinge of fair skin is due to the red pigment hemoglobin in vessels near the skin surface.

Caucasian melanocytes in tissue culture
Melanocytes in fair skin, like these lab-grown cells, have few cell extensions and make less melanin than those of darker skin.

Nerve

Epidermis

Dermis

Sebaceous gland

Basal epidermal layer

Pore

Sweat gland

Touch receptor

Scaly layer of keratin-rich cells

Structure of skin
This diagram shows the complex anatomy of human skin. Hair follicles, nerves, blood vessels and oil and sweat glands all are embedded in the dermis. The upper epidermis consists of dead, keratin-rich cells.

Hair follicle

Arrector pili muscle

Blood vessels

Subcutaneous fat

Derivatives of Skin

Hair, nails, oil and sweat glands—all these structures develop from the epidermis. Millions of hairs grow on the scalp, in the armpits, pubic area and elsewhere. Each flexible shaft consists mainly of keratin-rich cells and protrudes from a hair follicle that is rooted in the dermis. As a hair grows, cells in the outer shaft die and may become frayed. Fingernails and toenails contain an especially hard form of keratin. As they grow, the elongating nails move over the nail bed underneath. Except for the palms and soles of the feet, every part of an adult's skin has sebaceous glands, and the oily sebum they produce lubricates and softens skin and hair. Adults also have about 2.5 million sweat glands embedded in their skin. Sweat is mostly water, and its most essential role in the body is to carry away excess body heat as it evaporates.

Hair down deep

A hair follicle cycles between phases of growth and rest. During the growth phase, the hair lengthens as new cells arise in the root and push dead cells upward. After a resting phase, growth begins anew. A scalp hair may grow for up to six years before the follicle rests. Hair follicles respond to fluxes in sex hormones. Male pattern baldness, for example, reflects the effects of testosterone on the genes that regulate hair growth, while waning hormones result in thinning hair as both men and women age.

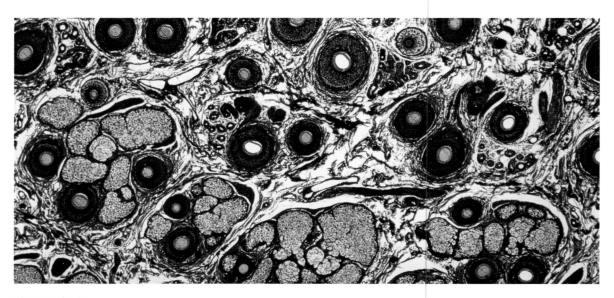

Sebaceous glands
Sebaceous (oil) glands produce oily sebum that lubricates hairs and the surface of the skin. They show up as small purple masses in this microscope image.

Sweat

Eccrine sweat glands populate much of human skin. From the scalp to the palm and the soles of the feet, most skin areas contain these glands, which can increase their output of watery sweat as needed to help dissipate body heat. Larger apocrine glands are concentrated in the armpits and groin. Their secretions may be triggered by sexual arousal and anxiety—producing the drenching "cold sweat" of stressful situations.

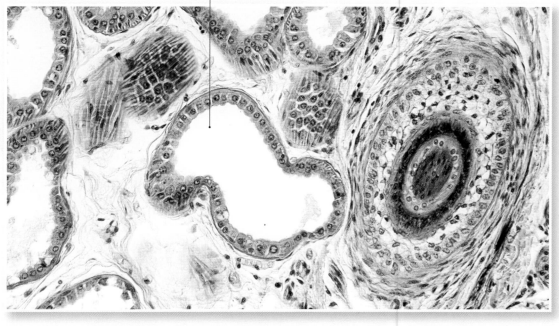

Apocrine sweat gland

Hair root

Sebaceous gland

Arrector pili muscle

Dermal papilla

Bulb

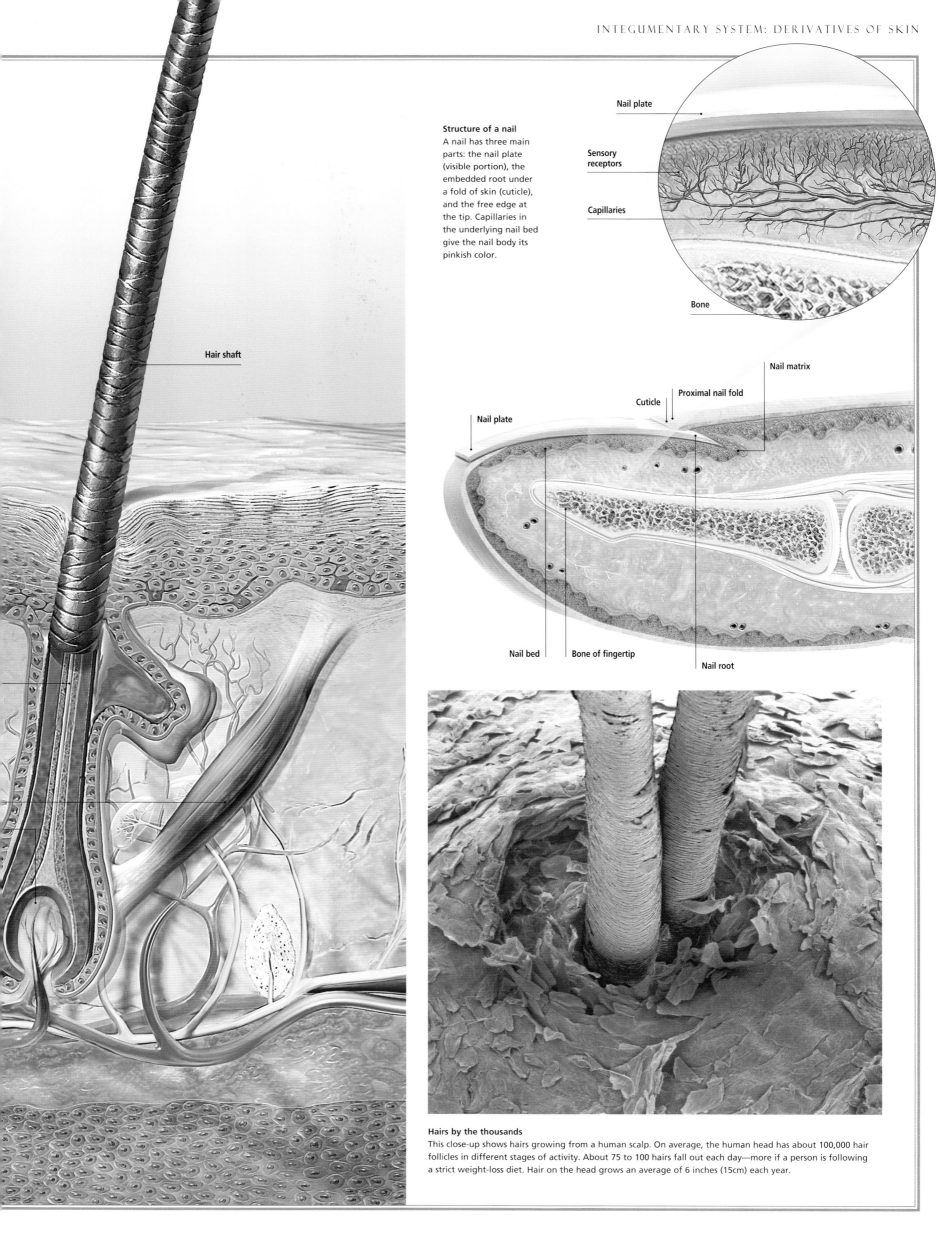

Nail plate

Structure of a nail
A nail has three main
parts: the nail plate
(visible portion), the
embedded root under
a fold of skin (cuticle),
and the free edge at
the tip. Capillaries in
the underlying nail bed
give the nail body its
pinkish color.

Sensory
receptors

Capillaries

Bone

Hair shaft

Nail matrix

Cuticle

Proximal nail fold

Nail plate

Nail bed

Bone of fingertip

Nail root

Hairs by the thousands
This close-up shows hairs growing from a human scalp. On average, the human head has about 100,000 hair
follicles in different stages of activity. About 75 to 100 hairs fall out each day—more if a person is following
a strict weight-loss diet. Hair on the head grows an average of 6 inches (15cm) each year.

Skin Diseases and Disorders

Skin is exposed to abrasion and contact with irritants, dangers such as sharp objects and hot stoves and bacteria and other pathogens. The most widespread skin disorders fall into the general category of dermatitis—mild to moderate inflammation that produces contact rashes and dandruff. Inflammation is a factor in many chronic skin ailments, including the itchy, scaly skin patches of eczema and facial redness and pustules that signal rosacea. Bacteria cause the crusting sores of impetigo, while fungi in the skin's epidermis produce the characteristic pattern of ringworm. Acne is one of several persistent problems that involve oil-clogged or infected hair follicles. Psoriasis is marked by thick, whitish, irritated patches that build up on the elbows, knees and elsewhere when the usual weeks-long life cycle of skin cells is compressed into a few days.

Vitiligo
The patchy loss of skin pigment is the main symptom of vitiligo. Causes are poorly understood but genetic factors may play a role in some cases. New treatments include transplanting melanin-producing cells to affected areas.

Burns

Burns harm or destroy the skin. Fire, hot liquids, chemicals, electricity and radiation all cause burns, which are graded according to the extent, depth and location of the damage. First-degree burns are superficial, and although red and painful, as with a mild sunburn (shown below), they usually heal quickly. Blistering is a sign of a deeper, second-degree burn. With third-degree burns, the skin often dies, exposing the affected area to infection. The more skin that is damaged, the greater the danger.

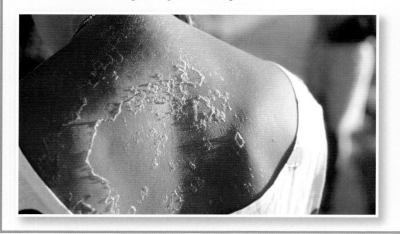

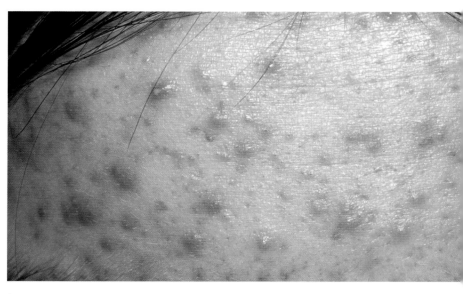

Acne
Acne is often associated with shifting hormones and a family history of the condition. In the most common form, sebaceous glands become inflamed and overproduce sebum that blocks hair follicles, forming red pustules.

Common Skin Disorders and Their Causes and Treatment		
Disorder	**Cause**	**Treatment**
Eczema	No known cause. Common triggers include soaps, weather, jewelry, creams, bacteria, stress, perspiration	Remove cause of reaction, avoid tight clothing, use lotion
Impetigo	Streptococcal and staphylococcus bacteria	Clean sores with antibacterial soap, take antibiotics
Psoriasis	Chronic autoimmune disorder. Attacks are often triggered by stress, trauma, infections, or hormones	Get plenty of sun, avoid irritating cosmetics and soaps, soak in warm bath with mosturizer
Ringworm	Fungal infection	Use antifungal medications
Vitiligo	Loss of melanocytes leads to uneven distribution of melanin, often due to genetics	Protect skin from sunlight, occasional use of cortisone creams can help, dermatologists can prescribe skin darkening agents
Acne	Inflammation of sebaceous glands	Cleansers or creams, dose of antibiotics or hormones

Eczema
Many people have a genetic predisposition to develop eczema, or recurring rashes, which may first appear in early childhood. Treatment advances include non-steroidal creams and lotions that temporarily soothe the irritation.

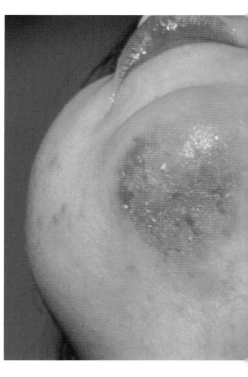

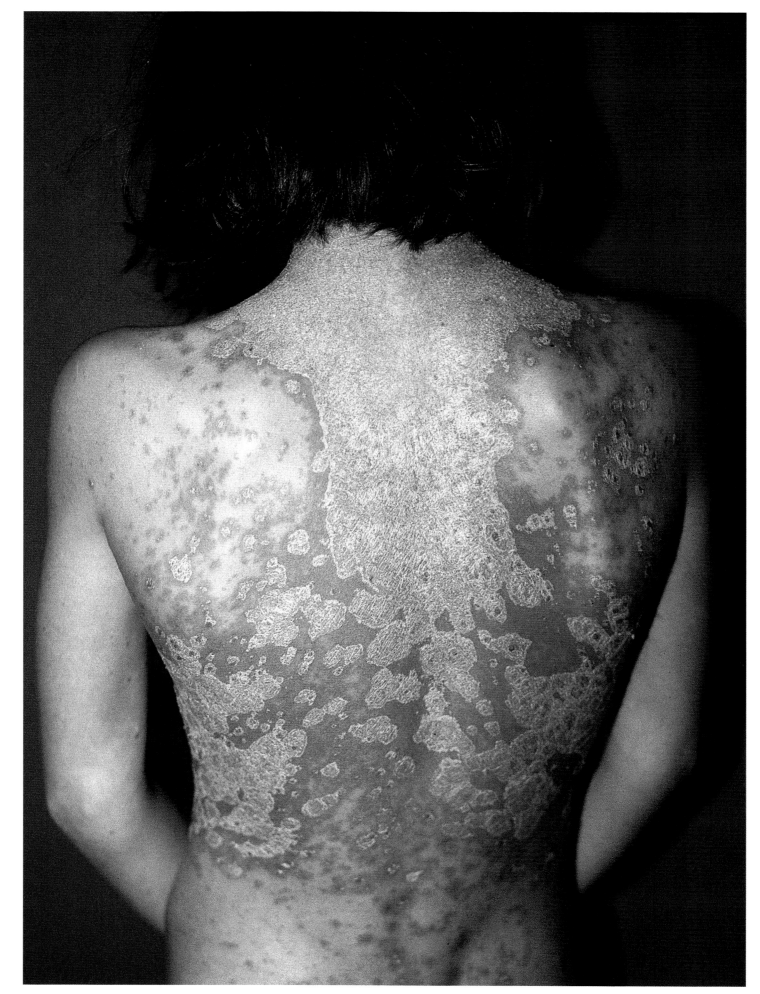

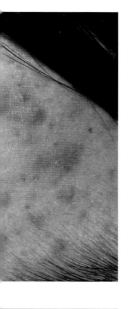

Treating problem skin

Chronic skin disorders such as rosacea, psoriasis (shown above) and eczema not only resist a cure but the root cause is unknown and the symptoms are notoriously difficult to treat. Symptoms may respond to a range of topical preparations including retinoic acid, coal tar, those containing a steroid such as cortisone and certain chemicals in the vitamin D family. More difficult cases may require oral medications or even drug injections. Often a combination of treatments is the most effective approach.

Skin Cancers

Skin cancers are the most common of all malignancies. All three main forms—basal cell carcinoma, squamous cell carcinoma and melanoma—are associated with overexposure to ultraviolet (UV) radiation, either from the sun or tanning beds. Most skin cancers are slow-growing basal cell carcinomas that are easily treatable by minor surgery in a doctor's office. Squamous cell carcinoma develops in the flattened cells at the skin surface. It is somewhat more dangerous because such cells grow more rapidly and may spread to nearby lymph nodes. Malignant melanoma is often mistaken for a harmless mole and may spread before a person realizes the growing blemish is abnormal. Cancer involving the skin's Merkel cells, which play a role in the sense of touch, is rarer but extremely aggressive, growing to considerable size within just a few weeks. Although anyone can develop skin cancer, people with fair complexions are at the greatest risk.

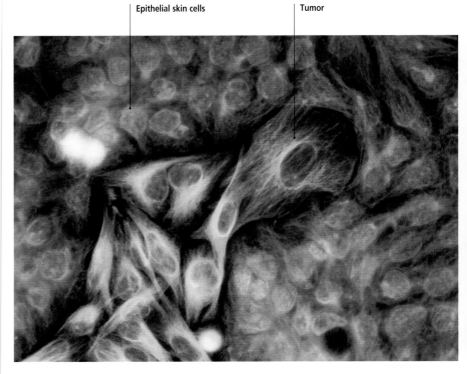

Epithelial skin cells   Tumor

Melanoma cancer cells
This micrograph shows melanoma cancer cells invading skin epithelium. Melanoma is a malignant cancer that proliferates wildly. It is made up of large undifferentiated cells that can divide rapidly and attack the healthy tissue that surrounds it.

Synthetic Skin

Synthetic skin grown in a laboratory can repair damage from cancer, burns and other problems. After a transplant is put into place, blood vessels migrate to the area, followed by epithelial cells. Over time, the synthetic skin decays, leaving behind a healthy, new patch of skin. Synthetic replacements must be made with materials such as silicon and collagen, which are less likely to trigger a reaction by the immune system.

Basal cell carcinoma
Prolonged exposure to ultraviolet rays can damage cells at the base of the epidermis, forming a mound of slow-growing, cancerous cells.

Squamous cells

Cancerous cells

Basal cells

Preventing and treating skin cancer

Because most skin cancers are caused by overexposure to ultraviolet light, they can be prevented by avoiding unnecessary sun exposure, especially at midday when the sun's rays are most intense. Dermatologists recommend wearing protective clothing and using a sunscreen that shields against both UVA and UVB rays. Early-stage basal and squamous cell carcinomas, along with precancerous growths called actinic keratosis, are usually removed with a laser or by cryosurgery.

Skin Cancer Risk Factors	Skin Cancer Signs
Exposure to a lot of natural or artificial sunlight or arsenic	Having a sore that does not heal
Having chronic skin inflammation or skin ulcers, a fair complexion, scars or burns	Having areas of the skin that are: small, raised, smooth, shiny, waxy; small, raised, red or reddish-brown; flat, rough, red or brown, scaly; scaly, bleeding, crusty; similar to a scar and firm
Receiving radiation treatment	
Taking immunosuppressive drugs	

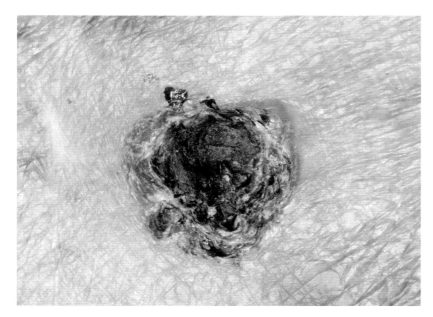

Squamous cell carcinoma
Rough, dark lesions are typical of squamous cell carcinoma, the second most common skin cancer. Precancerous lesions known as solar keratoses signal heavily sun-damaged skin and are an early warning sign. This type of cancer mostly impacts the elderly.

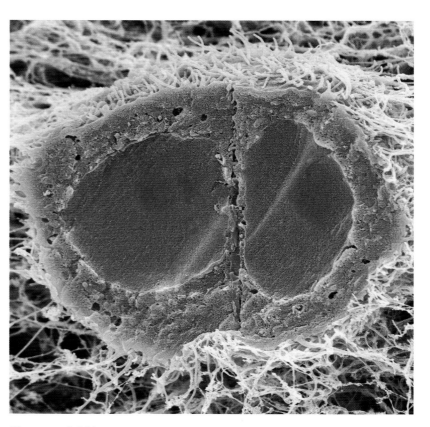

Skin cancer cell division
This colored scanning electron micrograph shows a slice through a skin cancer cell. It has recently undergone mitosis, or nuclear division, and has two nuclei (purple). The next stage is cytokinesis, which will produce two daughter cells and cause the cancer to spread.

Cancerous cells   Uneven pigmentation

Melanoma
Radiation damage to melanocytes, or pigment-producing cells, forms a dark, irregular mass. This type of cancer is highly metastatic.

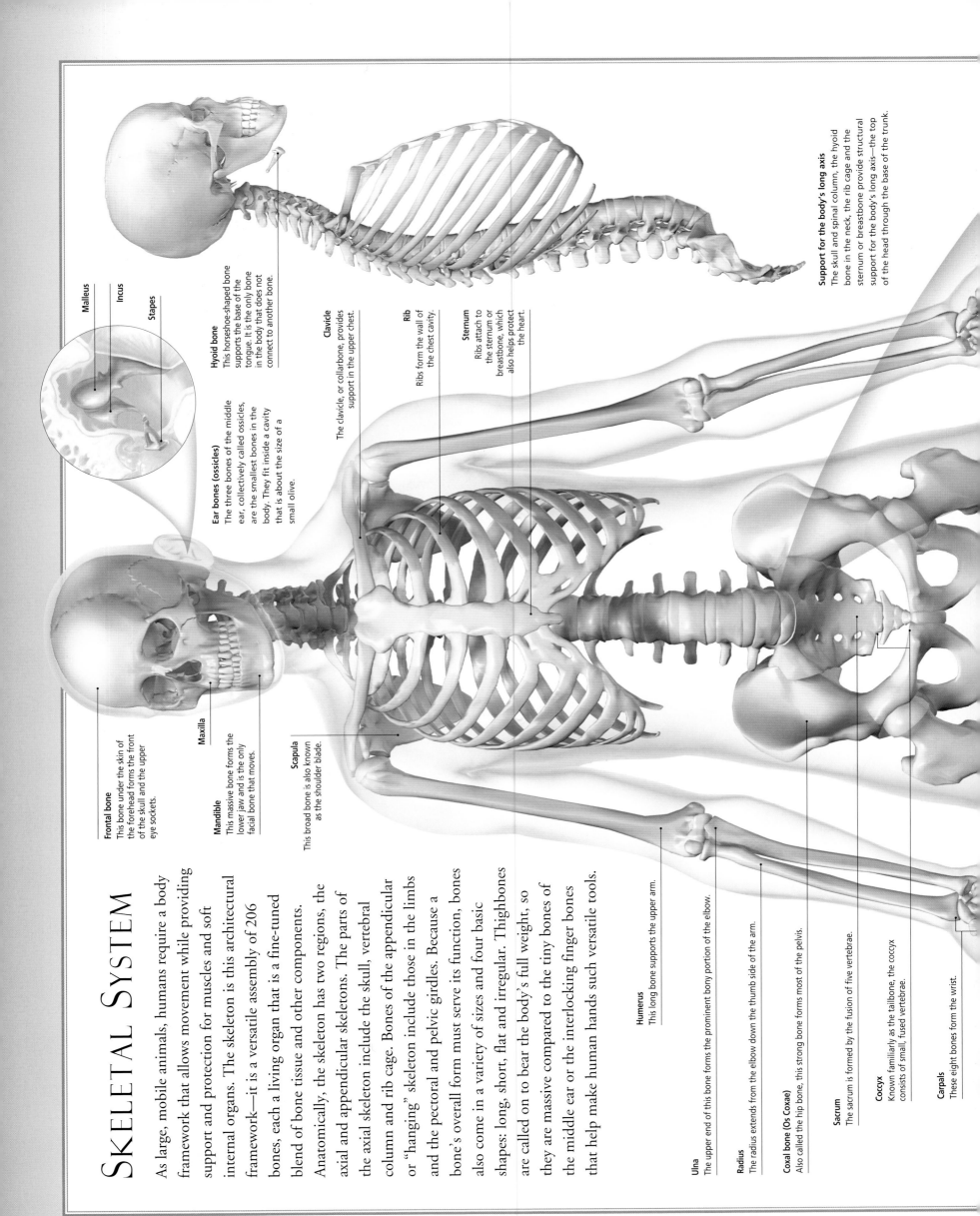

SKELETAL SYSTEM

As large, mobile animals, humans require a body framework that allows movement while providing support and protection for muscles and soft internal organs. The skeleton is this architectural framework—it is a versatile assembly of 206 bones, each a living organ that is a fine-tuned blend of bone tissue and other components. Anatomically, the skeleton has two regions, the axial and appendicular skeletons. The parts of the axial skeleton include the skull, vertebral column and rib cage. Bones of the appendicular or "hanging" skeleton include those in the limbs and the pectoral and pelvic girdles. Because a bone's overall form must serve its function, bones also come in a variety of sizes and four basic shapes: long, short, flat and irregular. Thighbones are called on to bear the body's full weight, so they are massive compared to the tiny bones of the middle ear or the interlocking finger bones that help make human hands such versatile tools.

Malleus

Incus

Stapes

Hyoid bone
This horseshoe-shaped bone supports the base of the tongue. It is the only bone in the body that does not connect to another bone.

Ear bones (ossicles)
The three bones of the middle ear, collectively called ossicles, are the smallest bones in the body. They fit inside a cavity that is about the size of a small olive.

Clavicle
The clavicle, or collarbone, provides support in the upper chest.

Rib
Ribs form the wall of the chest cavity.

Sternum
Ribs attach to the sternum or breastbone, which also helps protect the heart.

Support for the body's long axis
The skull and spinal column, the hyoid bone in the neck, the rib cage and the sternum or breastbone provide structural support for the body's long axis—the top of the head through the base of the trunk.

Frontal bone
This bone under the skin of the forehead forms the front of the skull and the upper eye sockets.

Mandible
This massive bone forms the lower jaw and is the only facial bone that moves.

Maxilla

Scapula
This broad bone is also known as the shoulder blade.

Humerus
This long bone supports the upper arm.

Ulna
The upper end of this bone forms the prominent bony portion of the elbow.

Radius
The radius extends from the elbow down the thumb side of the arm.

Coxal bone (Os Coxae)
Also called the hip bone, this strong bone forms most of the pelvis.

Sacrum
The sacrum is formed by the fusion of five vertebrae.

Coccyx
Known familiarly as the tailbone, the coccyx consists of small, fused vertebrae.

Carpals
These eight bones form the wrist.

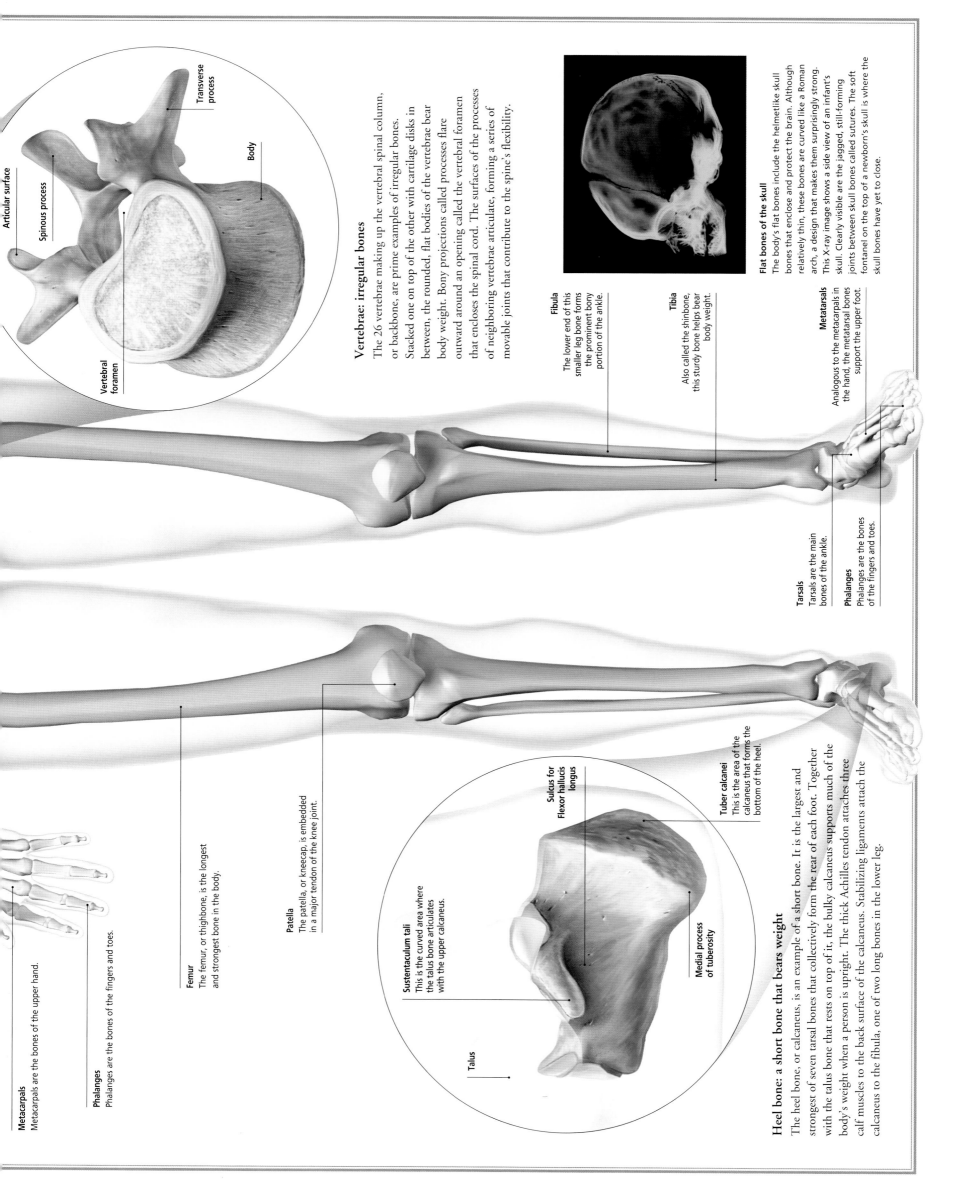

Transverse process

Body

Articular surface

Spinous process

Vertebral foramen

Vertebrae: irregular bones

The 26 vertebrae making up the vertebral spinal column, or backbone, are prime examples of irregular bones. Stacked one on top of the other with cartilage disks in between, the rounded, flat bodies of the vertebrae bear body weight. Bony projections called processes flare outward around an opening called the vertebral foramen that encloses the spinal cord. The surfaces of the processes of neighboring vertebrae articulate, forming a series of movable joints that contribute to the spine's flexibility.

Fibula
The lower end of this smaller leg bone forms the prominent bony portion of the ankle.

Tibia
Also called the shinbone, this sturdy bone helps bear body weight.

Metatarsals
Analogous to the metacarpals in the hand, the metatarsal bones support the upper foot.

Tarsals
Tarsals are the main bones of the ankle.

Phalanges
Phalanges are the bones of the fingers and toes.

Flat bones of the skull

The body's flat bones include the helmetlike skull bones that enclose and protect the brain. Although relatively thin, these bones are curved like a Roman arch, a design that makes them surprisingly strong. This X-ray image shows a side view of an infant's skull. Clearly visible are the jagged, still-forming joints between skull bones called sutures. The soft fontanel on the top of a newborn's skull is where the skull bones have yet to close.

Metacarpals
Metacarpals are the bones of the upper hand.

Phalanges
Phalanges are the bones of the fingers and toes.

Femur
The femur, or thighbone, is the longest and strongest bone in the body.

Patella
The patella, or kneecap, is embedded in a major tendon of the knee joint.

Sulcus for Flexor hallucis longus

Tuber calcanei
This is the area of the calcaneus that forms the bottom of the heel.

Sustentaculum tali
This is the curved area where the talus bone articulates with the upper calcaneus.

Medial process of tuberosity

Talus

Heel bone: a short bone that bears weight

The heel bone, or calcaneus, is an example of a short bone. It is the largest and strongest of seven tarsal bones that collectively form the rear of each foot. Together with the talus bone that rests on top of it, the bulky calcaneus supports much of the body's weight when a person is upright. The thick Achilles tendon attaches three calf muscles to the back surface of the calcaneus. Stabilizing ligaments attach the calcaneus to the fibula, one of two long bones in the lower leg.

STRUCTURE OF BONE

For the skeleton to support and protect soft body parts, bones must be strong and rigid. The structure of bone tissue helps satisfy these demands without making the skeleton too heavy. Like other connective tissues, bone consists of living cells in a extracellular matrix of fibers and other substances. The cells include osteoblasts, which form bone, and osteoclasts, which break it down. Bone matrix contains collagen fibers and crystals of hydroxyapatite— a mix of the minerals calcium and phosphate that makes the matrix rock-hard. These are the foundation for the two types of bone tissue. Dense compact bone forms the smooth outer part of bones while spongy bone, with large spaces amid bony struts, occurs in the interior. In some bones, marrow fills a cavity or the spaces in spongy bone. Red marrow in bones such as the sternum produces blood cells.

Bones as calcium depots

In a give-and-take process called remodeling, osteoblasts steadily form bone and osteoclasts steadily destroy it. Osteoclasts can also "mine" bone tissue to help ensure an adequate supply of calcium to meet the constant demand from muscles and the nervous system. When too little calcium circulates in the bloodstream, glands in the neck, the parathyroids, release the hormone parathyroid hormone (PTH). Osteoclasts respond by breaking down bone and releasing calcium that soon enters the blood. This effect is one reason why a diet chronically deficient in calcium can seriously weaken the skeleton.

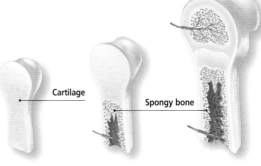

How a long bone forms
Initially a fetus has flexible "bones" of cartilage. As bone cells develop, spongy bone begins to replace cartilage and blood vessels invade. With time, a marrow cavity opens and knobby epiphyses form at the bone ends.

Cartilage · Spongy bone · Epiphysis · Epiphyseal plate · Diaphysis · Marrow cavity

BONE NUTRITION

Humans require vitamin D because it helps move calcium and phosphorus into the bloodstream. These minerals make bones hard and dense. Children deficient in vitamin D may develop rickets, a disorder in which bones soften, producing bowed legs and other skeletal problems.

This photo shows how rickets can deform the lower limb bones of a child who has a vitamin D deficiency.

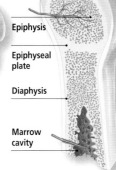

Bone marrow
Long bones of adults have yellow marrow, which stores fat.

Nerve
Nerves carry neural signals to and from the periosteum.

Blood vessels
Arteries (red) deliver blood rich in oxygen and nutrients to bone tissue and veins (blue) carry away wastes and other substances.

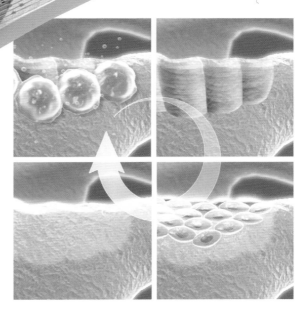

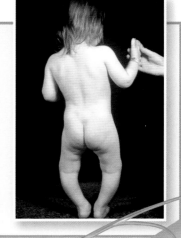

Remodeling bone tissue
Bones grow longer or wider, take on the proper proportions and heal from injuries as osteoblasts lay down bone tissue and osteoclasts selectively remove it. Remodeling continuously occurs, and over the span of several years virtually all of the body's bone mass is recycled as new bone replaces the old.

Periosteum
The inner layer of this membrane contains bone-forming cells that increase a long bone's girth.

Stress and bone strength
Healthy bones become stronger when they are subjected to load-bearing activities such as lifting weights. Such mechanical stress shifts the balance between osteoblasts and osteoclasts, so more bone is laid down than is removed during the normal cycle of remodeling.

Epiphysis
Each cartilage-covered end of a long bone, called the epiphysis, articulates in a joint.

Cartilage

Osteon
An osteon consists of layered rings of bone matrix around a central canal. Bone cells live in the rings inside chambers called lacunae. Tunnel-like caniculi weave through and between osteons, providing passageways for the movement of nutrients and wastes.

Compact bone
Compact bone consists of layered cylinders called osteons. Chambers between the layers hold bone cells, which are serviced by blood vessels and nerves that thread through channels in the matrix.

Spongy bone
Like the girders of a bridge, the many bony struts of spongy bone provide lightweight strength. In bones where blood cells form, such as the breastbone, hip bones and vertebrae, red marrow may fill the spaces.

Axial Skeleton

The axial skeleton is the body's overall framework. Aligned along a lengthwise axis, its 82 bones support the head, neck, chest and abdomen and protect the vital structures within, including the brain, spinal cord and organs such as the heart. Most axial skeleton bones are flat or have an irregular shape. Many are arranged to form protective cavities for delicate soft parts or to allow openings for blood vessels and nerves, including the spinal cord and nerves that link the central nervous system with the rest of the body. Skull bones encase the all-important brain and support the face. They also form protective chambers around the organs that provide our senses of vision, hearing, taste, smell and balance. Bones of the vertebral column, or spine, interlock in a flexible girder that helps support the weight of the trunk. Flaring, paired ribs provide a sturdy cage around the heart, lungs and the body's largest blood vessels.

Sinuses

Sinuses are cavities in skull bones that help reduce the skull's weight. Lined with mucous membranes, they connect via short passageways to the nasal cavity. Respiratory allergies and irritants can readily spread into the sinuses. The congestion, pressure and pain of sinusitis results when a bacterial infection takes hold.

Sinuses are located in the frontal, sphenoid, ethmoid and maxillary bones. People with severe sinus congestion sometimes feel as if their entire face aches.

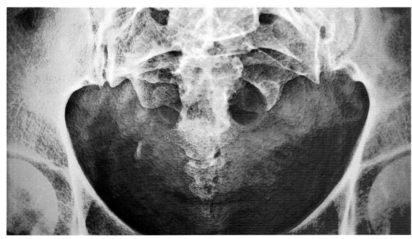

Tale of a tail bone
Small and pointed, the tailbone is a biological holdover from human forbears that had a tail serviced by nerves of the lower spinal cord. Today, the tailbone helps anchor several muscles, including the large gluteus maximus of the buttocks.

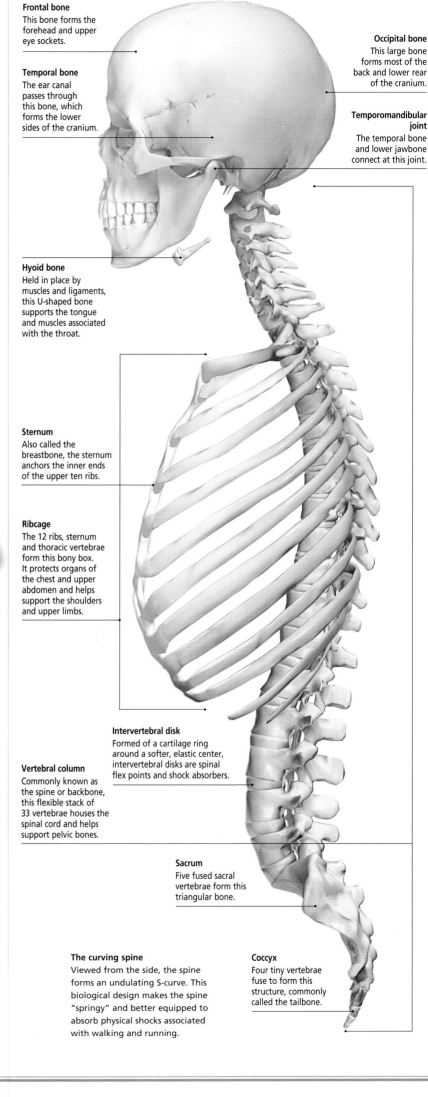

Frontal bone
This bone forms the forehead and upper eye sockets.

Occipital bone
This large bone forms most of the back and lower rear of the cranium.

Temporal bone
The ear canal passes through this bone, which forms the lower sides of the cranium.

Temporomandibular joint
The temporal bone and lower jawbone connect at this joint.

Hyoid bone
Held in place by muscles and ligaments, this U-shaped bone supports the tongue and muscles associated with the throat.

Sternum
Also called the breastbone, the sternum anchors the inner ends of the upper ten ribs.

Ribcage
The 12 ribs, sternum and thoracic vertebrae form this bony box. It protects organs of the chest and upper abdomen and helps support the shoulders and upper limbs.

Intervertebral disk
Formed of a cartilage ring around a softer, elastic center, intervertebral disks are spinal flex points and shock absorbers.

Vertebral column
Commonly known as the spine or backbone, this flexible stack of 33 vertebrae houses the spinal cord and helps support pelvic bones.

Sacrum
Five fused sacral vertebrae form this triangular bone.

The curving spine
Viewed from the side, the spine forms an undulating S-curve. This biological design makes the spine "springy" and better equipped to absorb physical shocks associated with walking and running.

Coccyx
Four tiny vertebrae fuse to form this structure, commonly called the tailbone.

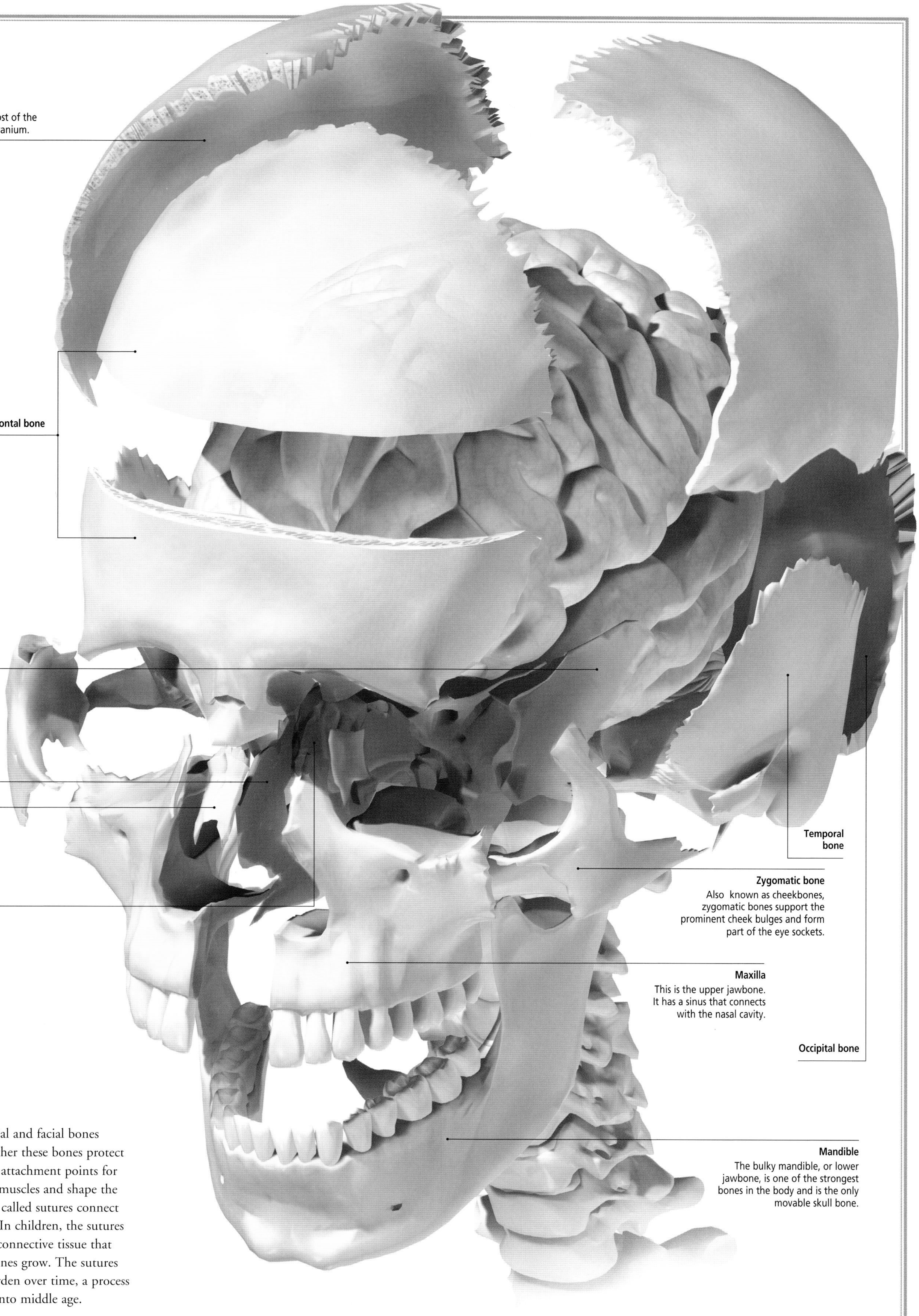

Parietal bone
Parietal bones form most of the roof and sides of the cranium.

Frontal bone

Sphenoid bone
This centrally located bone forms part of the floor of the cranium and connects with most other cranial bones.

Ethmoid bone
This bone forms a portion of the inner eye socket and helps support the nose.

Nasal bone
This pair of bones forms the upper portion of the bridge of the nose.

Lacrimal bone
Small and flat, this bone forms the inner eye sockets.

Temporal bone

Zygomatic bone
Also known as cheekbones, zygomatic bones support the prominent cheek bulges and form part of the eye sockets.

Maxilla
This is the upper jawbone. It has a sinus that connects with the nasal cavity.

Occipital bone

Mandible
The bulky mandible, or lower jawbone, is one of the strongest bones in the body and is the only movable skull bone.

The skull

There are 22 cranial and facial bones in the skull. Together these bones protect the brain, provide attachment points for the face and neck muscles and shape the face. Jagged joints called sutures connect some skull bones. In children, the sutures consist of fibrous connective tissue that flexes as cranial bones grow. The sutures mineralize and harden over time, a process that can last well into middle age.

APPENDICULAR SKELETON

The appendicular skeleton includes the bones of the limbs and the pectoral and pelvic girdles—all parts that attach to the axial skeleton and provide bony infrastructure for most major body movements. Human limbs, and especially the wrists and hands, have an intricate structure. Each hand contains 19 bones that articulate with each other or with the wrist bones, providing the dexterity to scratch an itch, play the piano or deftly communicate with sign language. The shoulder joint also is highly mobile, allowing the humerus, the long bone of the upper arm, to play its fundamental role in movements such as throwing a ball, swinging a golf club or lifting loads overhead. The pelvic girdle and lower limbs are bulkier and less flexible, but they also are sturdy enough to support the body's weight against gravity when a person is upright.

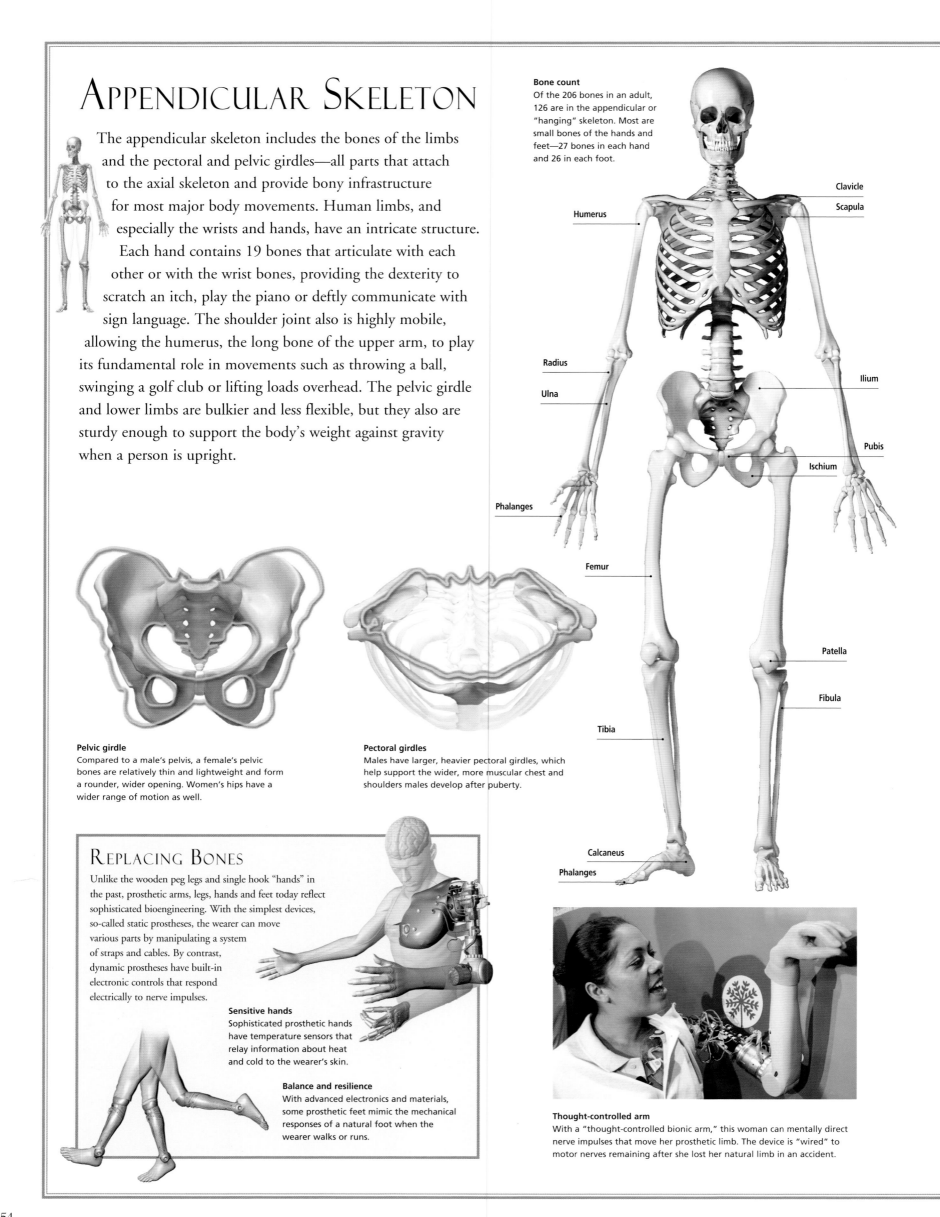

Bone count
Of the 206 bones in an adult, 126 are in the appendicular or "hanging" skeleton. Most are small bones of the hands and feet—27 bones in each hand and 26 in each foot.

Clavicle

Scapula

Humerus

Radius

Ulna

Ilium

Pubis

Ischium

Phalanges

Femur

Patella

Fibula

Tibia

Calcaneus

Phalanges

Pelvic girdle
Compared to a male's pelvis, a female's pelvic bones are relatively thin and lightweight and form a rounder, wider opening. Women's hips have a wider range of motion as well.

Pectoral girdles
Males have larger, heavier pectoral girdles, which help support the wider, more muscular chest and shoulders males develop after puberty.

REPLACING BONES

Unlike the wooden peg legs and single hook "hands" in the past, prosthetic arms, legs, hands and feet today reflect sophisticated bioengineering. With the simplest devices, so-called static prostheses, the wearer can move various parts by manipulating a system of straps and cables. By contrast, dynamic prostheses have built-in electronic controls that respond electrically to nerve impulses.

Sensitive hands
Sophisticated prosthetic hands have temperature sensors that relay information about heat and cold to the wearer's skin.

Balance and resilience
With advanced electronics and materials, some prosthetic feet mimic the mechanical responses of a natural foot when the wearer walks or runs.

Thought-controlled arm
With a "thought-controlled bionic arm," this woman can mentally direct nerve impulses that move her prosthetic limb. The device is "wired" to motor nerves remaining after she lost her natural limb in an accident.

What the skeleton reveals

A skeleton provides a bony biography of its owner. Overall, the bones and skeleton of a female are smaller and lighter than those of a male of the same age and size. Forensic scientists using skeletal remains to ascertain the gender of a person look immediately at the pelvis, which in females is shallower and wider, both specializations for childbearing. The size, shape and arthritic or other changes in bones also can reveal approximate age and insight into a person's health, and sometimes even the cause of death.

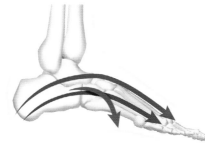

Supporting arches
Foot bones form weight-bearing arches in the feet—a transverse side-to-side arch and two longitudinal arches. "Flat feet" result when tendons and ligaments holding the inner, or medial, longitudinal arch weaken and the arch flattens or "falls."

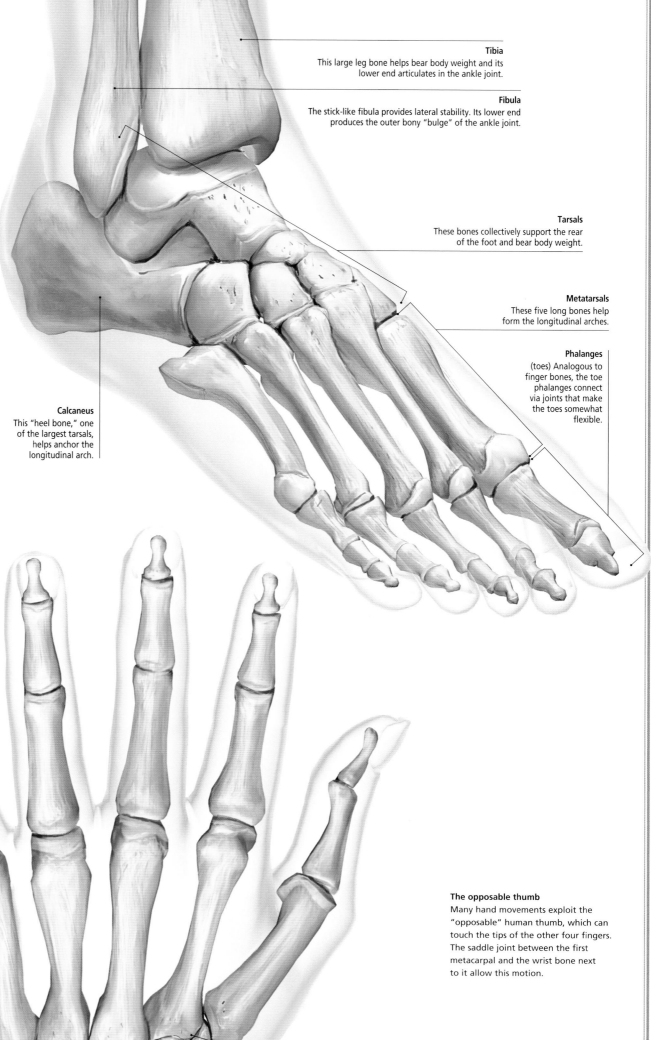

Tibia
This large leg bone helps bear body weight and its lower end articulates in the ankle joint.

Fibula
The stick-like fibula provides lateral stability. Its lower end produces the outer bony "bulge" of the ankle joint.

Tarsals
These bones collectively support the rear of the foot and bear body weight.

Metatarsals
These five long bones help form the longitudinal arches.

Phalanges
(toes) Analogous to finger bones, the toe phalanges connect via joints that make the toes somewhat flexible.

Calcaneus
This "heel bone," one of the largest tarsals, helps anchor the longitudinal arch.

Phalanges
(fingers) Joints between the finger phalanges allow tremendous manual dexterity.

Metacarpals
These slender bones support the palms and link to the finger phalanges at knuckles.

The opposable thumb
Many hand movements exploit the "opposable" human thumb, which can touch the tips of the other four fingers. The saddle joint between the first metacarpal and the wrist bone next to it allow this motion.

Carpals
These eight short wrist bones execute gliding movements. Only two of them articulate with the arm bones to form the wrist joint.

CONNECTIONS BETWEEN BONES

For the skeleton's parts to move, its bones must link at joints. The human skeleton has three main types of these connections. In freely movable or synovial joints, such as the knee and shoulder, a cavity separates the adjoining bones and the bone ends are covered with cartilage and ligaments add stability. Within the joint is a capsule filled with synovial fluid, which lubricates bone movements. Built to flex, extend and rotate, synovial joints are the mechanical foundation for the vast majority of body movements. Less mobile are cartilaginous joints, such as between vertebrae or between the ribs and sternum, where cartilage fills the space between bones. In fibrous joints, a seam of tough connective tissue essentially fuses abutting bones. Examples include tooth sockets and the sutures or "seams" joining the flat skull bones.

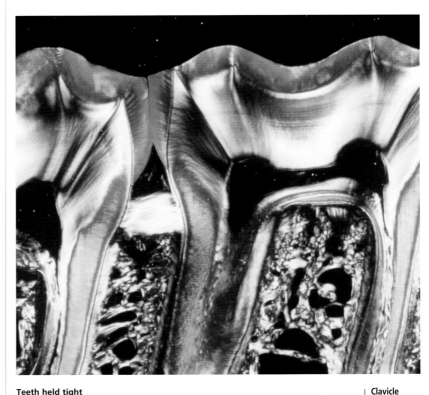

Teeth held tight
A fibrous joint holds each tooth in its socket. The joint consists of a periodontal "around the tooth" ligament that attaches on one surface to the tooth root and on the other surface to the underlying jaw bone.

Supportive ligaments
Ligaments that connect the hipbones to the thighbones, to the sacrum at the lower end of the spine and to each other at the pubic symphysis are exceedingly strong. The pelvis not only supports the spine but internal organs as well.

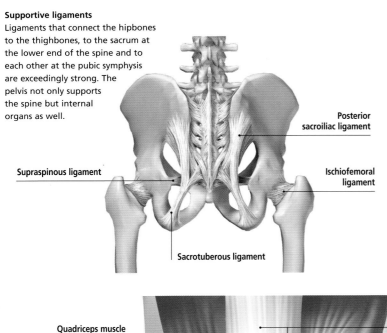

Posterior sacroiliac ligament

Supraspinous ligament

Ischiofemoral ligament

Sacrotuberous ligament

Fibrous capsule

Humerus

Clavicle

Bursa

Articular cartilage

Maximum motion
Of all synovial joints, the shoulder has the greatest range of motion. The anatomical price for this mobility is a "loose" joint reinforced by only a few ligaments. Tendons extending from the biceps muscle and from the muscles that form the rotator cuff around the joint provide additional stability.

Joint cavity

Articular capsule

Biceps tendon

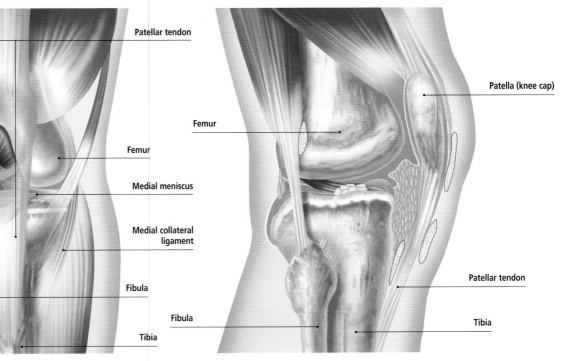

Quadriceps muscle

Patellar tendon

Lateral collateral ligament

Lateral meniscus

Stability vs mobility
Numerous ligaments, cartilage menisci of the tibia and tendons from the strong muscles of the thigh and leg all stabilize and strengthen the knee joint, but they limit the joint mainly to a hinge-like motion. Twisting or sideways movements can easily tear a ligament or cause some other knee injury.

Femur

Medial meniscus

Medial collateral ligament

Fibula

Tibia

Patella (knee cap)

Femur

Patellar tendon

Fibula

Tibia

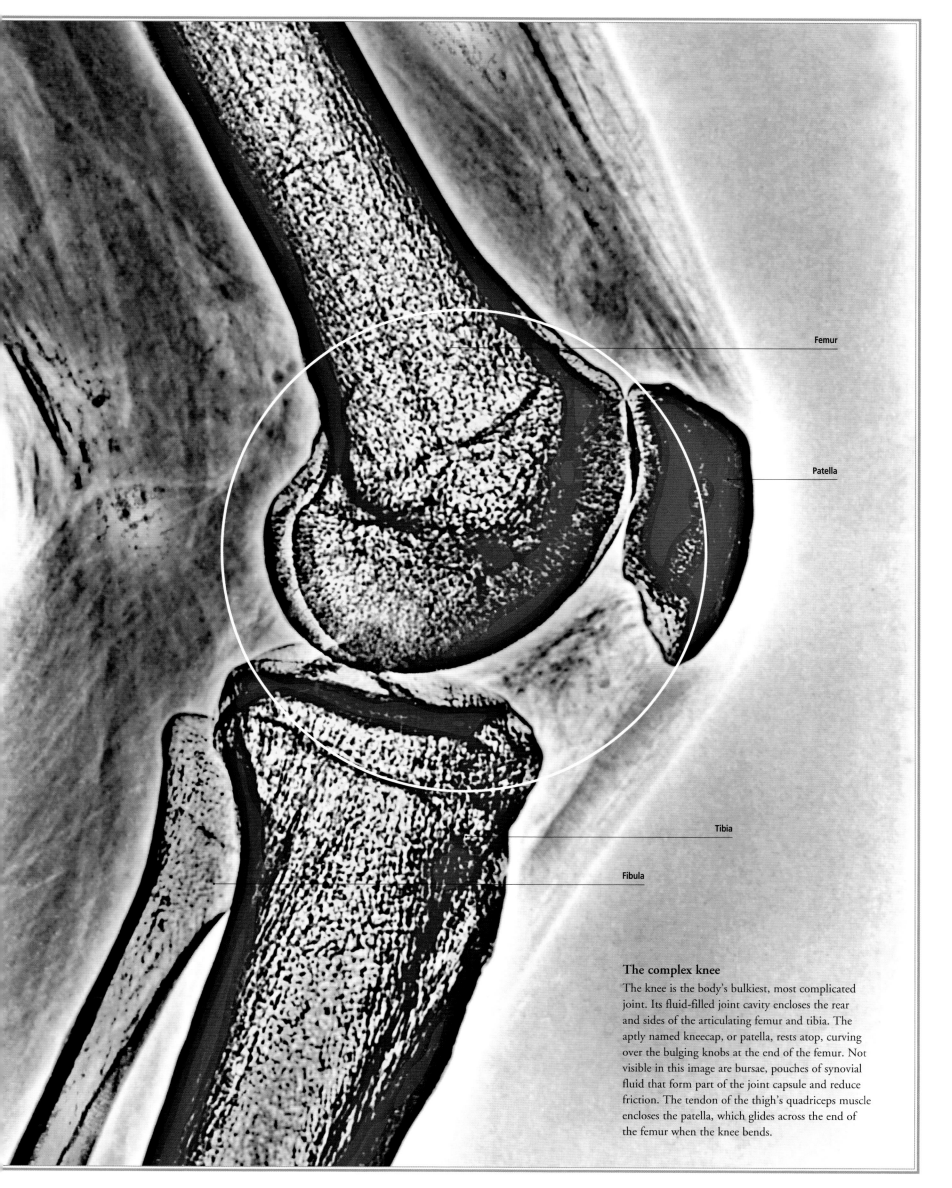

Femur

Patella

Tibia

Fibula

The complex knee

The knee is the body's bulkiest, most complicated joint. Its fluid-filled joint cavity encloses the rear and sides of the articulating femur and tibia. The aptly named kneecap, or patella, rests atop, curving over the bulging knobs at the end of the femur. Not visible in this image are bursae, pouches of synovial fluid that form part of the joint capsule and reduce friction. The tendon of the thigh's quadriceps muscle encloses the patella, which glides across the end of the femur when the knee bends.

SYNOVIAL JOINTS

Walking, eating, punching in numbers on a cell phone—these and a great variety of other movements exploit the tremendous versatility of synovial joints, the most common joints in the body. All share the same basic anatomy. A strong connective tissue capsule encloses the ends of the bones that form the joint and within it is a membrane-line cavity filled with lubricating synovial fluid. Both bone ends are cushioned with a layer of smooth cartilage, which helps prevent damage to the ends when the joint is in use.

Strong ligaments help support many synovial joints. These sturdy, well-lubricated skeletal connections allow articulating bones to glide past one another, increase or decrease the angle between them, rotate around the bone's long axis or perform special movements such as shrugging the shoulders or dropping the lower jaw in surprise. The configuration of the articulating bone surfaces, and the positioning of stabilizing ligaments largely determines the types of motions a given joint can perform with ease.

Plane
This type of joint connects flat bones such as the articulating processes of vertebrae and hand bones below the wrist. It allows the bones to glide past one another, but they cannot rotate.

Hypermobile joints
Everyone has the same number of joints, but some individuals are astonishingly flexible. In someone who has hypermobile joints, the bone articulations and ligaments in the spine, knees, shoulders or elsewhere are "looser" than normal. This "double-jointed" anatomical quirk allows an exceptional range of motion but also may mean that some joints are particularly susceptible to being dislocated.

Ball and socket
The hips and shoulders exemplify this type of joint. The curved socket of one bone cups the rounded head of the other. Ball-and-socket joints allow the greatest range of motion, including a variety of angular movements and rotation.

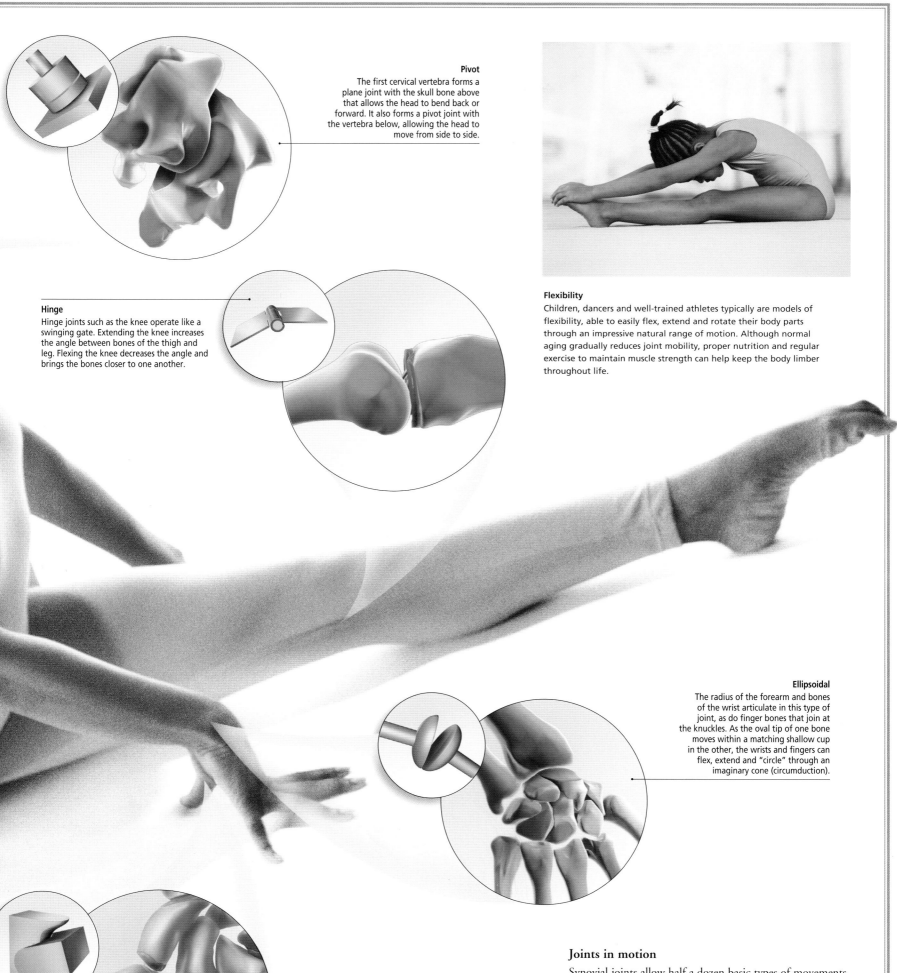

Pivot
The first cervical vertebra forms a plane joint with the skull bone above that allows the head to bend back or forward. It also forms a pivot joint with the vertebra below, allowing the head to move from side to side.

Hinge
Hinge joints such as the knee operate like a swinging gate. Extending the knee increases the angle between bones of the thigh and leg. Flexing the knee decreases the angle and brings the bones closer to one another.

Flexibility
Children, dancers and well-trained athletes typically are models of flexibility, able to easily flex, extend and rotate their body parts through an impressive natural range of motion. Although normal aging gradually reduces joint mobility, proper nutrition and regular exercise to maintain muscle strength can help keep the body limber throughout life.

Ellipsoidal
The radius of the forearm and bones of the wrist articulate in this type of joint, as do finger bones that join at the knuckles. As the oval tip of one bone moves within a matching shallow cup in the other, the wrists and fingers can flex, extend and "circle" through an imaginary cone (circumduction).

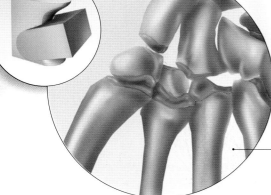

Saddle
In saddle joints the end of one articulating bone is roughly U-shaped and the end of the other bone fits into it like a rider in a saddle. The thumb articulates with the neighboring carpal bone in this type of joint, which allows humans to move their thumbs in several planes.

Joints in motion

Synovial joints allow half a dozen basic types of movements. Gliding movements are the simplest. Angle-changing movements include flexion, such as bending the chin toward the chest, and extension—the opposite movement, such as lifting the chin to its starting position. Abduction, such as spreading the fingers or raising an arm to the side, moves a body part outward from a central point, while adduction accomplishes the reverse. Rotation moves a bone around its vertical axis. Moving a limb, hand or digit so that the tip scribes an invisible cone is circumduction.

Bone Diseases and Disorders

Mineralized and hard, bones are quite sturdy, but they are far from indestructible. Bones may break or be attacked by microbes, weakened by osteoporosis, or affected by cancer and genetic disorders. Degenerative joint disease, especially osteoarthritis (OA), is responsible for more discomfort and disability than any other skeletal ailment, afflicting roughly 70 percent of people over age 65. Deep wounds, including a serious fracture, can allow entry of bacteria responsible for osteomyelitis, an infection of the bone and bone marrow. Teens and young adults are most susceptible to the aggressive bone cancer called osteosarcoma. The most common skeletal injuries, however, are simple joint sprains, strains and dislocations. Regardless of the cause, when any bone is injured or becomes diseased, the mobility and structural integrity of the whole skeleton are at stake.

Bone changes with age
Aging invariably alters bones and joints. With time nearly everyone suffers some loss of bone mass as natural bone-replenishing processes become less effective. Aging bones often develop spurs, projections that reduce the range of motion at joints and make movements feel stiff. Bone spurs also complicate osteoarthritis, which develops as mechanical stress wears away the cartilage coverings of bone ends in synovial joints. As unprotected bone ends rub against each other and break down, the joint becomes painfully inflamed.

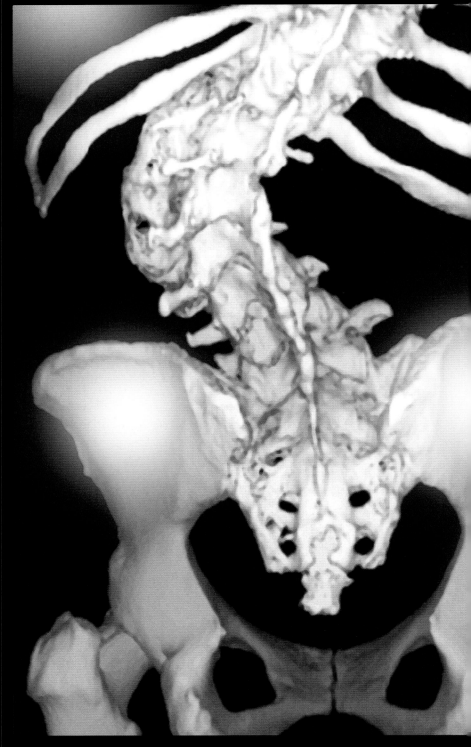

Spinal osteoporosis
Effects of osteoporosis often are worst in the spine, where spongy bone in vertebrae may become extremely fragile. A patient may suffer one or more compression fractures—the cracking and partial crumbling of vertebrae under the strain of a fall or simply of the patient's body weight.

Scoliosis
Scoliosis is an abnormal lateral bend in the spine. This puzzling disorder usually involves thoracic vertebrae and is most common in females. Scoliosis often develops in conjunction with muscle paralysis or when one leg is shorter than the other. In children a body brace or surgery can correct the spine's alignment.

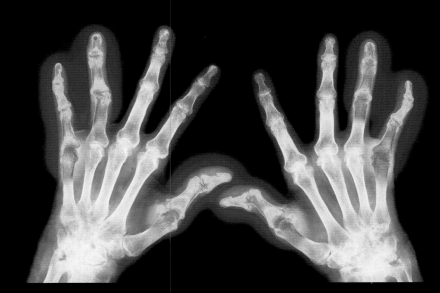

Rheumatoid arthritis
As with osteoarthritis, inflammation can also be a factor in rheumatoid arthritis, a progressive and painful autoimmune disease in which the person's own immune system mounts an attack on joint tissues. In severe cases the ends of bones in the fingers or toes fuse, often producing crippling deformities.

Bone fractures

Bone breaks fall into multiple categories, depending mainly on the positions of the bone ends and whether the fracture breaks the skin. An incomplete, closed or "simple" fracture is basically a crack running partly through a bone. A complete fracture separates the bone into two pieces. If a broken bone breaks the skin, the injury is considered an open complete or "compound" fracture. Comminuted fractures, in which a bone shatters, are among the most difficult to repair and the slowest to heal.

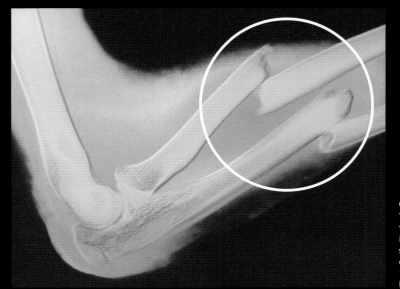

Osteoporosis
Over time osteoporosis may so weaken bones that they break under even modest pressure. This colorized image shows the jagged fracture of an affected limb bone, which has lost much of the mineralized tissue that would normally allow it to withstand a great deal of mechanical force.

Compound fracture
This X-ray displays the complete fracture of both the radius and ulna in a patient's forearm—an injury sometimes due to falling on an outstretched arm. The breaks are "transverse fractures" across each bone's long axis.

Complete fracture
This X-ray image shows a major fracture of the humerus, the usually strong upper arm bone, which has broken in two. When the skin above a fractured bone is broken the open wound may be colonized by infectious microbes.

HEALING AND REPLACING JOINTS

Joint injuries and arthritic changes often are extremely painful and seriously limit the mobility of hips, knees, shoulders, fingers and other joints. Today all manner of joint damage can be treated with an ever-increasing number of medical options. Improving technology is making joint surgery and replacement more efficient and less costly with longer-lasting effects. Minimally invasive procedures that require only a finger-length incision reduce blood loss and the trauma of surgery and speed the healing process. Newly developed materials for artificial joints, including alloys of titanium and of cobalt chromium, may last 20 years or longer, a major boon for younger patients. Extremely durable prosthetic joints may be built of a malleable metal called tantalum, which can be formed into an almost identical copy of a natural joint. All these advances are relieving crippling pain and helping people pursue active lives well into old age.

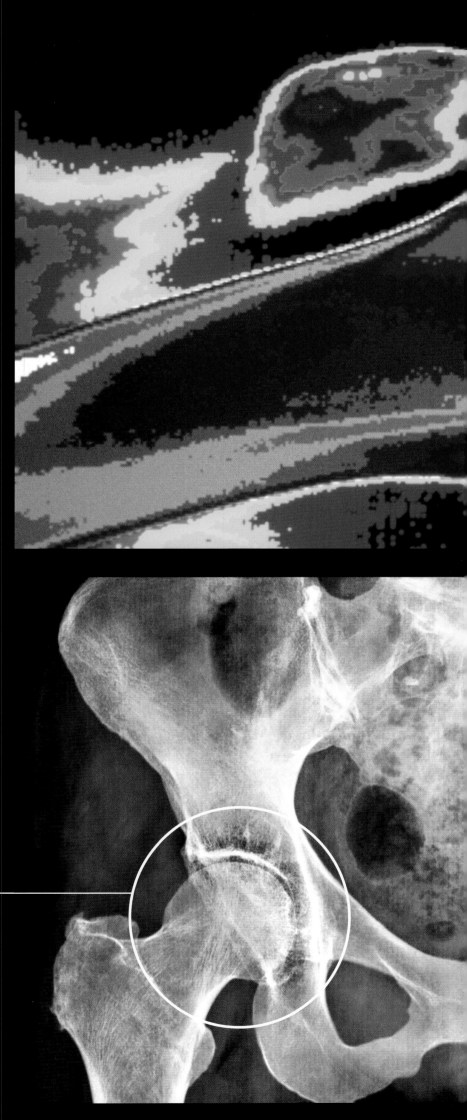

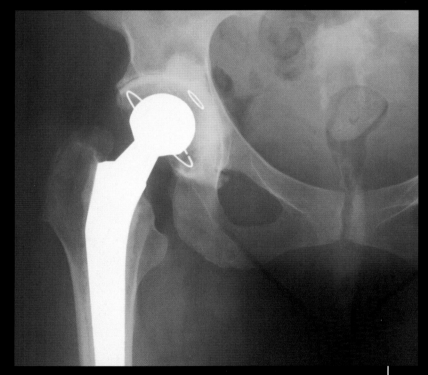

Total hip replacement
In total hip replacement, the diseased ball and socket (orange areas) are replaced with a metal ball and stem and a plastic socket. Traditionally, replacements were cemented in place, but many patients today receive a more durable, "cementless" prosthesis with minute pores. Bone tissue produced by cells in the femur grows into the pores, holding the new hip in place.

Replacing joints

Joint replacement is on the rise as the incidence of problems such as degenerative arthritis increases in aging populations and more people participate in sports that can stress and injure joints. When a hip, shoulder or knuckle joint is replaced, a surgeon replaces damaged cartilage and bone with artificial materials. Damaged areas in knee joints may be resurfaced with a device made of metal or other materials. Recovery time varies depending on the patient's age, physical condition and the complexity of the surgery.

Knee scan

This image shows a dislocated kneecap (top, center), its position skewed toward the outside of the leg. As a result the knee joint cannot extend and the patient cannot straighten the leg. Fortunately this injury usually responds well to rest, icing and other medical treatment.

Vulnerable ligaments

When the fibrous ligaments that stabilize shoulder joints, hips, knees and ankles overstretch or tear, the joint loosens and the bones it links fall out of alignment. A fall or direct blow, jumping, twisting and coming to a sudden stop all can produce this type of injury, which is most common among runners, skiers and football players. Although the reasons are unclear, women are most susceptible to these injuries. Healing a major tear may require surgery and months of intensive rehabilitation.

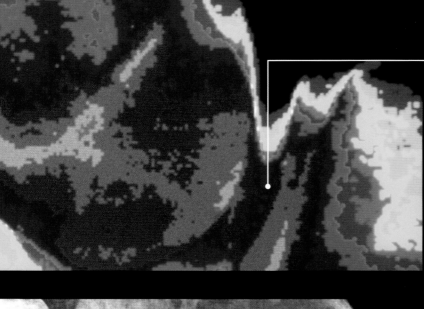

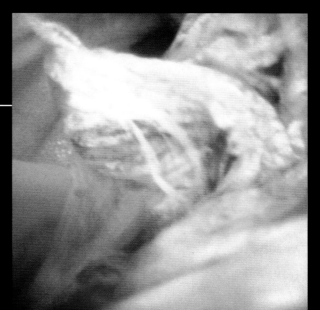

Torn ligament

Here, a severely torn knee ligament has been exposed for surgical repair. The anterior cruciate ligament, or ACL, is a common sports-related knee injury. Researchers are developing techniques for growing transplantable replacement ligaments, which may greatly speed recovery time.

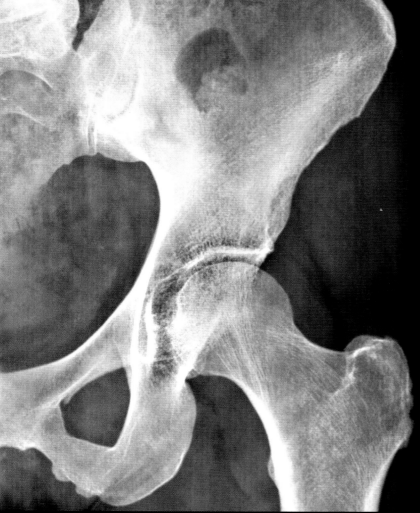

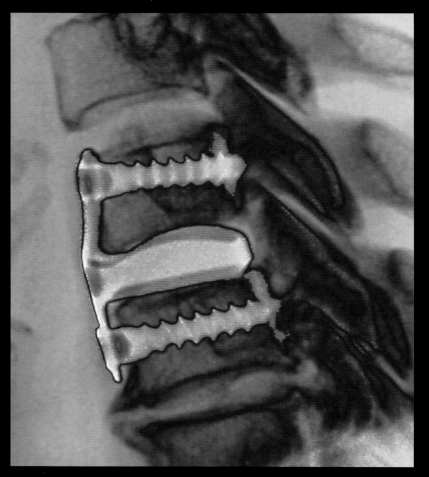

New spinal disks

Replacement of vertebral disks is becoming an option for patients who have untreatable degenerative disk disease. The procedure is used most often to replace disks in the lumbar spine. This artificial disk (orange) was attached with screws in the upper, cervical spine to treat arthritic changes that had severely limited the mobility of the patient's neck.

MUSCULAR SYSTEM

By weight, a human body is about 40 percent skeletal muscle. A few skeletal muscles attach to the skin, but most connect firmly to bones by way of tendons. All bear Latin names that describe one or more aspects of their shape, structure or action. For example, muscles that flex or extend a movable body part may have the terms *flexor* or *extensor* as part of their anatomical name. Terms such as *longus* (long), *maximus* (largest) and *minimus* (smallest) describe the relative size of a muscle. Unlike cardiac muscle or the smooth muscle of internal organs, skeletal muscles are under conscious control. When signals from the nervous system spark muscle contractions, the resulting force may move fingers on a keyboard, pucker lips for a kiss or propel a marathoner through a grueling race. Regardless, the force skeletal muscles exert is always a pull, never a push. This physiological work also generates much of the body's heat. Even at rest, skeletal muscles play a crucial role as stabilizers for the body's movable joints.

Gender differences in muscle mass

The body of an adult male is generally about 42 percent skeletal muscle, while that of an adult female averages about 36 percent skeletal muscle. Researchers attribute most of this difference to the fact that males produce more testosterone, which promotes the development of skeletal muscle fibers. Pound for pound, however, the skeletal muscles of females are just as strong as those of males.

Posterior muscles
Muscles of the upper and lower back have major roles in moving the head, neck, spine and arms, while those of the buttocks and backs of the thighs and legs generate much of the power humans require to move their hips and bend the knees. Not surprisingly, these muscles and muscle groups include some of the largest and strongest skeletal muscles.

Levator scapulae
Located under the trapezius, this muscle works with the trapezius to raise the shoulder blades.

Rhomboids
These muscles draw the shoulder blades back or downward and also help stabilize them.

Supraspinatus
Part of the muscle group forming the rotator cuff, this deep muscle helps stabilize the shoulder joint.

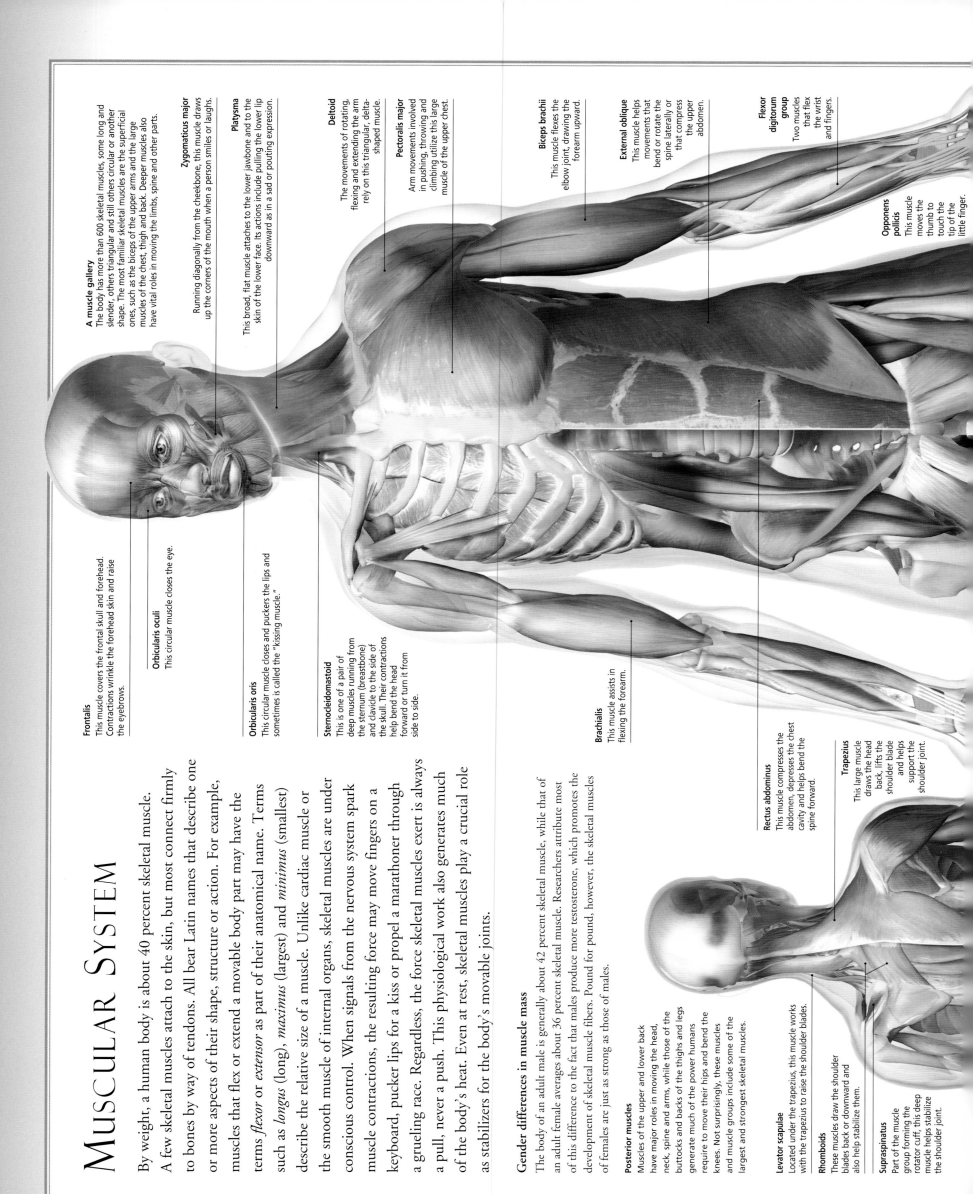

A muscle gallery
The body has more than 600 skeletal muscles, some long and slender, others triangular and still others circular or another shape. The most familiar skeletal muscles are the superficial ones, such as the biceps of the upper arms and the large muscles of the chest, thigh and back. Deeper muscles also have vital roles in moving the limbs, spine and other parts.

Zygomaticus major
Running diagonally from the cheekbone, this muscle draws up the corners of the mouth when a person smiles or laughs.

Platysma
This broad, flat muscle attaches to the lower jawbone and to the skin of the lower face. Its actions include pulling the lower lip downward as in a sad or pouting expression.

Deltoid
The movements of rotating, flexing and extending the arm rely on this triangular, delta-shaped muscle.

Pectoralis major
Arm movements involved in pushing, throwing and climbing utilize this large muscle of the upper chest.

Biceps brachii
This muscle flexes the elbow joint, drawing the forearm upward.

External oblique
This muscle helps movements that bend or rotate the spine laterally or that compress the upper abdomen.

Flexor digitorum group
Two muscles that flex the wrist and fingers.

Opponens pollicis
This muscle moves the thumb to touch the tip of the little finger.

Frontalis
This muscle covers the frontal skull and forehead. Contractions wrinkle the forehead skin and raise the eyebrows.

Orbicularis oculi
This circular muscle closes the eye.

Orbicularis oris
This circular muscle closes and puckers the lips and sometimes is called the "kissing muscle."

Sternocleidomastoid
This is one of a pair of deep muscles running from the sternum (breastbone) and clavicle to the side of the skull. Their contractions help bend the head forward or turn it from side to side.

Brachialis
This muscle assists in flexing the forearm.

Rectus abdominus
This muscle compresses the abdomen, depresses the chest cavity and helps bend the spine forward.

Trapezius
This large muscle draws the head back, lifts the shoulder blade and helps support the shoulder joint.

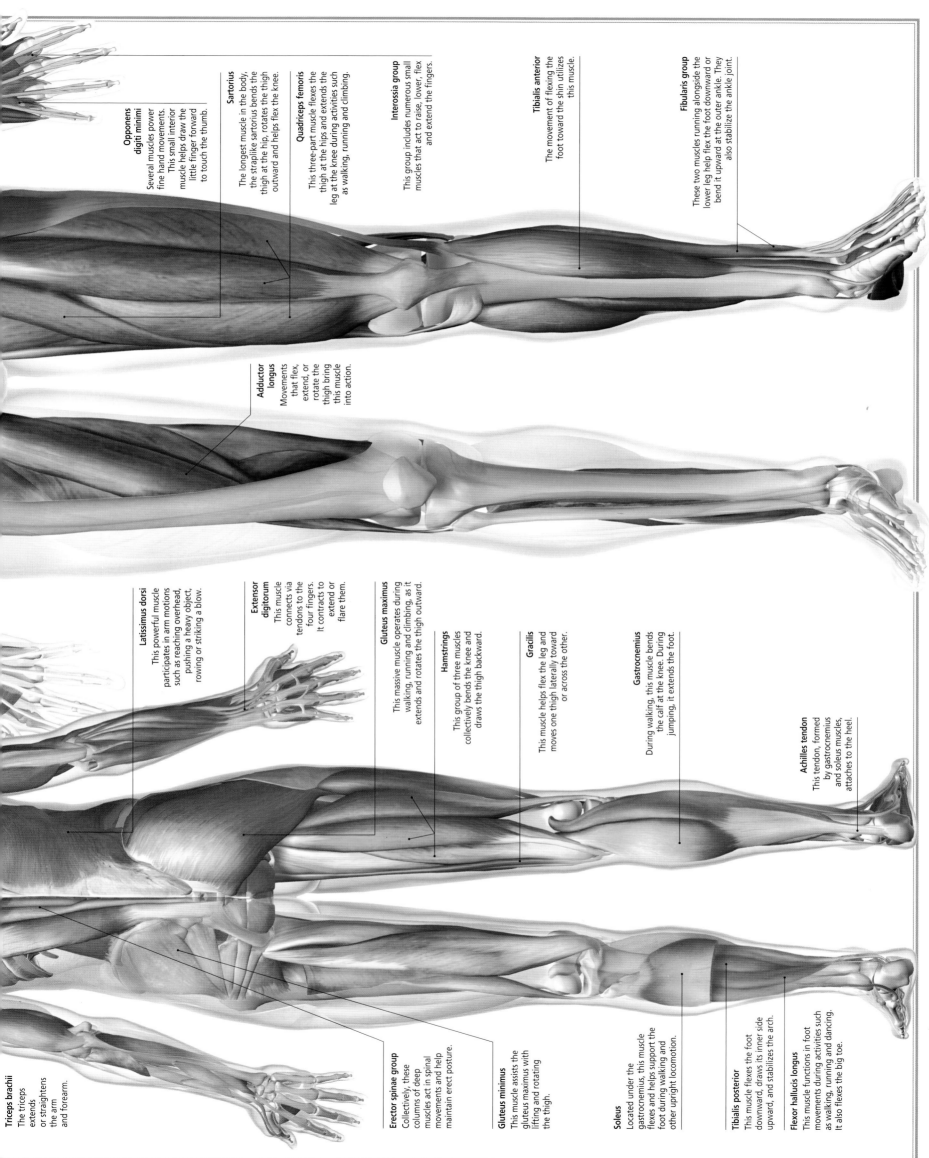

Opponens digiti minimi
Several muscles power fine hand movements. This small interior muscle helps draw the little finger forward to touch the thumb.

Sartorius
The longest muscle in the body, the straplike sartorius bends the thigh at the hip, rotates the thigh outward and helps flex the knee.

Quadriceps femoris
This three-part muscle flexes the thigh at the hips and extends the leg at the knee during activities such as walking, running and climbing.

Interossia group
This group includes numerous small muscles that act to raise, lower, flex and extend the fingers.

Tibialis anterior
The movement of flexing the foot toward the shin utilizes this muscle.

Fibularis group
These two muscles running alongside the lower leg help flex the foot downward or bend it upward at the outer ankle. They also stabilize the ankle joint.

Adductor longus
Movements that flex, extend, or rotate the thigh bring this muscle into action.

Latissimus dorsi
This powerful muscle participates in arm motions such as reaching overhead, pushing a heavy object, rowing or striking a blow.

Extensor digitorum
This muscle connects via tendons to the four fingers. It contracts to extend or flare them.

Gluteus maximus
This massive muscle operates during walking, running and climbing, as it extends and rotates the thigh outward.

Hamstrings
This group of three muscles collectively bends the knee and draws the thigh backward.

Gracilis
This muscle helps flex the leg and moves one thigh laterally toward or across the other.

Gastrocnemius
During walking, this muscle bends the calf at the knee. During jumping, it extends the foot.

Achilles tendon
This tendon, formed by gastrocnemius and soleus muscles, attaches to the heel.

Triceps brachii
The triceps extends or straightens the arm and forearm.

Erector spinae group
Collectively, these columns of deep muscles act in spinal movements and help maintain erect posture.

Gluteus minimus
This muscle assists the gluteus maximus with lifting and rotating the thigh.

Soleus
Located under the gastrocnemius, this muscle flexes and helps support the foot during walking and other upright locomotion.

Tibialis posterior
This muscle flexes the foot downward, draws its inner side upward, and stabilizes the arch.

Flexor hallucis longus
This muscle functions in foot movements during activities such as walking, running and dancing. It also flexes the big toe.

HOW SKELETAL MUSCLES WORK

Skeletal muscles are arranged to move limbs or other body parts as efficiently as possible. Nearly all pull on bones much like pulleys tugging on levers. The two ends of a muscle attach to different bones—one that moves at a joint, and another that usually remains immobile.

A muscle's "origin" is the site where it anchors to the stationary bone and its "insertion" is the place where it attaches to the movable bone. Contractions usually pull the moving bone toward the muscle's origin, and because muscles attach close to most joints, a small contraction can produce a major movement. Skeletal muscles often work in pairs or larger groups. One muscle serves as the "prime mover," providing most of the required force, and one or more assisting, or synergist, muscles may add force or stability. Conversely, when a prime mover contracts, one or more antagonist muscle on the opposite side of the joint can reverse or adjust the action.

MUSCLE CONTRACTIONS

A muscle contraction begins when nerve impulses cause sarcomeres in muscle fibers to compress lengthwise like accordions. The impulses trigger chemical changes that activate filaments built of myosin, a protein with a rounded "head." Millions of activated myosin heads attach to filaments of a different protein, actin, and slide them toward each other—making the sarcomere shorter. Repeated in hundreds or thousands of muscle fibers, this shortening of sarcomeres contracts the whole muscle. A muscle relaxes when myosin and actin disengage and sarcomeres and other parts lengthen once again.

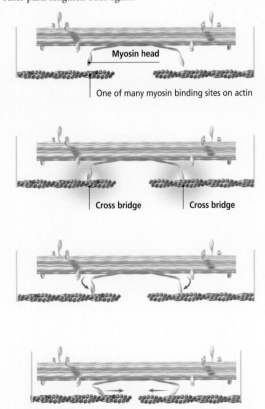

Myosin head

One of many myosin binding sites on actin

Cross bridge   **Cross bridge**

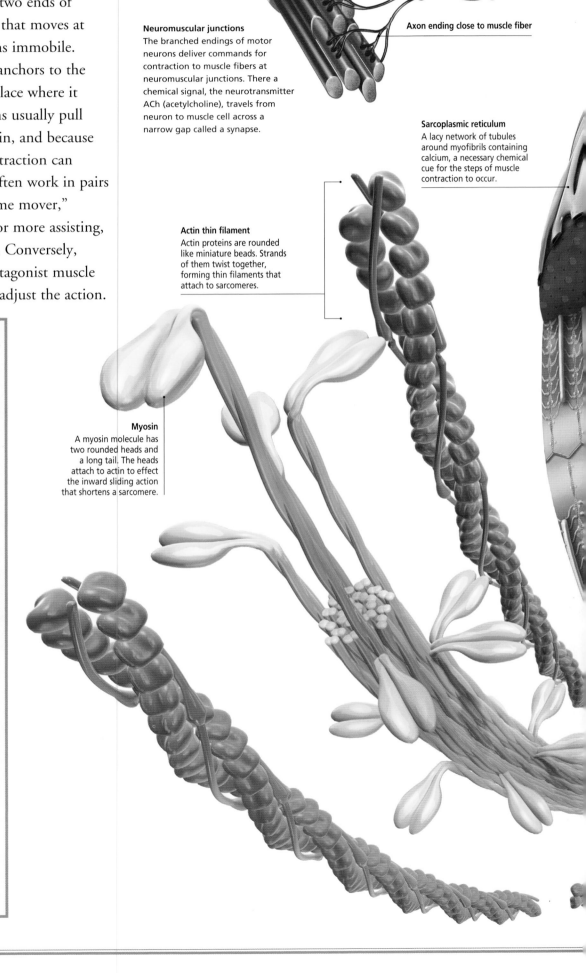

Bundled muscle fibers

Neuron axon

Axon ending close to muscle fiber

Neuromuscular junctions
The branched endings of motor neurons deliver commands for contraction to muscle fibers at neuromuscular junctions. There a chemical signal, the neurotransmitter ACh (acetylcholine), travels from neuron to muscle cell across a narrow gap called a synapse.

Sarcoplasmic reticulum
A lacy network of tubules around myofibrils containing calcium, a necessary chemical cue for the steps of muscle contraction to occur.

Actin thin filament
Actin proteins are rounded like miniature beads. Strands of them twist together, forming thin filaments that attach to sarcomeres.

Myosin
A myosin molecule has two rounded heads and a long tail. The heads attach to actin to effect the inward sliding action that shortens a sarcomere.

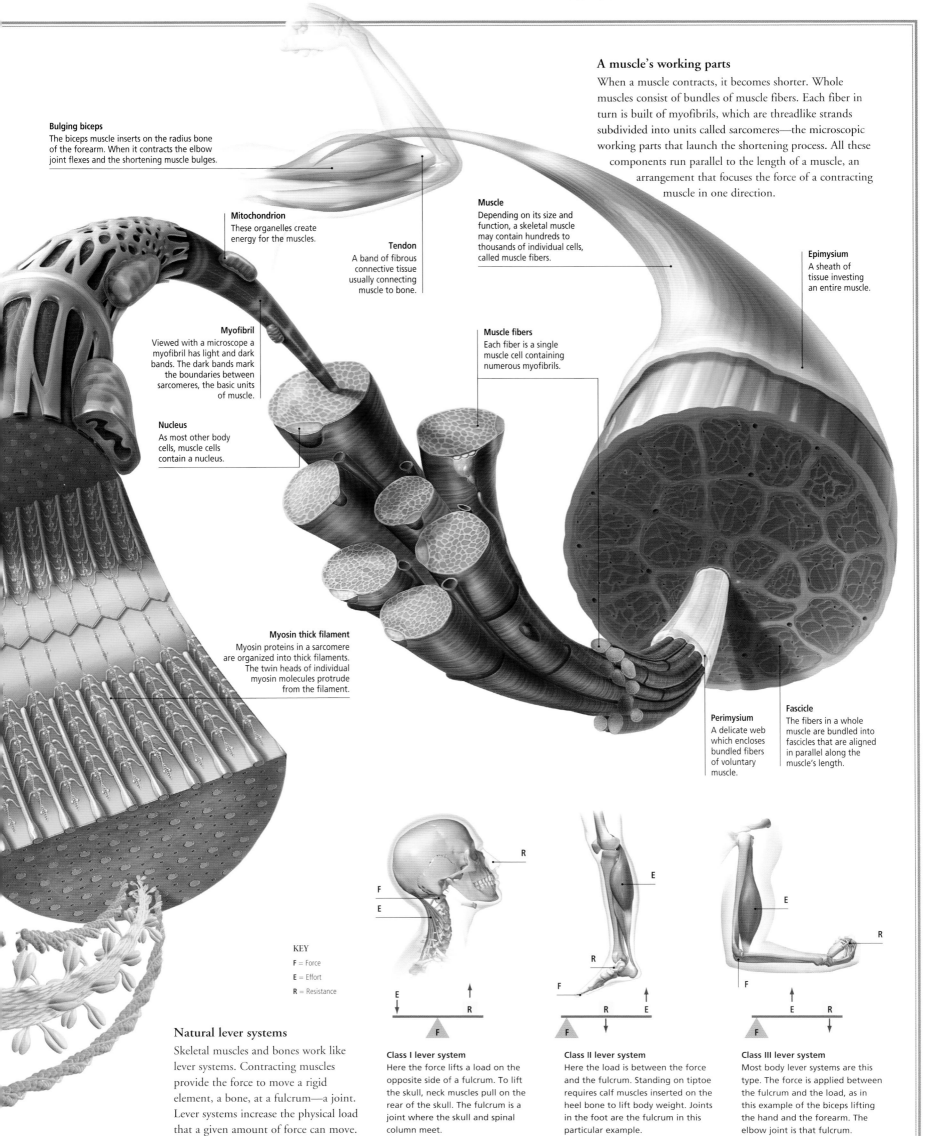

A muscle's working parts

When a muscle contracts, it becomes shorter. Whole muscles consist of bundles of muscle fibers. Each fiber in turn is built of myofibrils, which are threadlike strands subdivided into units called sarcomeres—the microscopic working parts that launch the shortening process. All these components run parallel to the length of a muscle, an arrangement that focuses the force of a contracting muscle in one direction.

Bulging biceps
The biceps muscle inserts on the radius bone of the forearm. When it contracts the elbow joint flexes and the shortening muscle bulges.

Mitochondrion
These organelles create energy for the muscles.

Tendon
A band of fibrous connective tissue usually connecting muscle to bone.

Muscle
Depending on its size and function, a skeletal muscle may contain hundreds to thousands of individual cells, called muscle fibers.

Epimysium
A sheath of tissue investing an entire muscle.

Myofibril
Viewed with a microscope a myofibril has light and dark bands. The dark bands mark the boundaries between sarcomeres, the basic units of muscle.

Muscle fibers
Each fiber is a single muscle cell containing numerous myofibrils.

Nucleus
As most other body cells, muscle cells contain a nucleus.

Myosin thick filament
Myosin proteins in a sarcomere are organized into thick filaments. The twin heads of individual myosin molecules protrude from the filament.

Perimysium
A delicate web which encloses bundled fibers of voluntary muscle.

Fascicle
The fibers in a whole muscle are bundled into fascicles that are aligned in parallel along the muscle's length.

KEY
F = Force
E = Effort
R = Resistance

Natural lever systems

Skeletal muscles and bones work like lever systems. Contracting muscles provide the force to move a rigid element, a bone, at a fulcrum—a joint. Lever systems increase the physical load that a given amount of force can move.

Class I lever system
Here the force lifts a load on the opposite side of a fulcrum. To lift the skull, neck muscles pull on the rear of the skull. The fulcrum is a joint where the skull and spinal column meet.

Class II lever system
Here the load is between the force and the fulcrum. Standing on tiptoe requires calf muscles inserted on the heel bone to lift body weight. Joints in the foot are the fulcrum in this particular example.

Class III lever system
Most body lever systems are this type. The force is applied between the fulcrum and the load, as in this example of the biceps lifting the hand and the forearm. The elbow joint is that fulcrum.

MUSCLES OF THE FACE

More than fifteen muscles form the sheet-like "flesh" of the face. Most of these muscles are part of our human capacity for nonverbal communication—smiles, frowns, smirks, furrowed brows and all manner of other facial expressions. Unlike most other skeletal muscles, which connect "bone to bone" to move joints, those used to make facial expressions connect skin to bone, or skin and muscles to bone. The muscles move the skin or other muscles when they contract. Humans also use their facial muscles for a variety of activities related to opening, closing and using some key openings in the skull, namely the eyes and mouth. Muscles around the mouth and linking the face and neck assist in taking in food, chewing and swallowing it. Others open and close the eyelids, purse a whistler's lips, and flare the nostrils in displeasure or in preparation for inhaling a long, deep breath.

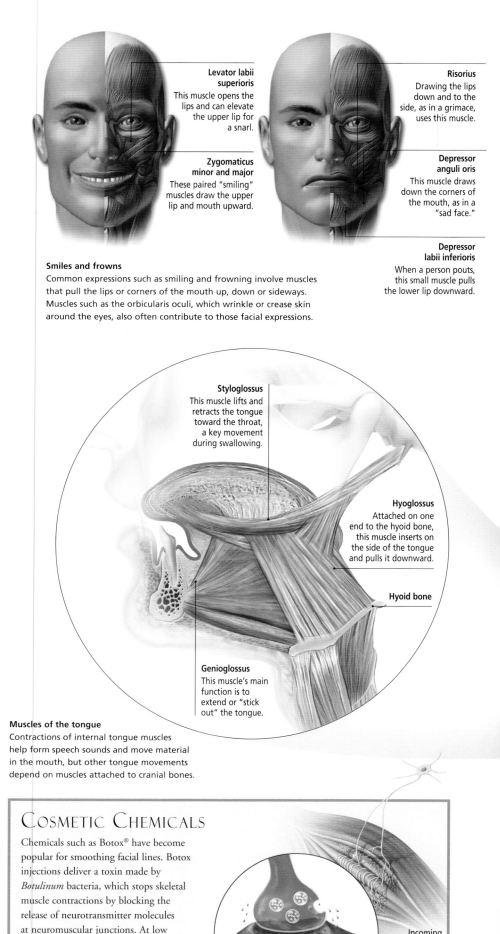

Levator labii superioris
This muscle opens the lips and can elevate the upper lip for a snarl.

Zygomaticus minor and major
These paired "smiling" muscles draw the upper lip and mouth upward.

Risorius
Drawing the lips down and to the side, as in a grimace, uses this muscle.

Depressor anguli oris
This muscle draws down the corners of the mouth, as in a "sad face."

Depressor labii inferioris
When a person pouts, this small muscle pulls the lower lip downward.

Smiles and frowns
Common expressions such as smiling and frowning involve muscles that pull the lips or corners of the mouth up, down or sideways. Muscles such as the orbicularis oculi, which wrinkle or crease skin around the eyes, also often contribute to those facial expressions.

Styloglossus
This muscle lifts and retracts the tongue toward the throat, a key movement during swallowing.

Hyoglossus
Attached on one end to the hyoid bone, this muscle inserts on the side of the tongue and pulls it downward.

Hyoid bone

Genioglossus
This muscle's main function is to extend or "stick out" the tongue.

Muscles of the tongue
Contractions of internal tongue muscles help form speech sounds and move material in the mouth, but other tongue movements depend on muscles attached to cranial bones.

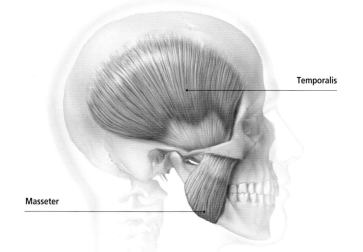

Temporalis

Masseter

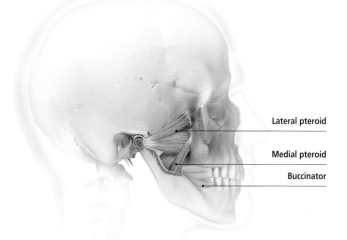

Lateral pteroid

Medial pteroid

Buccinator

Muscles of mastication
Mastication, or chewing, uses five major muscles plus the orbicularis oris, which opens the lips when a person eats. The powerful masseter draws up the lower jawbone to close the mouth. Side-to-side grinding movements use the temporalis and the two pteroid muscles. The buccinator muscles push food toward the rear teeth during chewing.

COSMETIC CHEMICALS

Chemicals such as Botox® have become popular for smoothing facial lines. Botox injections deliver a toxin made by *Botulinum* bacteria, which stops skeletal muscle contractions by blocking the release of neurotransmitter molecules at neuromuscular junctions. At low doses the toxin relaxes facial muscles that cause wrinkling.

Uninjected muscle
Neurotransmitter released

Incoming motor neuron impulse

Botox-injected muscle
Neurotransmitter blocked

Facial muscles

Together or in combination, facial muscles generate the movements that produce facial expressions. A single cranial nerve, the facial nerve (VII), innervates the muscles of facial expression. As a result, a stroke, injury or infection that damages the nerve can produce paralysis, usually on one side of the face.

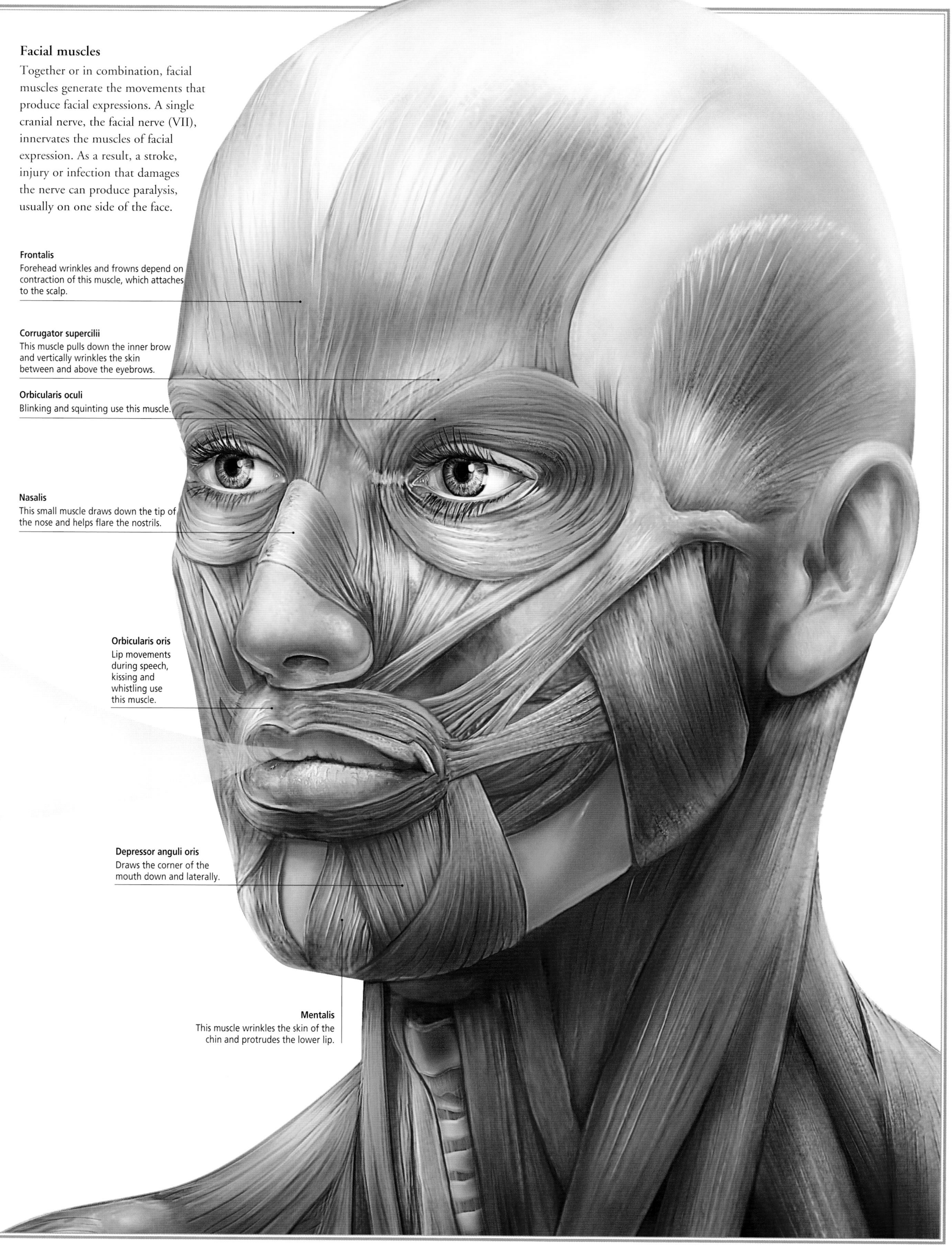

Frontalis
Forehead wrinkles and frowns depend on contraction of this muscle, which attaches to the scalp.

Corrugator supercilii
This muscle pulls down the inner brow and vertically wrinkles the skin between and above the eyebrows.

Orbicularis oculi
Blinking and squinting use this muscle.

Nasalis
This small muscle draws down the tip of the nose and helps flare the nostrils.

Orbicularis oris
Lip movements during speech, kissing and whistling use this muscle.

Depressor anguli oris
Draws the corner of the mouth down and laterally.

Mentalis
This muscle wrinkles the skin of the chin and protrudes the lower lip.

SMOOTH MUSCLE

Smooth muscle functions differently to skeletal muscle. Unlike skeletal muscle, its contractions do not help us move about in the world, and it is not under voluntary control. Instead, smooth muscle forms much of the walls of hollow organs, such as the stomach, intestine, bladder and uterus. It also is a key building material of body tubes including miles of small blood vessels, airways to the lungs, and the various types of ducts that transport substances from place to place in the digestive and reproductive systems. In the eyes, tiny bands of smooth muscle perform fine adjustments that focus light on the retina and dilate or contract the pupils. All these activities are coordinated as signals from the nervous system, hormones or from smooth muscle fibers themselves triggering slow contractions that provide the steady force to move food, blood or urine from place to place—or even bring a newborn into the world.

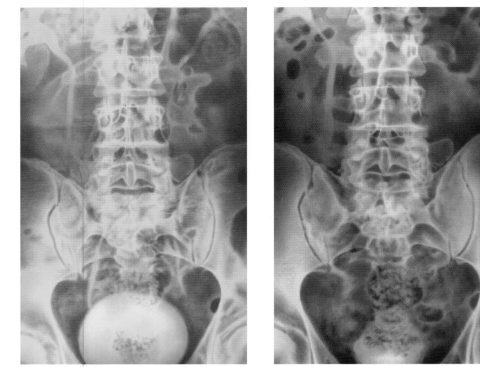

Slow, tireless and adaptable
Skeletal muscles contract rapidly, but their work is energy intensive and they fatigue quickly. By contrast, smooth muscle contracts slowly and uses far less energy. This low-demand operation allows most smooth muscle to contract steadily for long periods—in some instances, as in the walls of blood vessels, for years on end. And unlike other muscle types, smooth muscle can tolerate extended stretching. The bladder can expand with urine for hours, and the stomach and intestines can hold food long enough for it to be digested.

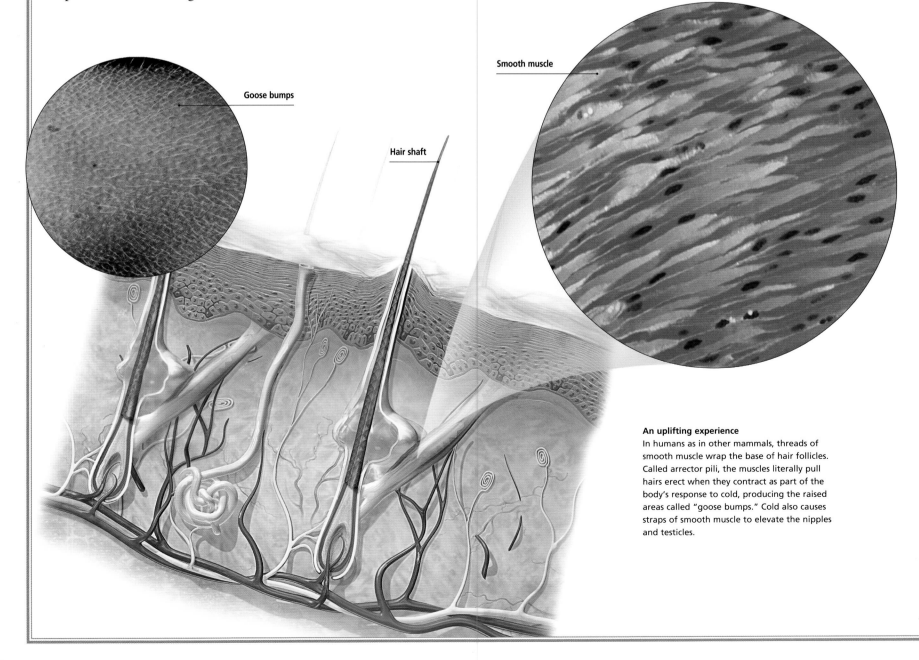

Goose bumps

Smooth muscle

Hair shaft

An uplifting experience
In humans as in other mammals, threads of smooth muscle wrap the base of hair follicles. Called arrector pili, the muscles literally pull hairs erect when they contract as part of the body's response to cold, producing the raised areas called "goose bumps." Cold also causes straps of smooth muscle to elevate the nipples and testicles.

Smooth muscle in the stomach
Just beneath the stomach's lining, layers of smooth muscle oriented at different angles form the stomach wall. Contractions of the muscles mix ingested food with digestive juices and move food into the intestines. As the stomach empties, the wall crumples into thick folds, only to expand again with the next meal.

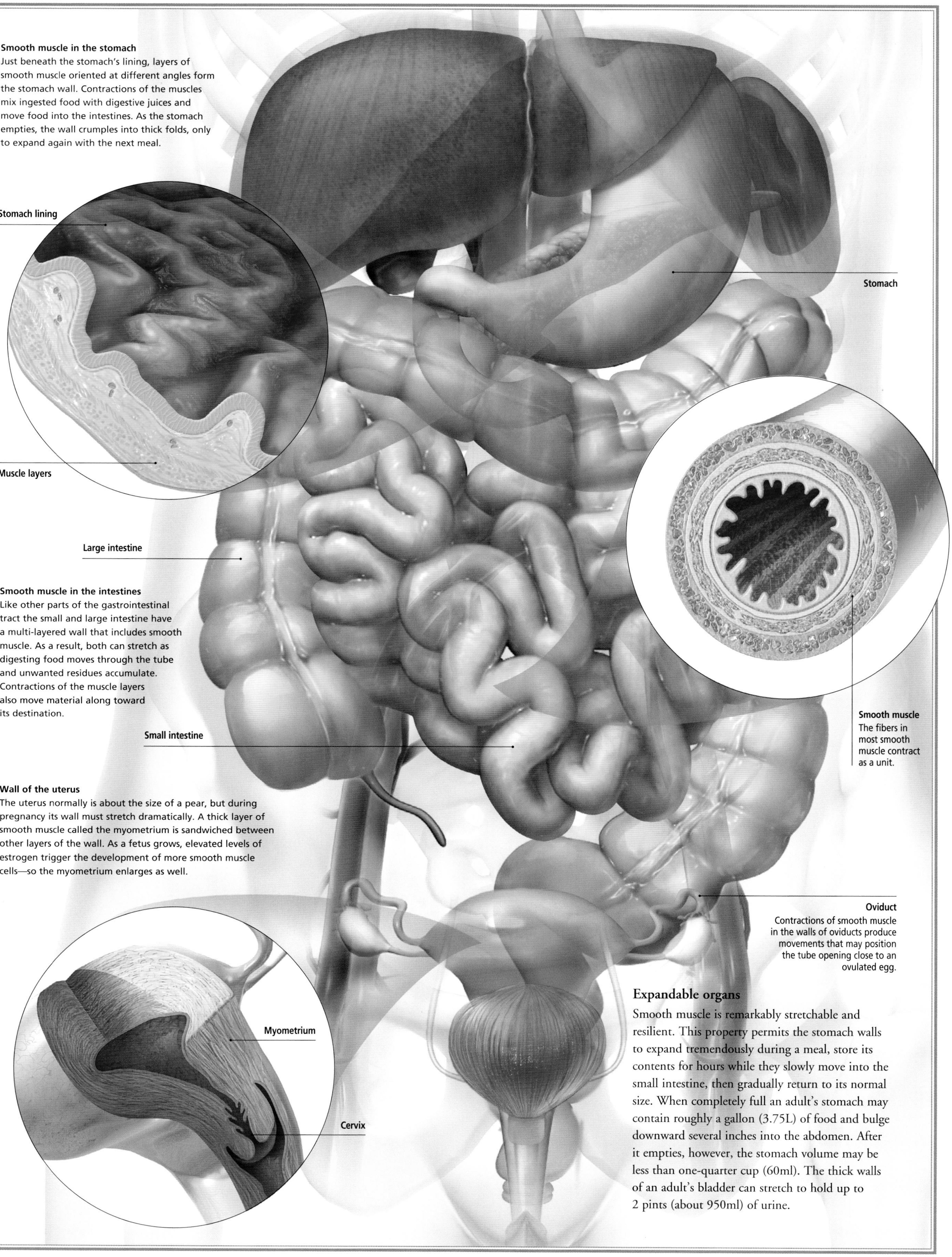

Stomach lining

Muscle layers

Stomach

Large intestine

Smooth muscle in the intestines
Like other parts of the gastrointestinal tract the small and large intestine have a multi-layered wall that includes smooth muscle. As a result, both can stretch as digesting food moves through the tube and unwanted residues accumulate. Contractions of the muscle layers also move material along toward its destination.

Small intestine

Smooth muscle
The fibers in most smooth muscle contract as a unit.

Wall of the uterus
The uterus normally is about the size of a pear, but during pregnancy its wall must stretch dramatically. A thick layer of smooth muscle called the myometrium is sandwiched between other layers of the wall. As a fetus grows, elevated levels of estrogen trigger the development of more smooth muscle cells—so the myometrium enlarges as well.

Oviduct
Contractions of smooth muscle in the walls of oviducts produce movements that may position the tube opening close to an ovulated egg.

Expandable organs

Smooth muscle is remarkably stretchable and resilient. This property permits the stomach walls to expand tremendously during a meal, store its contents for hours while they slowly move into the small intestine, then gradually return to its normal size. When completely full an adult's stomach may contain roughly a gallon (3.75L) of food and bulge downward several inches into the abdomen. After it empties, however, the stomach volume may be less than one-quarter cup (60ml). The thick walls of an adult's bladder can stretch to hold up to 2 pints (about 950ml) of urine.

Myometrium

Cervix

MUSCLE DISEASES AND DISORDERS

Movement is the casualty when skeletal muscles are damaged. Everyone experiences an occasional muscle spasm—the sudden, involuntary "jerk" of a skeletal muscle. The contraction can become a cramp if it does not release immediately. Cramps usually occur in the calf and thigh muscles and may indicate a deficiency of potassium, which is required for normal muscle contraction. When a movement, overexertion or blow tears too many of the fibers in a muscle, the result may be a low-level strain that heals within a week or two. The more fibers that tear, the more serious the strain and the longer the recuperation time. When a whole muscle is torn, healing may require many weeks or months and resulting scar tissue may prevent the muscle from ever regaining its previous strength and durability. With the progressive, genetic conditions called muscular dystrophies, skeletal muscle tissue irreversibly breaks down and muscles become wasted and weak.

Tetanus
"Lockjaw" and other symptoms of the disease tetanus may develop if a newborn's umbilical stump becomes infected by *Clostridium tetani*. The bacterium's toxin prevents contracted muscles from relaxing. Prompt administration of an antitoxin leads to full recovery.

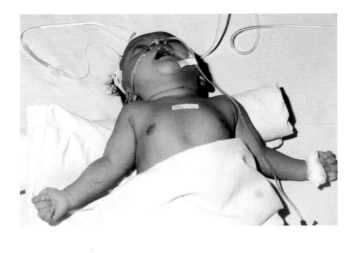

Muscular dystrophies
The most serious muscular dystrophy, called Duchenne muscular dystrophy or DMD, usually strikes children. DMD is fatal as skeletal muscles used in breathing stop functioning. Symptoms of myotonic muscular dystrophy (MMD) are more likely to develop in adults. MMD typically affects only muscles in the face, neck and lower limbs. Gradual wasting weakens the muscles, although many people with MMD remain quite mobile for many years. Movements may seem stiff because affected muscles cannot fully relax.

Wheelchair athletes
Athlete Huang Xuman shoots a basket during a match between China and Canada at the "Good Luck Beijing" 2008 Wheelchair Basketball International Tournament. The tournament is part of the international Paralympics program, which organizes Olympics-level competitions featuring disabled athletes. Huang's leg muscles are paralyzed but rigorous training has produced powerful skeletal muscles in his upper body.

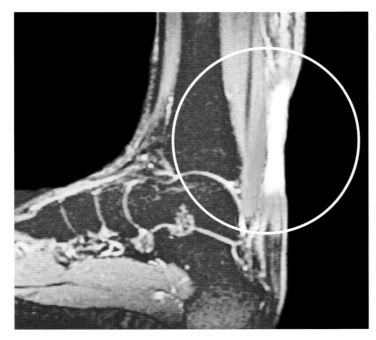

Achilles heel
An overstressed tendon can abruptly tear, separating muscles from bones. This image shows a ruptured Achilles tendon, which normally attaches the calf muscle to the heel bone. Surgery to mend the tear is the usual treatment.

Painful signal
Depending on the severity of a muscle injury, the pain can be minimal, agonizing or somewhere in between. Regardless, pain always signals damage. This player is in agony due to an acute injury—a severely torn thigh muscle.

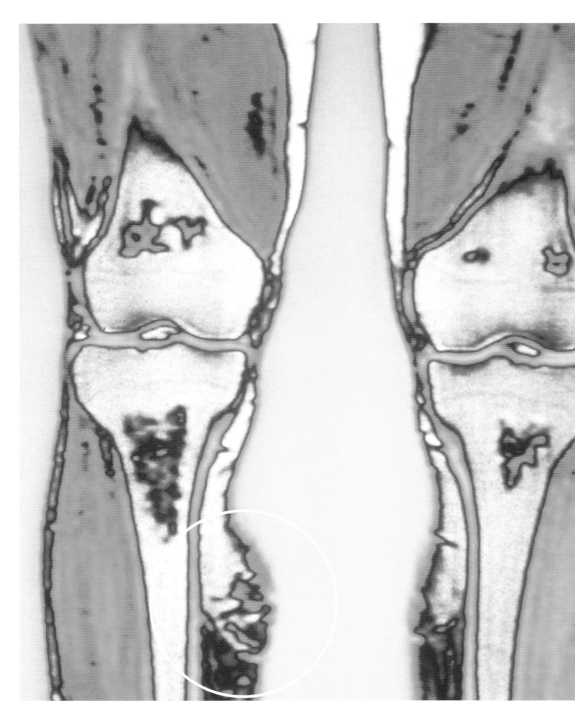

Preventing and treating tears
This MRI scan shows a torn calf muscle. Muscles are less likely to tear if they are strong from regular use and adequately warmed up before a workout. Exercisers should be alert for signs of excess muscle stress, especially pain. Rest is likely to be a major element of the treatment prescribed for a muscle injury.

From fatigue to injury

It is normal for some fibers in a muscle to tear when it contracts intensively, as in strenuous exercise or demanding physical work. This also produces lactic acid and depletes glycogen, a muscle's energy reserves. Both changes result in stiff and aching muscles, and several days may pass before a muscle regains full function. Pain signals an overstressed muscle, warning of more serious injury if the muscle is not allowed to recuperate.

NERVOUS SYSTEM

The human nervous system is a sophisticated command and control center, rising to the challenge of three tasks. First, its basic parts—tens of billions of neurons and a complex brain—continually monitor conditions both within the body and in the outside environment. Next, the steady flow of arriving information is integrated and assessed, usually very rapidly. Lastly, the nervous system issues instructions for any needed adjustments to the appropriate organs, tissues or cells.

A division of labor allows the nervous system to meet these demands. The brain and spinal cord form the central nervous system (CNS), and their role is to receive and evaluate information from sense organs and receptors, and if necessary, respond with signals that call for adjustments in some aspect of body functioning. Carrying signals to and from the CNS is the task of the peripheral nervous system (PNS), the elaborate network of nerves that services the rest of the body.

Communication via neurons
Neurons are the system's information carriers. Most communicate with their target cells by releasing chemical neurotransmitters from the endings of long axons. In this image the bulging, pink-colored cell body of one neuron is nearly covered by blue-colored axon endings extending toward it from other neurons.

Brain
Directly or indirectly, the brain controls all body functions.

Brain stem
The brain stem physically links other brain regions with the spinal cord.

Phrenic nerve
Movements of the diaphragm, a key muscle in breathing, depend on signals from this nerve.

Brachial plexus
A plexus is a group pf nerves. Nerves of the brachial plexus service the shoulders and arms.

Spinal cord
The spinal cord is a neural expressway that carries signals to and from the brain.

Radial nerve
This nerve helps control muscles of the forearm, wrist and fingers.

Vagus
Vagus nerves carry motor and sensory impulses. They serve pharynx and larynx muscles, the heart, lungs and abdominal organs.

Intercostal nerves
Intercostal nerves supply the skin, abdominal wall and muscles of the heart wall.

Genitofemoral nerve
This nerve supplies much of the genital area.

Median nerve
This nerve supplies several muscles of the forearm, wrist and fingers.

Iliohypogastric nerve
Signals to and from the lower back, abdomen and pubic region travel on this nerve.

Lumbar plexus
Nerves from this plexus service abdominal muscles and much of the thigh.

Ulnar nerve
This nerve runs from the brachial plexus through the forearm to muscles and skin of the ring finger and little finger.

Pudendal nerve
This nerve supplies muscles used in voluntary control of urination, in the anal area and in the erection of the penis.

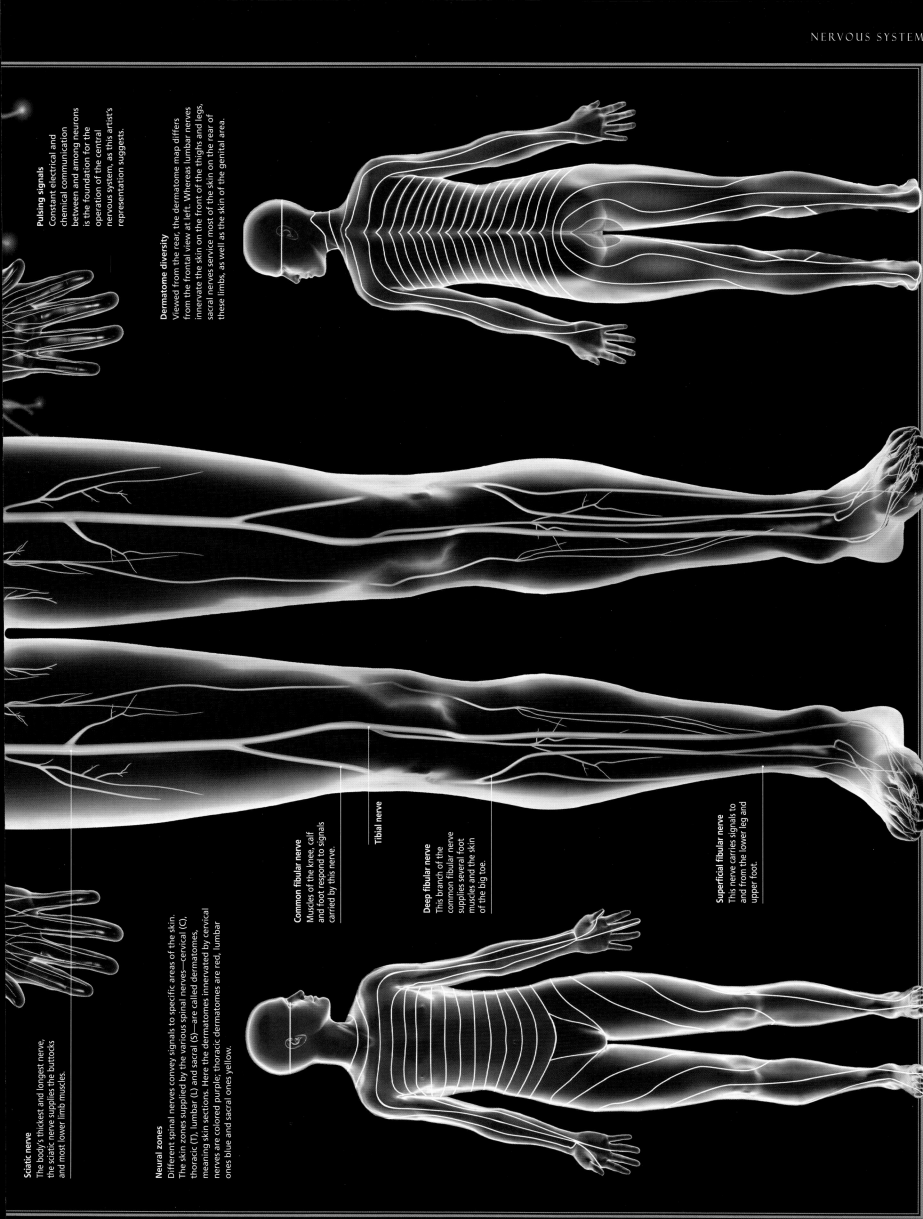

Pulsing signals
Constant electrical and chemical communication between and among neurons is the foundation for the operation of the central nervous system, as this artist's representation suggests.

Dermatome diversity
Viewed from the rear, the dermatome map differs from the frontal view at left. Whereas lumbar nerves innervate the skin on the front of the thighs and legs, sacral nerves service most of the skin on the rear of these limbs, as well as the skin of the genital area.

Sciatic nerve
The body's thickest and longest nerve, the sciatic nerve supplies the buttocks and most lower limb muscles.

Neural zones
Different spinal nerves convey signals to specific areas of the skin. The skin zones supplied by the various spinal nerves—cervical (C), thoracic (T), lumbar (L) and sacral (S)—are called dermatomes, meaning skin sections. Here the dermatomes innervated by cervical nerves are colored purple; thoracic dermatomes are red, lumbar ones blue and sacral ones yellow.

Common fibular nerve
Muscles of the knee, calf and foot respond to signals carried by this nerve.

Tibial nerve

Deep fibular nerve
This branch of the common fibular nerve supplies several foot muscles and the skin of the big toe.

Superficial fibular nerve
This nerve carries signals to and from the lower leg and upper foot.

THE SPINAL CORD AND BEYOND

The spinal cord is the vital information expressway between the brain and other body parts. It carries an unceasing flow of information—incoming sensory signals from the skin, muscles and glands as well as the brain's outgoing commands for body movements, the activity of the heart and other organs and other essentials of body functioning. Nerves of the peripheral nervous system deliver incoming signals and receive and send on responses. Threading throughout all body tissues, these communication lines fall into two groups. Many are somatic, or "body" nerves that directly link the spinal cord or brain with skeletal muscles and tendons and transmit impulses associated with movements of the head, trunk and limbs. Others are autonomic nerves that connect to the central nervous system indirectly by way of ganglia—clusters of nerve cell bodies outside the spinal cord or brain stem that serve as transfer points for signals to muscles and glands.

The autonomic nervous system

Autonomic nerves subdivide into two types that transmit counteracting signals to the heart and the smooth muscle of internal organs and glands. One type, parasympathetic nerves, manages "rest and digest" tasks that replenish the body's energy resources. Sympathetic nerves manage changes associated with more demanding activity, such as increasing the heart rate when a person is agitated. The shifting balance between these signals allows fine-tuned control of internal organs.

Fight or flight

Danger, excitement and stress prompt sympathetic nerves to mount a "fight-flight response." Tasks such as digestion slow while the heart rate, breathing, and sweating increase.

THE REFLEX ARC

In a reflex arc, a sensory neuron communicates directly or indirectly with a motor neuron to trigger an automatic, stereotyped movement such as the "knee-jerk" caused by a tap at the base of the kneecap. The tap activates stretch-sensitive receptors in a tendon attached to the patella, sending nerve impulses along sensory axons to the spinal cord. There, the signals pass to motor neurons that cause the quadriceps muscle to contract and briefly extend the lower leg.

Inside the spinal cord

Neuron axons sheathed in white, insulating myelin make up the outer portion of the spinal cord. Neuron cell bodies, dendrites and synapses make up its gray interior. Membranes called meninges and bony vertebrae protect these delicate neural parts. Cerebrospinal fluid fills the central canal.

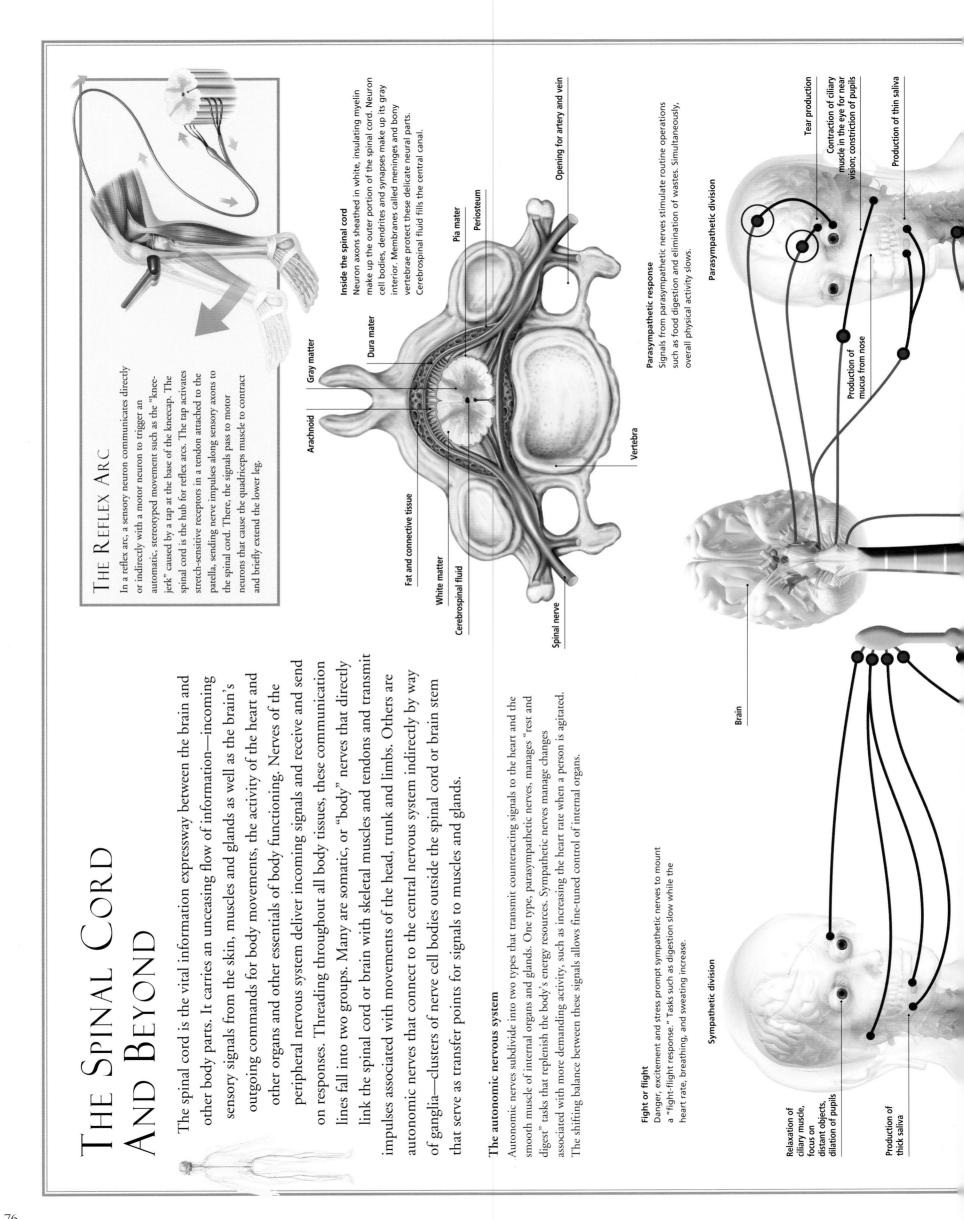

Pia mater

Periosteum

Opening for artery and vein

Dura mater

Gray matter

Arachnoid

Fat and connective tissue

White matter

Cerebrospinal fluid

Spinal nerve

Vertebra

Parasympathetic response

Signals from parasympathetic nerves stimulate routine operations such as food digestion and elimination of wastes. Simultaneously, overall physical activity slows.

Parasympathetic division

Tear production

Contraction of ciliary muscle in the eye for near vision; constriction of pupils

Production of thin saliva

Production of mucus from nose

Brain

Sympathetic division

Relaxation of ciliary muscle, focus on distant objects, dilation of pupils

Production of thick saliva

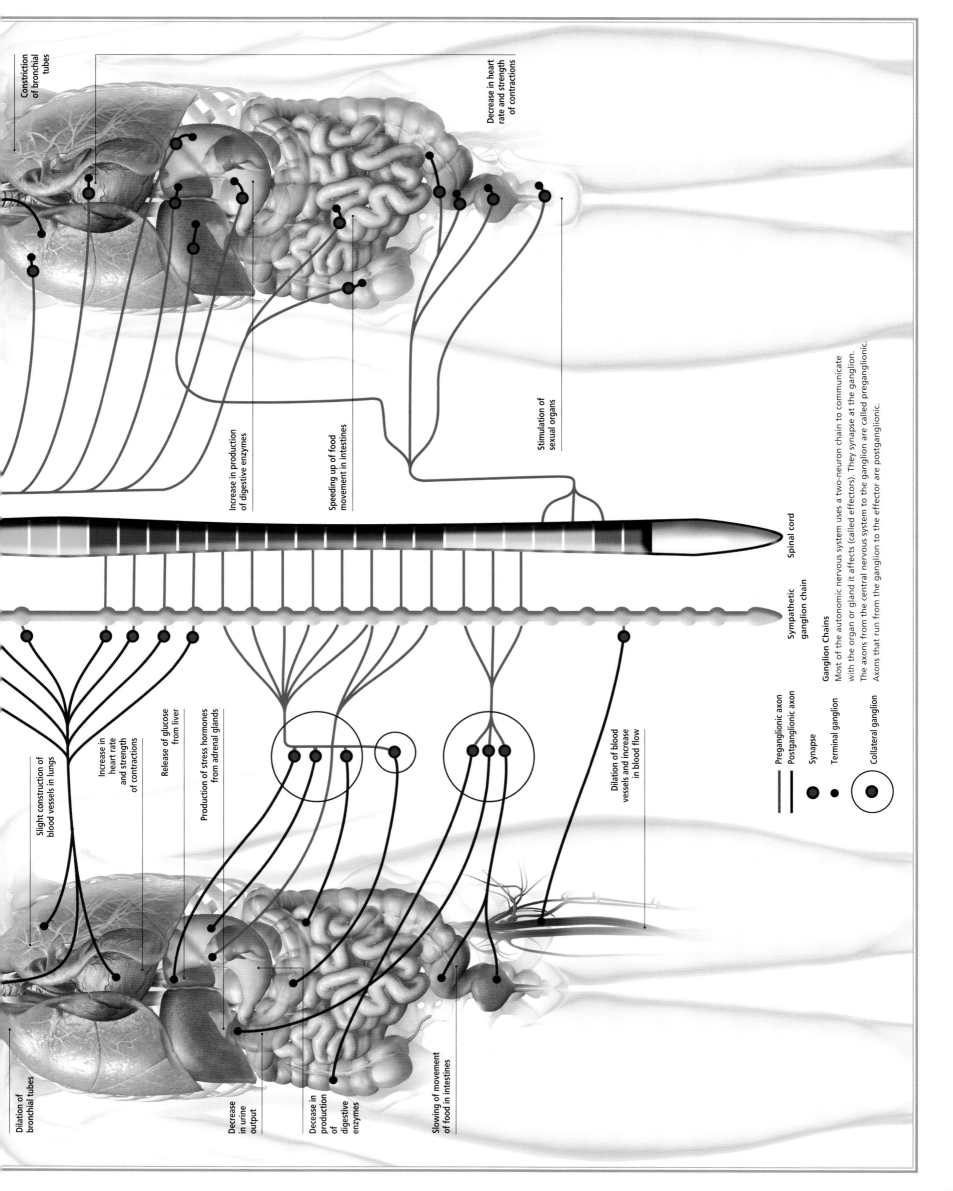

Constriction of bronchial tubes

Decrease in heart rate and strength of contractions

Increase in production of digestive enzymes

Speeding up of food movement in intestines

Stimulation of sexual organs

Spinal cord

Sympathetic ganglion chain

Ganglion Chains

Most of the autonomic nervous system uses a two-neuron chain to communicate with the organ or gland it affects (called effectors). They synapse at the ganglion. The axons from the central nervous system to the ganglion are called preganglionic. Axons that run from the ganglion to the effector are postganglionic.

Slight constriction of blood vessels in lungs

Increase in heart rate and strength of contractions

Release of glucose from liver

Production of stress hormones from adrenal glands

Dilation of blood vessels and increase in blood flow

Preganglionic axon
Postganglionic axon

Synapse

Terminal ganglion

Collateral ganglion

Dilation of bronchial tubes

Decrease in urine output

Decrease in production of digestive enzymes

Slowing of movement of food in intestines

Neurons and Nerves

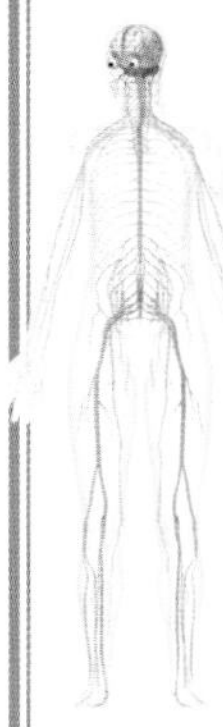

Neurons, the body's nerve cells, have a rounded cell body with two types of extensions: axons, which carry outgoing signals, and dendrites, which receive incoming ones. Axons bundled into long cable-like structures make up the body's nerves. The nervous system carries out its elaborate communication roles with only three basic types of neurons. Information about the stimuli responsible for vision, hearing, touch, taste and smell, as well as for pain and temperature changes, all reaches the central nervous system via sensory neurons that link receptors in the skin, eyes, ears, muscles and elsewhere with the spinal cord and brain. Motor neurons always carry impulses away from the central nervous system, conveying the countless signals necessary for muscles and glands to function properly. The vast majority of the body's neurons, however, are interneurons that carry signals in the brain and spinal cord and serve as intermediaries between sensory and motor neurons.

Neural circuitry

Neurons often are organized into circuits. In a converging circuit, impulses from several sources converge in a single receiving neuron, which thus receives a more powerful stimulus. In a diverging circuit, a signal is passed to a widening number of receiving cells, relaying sensory impulses to multiple brain centers. A reverberating circuit may underlie the rhythmic muscle contractions of breathing. A "downstream" neuron in the circuit has a forking axon, and as one branch passes the impulse onward the other loops back to the starting neuron—so the signal recycles.

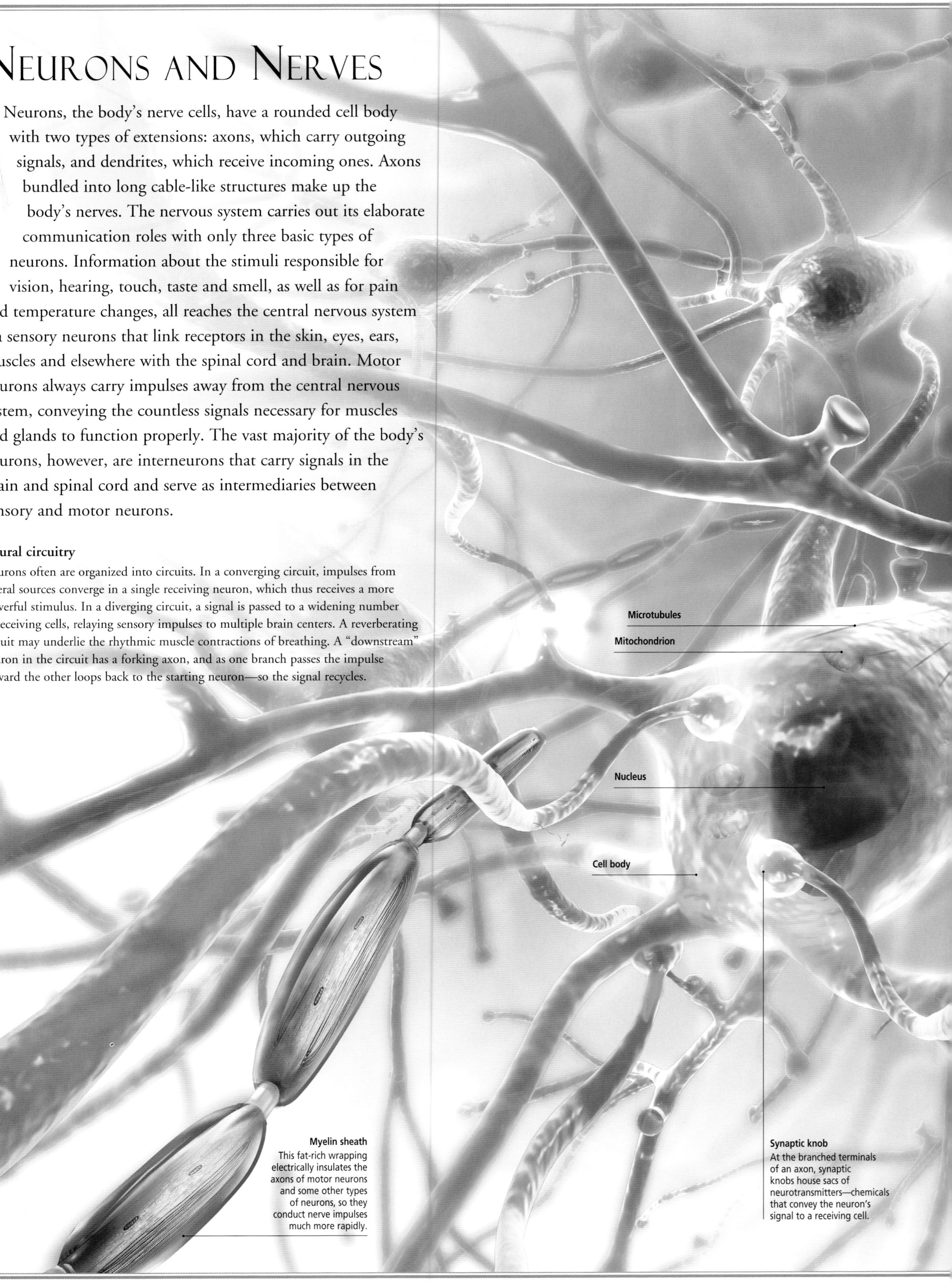

Microtubules

Mitochondrion

Nucleus

Cell body

Myelin sheath
This fat-rich wrapping electrically insulates the axons of motor neurons and some other types of neurons, so they conduct nerve impulses much more rapidly.

Synaptic knob
At the branched terminals of an axon, synaptic knobs house sacs of neurotransmitters—chemicals that convey the neuron's signal to a receiving cell.

GLIA: SUPPORT AND MORE

Glia make up at least half the volume of the central nervous system. The most abundant are astrocytes. These large star-shaped cells physically support neurons and also make chemical modifications in brain tissue. Among other functions, their adjustments help ensure the chemical conditions that allow neurons to fire. Astrocytes also may foster the neural connections involved in learning and memory.

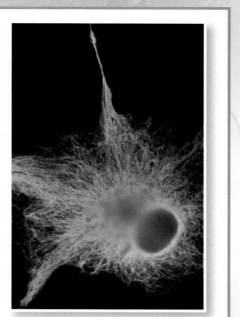

Astrocytes
Thread-like extensions from the main body of an astrocyte establish physical contact with neurons, blood capillaries and other structures in the brain.

Neuroglial cells
Called glia for short, various types of these cells physically or chemically support neurons, produce cerebrospinal fluid and defend against pathogens.

Axon
This long projection carries impulses away from the neuron's cell body and toward another neuron, a muscle cell or a gland cell.

Dendrite
Much shorter than axons, dendrites are "little trees" with many short branches that receive impulses arriving on axons from other neurons.

Nucleus

Nucleolus

Nerve cell body
Like other cells, a neuron must support itself biochemically in addition to performing its specialized roles. It contains a nucleus with DNA to guide the synthesis of proteins, mitochondria that form fuel molecules, supportive microtubules and membrane systems that manufacture substances and channel them through the cell.

Nerve Impulses and Synapses

A neuron is excitable: with the proper stimulus, it will fire off a nerve impulse. The stage is set for this response while the neuron is inactive and resembles a living battery. The chemical makeup of the tissue fluid outside the neuron makes that region electrically positive, while the fluid inside the cell has an opposite, negative charge. This electrical imbalance is called "resting potential" because if it shifts sufficiently, it has the potential to do physiological work. Resting potential transforms into an "action potential"—a nerve impulse—when a stimulus near the cell body sets in motion changes that briefly reverse the positive and negative charges. The impulse then travels down the axon to its branched tip. A synapse is a minute gap that separates its end of the branch of the axon from a neighboring neuron or some other type of cell. It prompts synaptic bulbs to release neurotransmitter molecules into the synapse, where they may trigger a response in the receiving cell.

Neural communication chemicals

Neurotransmitters include dozens of substances, virtually all made by neurons and stored in synaptic bulbs of axons until a nerve impulse sparks their release. Some neurotransmitters stimulate receiving cells, others inhibit them, and with some the effect depends on the type of receiving cell. Glutamate may convey as many as half of the signals that stimulate brain neurons while acetylcholine (ACh) provides the stimulus for all skeletal muscle contractions.

Nerve Impulses

Dendrites are the entry point to the "input zone" where neurotransmitter signals stimulate a neuron into action. In the nearby trigger zone, channels open in a patch of the cell membrane and positively charged sodium flows in. If this sodium shifts the electrical balance enough, it sparks a nerve impulse. Then the sodium abates and the membrane patch is once more at rest. Meanwhile, the impulse is traveling down the axon as the chemical flux repeats over and over.

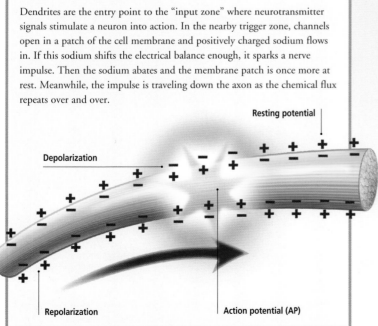

Resting potential

Depolarization

Repolarization

Action potential (AP)

Nucleus

Input zone
Here, incoming signals are received and a neurotransmitter contacts the postsynaptic or receiving cell. At some synapses in the brain, electrically charged particles, rather than chemical neurotransmitters, are the signals.

Trigger zone
Here, the axon membrane first responds to an arriving stimulus and triggers an initial action potential.

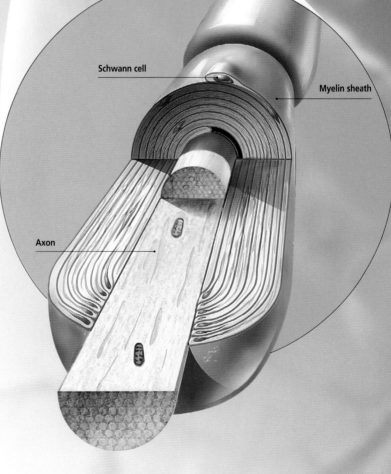

Schwann cell

Myelin sheath

Axon

Myelin sheath
In the peripheral nervous system, Schwann cells wrap axons with a sheath of fatty myelin. In the CNS, other glia provide this service. Nerve impulses occur at nodes where the axon is exposed, "jumping" along the axon as fast as 400 feet (120m) per second.

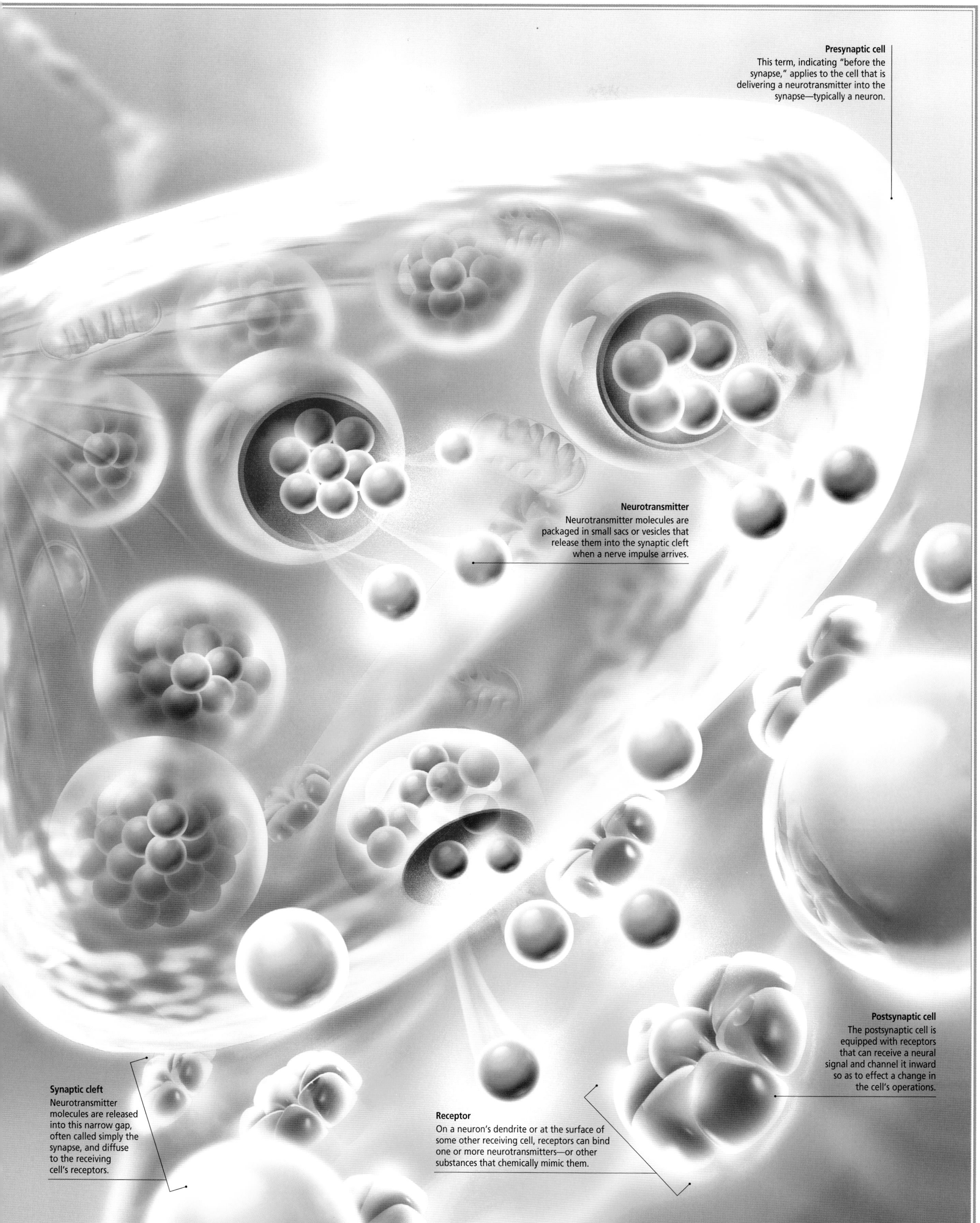

Presynaptic cell
This term, indicating "before the synapse," applies to the cell that is delivering a neurotransmitter into the synapse—typically a neuron.

Neurotransmitter
Neurotransmitter molecules are packaged in small sacs or vesicles that release them into the synaptic cleft when a nerve impulse arrives.

Postsynaptic cell
The postsynaptic cell is equipped with receptors that can receive a neural signal and channel it inward so as to effect a change in the cell's operations.

Synaptic cleft
Neurotransmitter molecules are released into this narrow gap, often called simply the synapse, and diffuse to the receiving cell's receptors.

Receptor
On a neuron's dendrite or at the surface of some other receiving cell, receptors can bind one or more neurotransmitters—or other substances that chemically mimic them.

BRAIN ANATOMY

The brain is not only the master controller for body functions but also provides humans with unparalleled cognitive and mental abilities. Weighing three to four pounds (1400–1800gm) in an adult, this astonishing organ's complex anatomy befits its sophisticated operations. The upper three-quarters of the brain is divided into two sides, the right and left hemispheres, linked by a thick band of nerve tracts called the corpus callosum. In each hemisphere, regions called the frontal, occipital, temporal and parietal lobes are named for the skull bones above them. Top to bottom, the brain has three tiers. The upper, convoluted forebrain is where the most advanced information processing occurs. Deeper areas in the midbrain coordinate reflexes and provide preliminary processing of information related to vision and hearing. Even deeper, the hindbrain helps control many basic reflexes and body functions.

Fluid-filled spaces
Cerebrospinal fluid fills four hollow brain chambers called ventricles. It cushions brain tissue against blows and is a reservoir for substances neurons require in order to generate nerve impulses.

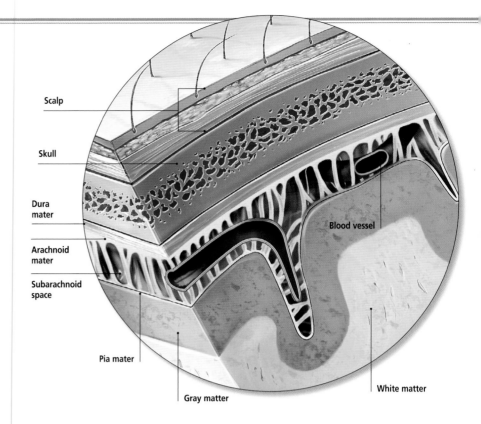

Scalp

Skull

Dura mater

Arachnoid mater

Subarachnoid space

Pia mater

Gray matter

Blood vessel

White matter

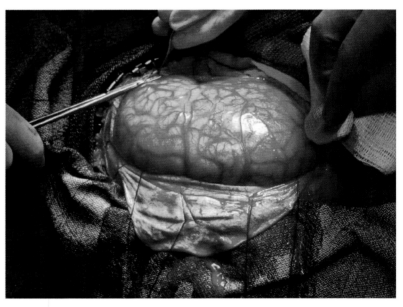

The brain's surface
Preparing for surgery on a patient with severe epilepsy, a physician has peeled back the two upper brain meninges to reveal the translucent pia mater and the lacework of blood vessels on the brain's surface.

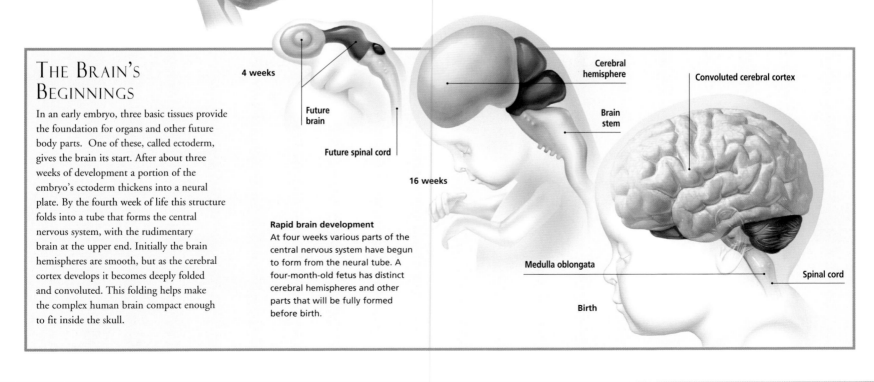

THE BRAIN'S BEGINNINGS

In an early embryo, three basic tissues provide the foundation for organs and other future body parts. One of these, called ectoderm, gives the brain its start. After about three weeks of development a portion of the embryo's ectoderm thickens into a neural plate. By the fourth week of life this structure folds into a tube that forms the central nervous system, with the rudimentary brain at the upper end. Initially the brain hemispheres are smooth, but as the cerebral cortex develops it becomes deeply folded and convoluted. This folding helps make the complex human brain compact enough to fit inside the skull.

4 weeks

Future brain

Future spinal cord

16 weeks

Rapid brain development
At four weeks various parts of the central nervous system have begun to form from the neural tube. A four-month-old fetus has distinct cerebral hemispheres and other parts that will be fully formed before birth.

Cerebral hemisphere

Brain stem

Convoluted cerebral cortex

Medulla oblongata

Spinal cord

Birth

Corpus callosum
This band of nerve tracts conveys signals between the two brain hemispheres and coordinates their respective activities.

Basal nuclei
These groups of neuron cell bodies have a vital role in relaying motor commands outward from the cerebral cortex.

Skull

Protective wrapping
In addition to skull bones, membranes called meninges protect the brain. The outer dura mater is thick and leathery while the thin, innermost pia mater sheaths brain tissue like plastic wrap. The arachnoid mater includes a shallow cavity containing cerebrospinal fluid. The meninges continue into the spine and wrap the spinal cord.

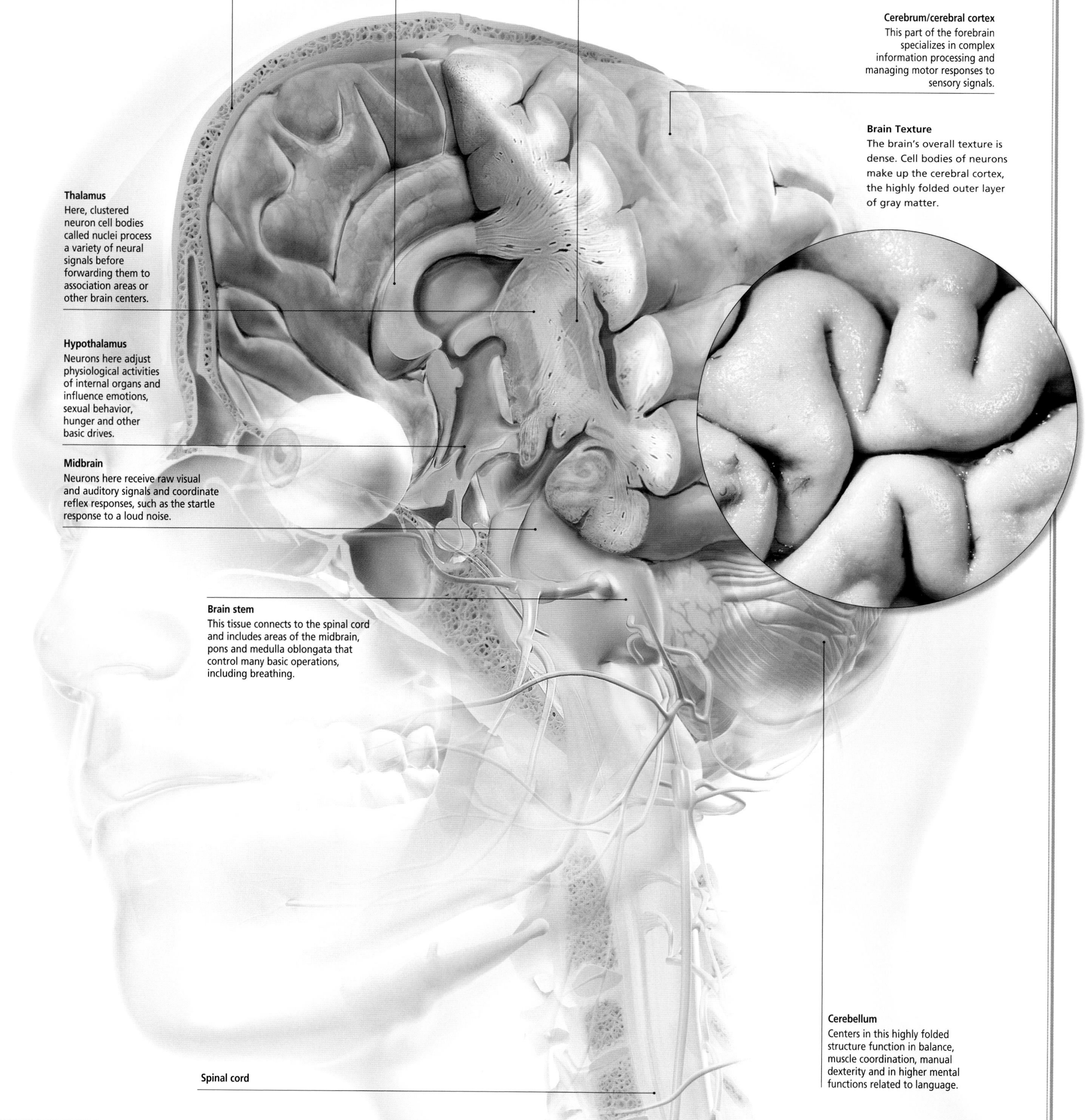

Cerebrum/cerebral cortex
This part of the forebrain specializes in complex information processing and managing motor responses to sensory signals.

Brain Texture
The brain's overall texture is dense. Cell bodies of neurons make up the cerebral cortex, the highly folded outer layer of gray matter.

Thalamus
Here, clustered neuron cell bodies called nuclei process a variety of neural signals before forwarding them to association areas or other brain centers.

Hypothalamus
Neurons here adjust physiological activities of internal organs and influence emotions, sexual behavior, hunger and other basic drives.

Midbrain
Neurons here receive raw visual and auditory signals and coordinate reflex responses, such as the startle response to a loud noise.

Brain stem
This tissue connects to the spinal cord and includes areas of the midbrain, pons and medulla oblongata that control many basic operations, including breathing.

Cerebellum
Centers in this highly folded structure function in balance, muscle coordination, manual dexterity and in higher mental functions related to language.

Spinal cord

THE BRAIN STEM

The brain stem, between the top of the spinal cord and the cerebrum, consists of the medulla oblongata, the pons and the midbrain—each only about 1 inch (2.5cm) long. Despite its small size, the brain stem is a crucial component in the central nervous system. The medulla oblongata, connected to the spinal cord, controls basic body function, such as breathing, heart rate and blood pressure. Located on the anterior of the medulla, the pons relays movement information between the cortex and the cerebellum. At the top of the brain stem, the midbrain coordinates and controls many sensory and motor functions of the body. Running lengthwise through the center of the brain stem is a network of neurons called the reticular formation. With long axons that spread outward to other parts of the brain, these neurons are key to the spectrum of brain states we call consciousness.

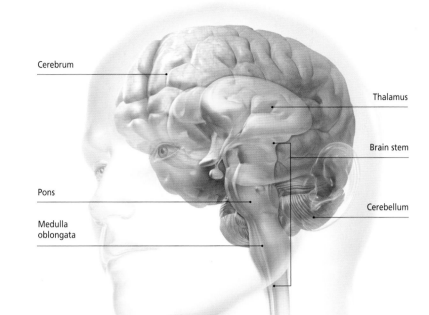

Cerebrum

Thalamus

Brain stem

Cerebellum

Pons

Medulla oblongata

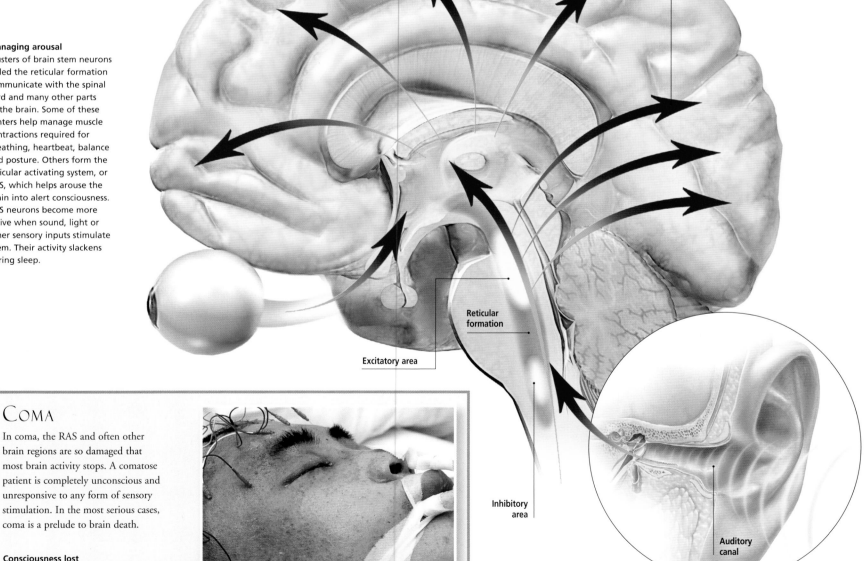

Radiating signals

Activating signals

Cerebral cortex

Managing arousal
Clusters of brain stem neurons called the reticular formation communicate with the spinal cord and many other parts of the brain. Some of these centers help manage muscle contractions required for breathing, heartbeat, balance and posture. Others form the reticular activating system, or RAS, which helps arouse the brain into alert consciousness. RAS neurons become more active when sound, light or other sensory inputs stimulate them. Their activity slackens during sleep.

Reticular formation

Excitatory area

Inhibitory area

Auditory canal

COMA

In coma, the RAS and often other brain regions are so damaged that most brain activity stops. A comatose patient is completely unconscious and unresponsive to any form of sensory stimulation. In the most serious cases, coma is a prelude to brain death.

Consciousness lost
The brain state called coma looks deceptively like sleep. Mild cases may be reversible.

Thalamus
The thalamus receives and sorts sensory signals from the brain stem before passing messages onward to the cerebral cortex. It also functions in arousal, memory and awareness.

Brain stem cross section
The bulge of the pons can be seen just above the cross section of the narrow medulla oblongata (blue). Coming off of both brain stem structures are some of the cranial nerves.

Midbrain
Neurons in the substantia nigra, a portion of the midbrain, release the neurotransmitter dopamine which coordinates subconscious muscle movements. Loss of these neurons creates the tremors and other symptoms of Parkinson's disease.

Occulomotor III
This nerve moves the eyeball and upper eyelid.

Trochlear IV
The smallest of the cranial nerves, this moves the eyeball down and laterally.

Pons
Nerve cells here work with the medulla to control breathing and to relay signals between the medulla and the midbrain.

Trigeminal V
This nerve carries motor and sensory impulses to and from the eye, jaws and face.

Facial VII
Among other functions, this nerve controls most facial expressions.

Vestibulocochlear VIII
This auditory nerve carries impulses for hearing and equilibrium.

Cranial nerves
Cranial nerves pass through the skull and connect directly to the brain. There are 12 pairs of cranial nerves, ten of which pass through the brain stem carrying sensory or motor signals or both, to and from the brain.

Abducens VI
This nerve "abducts" or turns the eye outward.

Vagus X
This nerve branches from the head and neck to the thorax and abdomen.

Hypoglossal XII
This motor nerve carries impulses to the tongue for speech and swallowing.

Glossopharyngeal IX
This nerve serves the throat and back of the tongue for taste and swallowing.

Medulla oblongata

Often simply called the medulla, this brain stem region is a hub for sensory and motor signals passing between the spinal cord and other parts of the brain. It coordinates muscle movements involved in swallowing, sneezing, hiccupping and vomiting, and with other parts of the brain stem it regulates the heartbeat, breathing and the constriction or widening of blood vessels. The medulla is also part of the pathway for reticular formation activity, related to arousal and consciousness. Serious damage to the medulla is often fatal.

Medulla oblongata

Spinal Accessory XI
This nerve conveys motor impulses to the shoulder and neck muscles.

THE CEREBELLUM

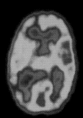

Outwardly the cerebellum resembles a layered, fan-shaped pad and sits behind the brain stem. Its name, meaning "little brain," reflects the fact that like the larger cerebrum, the cerebellum consists of two side-by-side hemispheres and its outer layer is deeply convoluted. Although it makes up only about 10 percent of human brain tissue, the cerebellum is a key central processing unit. Operating below the level of conscious awareness, the cerebellum constantly assesses signals from sense receptors that detect changes in the position of body parts. It manages these and other sensory information to ensure precise timing and patterns of skeletal muscle contractions. As a result, humans have the coordination and agility for rapid-fire movements associated with activities such as driving, playing video games, typing and dancing. Brain imaging studies show that the cerebellum also is active during some key types of conscious activity—an unexpected revelation that researchers are avidly exploring.

Normal brain activity

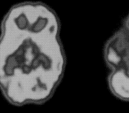 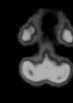

Brain activity of a marijuana user

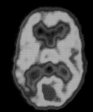 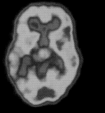 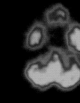

Brain activity scan
Contrasting brain scans show how THC, the psychoactive ingredient in marijuana, dampens cerebellum activity, impairing a user's motor coordination. The four scans on the bottom show progressively deeper levels of a user's brain. Blue areas indicate reduced activity in the cerebellum. In the unaffected brain on the top, the same areas glow red, signifying that neurons there are much more active.

Ataxia—a disordered cerebellum

Disease, injury and some psychoactive drugs all may impair cerebellum functions and cause ataxia, a condition in which properly coordinated movements become difficult or impossible. Symptoms include an abnormal gait, difficulty maintaining appropriate posture and balance, and an inability to sense the location of body parts in space. In some people, consuming even a moderate amount of alcohol can produce telltale signs of ataxia, including lurching, the inability to walk a straight line and difficulty in performing physical sobriety tests such as closing the eyes and touching the nose.

Monitoring and adjusting movements

In humans, the cerebellum sits behind the brain stem, receiving inputs about the activities of muscles and joints from the pons and medulla. After assessing the position, balance and momentum of body parts, the cerebellum sends a message to the thalamus, which forwards the information to the premotor cortex. This feedback allows the cortex to fine-tune the speed, force and direction of muscle contractions so that bodily posture and movements—such as typing at a keyboard and manipulating a computer mouse—are precisely geared to the task at hand.

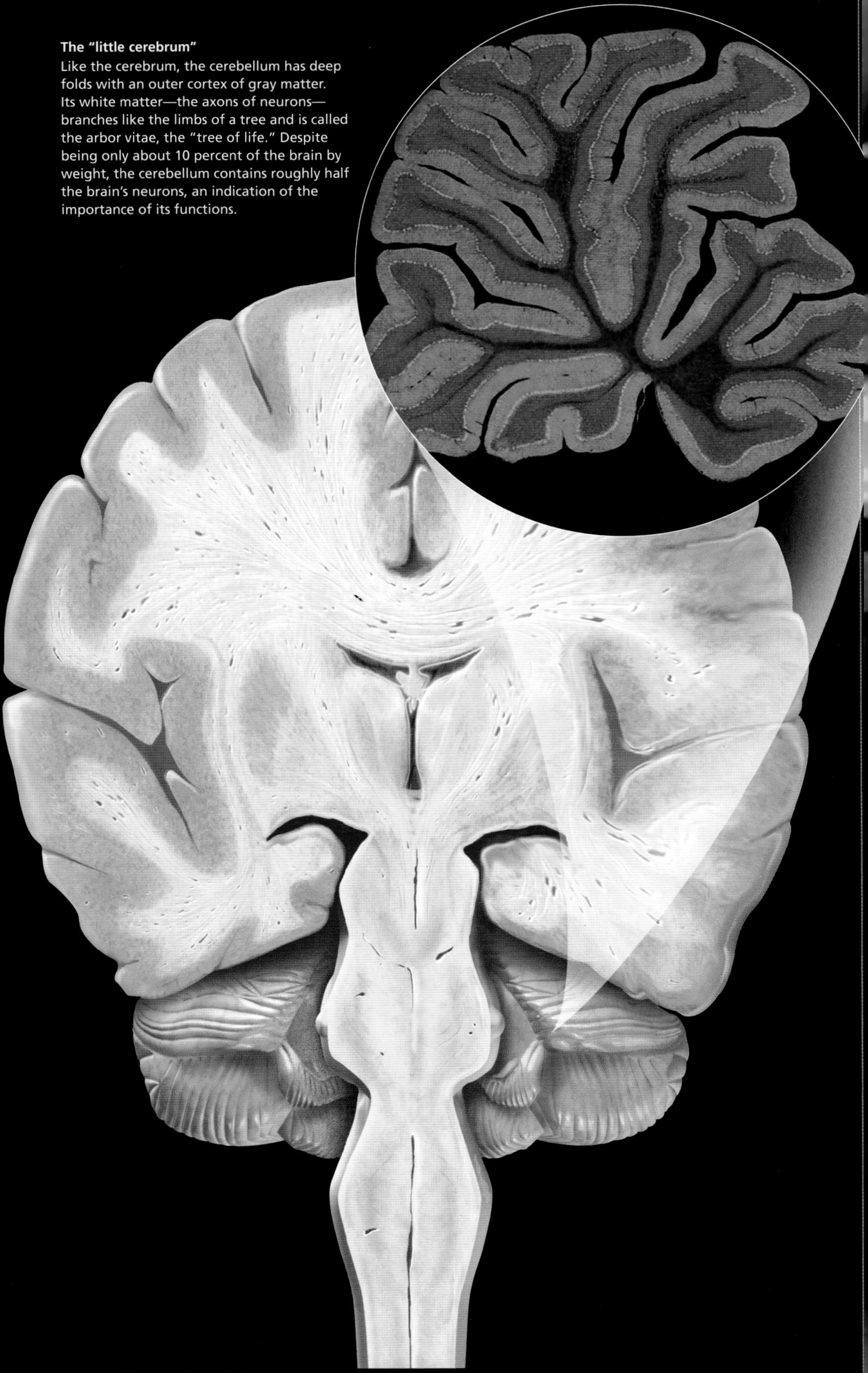

The "little cerebrum"
Like the cerebrum, the cerebellum has deep folds with an outer cortex of gray matter. Its white matter—the axons of neurons— branches like the limbs of a tree and is called the arbor vitae, the "tree of life." Despite being only about 10 percent of the brain by weight, the cerebellum contains roughly half the brain's neurons, an indication of the importance of its functions.

The ancient cerebellum
A version of the cerebellum arose millions of years ago as animals began evolving complex nervous systems—an indication of the importance of brain centers for adjusting posture, regulating balance and micromanaging muscle contractions. Functional brain scans have revealed another, still mysterious role for the cerebellum—it also is active when a person is using language or performing tasks that require problem solving.

BRAIN POWER

Many qualities associated with "humanness" stem from the activity of the cerebral cortex—the cerebrum's thin outer region of gray matter. Only one-eighth of an inch (.5cm) thick, the cerebral cortex consists of several fine layers and is convoluted into deep, curving folds containing billions of neurons—in all, approximately 40 percent of the brain's tissue. Signals from the cortex control conscious behavior and thought, language and understanding. The complicated interactions among neurons that underlie reasoning and learning, planning, personality, judgment, aspects of memory and the thought patterns of "conscience" are centered in the prefrontal cortex. This cortical area communicates intimately with the limbic system, the seat of emotions. The cerebral cortex also contains primary motor and sensory areas where neurons are arranged in patterns that map the entire body. The sensory areas receive and process information from the muscles and skin, while primary motor areas are responsible for voluntary muscle movements.

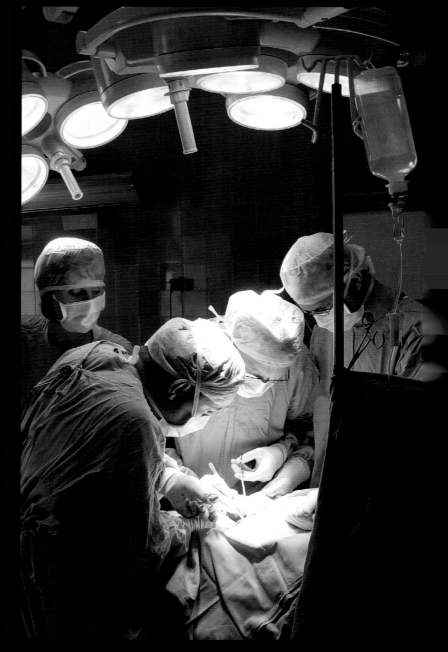

Mental focus and motor skills
A surgeon's arsenal of expertise exploits the operational power of the prefrontal cortex. Mental focus, the ability to draw upon past experience and the capacity to mobilize hand muscles to perform intricate motor activities all emerge from interacting cerebral neurons.

Language and math
Mathematical reasoning and language skills, such as reading and writing, involve the cerebral capacity to recognize and assemble abstract symbols into meaningful sequences. Due to lateralization of the brain hemispheres, language and mathematical abilities are usually centered in the left hemisphere, while musical and artistic skills are typically right-brain specialties.

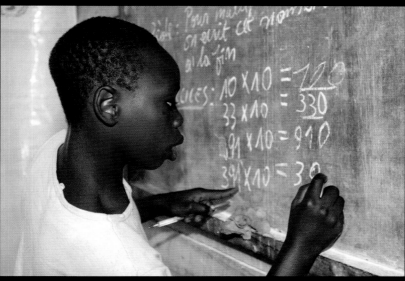

Concentration and strategy
Playing chess utilizes various parts of the cerebrum to analyze previous experiences and use that information to imagine possible future outcomes and plan a strategy to achieve a desired outcome. Good chess players also exert exacting control over emotional responses to an opponent's moves as such reactions can give an opponent a mental "edge."

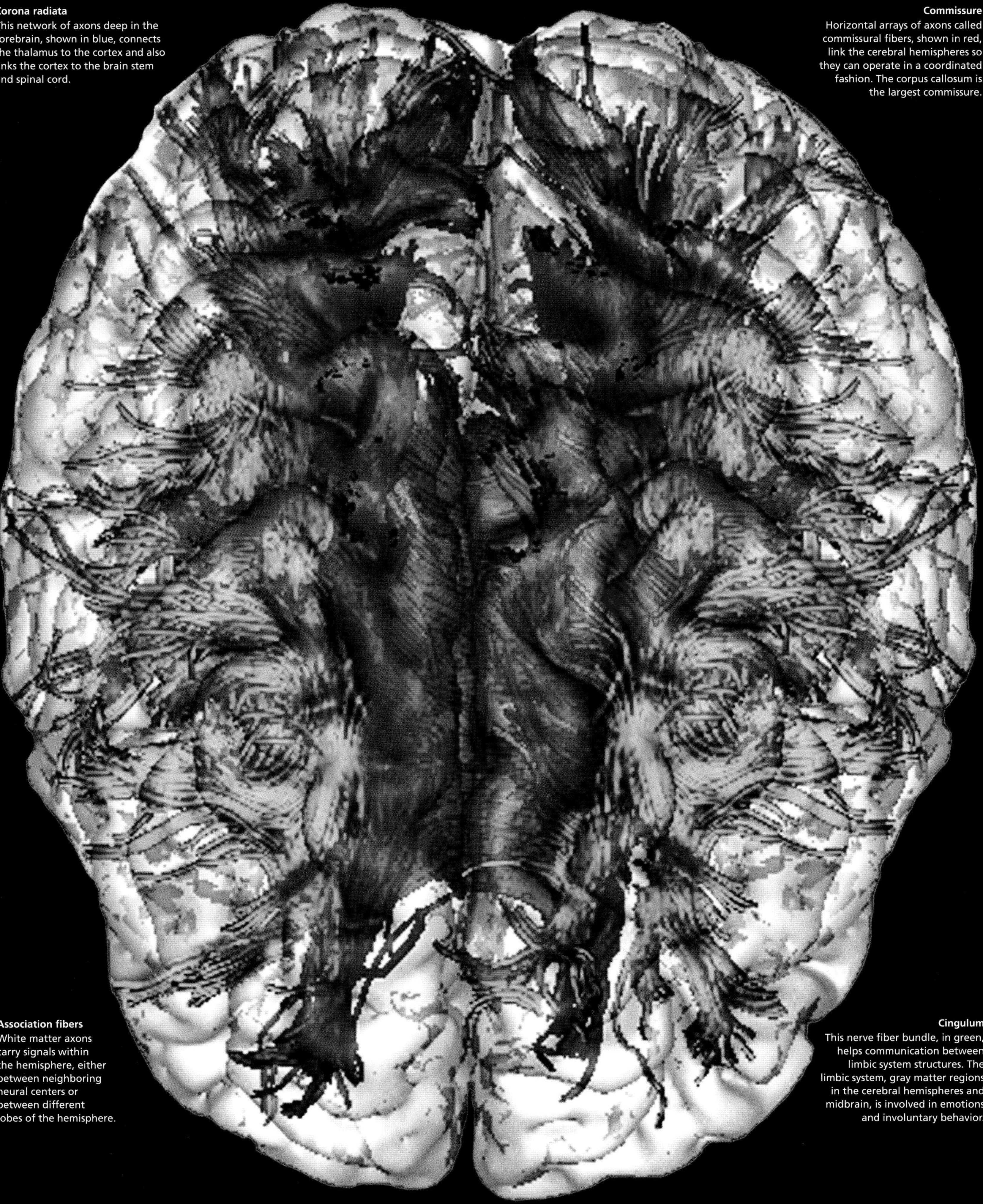

Corona radiata
This network of axons deep in the forebrain, shown in blue, connects the thalamus to the cortex and also links the cortex to the brain stem and spinal cord.

Commissure
Horizontal arrays of axons called commissural fibers, shown in red, link the cerebral hemispheres so they can operate in a coordinated fashion. The corpus callosum is the largest commissure.

Association fibers
White matter axons carry signals within the hemisphere, either between neighboring neural centers or between different lobes of the hemisphere.

Cingulum
This nerve fiber bundle, in green, helps communication between limbic system structures. The limbic system, gray matter regions in the cerebral hemispheres and midbrain, is involved in emotions and involuntary behavior.

Cerebral white matter

The myelinated axons of neurons make up much of the cerebrum's white matter. These nerve fibers are bundled in nerve tracts which carry nerve impulses between brain regions and from the brain to the spinal cord. Horizontal tracts connect the brain's two hemispheres. Vertical tracts connect the brain stem and motor and sensory association areas of the cerebral cortex.

MOTOR AREAS

The primary motor cortex is the arbiter for voluntary muscle movements. Occupying a broad, curving region at the rear of the frontal lobe, the motor cortex houses neurons that extend their axons directly to the spinal cord. The axons from each side of the cortex cross over, so that the right side of the cortex controls muscles on the left side of the body and vice versa. Gross motor activities do not require as exacting neural control as delicate ones. Accordingly, a greater proportion of motor cortex neurons are assigned to body parts that require extremely precise motor control, such as the hands, eyes and face. Interacting groups of neurons coordinate movements of opposing muscle groups, such as those used to flex and extend the forearms or legs.

Beyond the primary cortex

The premotor cortex, located anterior to the primary motor cortex, functions as a memory bank for operating muscles used in learned motor activities, such as writing. Such skills require muscles to contract in a specific, unvarying sequence. Nearby, neurons in the frontal eye field control voluntary eye movements. Broca's area in the left cerebral hemisphere is active both when a person prepares to speak and when muscles move the lips, tongue and other parts to make speech sounds.

Mapping the motor cortex

This diagram, called a somatotopy (body place), shows the proportions of the motor cortex devoted to movements of various body parts. A distinct majority of neurons manage the complex, refined movements performed by muscles of the face, mouth structures and hands.

Fingers
Face
Brow
Neck
Hand
Eye
Wrist
Lips
Elbow
Shoulder
Jaw
Trunk
Tongue
Hip
Swallowing
Knee
Ankle
Toes

Motor pathways

Bundles of axons with the same beginning or end point are called nerve tracts. Voluntary body movements depend on motor tracts that convey signals from the brain to skeletal muscles via the spinal cord. Two tracts carry impulses for voluntary movements directly from the primary motor cortex to the spinal cord. Several other tracts transport motor signals from other parts of the brain.

Premotor cortex

Primary motor cortex

Frontal eye field

Broca's area

Upper motor neurons

Primary motor area of cerebral cortex

Cerebrum

Primary motor area of cerebral cortex

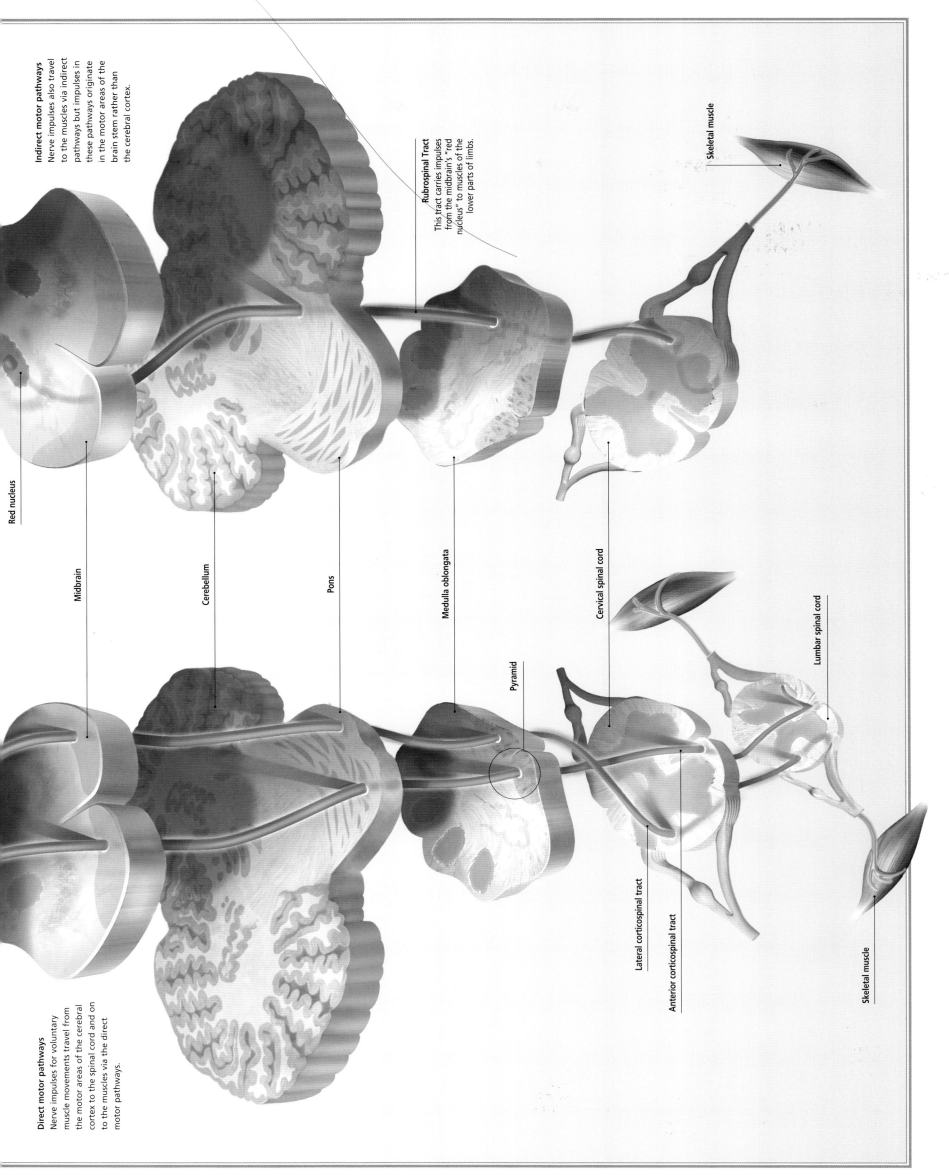

Indirect motor pathways
Nerve impulses also travel to the muscles via indirect pathways but impulses in these pathways originate in the motor areas of the brain stem rather than the cerebral cortex.

Rubrospinal Tract
This tract carries impulses from the midbrain's "red nucleus" to muscles of the lower parts of limbs.

Skeletal muscle

Red nucleus

Midbrain

Cerebellum

Pons

Medulla oblongata

Cervical spinal cord

Pyramid

Lumbar spinal cord

Lateral corticospinal tract

Anterior corticospinal tract

Skeletal muscle

Direct motor pathways
Nerve impulses for voluntary muscle movements travel from the motor areas of the cerebral cortex to the spinal cord and on to the muscles via the direct motor pathways.

The Conscious Brain

Brain neurons begin their electrical signaling well before birth and continue this biological work until the moment of death. In a healthy brain, the life-long spectrum of neural activity includes various states of consciousness, from full alertness to drowsiness and sleep. Electroencephalograms (EEGs) and brain scans can record the brain's electrical operations, although they do not reveal the physical underpinnings of "the mind." Thinking, fantasizing, understanding, planning, making judgments, worrying—these and similar kinds of cognitive activity all take place in association areas of the prefrontal cortex, where information from elsewhere in the brain is processed and integrated. Yet no particular group of neurons can be pinpointed as the mind, and imaging studies confirm that many parts of the brain are involved during thinking, long-term planning and other high-level mental tasks. In all likelihood, the mind is the sum total of activity in many parts of the brain.

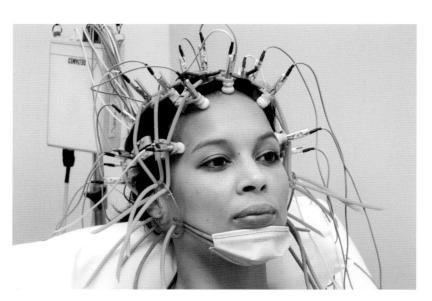

Measuring brain activity
An EEG helps diagnose a variety of brain disorders. The test is usually administered in a quiet room while the patient rests or performs mental tasks such as answering simple questions. Electrodes positioned on the scalp record the associated electrical activity in various parts of the brain.

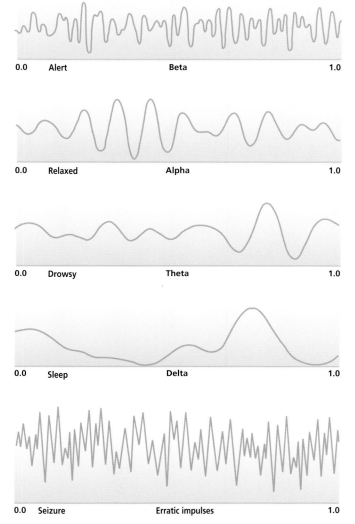

0.0	Alert	Beta	1.0

0.0	Relaxed	Alpha	1.0

0.0	Drowsy	Theta	1.0

0.0	Sleep	Delta	1.0

0.0	Seizure	Erratic impulses	1.0

Brain waves/epilepsy
Brain waves reflect the electrical activity of brain neurons. When a person is alert and processing ample sensory input, the pattern consists of relatively fast-paced, irregular beta waves. A relaxed mental state, such as daydreaming with closed eyes, generates slower, more regular alpha waves. Drowsiness brings a shift to the slower and less regular pattern of theta waves, while even slower delta waves predominate during deep sleep, coma or general anesthesia. During an epileptic seizure brain neurons fire an abnormal barrage of impulses.

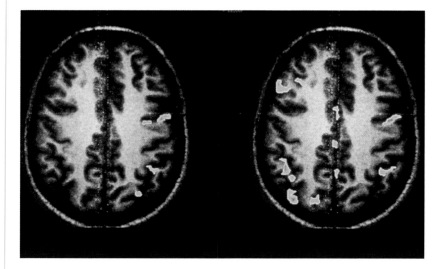

The mathematical brain
Orange areas in these images highlight parts of the brain that are most active while a subject is performing different mathematical tasks. Reciting multiplication tables elicits activity only in one brain hemisphere (left), while doing a series of subtractions engages neurons in both hemispheres (right). This type of study is helping to provide a much fuller understanding of how the brain performs certain problem-solving tasks.

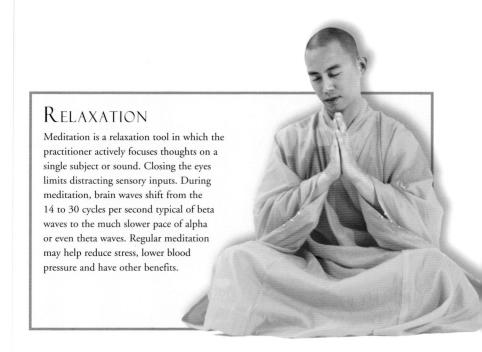

Relaxation

Meditation is a relaxation tool in which the practitioner actively focuses thoughts on a single subject or sound. Closing the eyes limits distracting sensory inputs. During meditation, brain waves shift from the 14 to 30 cycles per second typical of beta waves to the much slower pace of alpha or even theta waves. Regular meditation may help reduce stress, lower blood pressure and have other benefits.

Finding the mind

The physical basis for conscious experience is the brain's most enduring mystery. In attempting to explain this enigma, methods such as functional magnetic resonance imaging (fMRI) are advancing understanding of cognitive functions. This technology exploits the fact that highly active cells use more oxygen than less active ones. In revealing color, fMRI provides a window into the activity levels in different brain regions when a subject is performing a particular mental task.

Rapt concentration
Fascinated by a dinosaur's skeleton, children's mental faculties are fully aroused. Beta waves are typical of this high level of concentration and focus.

LANGUAGE

The capacity to communicate using complex language is one of the traits that sets humans apart from their closest relatives in the animal world. In most people, this profoundly important aspect of humanness resides mainly in the brain's left hemisphere, where linked centers in the prefrontal cortex and temporal lobe play vital roles in our ability to produce and comprehend speech and the written word. The neurons in a region called Broca's area manage muscle movements required to form speech sounds with the throat, tongue and lips. Stroke victims and others who suffer damage to this area lose the ability to produce speech. Wernicke's area encompasses parts of the left temporal and parietal lobes. Its functions include assigning meaning to spoken words, managing the arrangement of a speaker's words into coherent sentences and integrating the spoken words of others into the listener's thoughts.

Sign language

In sign language, meaning is conveyed by visual signals, such as gestures and facial expressions. Although the left hemisphere is most active when someone speaks, sign language mobilizes both hemispheres. Chinese, for example, relies heavily on tonal quality to distinguish between similar spoken words; in Chinese sign language tones are expressed by slight eye or head movements.

Studying human language

PET and functional MRI technology have dramatically expanded scientific understanding of the roles different parts of the brain play in producing and comprehending language. By generating images that reflect the relative use of oxygen or other substances by metabolically active cells, researchers can track the shifting operations of brain neurons in real time. Research has also proven that, far from being the province of independent language "centers," many language skills involve coordinated interactions of several different brain regions.

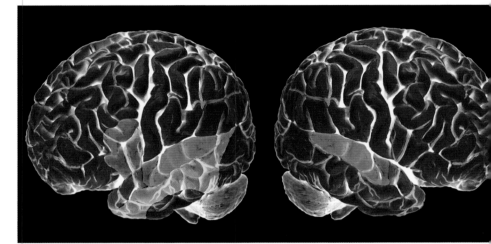

Dominant left

While the left side of the brain dominates speech and comprehension for most people, the right cerebral hemisphere helps process emotional components of language. This scan shows brain activity while hearing and understanding language. On the left side of the brain (on left), more areas are active, including Broca's area (pink) and temporal lobe areas dealing with comprehension (yellow). Auditory centers are active in both hemispheres.

Brain activity
PET scans show activated areas of the brain (red-orange) during various language tasks. Parts of the temporal lobe, center for auditory processing, are active in bottom scan. Broca's area (speech production) and Wernicke's area (language comprehension) are shown in the top scan.

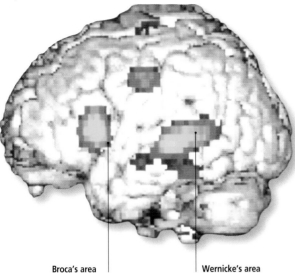

Broca's area   Wernicke's area

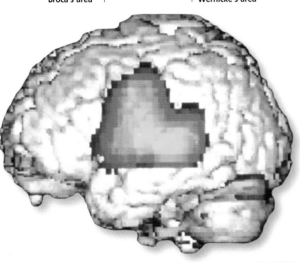

Relearning to write
Here a formerly right-handed stroke patient is relearning to write using her left hand. A stroke may result in muscle paralysis and interfere with processes required to formulate written words.

APHASIA

Aphasia is loss of the ability to produce or understand language. Damage to certain areas of the brain from disease or injury can cause aphasia. In Broca's aphasia, the ability to produce speech is lost, although the person may still understand spoken words. In Wernicke's aphasia, the ability to understand language is lost. People with Wernicke's aphasia often speak nonsensical words or sounds. This MRI shows the brain of a patient with sudden onset of Broca's aphasia following a stroke.

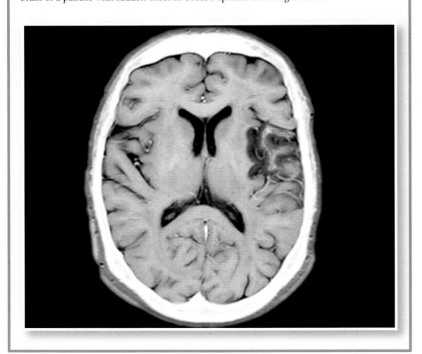

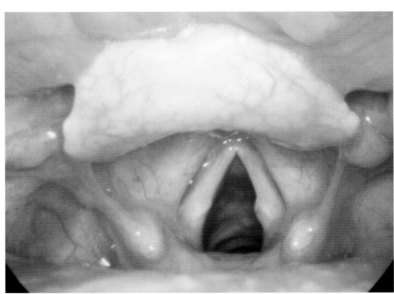

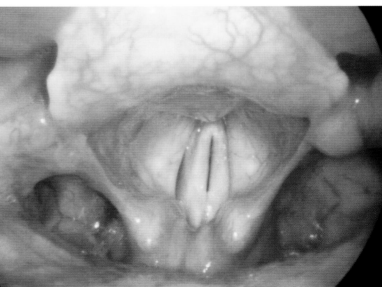

Producing sounds
Like a musical instrument, the human voice produces sound by vibration and resonating air. The larynx, or voice box, contains the vocal cords, two elastic bands of muscle that relax, tense and lengthen. When breathing normally, vocal cords are relaxed (top) and do not produce any vocal sounds. When tense (bottom), vocal cords are in a sound-producing position. Voice volume varies depending on the force of the air across the vocal cords.

SLEEP

Sleep is a state of altered consciousness that seems to be a biological essential. Centers in the brain stem's reticular formation govern both sleeping and waking, with different groups of neurons releasing neurotransmitters that promote or inhibit sleep. As a person falls asleep, the cerebral cortex becomes less active. Unlike true unconsciousness, however, it is readily aroused again when a sleeper is exposed to a stimulus, such as a ringing alarm clock or light streaming in through a window. During sleep, non-rapid eye movement (NREM) sleep alternates with rapid eye movement (REM) sleep, when the eyeballs seem to move back and forth. Most of the time spent sleeping is a "slow wave" NREM sleep stage during which a person is easily aroused and basic functions, such as breathing and heart rate, are only slightly reduced. About every 90 minutes, the pattern typically shifts to REM sleep, when dreaming occurs.

SLEEP DISORDERS

Anxiety, aging and other factors can cause chronic insomnia. By contrast, a person with narcolepsy unpredictably shifts between alert wakefulness and REM sleep. With sleep apnea, a sleeper repeatedly awakens when breathing stops for an extended period due to weakness in the muscles of the upper airway. In restless legs syndrome, intense burning or other sensations trigger an urge to move the legs, but because symptoms only occur when one lies down, a person often has great difficulty sleeping.

Brain waves during sleep
This image shows a polysomnogram, a graphic that correlates brain and eye activity during sleep testing. The blue trace is data from an electroencephalogram (EEG) tracking brain waves, while the green trace records rapid eye movements.

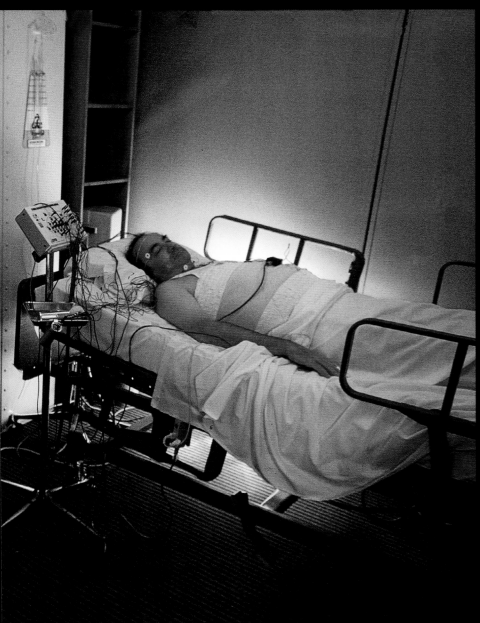

Sleep research
Sleep testing has revealed that during REM sleep, when people usually dream, the limbic system and visual association areas of the brain are highly active. This discovery correlates with the intense visual imagery and charged emotions often associated with dreams.

Circadian rhythm

The body's biological clock regulates sleep and other physiological states in cycles of about 24 hours that roughly follow daily shifts in external light and dark periods. The clock is a cluster of nerve cell bodies in the hypothalamus called the suprachiasmatic nucleus (SCN). It receives signals from special photoreceptors in the retina that communicate rising or falling light levels. The SCN in turn signals the pineal gland to stimulate or inhibit the release of melatonin—the hormone that induces sleep at night.

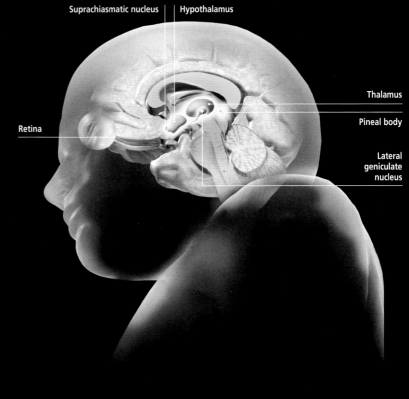

Suprachiasmatic nucleus | Hypothalamus

Retina

Thalamus

Pineal body

Lateral geniculate nucleus

NREM

REM

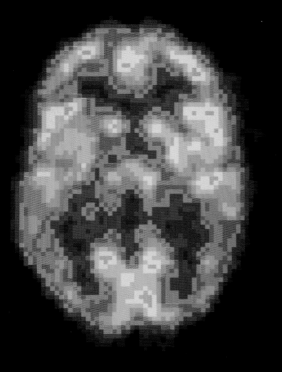

Stages of sleep

Researchers have discovered that the stages of sleep are highly organized. NREM sleep has four stages that unfold in sequence. During NREM Stage 1, a person sleeps lightly and is easily awakened. Sleep then progressively deepens. It is most difficult to rouse a sleeper during the deepest phase, NREM Stage 4. NREM sleep alternates with shorter periods of REM sleep during the night. Dreams occur almost entirely during REM sleep. The colored PET scans show the brain in NREM (left) and REM (right) sleep. Active parts of the cerebral cortex are shown in red. In NREM sleep the brain is inactive while the REM phase shows activity similar to the awake brain.

EMOTIONS

From infancy onward, the functions of emotions and other basic aspects of human life and experience rely on a ring of small structures collectively called the limbic system. The system's parts, which have long been known as the "emotional brain," include the almond-shaped amygdala, the hippocampus, a curved fold of tissue called the cingulate gyrus, and the hypothalamus and thalamus. Looping around the upper brain stem, these parts collectively govern the full gamut of human emotions—feelings of joy, rage, fear, love, grief, desire and empathy among others. They also have key roles in memory and influence a person's capacity to perceive and pay attention to events in the outside world. Communications between the limbic system and the prefrontal cortex help regulate emotions. Brain imaging technologies, such as functional magnetic resonance imaging (fMRI), are also providing clues about how emotions shape patterns of thought.

EMOTIONS AND STRESS

The limbic system's links with the hypothalamus may help explain why negative stressors, such as financial difficulties, a problem relationship or the illness of a loved one, sometimes manifest with physical illnesses. The hypothalamus secretes a hormone called corticotrophin-releasing hormone (CRH) that indirectly causes the adrenal glands to release the "stress hormone" cortisol, a potent immune system suppressor that also elevates blood pressure. Some researchers speculate that chronically stressed people may be more susceptible to disease, including hypertension, infections and cancer.

Mature adults
Neural connections between the emotional and thinking brain are not fully formed until the mid-twenties. From then on, most people increasingly display typically "adult" behaviors, including improved impulse control and assuming more mature responsibilities, such as the ability to respond calmly and professionally in a disaster situation.

Tantrum time
A toddler's tantrum reflects the fact that the limbic system has developed to a stage where the child is capable of experiencing, but not controlling, strong emotions—including rage and fear. Further development of the limbic system solidifies the neural connections that underlie long-term memory.

Risky teen behaviors
In a teenager the limbic system, including the brain's pleasure centers, is fully developed, but the "rational" prefrontal cortex is only partially mature, giving teenagers less neural control over impulsive pleasure-seeking behaviors such as experimenting with drugs.

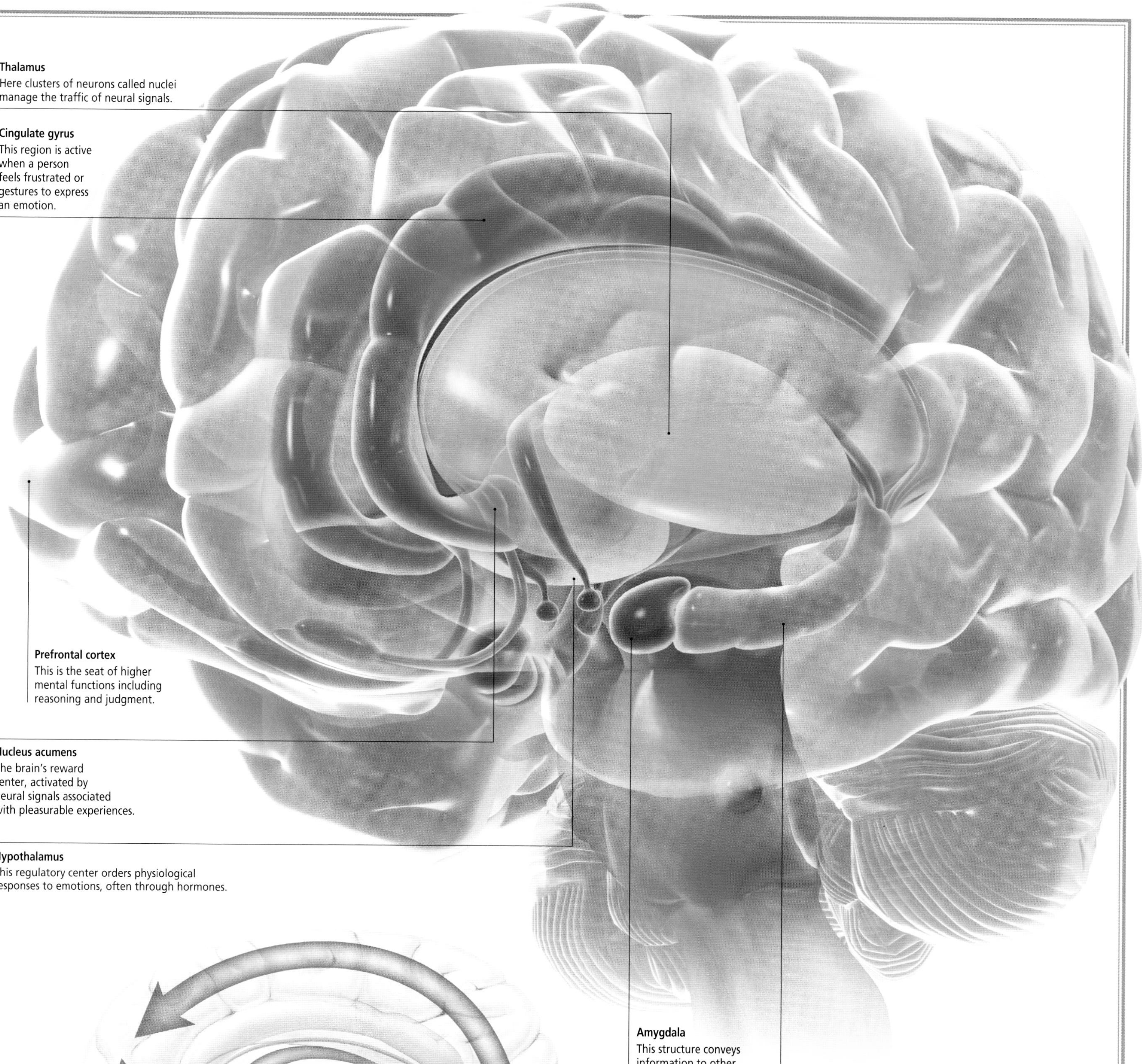

Thalamus
Here clusters of neurons called nuclei manage the traffic of neural signals.

Cingulate gyrus
This region is active when a person feels frustrated or gestures to express an emotion.

Prefrontal cortex
This is the seat of higher mental functions including reasoning and judgment.

Nucleus acumens
The brain's reward center, activated by neural signals associated with pleasurable experiences.

Hypothalamus
This regulatory center orders physiological responses to emotions, often through hormones.

Amygdala
This structure conveys information to other brain regions about experiences that have emotional content.

Hippocampus
This C-shaped limbic system structure is involved mainly in memory.

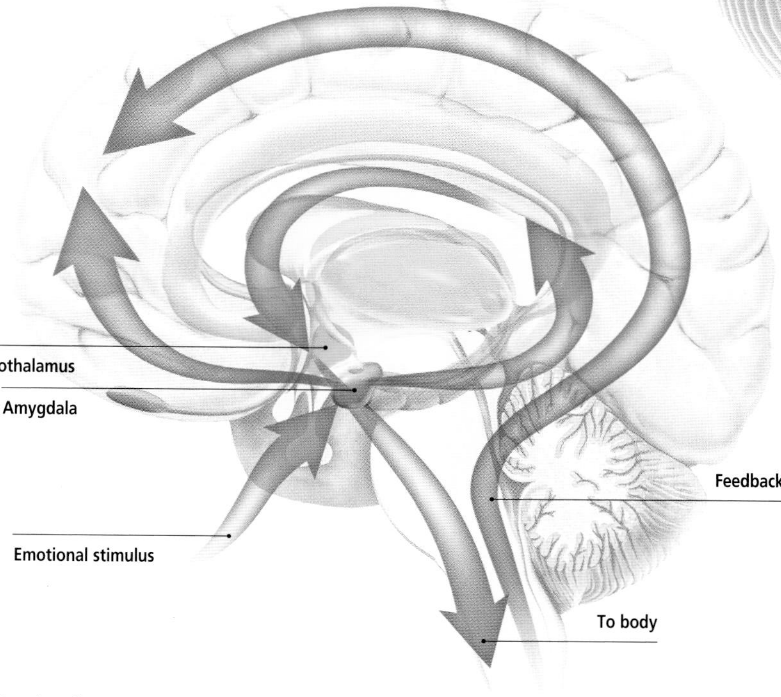

Hypothalamus

Amygdala

Feedback from body

Emotional stimulus

To body

Emotional pathways
Fear, joy and other emotions are a mix of feelings and physiological responses, such as a racing heart, a burst of tears or waves of nausea. These responses are coordinated by the amygdala, which processes the triggers and forwards them on to the hypothalamus, where signals are issued evoking physical responses. As affected organs "report back" to the frontal cortex, a person experiences the emotion and its physical impacts.

Linking emotions and thoughts

Research in cognitive neuroscience suggests that the amygdala and other parts of the limbic system are involved in brain operations such as reasoning, judgment and decision-making. In one study, investigators used functional magnetic resonance imaging (fMRI) to observe whether the emotional content of a situation affected subjects' choices. The images revealed "crosstalk" between the amygdala and parts of the prefrontal cortex. The hippocampus, which functions in memory, may also be influencing higher brain centers, according to preliminary studies.

MEMORY

Memory is the brain's capacity to store and retrieve information, a basic requirement for learning facts and skills, and for the human ability to modify behavior in response to experience. Although studying the details of memory has proved challenging, it is clear that no single part of the brain manages these processes. Instead, memories form as sensory processing areas of the cerebral cortex interact in complex ways with deeper brain structures, including the limbic system. Throughout life, the brain constantly sorts and assesses the sensory information it receives. Some of this information, such as the number on a door in a hotel corridor, is likely to be stored only briefly as a short-term memory. Other more complex sensory input, such as a wedding ceremony or the sights and sounds of an accident scene, become long-term memories that may be retained for decades.

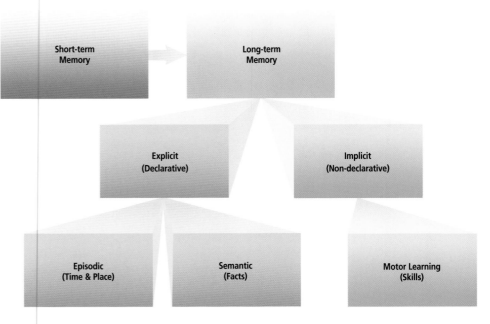

Types of memory
Short-term memory, such as a taxi company's phone number, lasts at most a few hours. Long-term memory storage involves more complex neural circuitry. Depending on circumstances, these memories are stored as facts or motor skills.

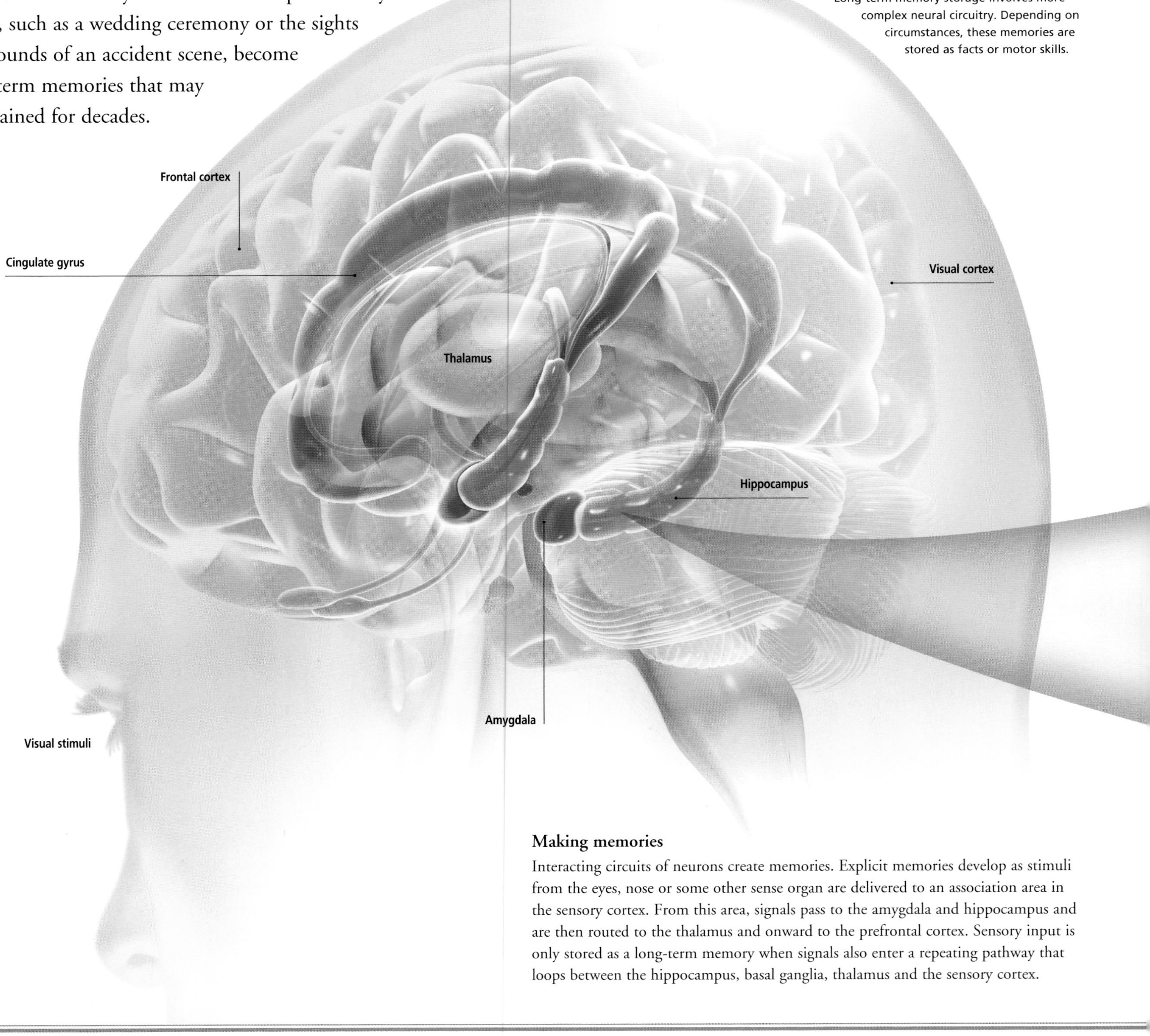

Frontal cortex

Cingulate gyrus

Visual cortex

Thalamus

Hippocampus

Amygdala

Visual stimuli

Making memories

Interacting circuits of neurons create memories. Explicit memories develop as stimuli from the eyes, nose or some other sense organ are delivered to an association area in the sensory cortex. From this area, signals pass to the amygdala and hippocampus and are then routed to the thalamus and onward to the prefrontal cortex. Sensory input is only stored as a long-term memory when signals also enter a repeating pathway that loops between the hippocampus, basal ganglia, thalamus and the sensory cortex.

Explicit memory

The ability to recall explicit information—two plus two equals four, someone's name or age—is the essence of explicit memory, also known as fact or declarative memory. Fact memories are embodied in words, symbols and images. Information associated with strong emotions or repeated activities, such as memorizing a list, are more likely to become stored in long-term memory.

Hippocampus tissue

This image highlights neurons (nerve cells) of the hippocampus in fluorescent green.

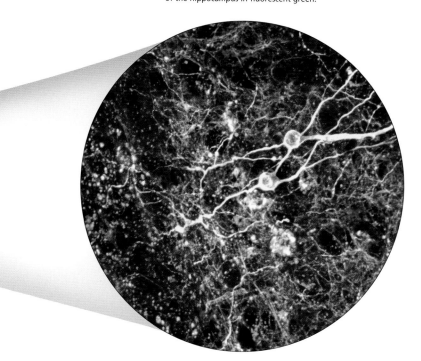

Implicit memory

Skill memory, also called implicit memory, can be defined as unconscious long-term memory. Skill memories are created by repeating a precise sequence of motor activities, such as dance steps. With time, that motor sequence becomes second nature and no longer requires conscious thought. The neural circuits involved in strengthening and consolidating skill memories involve basal ganglia and the cerebellum, which controls automatic motor activities.

Nervous System Disorders

Wear and tear, injuries, disease, autoimmune disorders—all of these factors and more can prevent neurons of the central nervous system from communicating normally. Countless people suffer from conditions such as spinal arthritis or a herniated disc, which puts pressure on nerves issuing from the spine. Such a "pinched" nerve is not life threatening, but it can produce debilitating pain or numbness that hampers normal life activities. Spinal cancer, often a metastasis from a primary cancer elsewhere in the body, can mimic these symptoms. Viruses and bacteria that invade the central nervous system cause different forms of meningitis, a dangerous but usually treatable inflammation of the meninges that surround the spinal cord and brain. Other causes produce the gradual neuron destruction associated with multiple sclerosis (MS) and amyotrophic lateral sclerosis (ALS), a condition also known as Lou Gehrig's disease. Devastating spinal damage may result in partial or total paralysis, or even death.

Meningitis
A physician can confirm a diagnosis of meningitis by obtaining and analyzing a sample of cerebrospinal fluid (CSF). In a procedure known as a lumbar puncture or spinal tap, an anesthetic is administered and then the fluid is withdrawn using a hollow needle inserted into the CSF-filled space above or below the fourth lumbar vertebra.

Neuron damage in multiple sclerosis
In MS, the immune system attacks proteins in the myelin sheath insulating a neuron's long axon. As multiple scarlike patches called scleroses develop, nerve impulses begin to travel more slowly and eventually come to a halt.

Axon (nerve fiber)

Myelin sheath

Amyotrophic lateral sclerosis
In amyotrophic lateral sclerosis, or ALS, neurons in motor pathways of the spine and parts of the brain degenerate. Gene mutations, autoimmune responses, damage from free radicals and numerous other factors have been implicated in the cause. Affected muscles quickly atrophy and most patients die within 5 years of diagnosis. A remarkable exception is astrophysicist Stephen Hawking, who has lived with ALS for decades.

Sheath breaking down

Spinal cord injury
An injury that cracks or breaks vertebrae (shown at the right) risks damage to the delicate spinal cord within. Depending on the severity and location of the trauma, temporary or permanent paralysis may result. If the cord is severed, the patient loses all sensation and voluntary muscle movements below the injury site. Quadriplegia affects all limbs, paraplegia only the lower limbs.

Multiple sclerosis

Multiple sclerosis, or MS, is a progressive autoimmune disease in which the immune system mistakenly attacks neurons in the spinal cord and brain. Viral infection and heredity may also be contributing factors. A major symptom is muscle weakness that progresses to paralysis. Many patients eventually are unable to walk and develop other symptoms related to fading neural control of muscles. MS usually appears in young adulthood, but sufferers may have periods of remission and medications can help moderate symptoms. Worldwide, several million people, most of them women, live with MS.

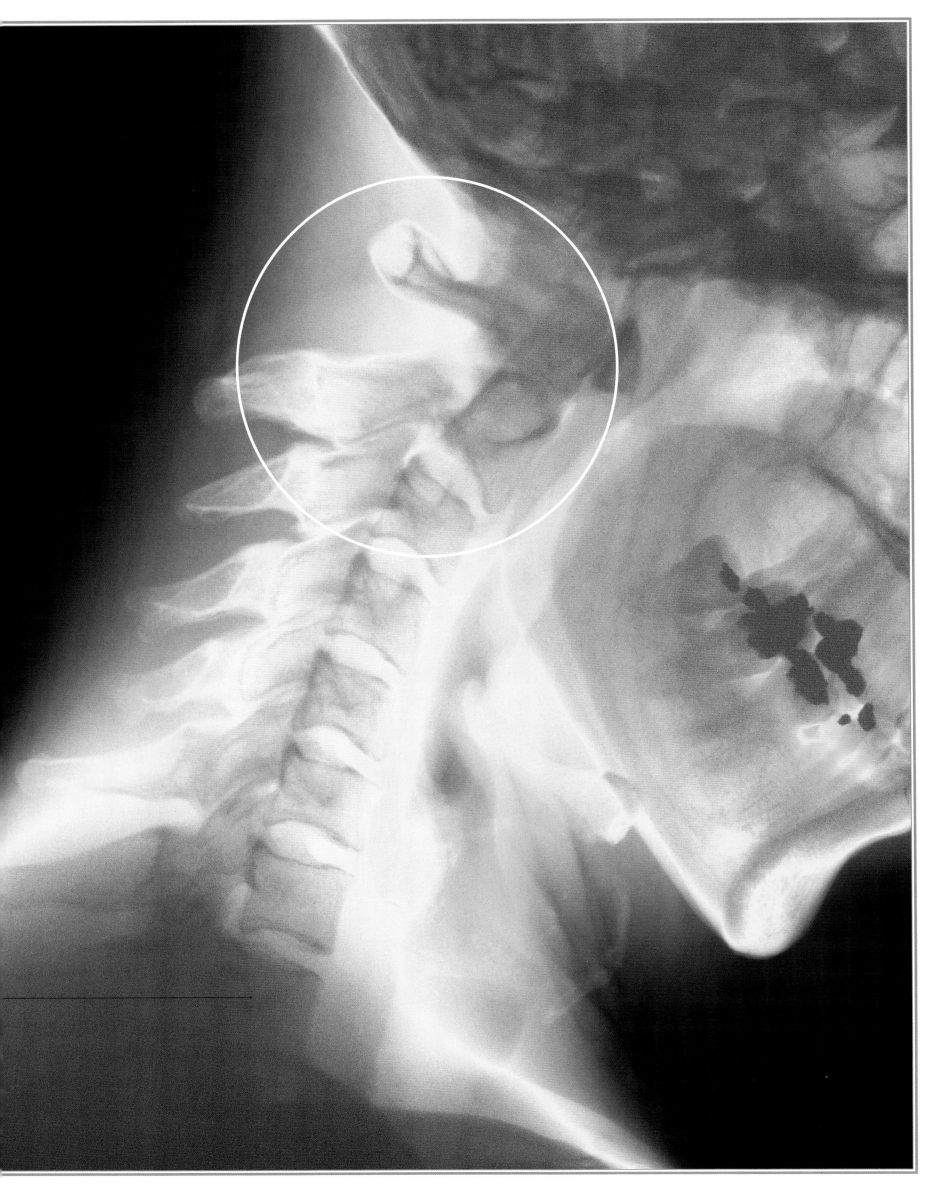

THE BRAIN UNDER ATTACK

Well-known disorders that affect the brain include concussion, Parkinson's disease and forms of dementia such as Alzheimer's disease. One of the most common illnesses is stroke, which afflicts many millions of people worldwide each year and is a leading cause of disability and death. Benign and cancerous tumors may cause symptoms only when they begin to put pressure on normal brain tissue. In epilepsy, certain brain neurons malfunction. Brain disorders have far-reaching impacts on both mental and physical functions. Serious problems may strike with little or no warning because the brain lacks sensory receptors for pain.

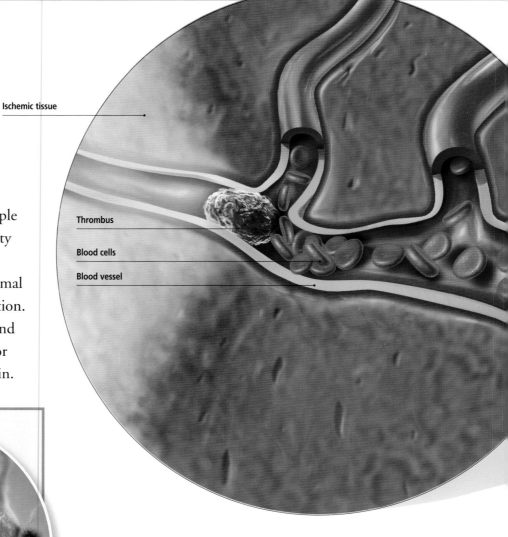

Ischemic tissue

Thrombus

Blood cells

Blood vessel

ALZHEIMER'S DISEASE

In Alzheimer's disease, structural changes in brain tissue lead to progressive memory loss and severe dementia. Neurons that release acetylcholine, an essential neurotransmitter, break down, disrupting neural functioning in the cerebral cortex and limbic system. Abnormal clumps of protein filaments, called neurofibrillary tangles, form inside other neurons. The affected brain tissue also becomes riddled with hard, insoluble protein fragments called amyloid plaques—shown here in an artist's representation.

STROKE DANGER SIGNS
• Abrupt, severe headache
• Numbness in the face, arms or legs (particularly on one side)
• Trouble walking or lack of balance
• Blurred vision or slurred speech
• Sudden mental confusion
• Unexplained nausea or vomiting
• Sudden muscle weakness
• Brief loss or reduction of consciousness

Hematoma
When a blood vessel in the brain ruptures, the clotted pool of blood, called a hematoma, can press on brain tissue and cause symptoms including headache, dizziness and seizure. Surgery may be required to remove a large hematoma.

Subdural hematoma
This type of hematoma forms between the two upper meninges, the dura mater and the arachnoid mater.

Epidural hematoma
Here blood collects between the skull and the brain.

Intracranial hematoma
The clotted blood pools inside the brain.

Blood clots and the brain
Most ischemic strokes occur when a blood clot forms in the brain itself. Called a thrombus, this clot may arise due to advancing atherosclerosis, in which formation of fatty plaques in vessels encourages clot formation.

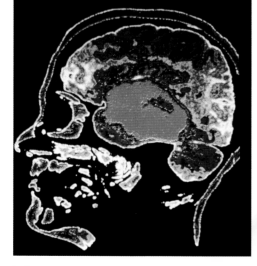

Brain cancer
Various types of cancers can occur in the brain. Some are secondary tumors resulting from metastasis of primary tumors elsewhere, while others begin in the brain. The most aggressive and deadly primary brain cancer is glioblastoma multiforme, which arises from glial cells and spreads rapidly. This image shows the scan of a brain with a tumor.

Stroke
A stroke is a sudden halt in the blood supply to some region of the brain. About 20 percent of strokes occur when a blood vessel bursts, causing a hemorrhage. The vast majority are ischemic—they occur when a clot lodges in a blood vessel and blocks the flow of blood. Emergency treatment is crucial because brain cells can survive only a few minutes without the oxygen blood delivers. Received in time, clot-dissolving medication can help restore blood flow and limit irreversible damage to brain tissue.

MENTAL HEALTH DISORDERS

Conditions that disturb mental functioning are among the most challenging health concerns for medical researchers and society at large. Many, if not most, common mental disorders reflect a combination of biological malfunctioning and stressful external events. In several of the most common mental illnesses, neuroscientists either suspect or have documented the role of abnormal brain chemistry in skewing mental functions. Relatively few people suffer from severe mental illnesses such as schizophrenia, but mood disorders such as depression and bipolar disorder are diagnosed in millions of adults, adolescents and children. Both can involve disabling symptoms that interfere with work, school or social interaction. Phobias, obsessive-compulsive disorder and post-traumatic stress disorder (PTSD) are anxiety disorders that also may disrupt the usual rhythms of daily life. Perhaps most mysterious are autism spectrum disorders (ASD), which typically begin to produce symptoms of profound developmental delays in early childhood.

Neurotransmitters and mental functioning

Neurotransmitters, the chemical intermediaries between neurons, play a major part in mental illness. Their usual role is to excite or inhibit the firing of nerve impulses. When there is either too little or too much of a given neurotransmitter, those communications go awry. For example, low levels of serotonin, norepinephrine and the neurotransmitter known as GABA are linked to clinical depression. Antidepressants increase levels of those neurotransmitters in the brain.

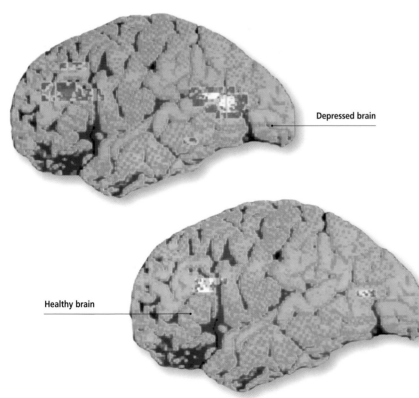

Depressed brain

Healthy brain

Healthy brain vs depressed brain
In a PET scan of a depressed person's prefrontal cortex (top), large red-yellow areas mark abnormally reduced neural activity. Those same areas are much more active in the brain of a person successfully treated for depression.

Depression
Clinical depression can be a stealthy and disabling disease. Symptoms include feelings of deep despair, difficulty concentrating, insomnia, lethargy and loss of appetite. Depressed individuals often experience distorted thinking that includes thoughts of suicide. These symptoms correlate with low levels of serotonin and several other neurotransmitters.

Phobias
Many individuals fear snakes, spiders and heights. A true phobia—an irrational, intense fear of particular objects or situation—may be due to inherited quirks of brain chemistry combined with unpleasant personal experiences.

Schizophrenia
Paranoid delusions, disorganized thinking and auditory hallucinations are classic symptoms of schizophrenia. Researchers are investigating the genetic basis of this devastating mental illness, which usually develops in young adulthood.

ADDICTIONS

In addiction, the brain becomes profoundly dependent on the chemical effects of a substance, such as alcohol, nicotine, cocaine, painkillers or some other psychoactive drug. The drug affects activity of one or more neurotransmitters, either by blocking its receptors, slowing its re-uptake by neurons or boosting its release. All major addictive drugs stimulate the release of the neurotransmitter dopamine, which is part of the brain's pleasure-signaling system. Individuals vary greatly in their susceptibility to addiction, and in some cases, genetic factors increase the risk.

Bipolar disorder
Bipolar disorder (formerly, manic depression) causes severe mood swings between euphoria and depression. This debilitating illness may have a genetic basis. Some experts speculate that it contributed to the suicide of artist Vincent van Gogh.

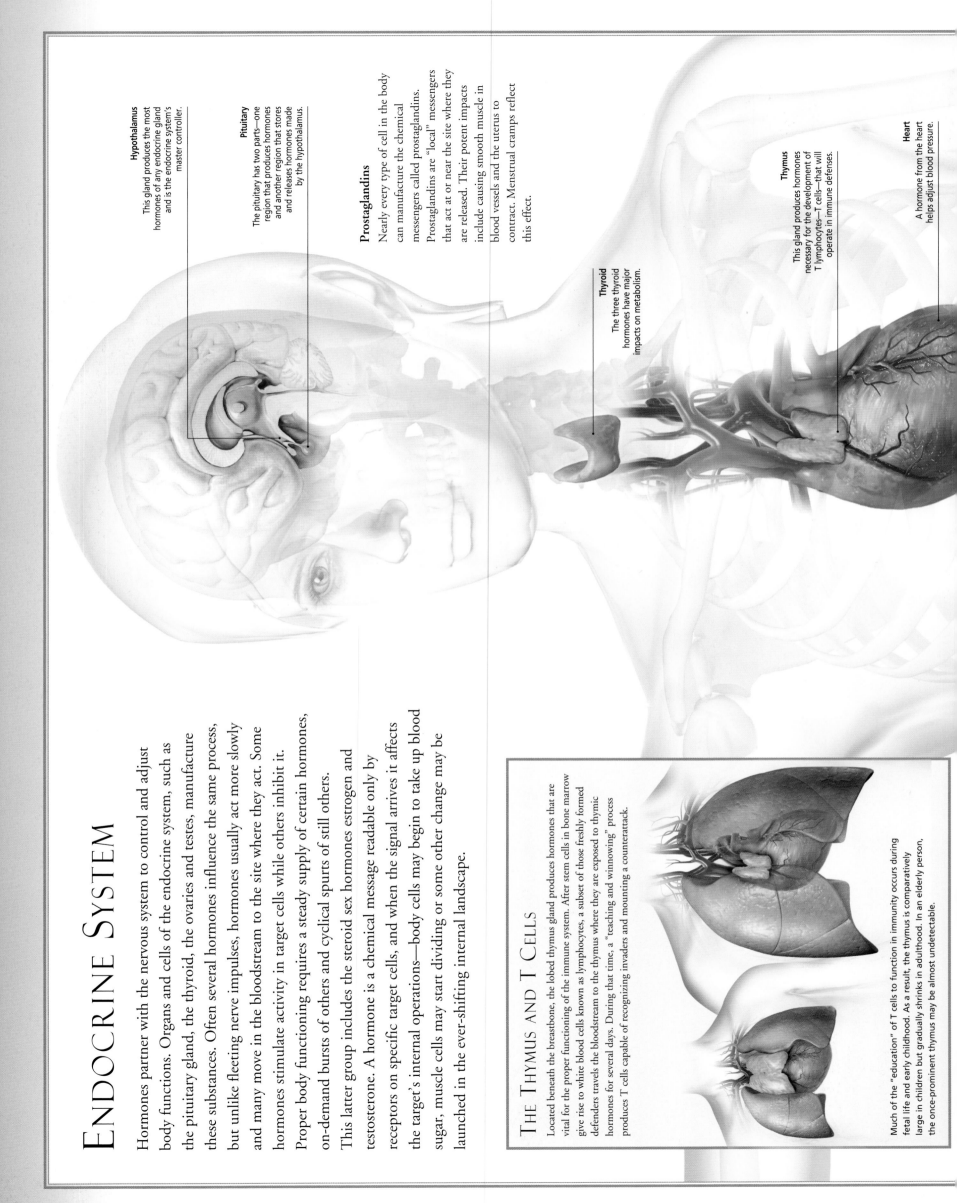

ENDOCRINE SYSTEM

Hormones partner with the nervous system to control and adjust body functions. Organs and cells of the endocrine system, such as the pituitary gland, the thyroid, the ovaries and testes, manufacture these substances. Often several hormones influence the same process, but unlike fleeting nerve impulses, hormones usually act more slowly and many move in the bloodstream to the site where they act. Some hormones stimulate activity in target cells while others inhibit it. Proper body functioning requires a steady supply of certain hormones, on-demand bursts of others and cyclical spurts of still others.

This latter group includes the steroid sex hormones estrogen and testosterone. A hormone is a chemical message readable only by receptors on specific target cells, and when the signal arrives it affects the target's internal operations—body cells may begin to take up blood sugar, muscle cells may start dividing or some other change may be launched in the ever-shifting internal landscape.

THE THYMUS AND T CELLS

Located beneath the breastbone, the lobed thymus gland produces hormones that are vital for the proper functioning of the immune system. After stem cells in bone marrow give rise to white blood cells known as lymphocytes, a subset of those freshly formed defenders travels the bloodstream to the thymus where they are exposed to thymic hormones for several days. During that time, a "teaching and winnowing" process produces T cells capable of recognizing invaders and mounting a counterattack.

Much of the "education" of T cells to function in immunity occurs during fetal life and early childhood. As a result, the thymus is comparatively large in children but gradually shrinks in adulthood. In an elderly person, the once-prominent thymus may be almost undetectable.

Hypothalamus
This gland produces the most hormones of any endocrine gland and is the endocrine system's master controller.

Pituitary
The pituitary has two parts—one region that produces hormones and another region that stores and releases hormones made by the hypothalamus.

Prostaglandins
Nearly every type of cell in the body can manufacture the chemical messengers called prostaglandins. Prostaglandins are "local" messengers that act at or near the site where they are released. Their potent impacts include causing smooth muscle in blood vessels and the uterus to contract. Menstrual cramps reflect this effect.

Thyroid
The three thyroid hormones have major impacts on metabolism.

Thymus
This gland produces hormones necessary for the development of T lymphocytes—T cells—that will operate in immune defenses.

Heart
A hormone from the heart helps adjust blood pressure.

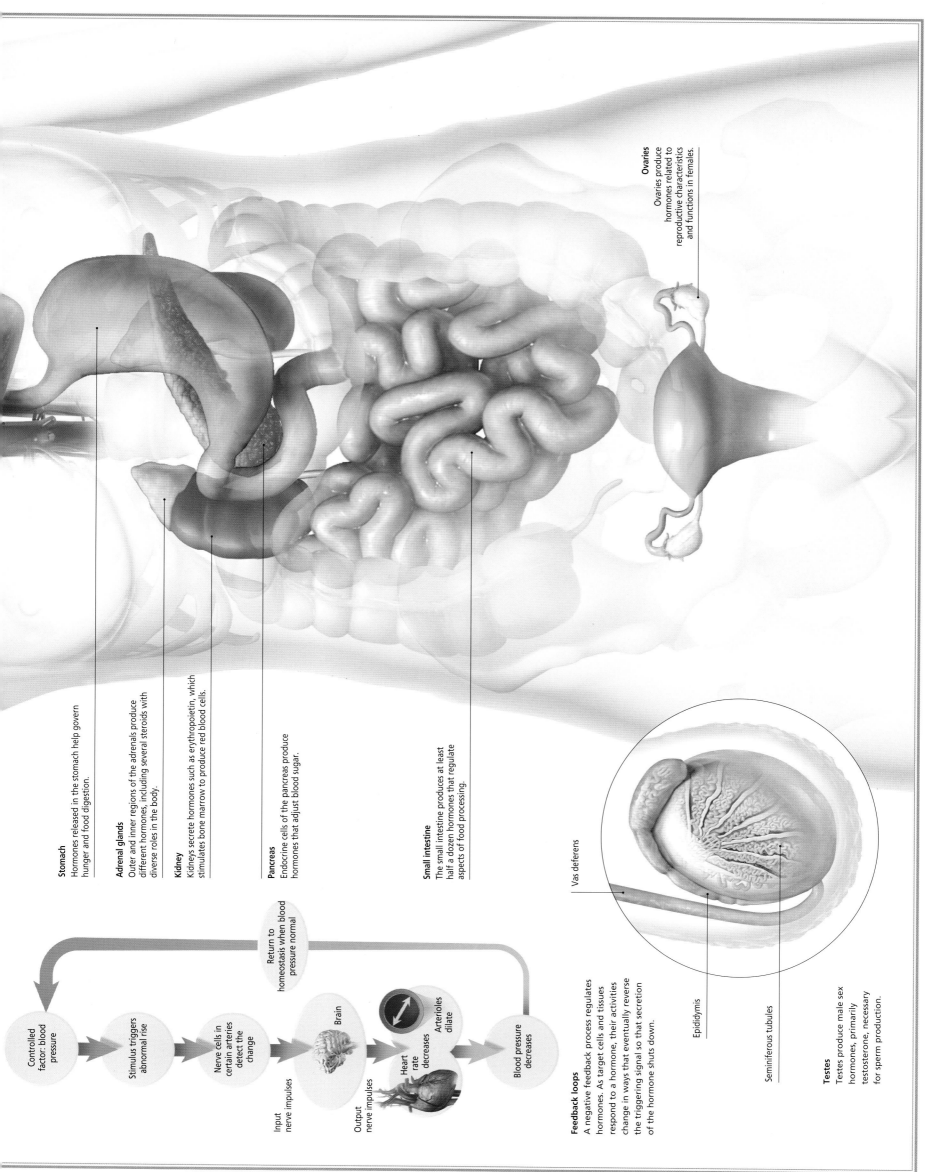

Stomach
Hormones released in the stomach help govern hunger and food digestion.

Adrenal glands
Outer and inner regions of the adrenals produce different hormones, including several steroids with diverse roles in the body.

Kidney
Kidneys secrete hormones such as erythropoietin, which stimulates bone marrow to produce red blood cells.

Pancreas
Endocrine cells of the pancreas produce hormones that adjust blood sugar.

Small intestine
The small intestine produces at least half a dozen hormones that regulate aspects of food processing.

Ovaries
Ovaries produce hormones related to reproductive characteristics and functions in females.

Vas deferens

Epididymis

Seminiferous tubules

Testes
Testes produce male sex hormones, primarily testosterone, necessary for sperm production.

Feedback loops
A negative feedback process regulates hormones. As target cells and tissues respond to a hormone, their activities change in ways that eventually reverse the triggering signal so that secretion of the hormone shuts down.

Controlled factor: blood pressure

Stimulus triggers abnormal rise

Nerve cells in certain arteries detect the change

Input nerve impulses

Brain

Output nerve impulses

Heart rate decreases

Arterioles dilate

Blood pressure decreases

Return to homeostasis when blood pressure normal

THE PITUITARY AND HYPOTHALAMUS

Normal body growth, the day-to-day metabolic activities of cells, the development and functioning of reproductive organs, bodily responses to stress—all these processes depend on the two major glands of the endocrine system, the hypothalamus and its subsidiary, the pituitary gland. The hypothalamus is a dual-purpose organ. Some of its neurons regulate conditions such as body temperature, hunger and thirst that are vital for internal homeostasis. Others function in the endocrine system and produce hormones. Several of these chemical messengers control the pituitary, while others influence tissues elsewhere and are merely stored in the pituitary until they are secreted to the bloodstream. The pituitary's rear or posterior lobe houses the axons of hormone-secreting hypothalamus neurons. The forward or anterior pituitary lobe is a true endocrine gland that produces six hormones that have major effects on tissues and organs.

Pituitary gland
The pituitary gland is about one-half inch (1cm) in diameter, the size of a cherry pit. It is located in a hollow of the sphenoid bone, which is part of the floor of the skull. Networks of small arteries and veins transport hormones from the hypothalamus to the anterior pituitary and other hormones from the pituitary into the general circulation.

Hypothalamus

Pituitary gland

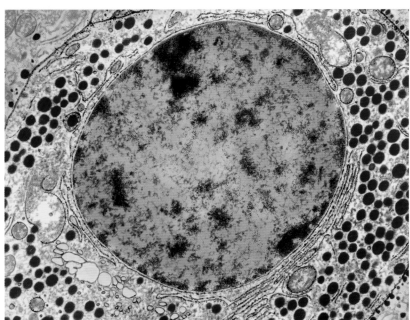

Breast feeding
Nursing an infant might seem like a simple process, but it requires the interaction of two maternal hormones— prolactin to stimulate the formation of milk, and oxytocin to stimulate the flow of milk into the ducts that open at the nipple.

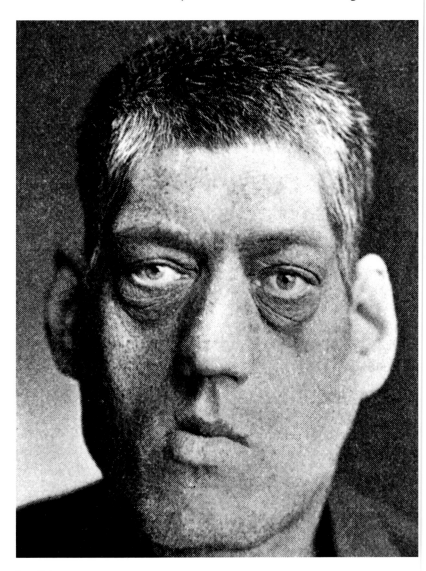

Growth to excess
When too much growth hormone (GH) is secreted in adulthood, the result is acromegaly, a condition in which epithelial tissue in the skin, nose, tongue and lips thickens abnormally, as do bones, cartilage and other connective tissues in the jaw, feet and hands.

Growth hormone
This anterior pituitary cell has stored growth hormone (GH) inside small vesicles (brown). As indicated by its name, growth hormone stimulates the growth of muscle, bones and other tissues. It is also used in treating cancer and AIDS.

The endocrine regulatory center

Linked by a slender stalk, the hypothalamus and pituitary are located at the base of the brain and operate jointly as an endocrine control center. Regulator hormones from the hypothalamus govern the release of anterior pituitary hormones such as growth hormone, which affects virtually all body cells, and hormones that stimulate other endocrine organs including the thyroid, adrenals, ovaries and testes. Hypothalamus neurons make the hormones oxytocin and ADH (antidiuretic hormone). They are released from the terminals of the neurons' axons, which are clustered in the posterior pituitary.

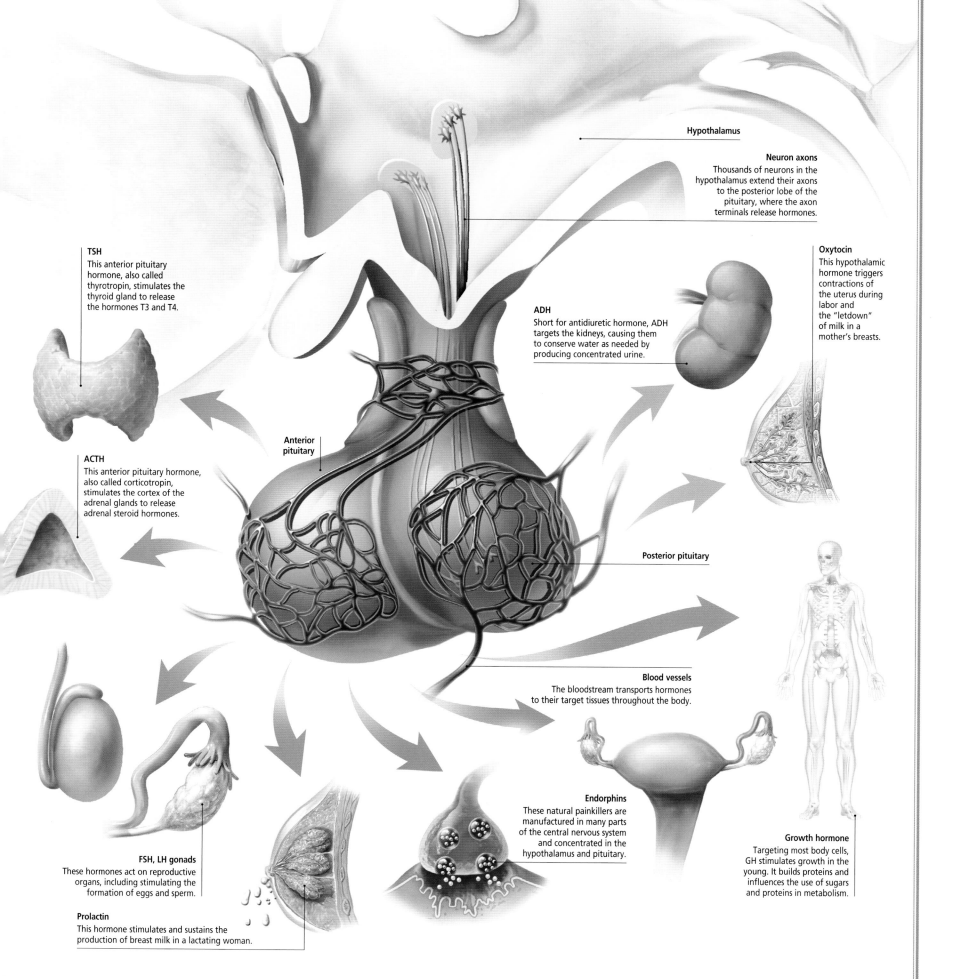

Hypothalamus

Neuron axons
Thousands of neurons in the hypothalamus extend their axons to the posterior lobe of the pituitary, where the axon terminals release hormones.

TSH
This anterior pituitary hormone, also called thyrotropin, stimulates the thyroid gland to release the hormones T3 and T4.

Oxytocin
This hypothalamic hormone triggers contractions of the uterus during labor and the "letdown" of milk in a mother's breasts.

ADH
Short for antidiuretic hormone, ADH targets the kidneys, causing them to conserve water as needed by producing concentrated urine.

ACTH
This anterior pituitary hormone, also called corticotropin, stimulates the cortex of the adrenal glands to release adrenal steroid hormones.

Anterior pituitary

Posterior pituitary

Blood vessels
The bloodstream transports hormones to their target tissues throughout the body.

FSH, LH gonads
These hormones act on reproductive organs, including stimulating the formation of eggs and sperm.

Prolactin
This hormone stimulates and sustains the production of breast milk in a lactating woman.

Endorphins
These natural painkillers are manufactured in many parts of the central nervous system and concentrated in the hypothalamus and pituitary.

Growth hormone
Targeting most body cells, GH stimulates growth in the young. It builds proteins and influences the use of sugars and proteins in metabolism.

THE THYROID AND PANCREAS

Few of the body's endocrine glands make hormones that influence cells and tissues throughout the body. One of them is the thyroid, a gland located below the shield-shaped thyroid cartilage of the larynx best known as the Adam's apple. Flaring around the base of the trachea, the thyroid makes three hormones. Two of these, triiodothyronine (T3) and thyroxine (T4), are jointly labeled as thyroid hormone (TH). Nearly every cell in the body has TH receptors, so unlike most other hormones TH affects most body tissues, helping to regulate their metabolism, growth and development. The third thyroid hormone, calcitonin, helps maintain sufficient calcium in the blood for processes such as muscle contraction that require it. Much of the finger-shaped pancreas is devoted to making enzymes used in food digestion, but it also contains small islets of hormone-producing cells. Three islet hormones collectively manage the body's ever-shifting supply of blood sugar.

The pancreas

When blood levels of the sugar glucose fall below a set point, alpha cells in pancreatic islets make the hormone glucagon, which acts in the liver and muscles to make glucose from the storage compound glycogen. When blood glucose is high, beta cells secrete insulin, which stimulates body cells to take up sugar from the bloodstream. A third group of islet cells called delta cells secretes somatostatin, which adjusts the activity of alpha and beta cells as needed.

HORMONES FROM THE THYROID AND PANCREAS		
HORMONE	**RELEASED FROM**	**FUNCTION**
Calcitonin	Thyroid	Slows the release of calcium from the bones into the blood
Triiodothyronine (T3)	Thyroid	Regulates metabolism
Thyroxine (T4)	Thyroid	Stimulates metabolism
Insulin	Pancreas	Promotes the absorption of glucose, which lowers blood sugar levels
Glucagon	Pancreas	Helps keep amount of glucose in the blood at a set point by raising blood sugar levels
Somatostatin	Pancreas	Regulates the alpha and beta cells of the pancreatic islets

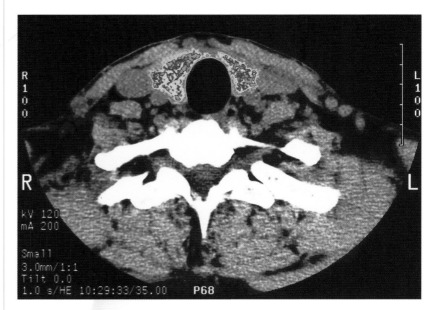

The thyroid
The thyroid, highlighted here as two reddish-orange masses in front of the trachea, is the body's largest endocrine gland, with two lobes that connect in front of the trachea. The lobes contain numerous round, hollow sacs where cells produce the thyroid's three hormones.

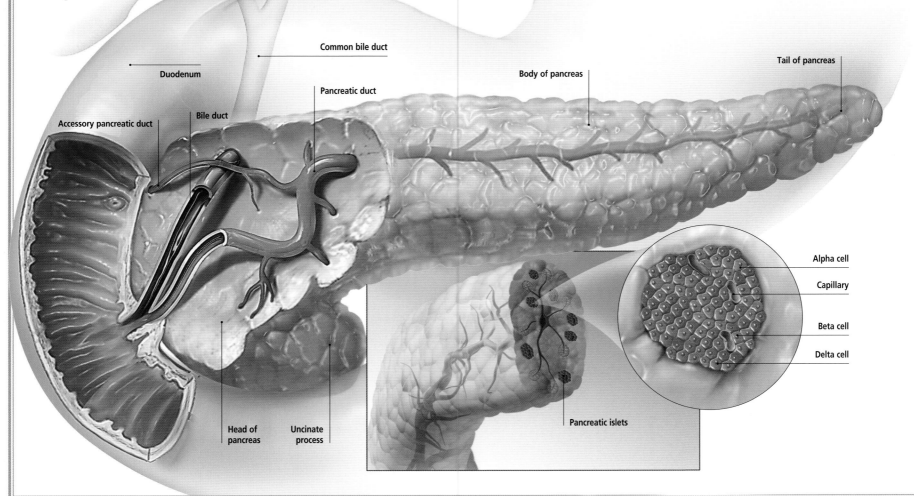

Common bile duct

Duodenum

Pancreatic duct

Body of pancreas

Tail of pancreas

Accessory pancreatic duct

Bile duct

Alpha cell

Capillary

Beta cell

Delta cell

Pancreatic islets

Head of pancreas

Uncinate process

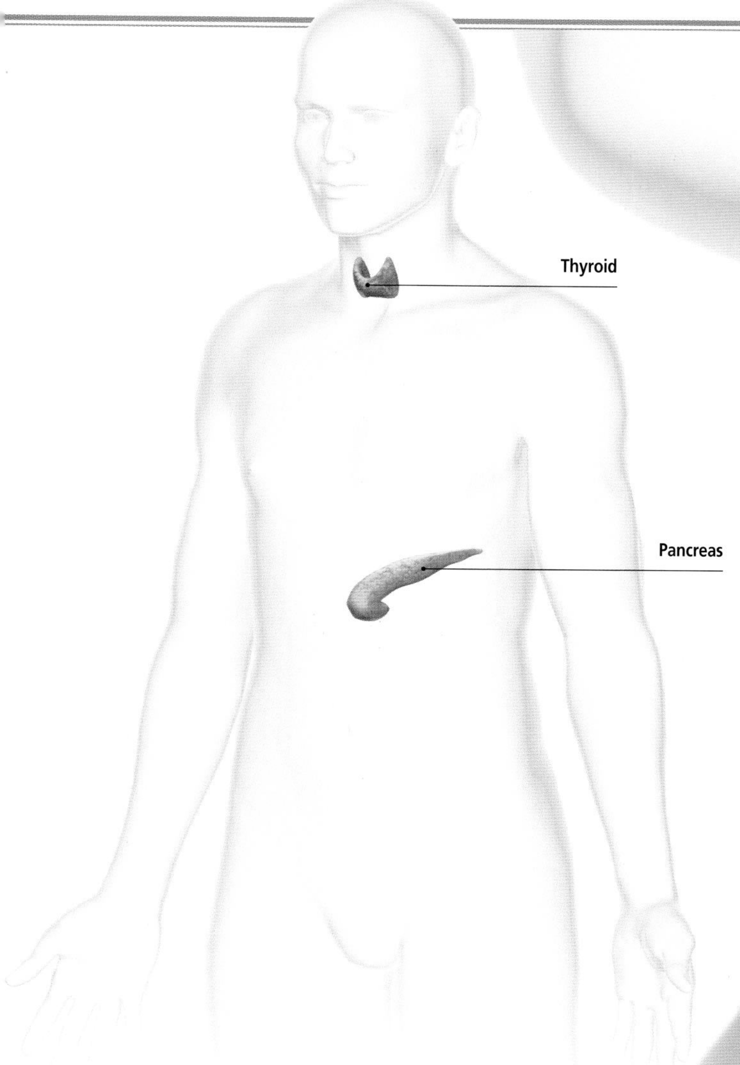

Thyroid

Pancreas

Metabolism and the thyroid

Thyroid hormone (TH) is involved in many metabolic processes. It regulates cells' use of blood sugar and oxygen to manufacture ATP, the chemical fuel that cells use to power their activities. It also adjusts body temperature by way of setting the basal metabolic rate, or BMR—the amount of energy used to sustain basic body operations. Without TH, virtually no major body system can function normally.

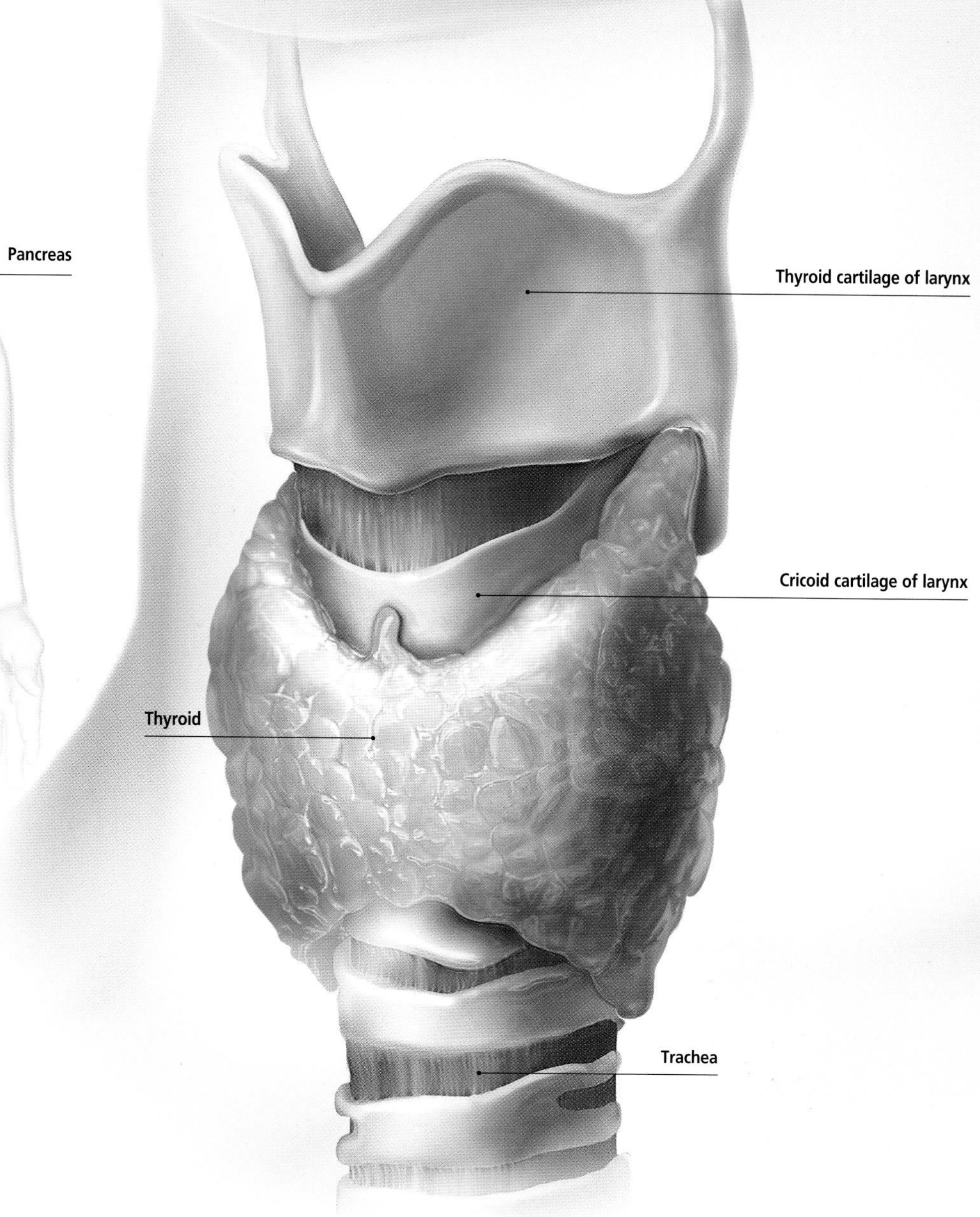

Thyroid cartilage of larynx

Cricoid cartilage of larynx

Thyroid

Trachea

Balancing blood sugar

Insulin lowers blood sugar and glucagon increases it. Together these hormones interact to keep blood glucose levels within a normal range. This balancing act is a key factor in weight control and maintaining overall health. It is especially crucial for the brain to have steady access to adequate blood glucose, which is the only fuel brain cells can use.

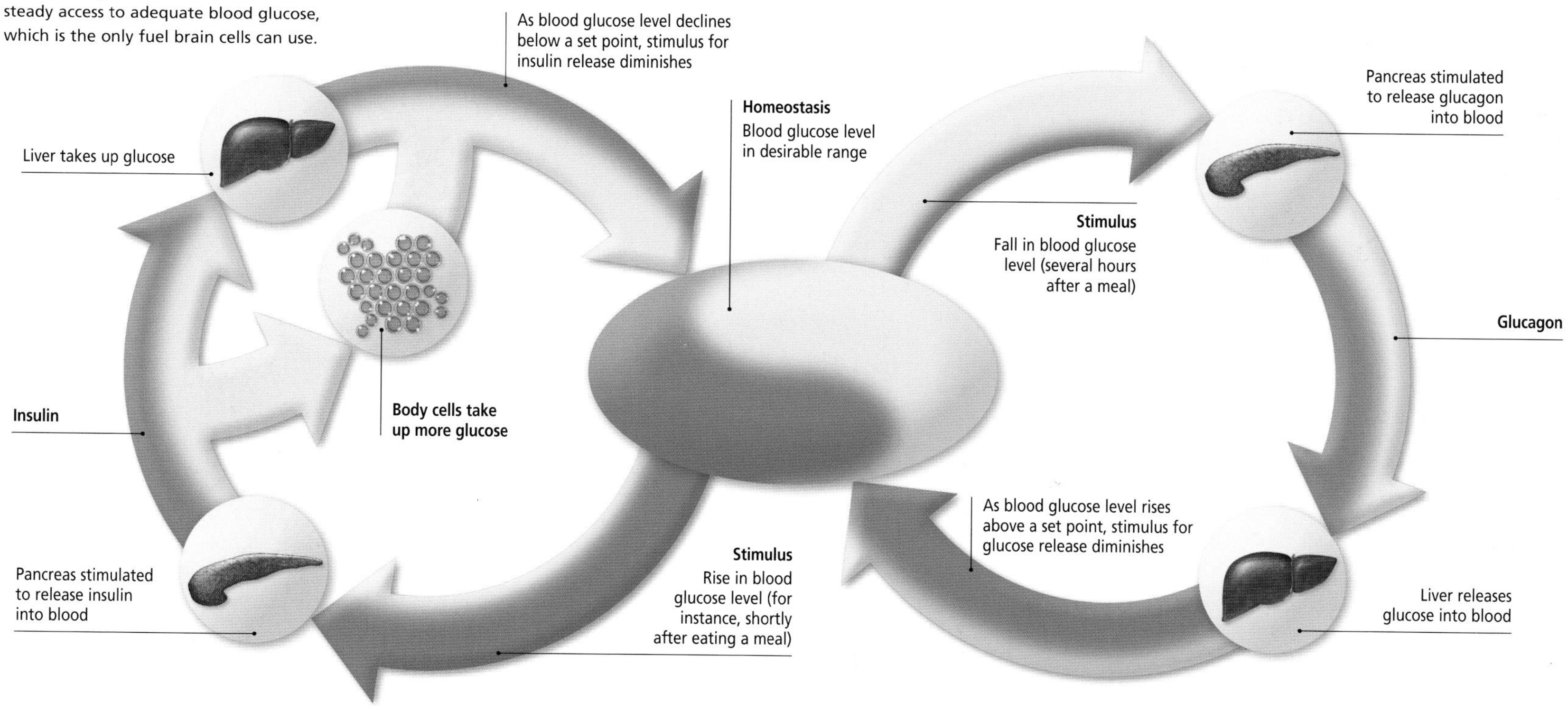

Liver takes up glucose

Insulin

Pancreas stimulated to release insulin into blood

Body cells take up more glucose

As blood glucose level declines below a set point, stimulus for insulin release diminishes

Homeostasis
Blood glucose level in desirable range

Stimulus
Rise in blood glucose level (for instance, shortly after eating a meal)

Pancreas stimulated to release glucagon into blood

Stimulus
Fall in blood glucose level (several hours after a meal)

Glucagon

As blood glucose level rises above a set point, stimulus for glucose release diminishes

Liver releases glucose into blood

PARATHYROIDS AND ADRENALS

Like most other endocrine glands, the parathyroids and adrenal glands both respond to control signals from the pituitary. The parathyroids consist of two, tiny, bean-shaped masses of tissue on either side of the rear of the thyroid. With the thyroid, they contribute to a never-ending balancing act that helps assure the proper level of calcium in the blood. When the calcium level falls too low, the parathyroids secrete parathyroid hormone or PTH, which acts to release calcium and other minerals that are stored in bone tissue. Rising blood calcium eventually prompts the thyroid to secrete calcitonin, which shuts off the action of PTH. The adrenal glands are located just above the kidneys. They produce several hormones, including steroids that help maintain blood pressure; adjust the use of fuel molecules in metabolism; and influence reproductive and sexual functions. Other adrenal hormones prepare the body to cope with stress.

Parathyroid glands

Parathyroid hormone (PTH) from the parathyroids is the body's main internal calcium regulator. When the level of calcium in the blood falls below a set point, PTH stimulates osteoclasts in bone tissue to break down parts of the mineralized bone matrix and release calcium into the blood. Simultaneously, it prompts the kidneys to excrete less calcium in urine. When the blood contains enough calcium to meet body needs, PTH secretion stops until calcium levels dip again.

HORMONES FROM THE ADRENAL AND PARATHYROID GLANDS		
HORMONE	**RELEASED FROM**	**FUNCTION**
Aldosterone	Adrenal cortex	Helps conserve water to maintain blood volume and pressure
Cortisol	Adrenal cortex	Regulates use of protein, fats, carbohydrates and some minerals
Epinephrine and Norepinephrine	Adrenal medulla	Elevate heart rate and blood pressure to help sustain fight-or-flight response
Androgens	Adrenal cortex	Influence sperm production in males and ovulation and menstruation in females
Parathyroid hormone (PTH)	Parathyroids	Helps regulate blood calcium and calcium uptake by cells

Calcium intake
Nearly all body cells need a steady, bloodborne supply of calcium to function properly. Parathyroid hormone (PTH) facilitates this process by triggering the breakdown of bone when calcium consumed in the diet does not meet the demand.

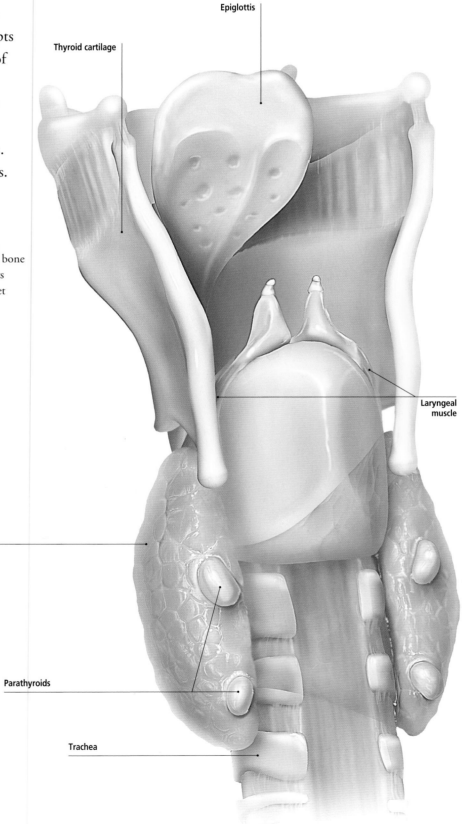

Epiglottis

Thyroid cartilage

Laryngeal muscle

Thyroid

Parathyroids

Trachea

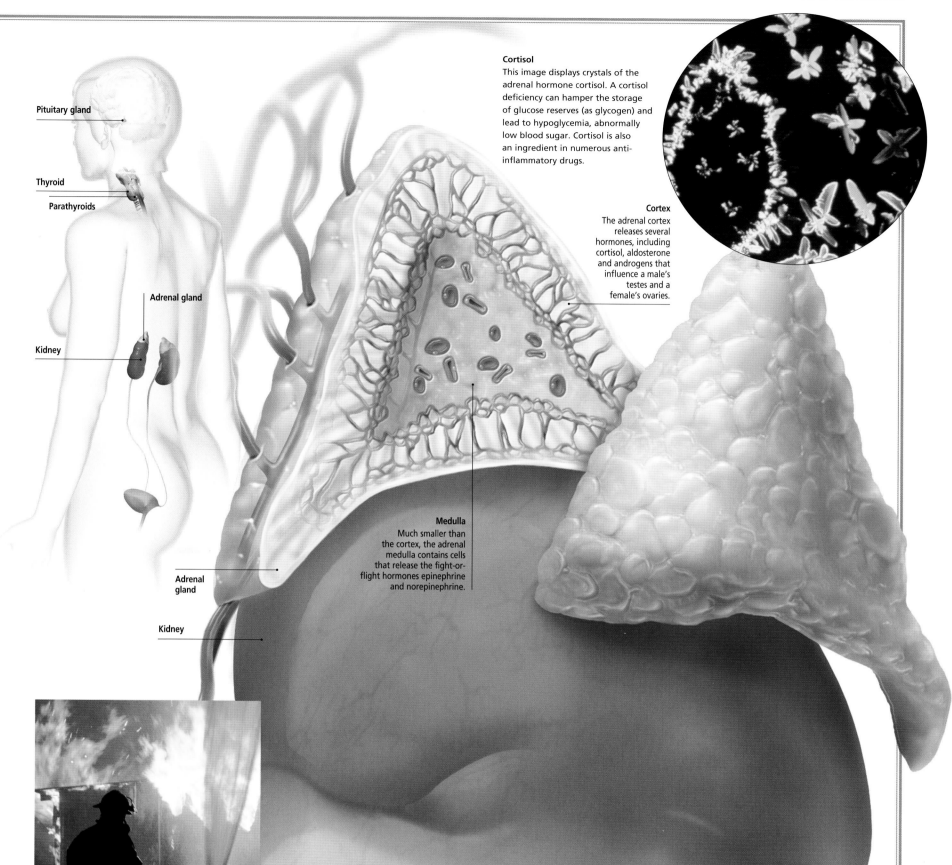

Pituitary gland

Thyroid

Parathyroids

Adrenal gland

Kidney

Adrenal gland

Kidney

Cortisol
This image displays crystals of the adrenal hormone cortisol. A cortisol deficiency can hamper the storage of glucose reserves (as glycogen) and lead to hypoglycemia, abnormally low blood sugar. Cortisol is also an ingredient in numerous anti-inflammatory drugs.

Cortex
The adrenal cortex releases several hormones, including cortisol, aldosterone and androgens that influence a male's testes and a female's ovaries.

Medulla
Much smaller than the cortex, the adrenal medulla contains cells that release the fight-or-flight hormones epinephrine and norepinephrine.

Fight or flight
When danger looms, the nervous system commands the adrenal medullas to pump out epinephrine, also known as adrenalin, and norepinephrine. They jointly trigger the "fight-or-flight" response—faster breathing and heartbeat—that primes the body to respond to an emergency.

Adrenal glands

Each adrenal gland has an inner medulla and a thick outer cortex that produces several steroid hormones. Glucocorticoids, including cortisol, regulate the use of proteins and fat in metabolism, help the liver store excess glucose as glycogen and dampen inflammation. Aldosterone, a mineralocorticoid, helps regulate blood pressure. The cortex androgen DHEA (dehydroepiandrosterone) acts during fetal development of reproductive organs. Later on it is a building block for estrogen, which is secreted by the ovaries in females.

HORMONES FROM OTHER SOURCES

In the body, chemical communication is a well-honed tool. In addition to familiar hormone sources such as the hypothalamus, pituitary, thyroid gland and reproductive organs, numerous other glands and scattered patches of tissue produce hormones. This arsenal of chemical messengers includes specialized cells in the digestive tract that secrete hormones that stimulate the release of digestive juices or have roles in adjusting appetite.

The skin acts like an endocrine gland when it makes cholecalciferol, a precursor of vitamin D, and then releases vitamin D into the blood stream. Tissues in the heart, kidneys, thymus and elsewhere release other hormones. This cadre of communication molecules also includes melatonin, the "jet lag" hormone produced by the tiny pineal gland when the environment becomes dark that helps induce sleep. All these substances have the capacity to alter body functioning in ways small and large.

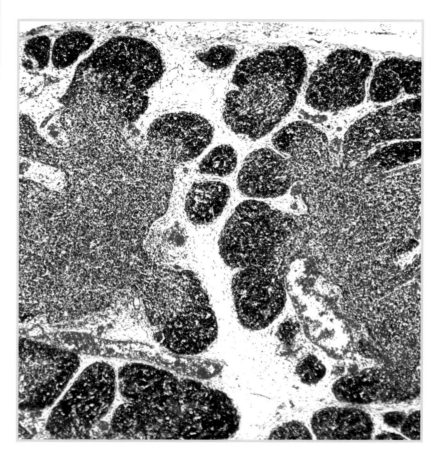

T is for thymus
T cells arise in bone marrow, and then they move via the bloodstream to the thymus where they are briefly exposed to hormones that guide their maturation into functional infection fighters. This process occurs mainly during childhood, when the thymus is largest, achieving maximum size during puberty. As a person grows to adulthood the thymus shrinks dramatically, eventually almost disappearing.

Hot water and "the call of nature"
A warm bath may trigger a desire to urinate. As warming blood fills the left atrium, that heart chamber registers the change as an increase in blood volume. The heart releases atrial natriuretic hormone, or ANH, in response, the kidneys form dilute urine and the bladder begins to fill.

Erythropoietin
The kidneys make the hormone erythropoietin, or EPO, which the bone marrow uses to produce new red blood cells. Although most track and field athletes compete fairly, some are unethical and resort to blood doping—withdrawing and storing a quantity of blood and then re-injecting after EPO has generated replacement cells. This practice increases oxygen in the bloodstream.

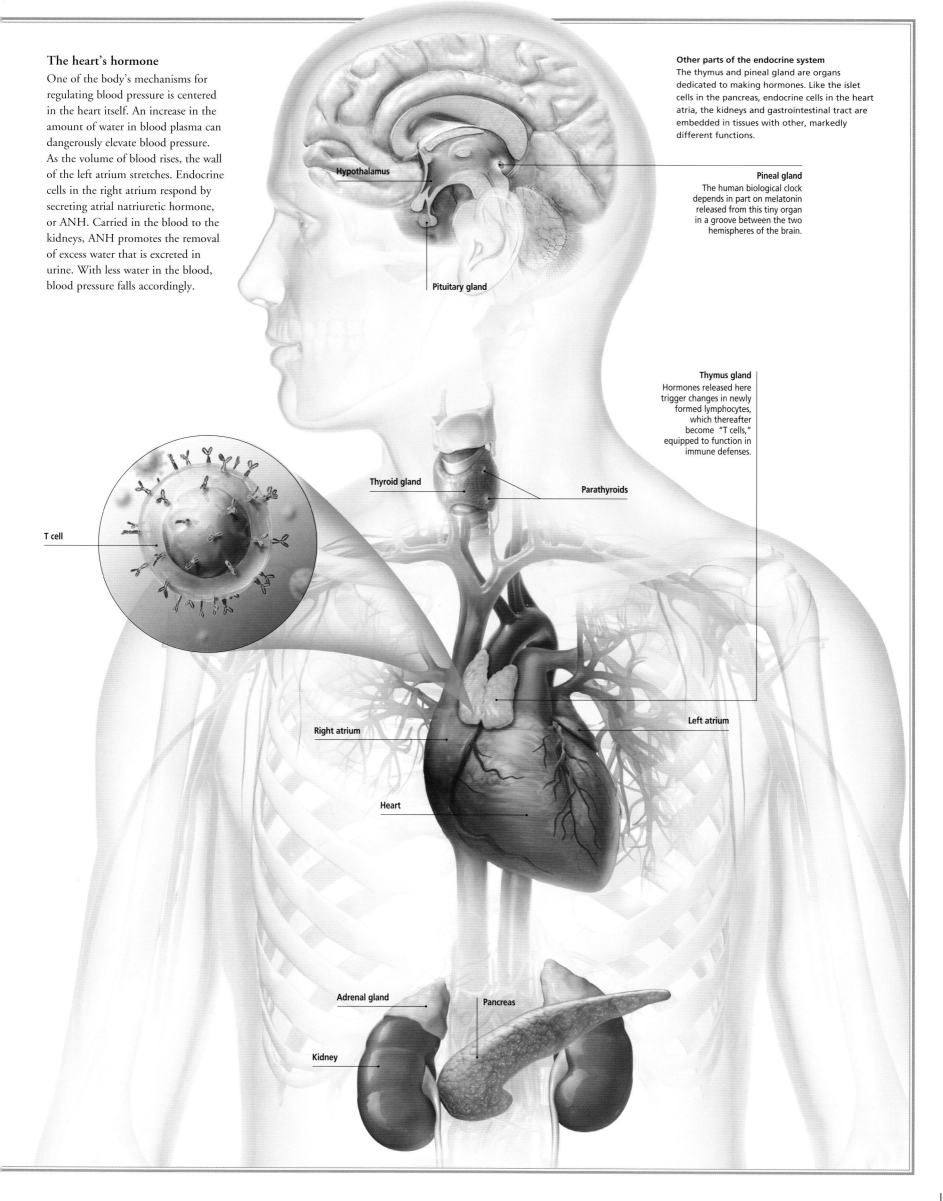

The heart's hormone

One of the body's mechanisms for regulating blood pressure is centered in the heart itself. An increase in the amount of water in blood plasma can dangerously elevate blood pressure. As the volume of blood rises, the wall of the left atrium stretches. Endocrine cells in the right atrium respond by secreting atrial natriuretic hormone, or ANH. Carried in the blood to the kidneys, ANH promotes the removal of excess water that is excreted in urine. With less water in the blood, blood pressure falls accordingly.

Other parts of the endocrine system
The thymus and pineal gland are organs dedicated to making hormones. Like the islet cells in the pancreas, endocrine cells in the heart atria, the kidneys and gastrointestinal tract are embedded in tissues with other, markedly different functions.

Pineal gland
The human biological clock depends in part on melatonin released from this tiny organ in a groove between the two hemispheres of the brain.

Thymus gland
Hormones released here trigger changes in newly formed lymphocytes, which thereafter become "T cells," equipped to function in immune defenses.

Hypothalamus

Pituitary gland

T cell

Thyroid gland

Parathyroids

Right atrium

Left atrium

Heart

Adrenal gland

Pancreas

Kidney

HORMONES AND HUNGER

Hunger is a drive to eat in order to replenish the body's declining energy stores. Appetite adds another dimension to this biological basic—it involves a desire to eat because doing so brings pleasure. The nervous system helps control food intake, just as it does other life processes. More surprising is the discovery that hormones also play a major role in regulating eating behavior. The bloodstream carries a variety of hormones produced in the digestive tract or by fat cells to receptors in the hypothalamus. When the system operates normally, some of these signals promote food intake when blood sugar declines, and others reduce the desire to eat when a person has consumed enough to satisfy metabolic needs. Although many aspects of the mechanisms that regulate normal eating patterns remain unknown, scientists are actively exploring ways of using the growing understanding of hunger hormones to combat obesity, eating disorders and other health concerns.

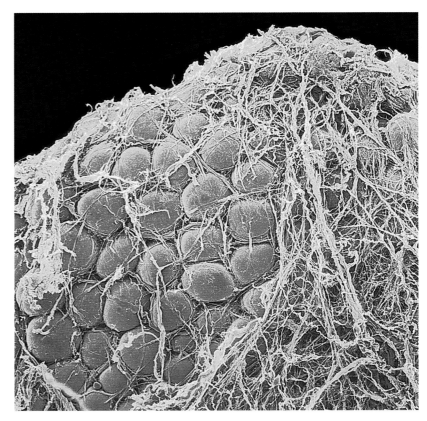

Storing fat
Wrapped in a mesh of connective tissue, these human fat cells are genetically programmed to take up and store excess blood sugar as fat that can be used in case other energy supplies run low. Fat cells expand or shrivel as fat is added or used.

EMOTIONAL EATING

Most people occasionally indulge in emotional eating—consuming food as a way to dampen boredom, stress, loneliness, anger or other feelings. Eating for emotional comfort rather than to satisfy hunger is an impulsive behavior and often the eater will crave a particular food item, such as ice cream, pizza or a favorite casserole. Chocolate is among the foods that contain chemicals with mood-elevating effects in the brain.

Snacking is a common nervous habit. Calories obtained in late-night snacking generally lead to weight gain because the body's metabolism slows down during sleep.

Self-starvation
Anorexia is any reduction in the normal desire to eat. In anorexia nervosa, deep-seated psychological factors skew the condition into a chronic and dangerous disorder in which the affected person purposely starves and may overexercise as well. Some patients starve themselves to death, but others respond to counseling and eventually are able to resume normal eating patterns.

Eating to extremes
Obesity is an unhealthy excess of body fat. Some obese people struggle with unwanted weight due to genetic or hormonal factors. Most often, however, the issue is a metabolic imbalance caused by consuming much more food than the body can use for energy. The World Health Organization has declared obesity to be a major global health crisis, with links to a number of chronic diseases such as diabetes, heart disease and even some cancers. The incidence of obesity is on the rise around the world, especially in cities.

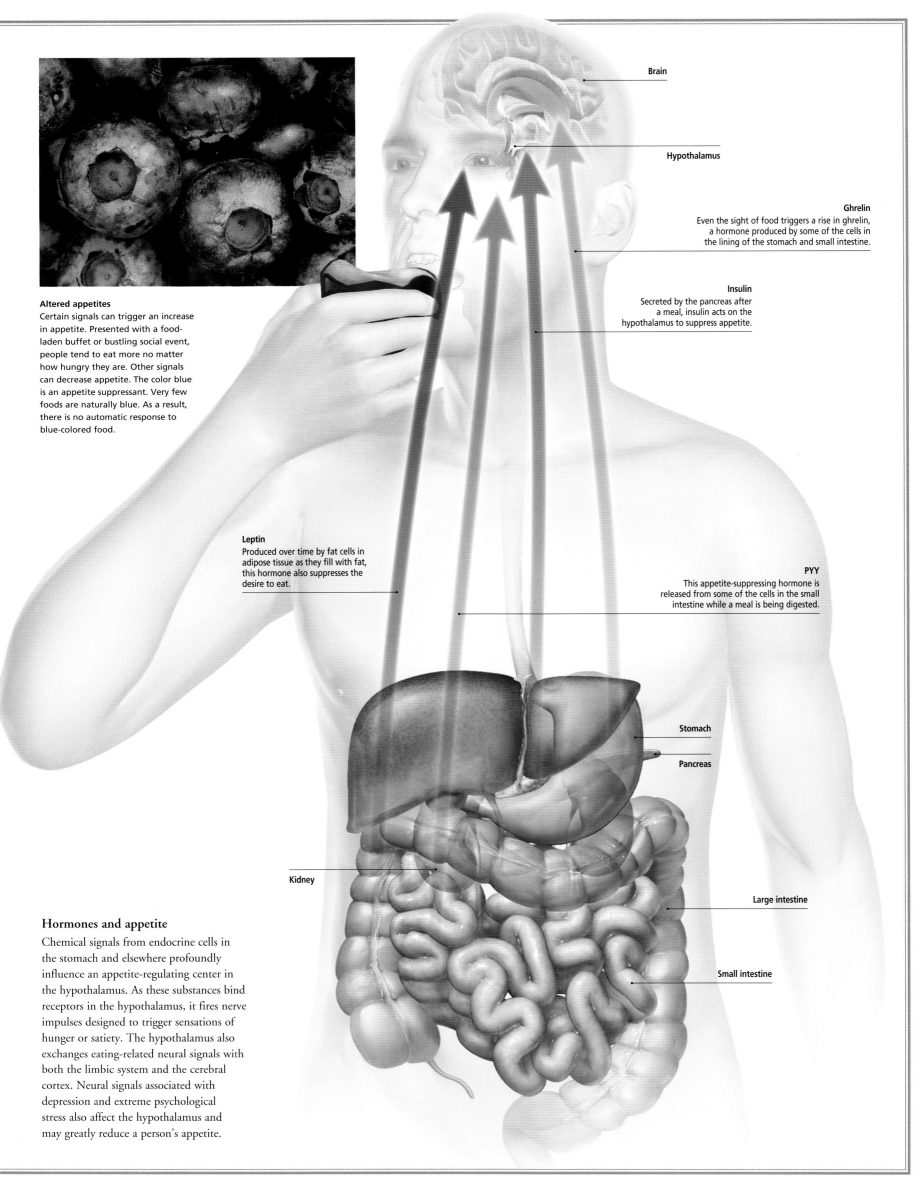

Altered appetites
Certain signals can trigger an increase in appetite. Presented with a food-laden buffet or bustling social event, people tend to eat more no matter how hungry they are. Other signals can decrease appetite. The color blue is an appetite suppressant. Very few foods are naturally blue. As a result, there is no automatic response to blue-colored food.

Brain

Hypothalamus

Ghrelin
Even the sight of food triggers a rise in ghrelin, a hormone produced by some of the cells in the lining of the stomach and small intestine.

Insulin
Secreted by the pancreas after a meal, insulin acts on the hypothalamus to suppress appetite.

Leptin
Produced over time by fat cells in adipose tissue as they fill with fat, this hormone also suppresses the desire to eat.

PYY
This appetite-suppressing hormone is released from some of the cells in the small intestine while a meal is being digested.

Stomach

Pancreas

Kidney

Large intestine

Small intestine

Hormones and appetite

Chemical signals from endocrine cells in the stomach and elsewhere profoundly influence an appetite-regulating center in the hypothalamus. As these substances bind receptors in the hypothalamus, it fires nerve impulses designed to trigger sensations of hunger or satiety. The hypothalamus also exchanges eating-related neural signals with both the limbic system and the cerebral cortex. Neural signals associated with depression and extreme psychological stress also affect the hypothalamus and may greatly reduce a person's appetite.

ENDOCRINE DISEASES AND DISORDERS

Endocrine glands produce exceedingly small quantities of hormones in short, intricately timed bursts. Often several hormones must interact in some way to produce a given effect. Several key endocrine organs such as the thyroid gland, the adrenals and male and female reproductive organs are controlled by pituitary hormones. Usually, controls over these processes keep hormones in balance, preventing either too much or too little of any hormone from circulating in the blood. If some factor disrupts the controls, the result may be an abnormal change in body form or in the workings of tissues and organs. For example, pituitary tumors which produce either too much or too little growth hormone may lead to conditions such as acromegaly, gigantism or dwarfism. In some cases the underlying problem is an autoimmune disorder in which the immune system attacks endocrine cells or otherwise interferes with their functioning.

Pituitary gland
Pituitary tumors can lead to acromegaly, gigantism and dwarfism.

Thyroid gland
Possible disorders include hyperthyroidism and hypothyroidism.

Parathyroid gland
Hyperparathyroidism is a rare disorder that affects this gland.

Adrenal gland
Possible disorders include Addison's disease, Cushing's syndrome and Hyperaldosteronism.

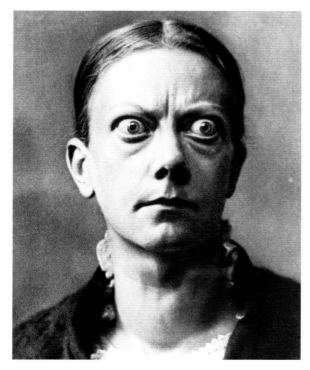

Effects of endocrine disorders
Some of the most common endocrine disorders involve altered body growth or metabolism due to malfunctions of the pituitary or the thyroid. Often the impacts of these conditions are wide-ranging, because cells in many types of tissues respond to the hormones those glands release. Fortunately many endocrine disorders are treatable with replacement hormones or other therapeutic drugs, or by surgery to remove all or part of a diseased gland.

Graves' disease
Bulging eyes, brittle hair and a racing metabolism are hallmarks of Graves' disease, which results from an overactive thyroid. This relatively common disorder is likely an autoimmune condition in which antibodies of the immune system stimulate thyroid gland cells to generate a constant oversupply of thyroid hormone. Radiation therapy or surgery can eliminate the malfunctioning tissue.

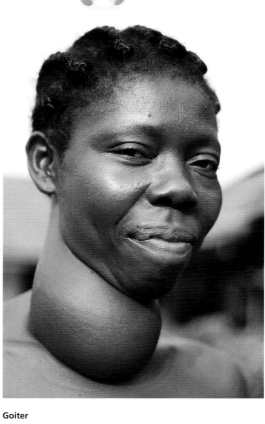

Goiter
A goiter is an extreme enlargement of the thyroid gland. A dietary deficiency of iodine may be the cause, but more often the growth is due to the failure of the thyroid to release thyroid hormone in response to a stimulating hormone, TSH, from the pituitary. Over time continued stimulation by TSH causes the thyroid to greatly enlarge.

DISEASE	SYMPTOMS
Acromegaly A tumor in the pituitary gland increases growth hormone	Enlarged body parts, such as hands, feet, jaw, lips
Addison's Disease The adrenal glands do not produce enough cortisol	Weight loss, fatigue, muscle weakness, low blood pressure
Hyperaldosteronism The adrenal glands produce too much aldosterone	Fluid retention, high blood pressure, weakness, muscle spasms
Hyperparathyroidism A rare condition in which the parathyroid glands secrete too much parathormone	Fatigue, bone loss, osteoporosis
Prolactinoma Pituitary tumor leads to excess prolactin, the hormone that stimulates production of breast milk	Abnormal lactation, infertility, headache, decreased sexual interest

Gigantism and dwarfism

The condition known as pituitary gigantism develops when the long bones grow excessively during childhood because the anterior pituitary overproduces growth hormone. An affected person may grow as tall as 8 feet (2.4m). In pituitary dwarfism the long bones grow unusually slowly and maximum height is around 4 feet (1.2m). People with either disorder generally have normal body proportions.

Cushing's disease

This photo shows muscle tissue damaged by excess cortisol, one of many health problems typical of Cushing's disease. This and other symptoms, such as fat deposits in the trunk and face, develop when the adrenal cortex overproduces cortisol. The root cause may be a pituitary tumor that boosts the output of ACTH, a hormone that controls cortisol release.

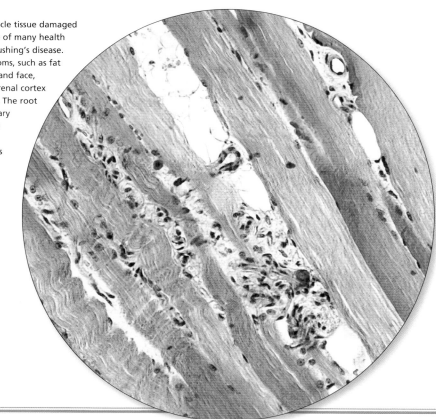

DIABETES

Diabetes mellitus is one of the most common and serious endocrine disorders. In diabetes, tissues and cells throughout the body cannot correctly process glucose (sugar) in the bloodstream. If the condition is not corrected or controlled, it leads to widespread, permanent damage in tissues and organs. Type 1 diabetes causes the immune system to destroy insulin-producing beta cells in the pancreas. This autoimmune disorder often develops in adolescence and may be triggered by a viral infection in combination with genetic susceptibility. In type 2 diabetes, the pancreas produces adequate insulin but body cells cannot respond normally to it and do not take up enough sugar from the blood. Often associated with obesity and an elevated risk of heart disease, type 2 diabetes has become a global health crisis. Worldwide, tens of millions of people exhibit a range of symptoms called metabolic syndrome—an early indicator of increased diabetes risk.

A global epidemic

The World Health Organization (WHO) has documented a dramatic global increase in reported cases of diabetes—a trend linked to the worldwide increase in major risk factors, particularly obesity. Sedentary lifestyles and calorie-dense (but often nutrient-poor) convenience foods and sugary beverages have contributed to the dramatic increase of diabetes. Effects include rapidly rising rates of diabetes-related illnesses. The WHO is promoting international educational efforts to encourage preventive measures and to help raise awareness.

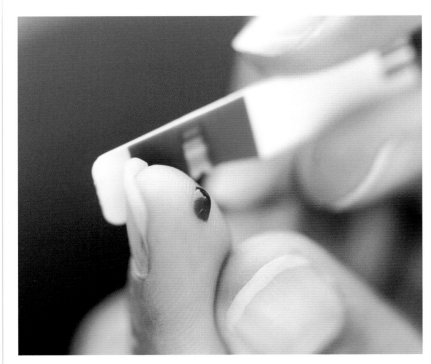

Monitoring blood sugar
Proper self-management of diabetes is key to preventing complications of the disease. Various home monitors are available that allow patients to regularly test a small blood sample to determine how much glucose it contains.

Worldwide impact
Statistics gathered by the World Health Organization show the growing impact of diabetes on every continent, especially the world's most populous nations.

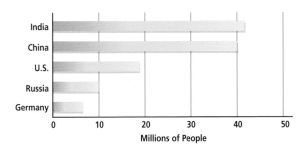

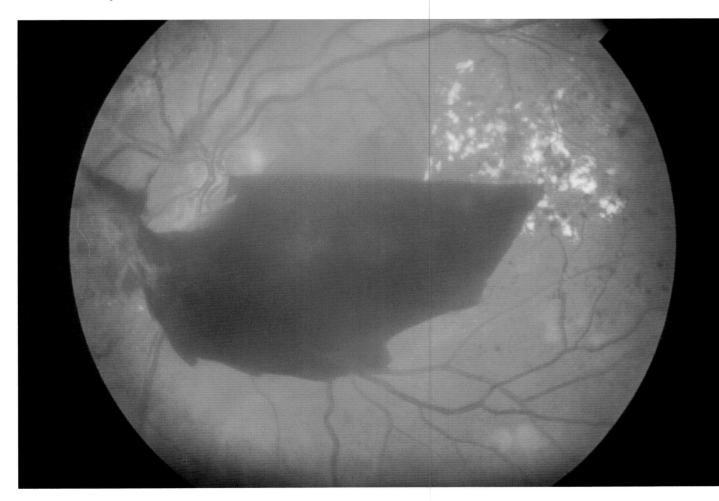

Retina damage
In diabetic retinopathy, damaged blood vessels of the retina may leak fluid, causing swelling and blurred vision. Abnormally fragile blood vessels may develop and leak blood in the retina. This disorder usually affects both eyes and causes blindness as it worsens.

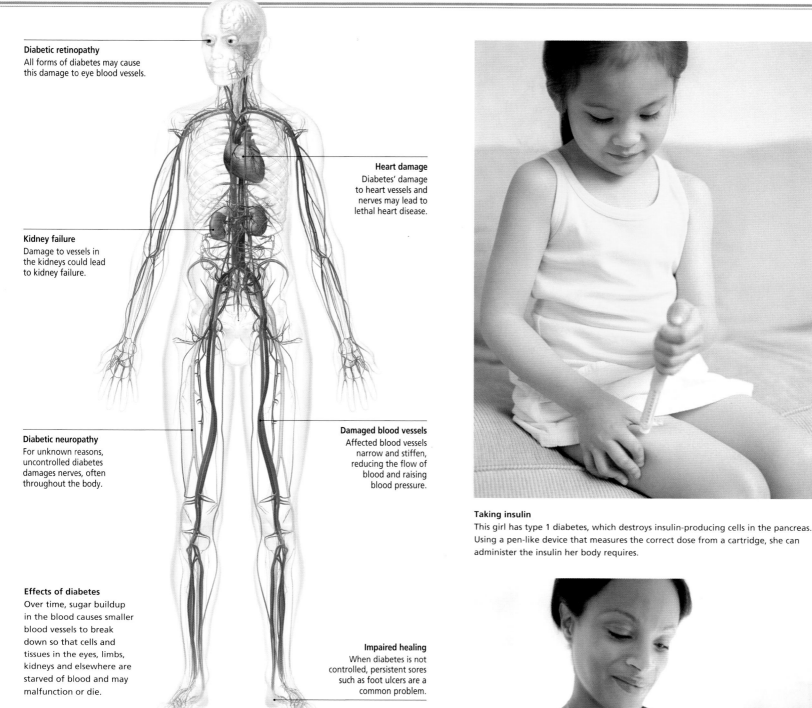

Diabetic retinopathy
All forms of diabetes may cause this damage to eye blood vessels.

Kidney failure
Damage to vessels in the kidneys could lead to kidney failure.

Diabetic neuropathy
For unknown reasons, uncontrolled diabetes damages nerves, often throughout the body.

Effects of diabetes
Over time, sugar buildup in the blood causes smaller blood vessels to break down so that cells and tissues in the eyes, limbs, kidneys and elsewhere are starved of blood and may malfunction or die.

Heart damage
Diabetes' damage to heart vessels and nerves may lead to lethal heart disease.

Damaged blood vessels
Affected blood vessels narrow and stiffen, reducing the flow of blood and raising blood pressure.

Impaired healing
When diabetes is not controlled, persistent sores such as foot ulcers are a common problem.

Taking insulin
This girl has type 1 diabetes, which destroys insulin-producing cells in the pancreas. Using a pen-like device that measures the correct dose from a cartridge, she can administer the insulin her body requires.

METABOLIC SYNDROME

Features collectively called metabolic syndrome increase a person's risk of type 2 diabetes. One indicator is an "apple" shape—a waist measuring more than 35 inches (88.9cm) for females and more than 40 inches (101.6cm) for males. Others include resting blood pressure at or above 135/85, low HDL ("good") cholesterol and elevated levels of blood sugar and triglyceride fats.

Lowering risk
Losing pounds and inches by combining regular exercise with reduced intake of sugary and fatty foods is key for reducing one's diabetes risk.

Gestational diabetes
Some pregnant women develop gestational diabetes. The risk is greatest for those with a family history of diabetes. The standard treatment is a low-sugar diet and regular exercise. Gestational diabetes usually disappears after pregnancy, but it may signal increased risk for type 2 diabetes later on.

CIRCULATORY SYSTEM

Blood, with its cargoes of oxygen, nutrients from food, hormones and other substances is literally the "river of life," and transporting it to and from every living body cell is the sole role of the circulatory or cardiovascular system. The circulatory system picks up oxygen in the lungs and off-loads waste carbon dioxide there. It also must reach to within a short distance of each of the body's trillions of living cells. The circulatory system is biologically engineered to meet all these needs. The heart is a double pump that transports blood both to the lungs and to other tissues under pressure. Pumped blood moves into a vast closed network of branching vessels that distribute it to within less than a hair's breadth of nearly every body cell, and then transport it back to the heart where the journey begins anew.

Blood vessel pathways

Roughly matching sets of arteries and veins follow the same routes through the body. Often the name of a vessel changes as its path moves through different body parts. In general, arteries are large vessels carrying blood away from the heart and veins transport blood returning to the heart. In the pulmonary circuit, however, the situation is reversed. Here, arteries deliver oxygen-poor blood to the lungs, and veins transport oxygenated blood back to the heart to be pumped outward to body tissues.

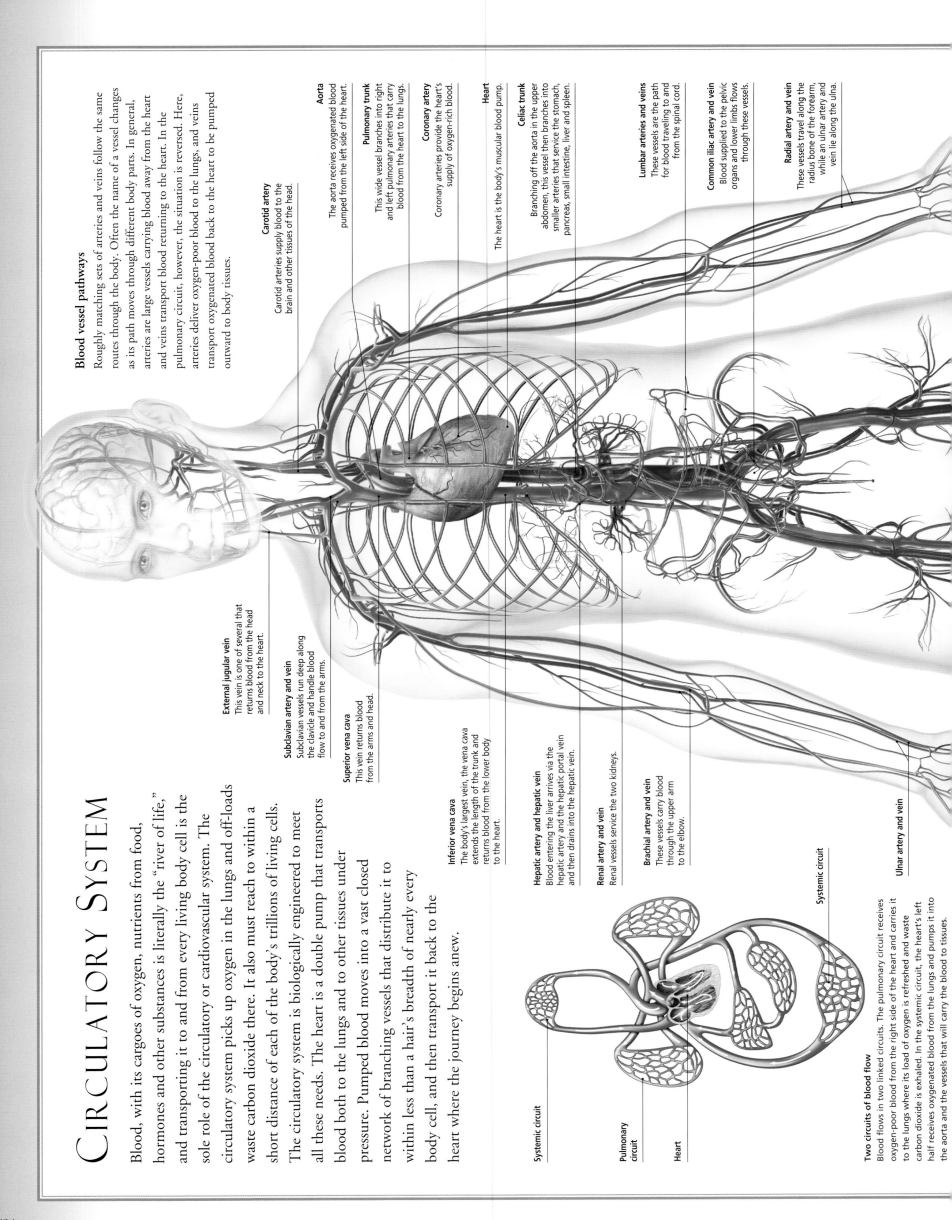

Carotid artery
Carotid arteries supply blood to the brain and other tissues of the head.

Aorta
The aorta receives oxygenated blood pumped from the left side of the heart.

Pulmonary trunk
This wide vessel branches into right and left pulmonary arteries that carry blood from the heart to the lungs.

Coronary artery
Coronary arteries provide the heart's supply of oxygen-rich blood.

Heart
The heart is the body's muscular blood pump.

Celiac trunk
Branching off the aorta in the upper abdomen, this vessel then branches into smaller arteries that service the stomach, pancreas, small intestine, liver and spleen.

Lumbar arteries and veins
These vessels are the path for blood traveling to and from the spinal cord.

Common iliac artery and vein
Blood supplied to the pelvic organs and lower limbs flows through these vessels.

Radial artery and vein
These vessels travel along the radius bone of the forearm, while an ulnar artery and vein lie along the ulna.

External jugular vein
This vein is one of several that returns blood from the head and neck to the heart.

Subclavian artery and vein
Subclavian vessels run deep along the clavicle and handle blood flow to and from the arms.

Superior vena cava
This vein returns blood from the arms and head.

Inferior vena cava
The body's largest vein, the vena cava extends the length of the trunk and returns blood from the lower body to the heart.

Hepatic artery and hepatic vein
Blood entering the liver arrives via the hepatic artery and the hepatic portal vein and then drains into the hepatic vein.

Renal artery and vein
Renal vessels service the two kidneys.

Brachial artery and vein
These vessels carry blood through the upper arm to the elbow.

Ulnar artery and vein

Systemic circuit

Pulmonary circuit

Heart

Two circuits of blood flow
Blood flows in two linked circuits. The pulmonary circuit receives oxygen-poor blood from the right side of the heart and carries it to the lungs where its load of oxygen is refreshed and waste carbon dioxide is exhaled. In the systemic circuit, the heart's left half receives oxygenated blood from the lungs and pumps it into the aorta and the vessels that will carry the blood to tissues.

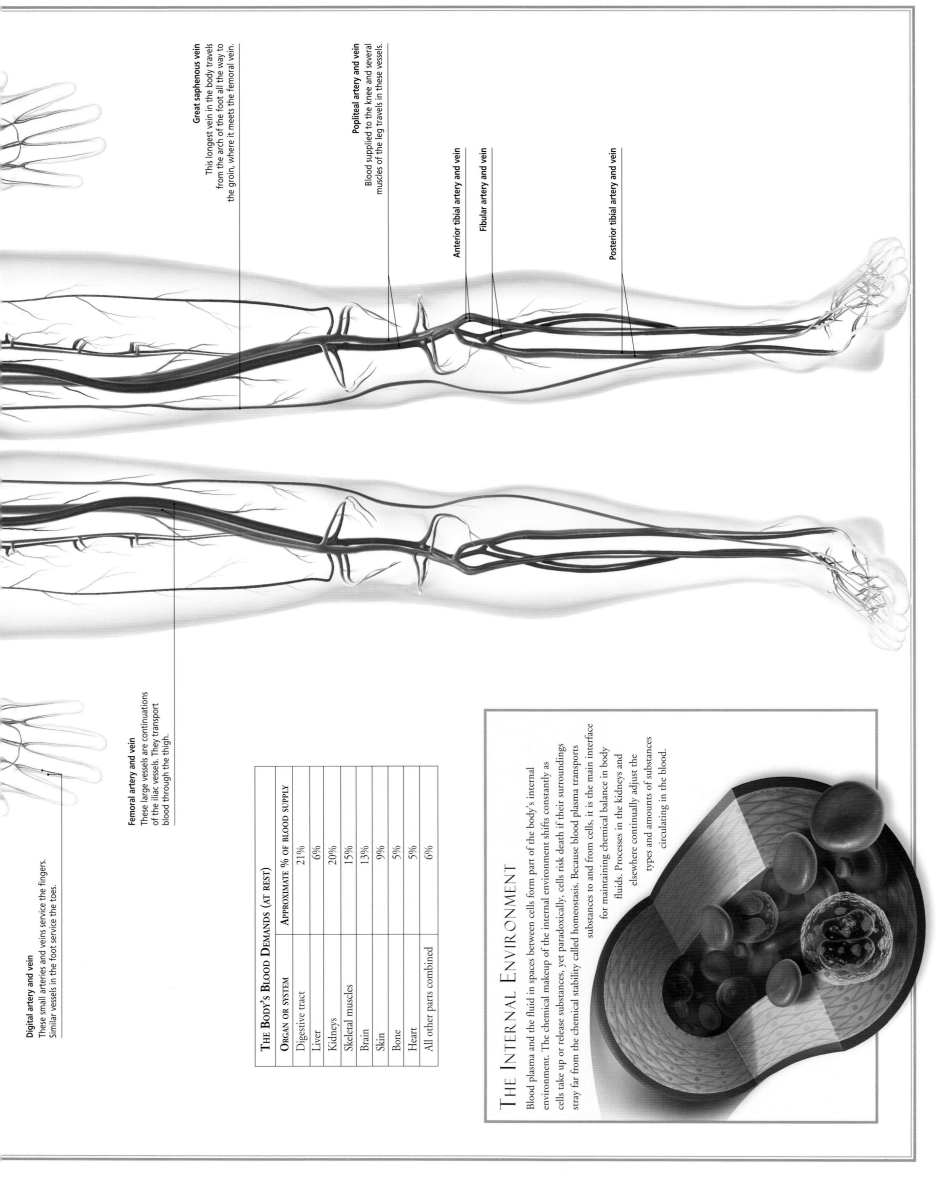

Great saphenous vein
This longest vein in the body travels from the arch of the foot all the way to the groin, where it meets the femoral vein.

Popliteal artery and vein
Blood supplied to the knee and several muscles of the leg travels in these vessels.

Anterior tibial artery and vein

Fibular artery and vein

Posterior tibial artery and vein

Femoral artery and vein
These large vessels are continuations of the iliac vessels. They transport blood through the thigh.

Digital artery and vein
These small arteries and veins service the fingers. Similar vessels in the foot service the toes.

THE BODY'S BLOOD DEMANDS (AT REST)

ORGAN OR SYSTEM	APPROXIMATE % OF BLOOD SUPPLY
Digestive tract	21%
Liver	6%
Kidneys	20%
Skeletal muscles	15%
Brain	13%
Skin	9%
Bone	5%
Heart	5%
All other parts combined	6%

THE INTERNAL ENVIRONMENT

Blood plasma and the fluid in spaces between cells form part of the body's internal environment. The chemical makeup of the internal environment shifts constantly as cells take up or release substances, yet paradoxically, cells risk death if their surroundings stray far from the chemical stability called homeostasis. Because blood plasma transports substances to and from cells, it is the main interface for maintaining chemical balance in body fluids. Processes in the kidneys and elsewhere continually adjust the types and amounts of substances circulating in the blood.

125

THE HEART

The heart is about the size of a clenched fist and weighs about one pound (450 grams). It is located in the pericardial cavity between the two pleural cavities, which each contain a lung. A delicate sac called the pericardium wraps around the heart and lines the pericardial cavities and a film of fluid within the pericardial cavities prevents friction as the heart muscle contracts and relaxes. In effect, the heart is two pumps in one. It has two halves, right and left. Each half is divided further into two hollow chambers, an atrium and a ventricle. The two ventricles each pump blood into vessels with different destinations. While the heart's atria have relatively thin walls, the ventricles have thick, muscular walls, a structure that befits their constant function of circulating blood.

From the outside

Although it is only about the size of a human fist, the heart accounts for about eight percent of the body's total oxygen consumption. The heart does not absorb oxygen from the blood it pumps. Instead a steady supply of oxygen to the heart muscle comes via the right and left coronary arteries, which direct blood from the aorta. The main arteries divide into several smaller blood vessels and eventually into numerous capillaries. Oxygen-poor blood returns to the right atrium via coronary veins and the coronary sinus, which only draws about 60 percent of the blood. The rest returns via tiny veins directly into the chambers of the heart.

Heart valves
The "heart strings," or chordae tendineae, are stabilizers built from collagen. They hold the valves between the atria and the ventricles closed while blood is propelled into an artery.

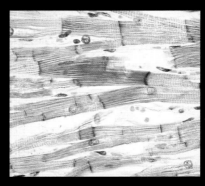

Heart muscle
Muscle fibers in the heart are linked by specialized junctions. These junctions, called intercalated discs, are visible as dark purple lines in this microscope photograph. They knit the fibers tightly together in a fashion that allows nerve impulses to travel easily from fiber to fiber.

Start pumping

Signals from the SA node travel to both atria and also to the AV node. From there, a network of Purkinje fibers extends down through the thick wall that separates the two ventricles, then branches upward, distributing the pacemaker's signals throughout the heart.

Superior vena cava

Sinoatrial (SA) node

The small clusters of cells in the SA node are the heart's natural pacemaker. If the SA node malfunctions, battery powered pacemakers can be surgically implanted. They emit electrical signals that trigger a normal rhythm of heart contractions.

Pulmonary valve

Right coronary artery

Right atrium

Antrioven-tricular (AV) node

This cluster, called the AV node, transfers the commands for contraction.

Purkinje cell

From the AV node, the commands spread through the ventricles along a branching system of conducting fibers called Purkinje cells.

Right ventricle

The heart's pacemaker

Unlike other muscles, cardiac muscle contracts and relaxes—and the heart beats—without commands from the nervous system. This property comes from the heart's pacemaker, a small cluster of cells called the sinoatrial (SA) node. Located near the top of the right atrium, the pacemaker cells are generally programmed to produce electrical signals 70 to 80 times a minute, or more if the situation warrants. The pacemaker continues to stimulate a heartbeat even if all nerves to the heart have been severed. The cardiac plexus, a network of nerves near the aorta and pulmonary artery, also modifies heart rate by increasing the rate and force of contractions.

Aorta

This is the body's main artery. It can withstand great pressure from blood.

Left Pulmonary artery

This artery carries oxygen-poor blood to left lung from the right ventricle.

Pulmonary trunk

Pulmonary vein

In time

Following commands from the Purkinje cells, the heart's chambers can contract in the coordinated fashion that keeps blood flowing steadily through the cardiovascular system.

Left atrium

Great cardiac vein

Left ventricle

Spreading fast

It takes only 30 one-thousandths of a second for Purkinje cells to transmit impulses to all the muscle fibers in the ventricles.

Papillary muscle

CARDIAC CYCLE

Over the course of a day, the heart beats about 100,000 times—and over an average lifetime, it produces 2.6 billion beats or more. Each beat is a rapid sequence of contraction and relaxation, first of the heart atria, then of the larger ventricles. This sequence, the cardiac cycle, takes less than a second. Electrical signals from the heart itself stimulate contraction, then briefly shut off only to commence again. The medical terms for these phases are systole (contraction) and diastole (relaxation). The movements of contracting heart chambers generate the familiar "lub-dup" heart sounds heard through a stethoscope. Blood pressure measurements also reflect the cardiac cycle. The top number in a blood pressure reading is systolic pressure, the maximum value when the ventricles are fully contracted. The bottom value is diastolic pressure, the amount of pressure in vessels when heart chambers are relaxed.

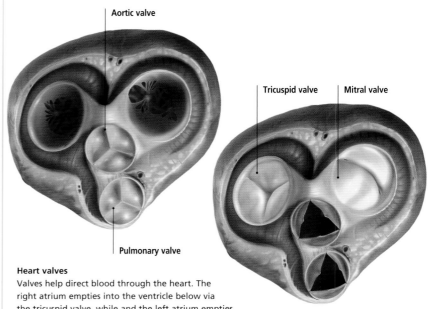

Heart valves
Valves help direct blood through the heart. The right atrium empties into the ventricle below via the tricuspid valve, while and the left atrium empties via the mitral valve. The right and left ventricles respectively pump blood through the "half" shaped pulmonary and aortic valves.

Testing heart stress
A stress test gauges heart health by monitoring the heart's electrical activity during progressively more strenuous exercise. Sensors attached to the patient reveal how well the heart adjusts to increasing demands for it to pump blood.

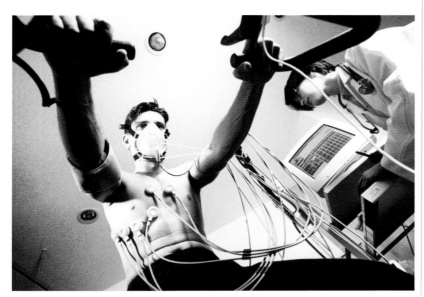

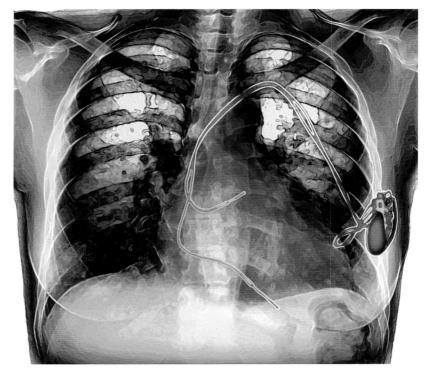

Setting the pace
A cluster of nerve cells called the sinoatrial node make up the heart's built-in pacemaker. The node sends out waves of electrical impulses that coordinate the heartbeat. An implanted electronic pacemaker, about the size of a pocket watch, can stimulate or normalize the heart rate in patients who suffer some types of heart irregularities.

Aerobic fitness
Activities such as fast walking, jogging, or swimming for 20 minutes or more are aerobic—they work muscles at a rate that allows the circulatory system to keep them supplied with oxygen. Aerobic exercise also promotes heart health by lowering a person's resting heart rate.

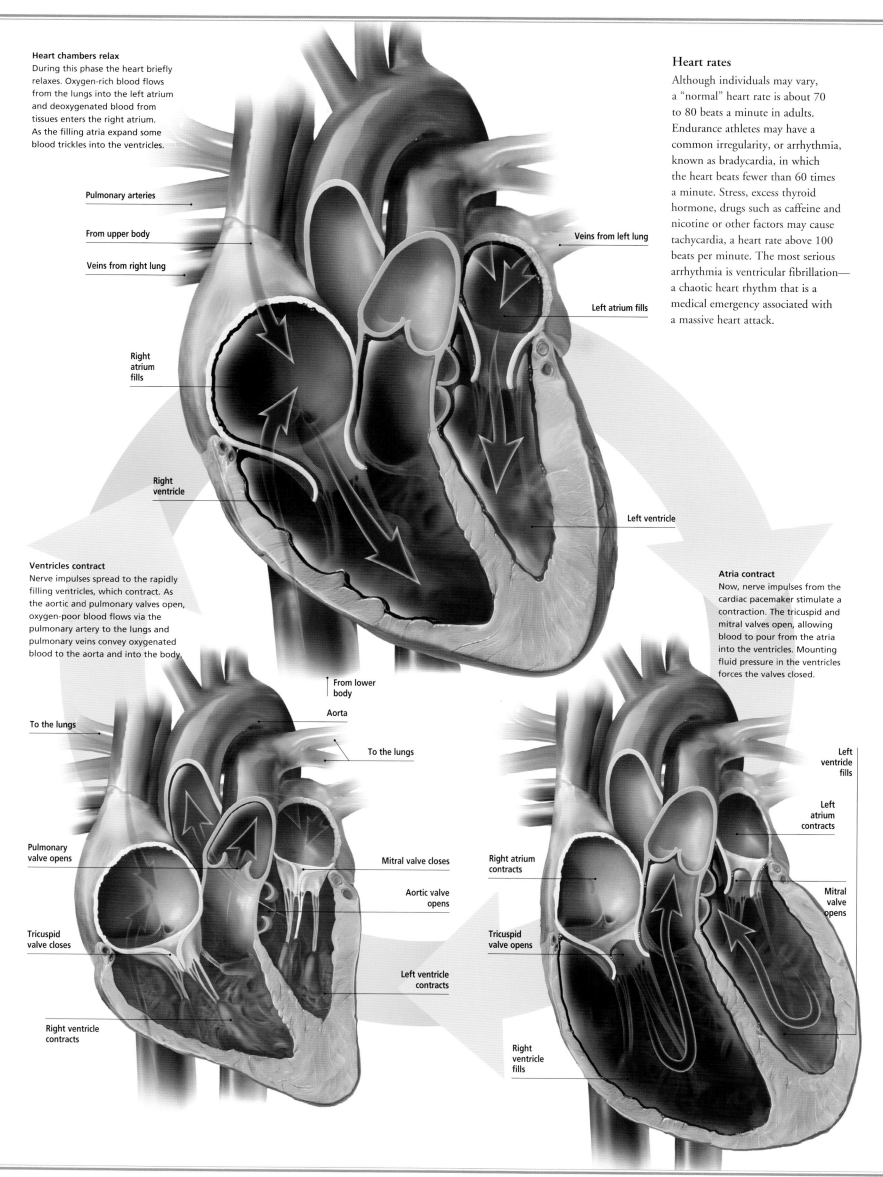

Heart chambers relax
During this phase the heart briefly relaxes. Oxygen-rich blood flows from the lungs into the left atrium and deoxygenated blood from tissues enters the right atrium. As the filling atria expand some blood trickles into the ventricles.

Pulmonary arteries

From upper body

Veins from right lung

Right atrium fills

Right ventricle

Veins from left lung

Left atrium fills

Left ventricle

Heart rates
Although individuals may vary, a "normal" heart rate is about 70 to 80 beats a minute in adults. Endurance athletes may have a common irregularity, or arrhythmia, known as bradycardia, in which the heart beats fewer than 60 times a minute. Stress, excess thyroid hormone, drugs such as caffeine and nicotine or other factors may cause tachycardia, a heart rate above 100 beats per minute. The most serious arrhythmia is ventricular fibrillation— a chaotic heart rhythm that is a medical emergency associated with a massive heart attack.

Ventricles contract
Nerve impulses spread to the rapidly filling ventricles, which contract. As the aortic and pulmonary valves open, oxygen-poor blood flows via the pulmonary artery to the lungs and pulmonary veins convey oxygenated blood to the aorta and into the body.

To the lungs

Pulmonary valve opens

Tricuspid valve closes

Right ventricle contracts

From lower body

Aorta

To the lungs

Mitral valve closes

Aortic valve opens

Left ventricle contracts

Atria contract
Now, nerve impulses from the cardiac pacemaker stimulate a contraction. The tricuspid and mitral valves open, allowing blood to pour from the atria into the ventricles. Mounting fluid pressure in the ventricles forces the valves closed.

Left ventricle fills

Left atrium contracts

Mitral valve opens

Right atrium contracts

Tricuspid valve opens

Right ventricle fills

Blood Vessels

Blood vessels come in five types, each structurally matched to its function. The largest are major arteries including the aorta, the brachial arteries in the arms and the femoral arteries in the thighs. Thick, slightly stretchy walls allow these vessels to flex while they sustain the pressure of blood freshly pumped by the heart. Arteries diverge into narrower arterioles, which have thinner walls and therefore can contract and relax more readily. Arterioles are the major managers of blood flow in the body, increasing or decreasing their internal diameter to adjust the volume of blood entering tissues as the demand warrants. Blood from arterioles disperses into slender capillaries, which travel close to every body cell in order to deliver or pick up substances such as oxygen or wastes. Blood moves from capillaries into almost equally narrow venules, which merge with veins that can transport a large volume of blood back to the heart.

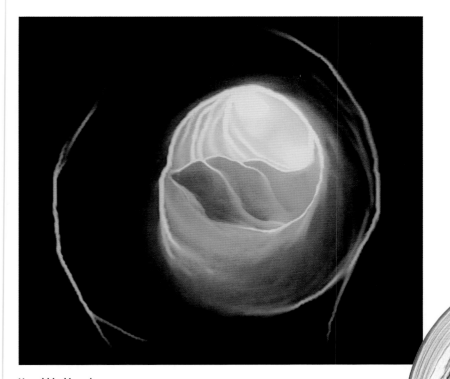

Vessel-blocking plaques
Ridges rising from the lining of an artery are fatty cholesterol plaques, which are thought to develop in part due to inflammation in vessels. Many heart attacks occur when plaques restrict blood flow in coronary arteries.

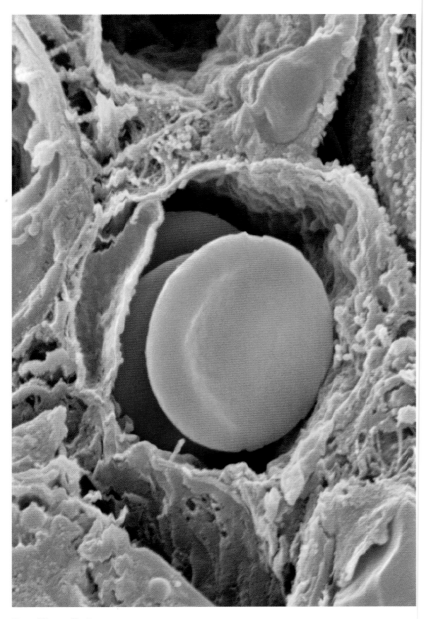

Threadlike capillaries
Capillaries are the smallest, most numerous blood vessels and many substances move easily across their thin, leaky walls. Their interior space is so narrow that red blood cells often must pass through in single file as seen in this image.

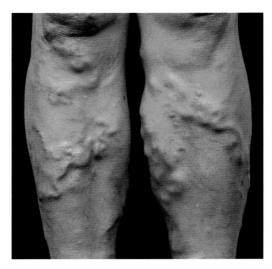

Valves gone awry
Varicose veins develop when weakened valves chronically allow blood to pool and overstretch the vessel wall. They may form due to extra weight from pregnancy or obesity, which increases pressure on the legs, or to hours of standing, walking or running on hard surfaces.

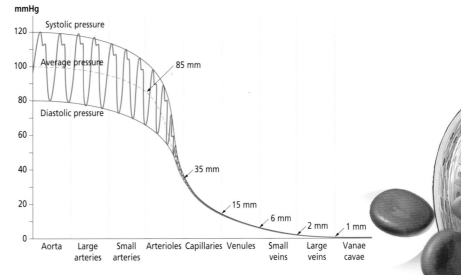

Shifting blood pressure
Blood pressure is highest in the aorta and drops as blood flows onward into arterioles and capillaries. When blood enters veins for its return to the heart, its pressure is a small fraction of the starting value.

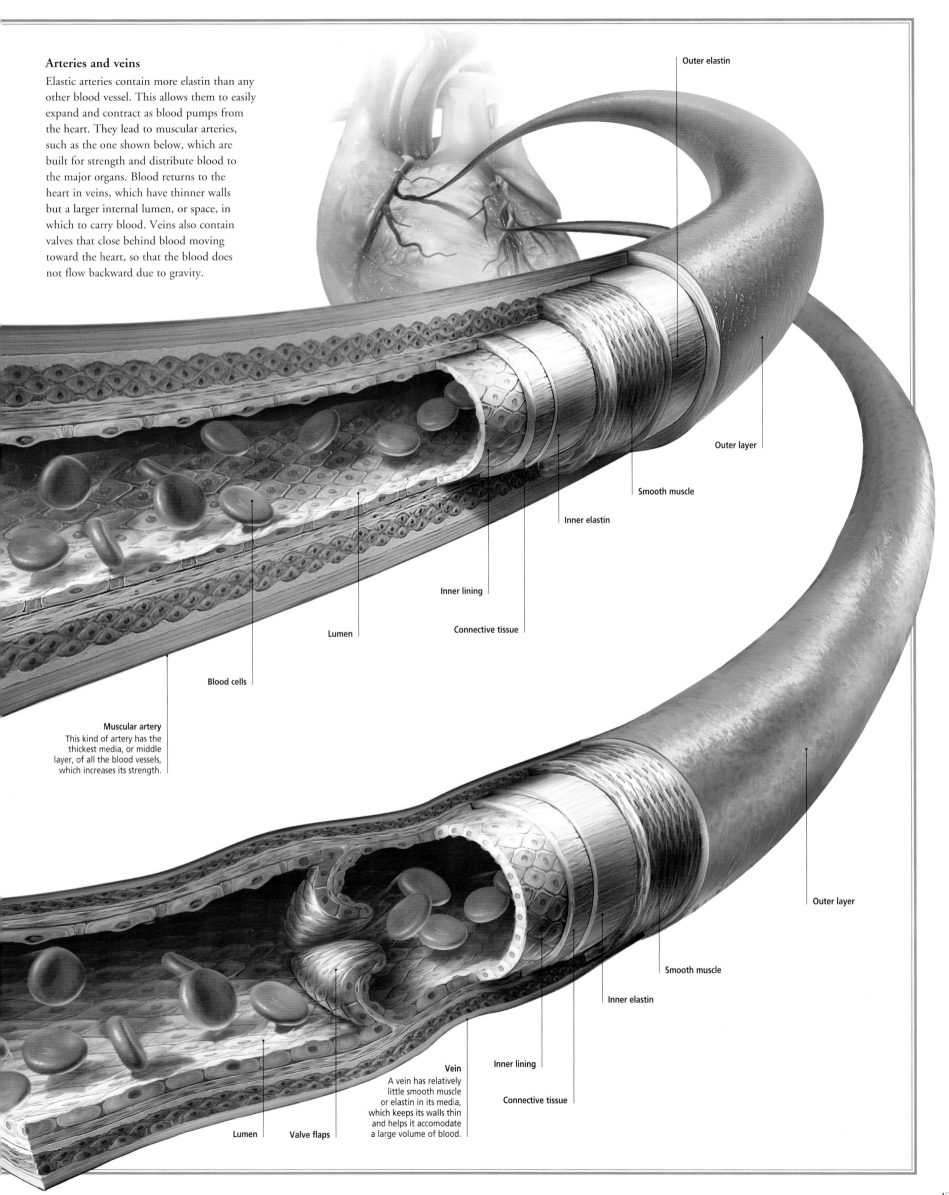

Arteries and veins

Elastic arteries contain more elastin than any other blood vessel. This allows them to easily expand and contract as blood pumps from the heart. They lead to muscular arteries, such as the one shown below, which are built for strength and distribute blood to the major organs. Blood returns to the heart in veins, which have thinner walls but a larger internal lumen, or space, in which to carry blood. Veins also contain valves that close behind blood moving toward the heart, so that the blood does not flow backward due to gravity.

Outer elastin

Outer layer

Smooth muscle

Inner elastin

Inner lining

Connective tissue

Lumen

Blood cells

Muscular artery
This kind of artery has the thickest media, or middle layer, of all the blood vessels, which increases its strength.

Outer layer

Smooth muscle

Inner elastin

Inner lining

Connective tissue

Lumen

Valve flaps

Vein
A vein has relatively little smooth muscle or elastin in its media, which keeps its walls thin and helps it accomodate a large volume of blood.

BLOOD COMPONENTS

The average adult contains about six quarts (5.6L) of blood that circulates through the body three times every minute. Circulating large quantities of blood is vital because blood brings oxygen, nutrients, hormones and other substances to cells and carries away the steady stream of metabolic wastes those cells produce. It also circulates body heat to and from internal organs, helping to maintain normal core temperature. By volume, nearly half of blood is plasma, a blend of water and a variety of proteins. Erythrocytes, or red blood cells, transport oxygen throughout the body, and make up most of the remainder of blood. Whole blood also contains platelets that assist in blood clotting, and various types of leukocytes or white blood cells. Although different types of white blood cells make up a mere one percent of the total, they are an important part of the immune system.

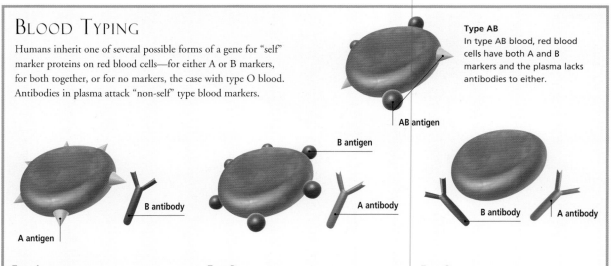

BLOOD TYPING

Humans inherit one of several possible forms of a gene for "self" marker proteins on red blood cells—for either A or B markers, for both together, or for no markers, the case with type O blood. Antibodies in plasma attack "non-self" type blood markers.

Type AB
In type AB blood, red blood cells have both A and B markers and the plasma lacks antibodies to either.

AB antigen

B antigen

A antibody

B antibody

A antigen

B antibody   A antibody

Type A
In type A blood, the red blood cells have A markers and the blood plasma contains antibodies against B markers.

Type B
In type B blood, the red blood cells have B markers and the blood plasma contains antibodies against A markers.

Type O
In type O blood, red blood cells have neither A nor B markers and the plasma contains antibodies to both.

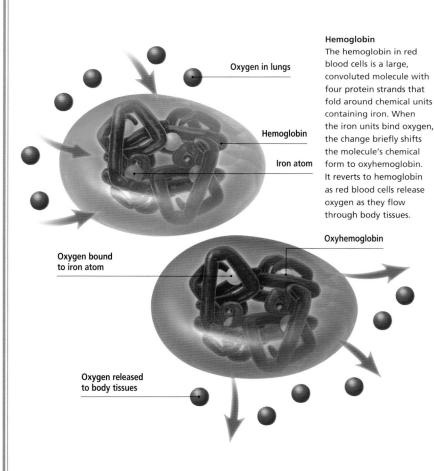

Oxygen in lungs

Hemoglobin

Iron atom

Oxygen bound to iron atom

Oxyhemoglobin

Oxygen released to body tissues

Hemoglobin
The hemoglobin in red blood cells is a large, convoluted molecule with four protein strands that fold around chemical units containing iron. When the iron units bind oxygen, the change briefly shifts the molecule's chemical form to oxyhemoglobin. It reverts to hemoglobin as red blood cells release oxygen as they flow through body tissues.

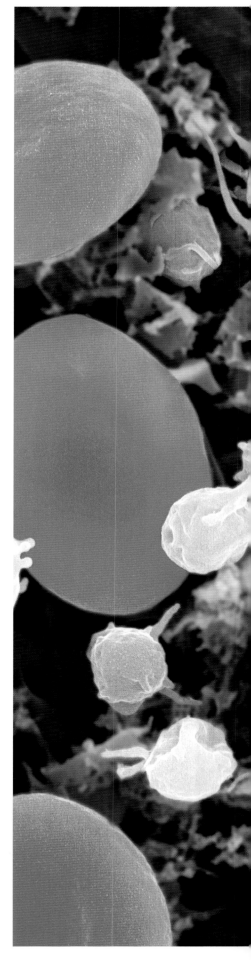

Separating the parts
The different components of whole blood become visible when a laboratory technician treats a sample with an anti-clotting agent and whirls it at high speed in a centrifuge. Pale yellow plasma rises to the top and dark-colored red blood cells and platelets fall to the bottom. In between is a thin layer of white blood cells.

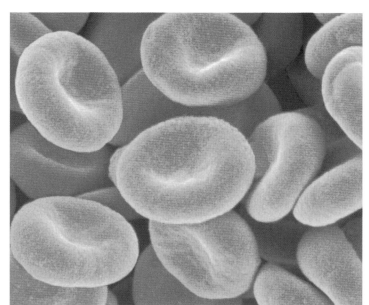

Red blood cells

Red blood cells resemble crimson disks indented on both sides. Packed with the iron-rich protein hemoglobin that binds oxygen, they have but one main role—to load up on oxygen in the lungs and deliver it to tissues. Red blood cells live about four months.

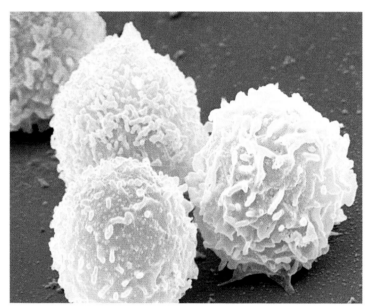

White blood cells

White blood cells specialize in bodily defense. Some types, such as lymphocytes, combat threats such as bacteria, viruses and parasites. Others remove debris and foreign material. Certain white blood cells die and are replaced after a few days, but other types function for years.

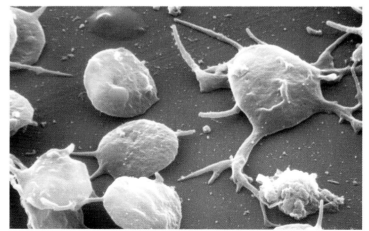

Platelets

Platelets are jagged fragments shed by precursor cells in bone marrow. They plug small tears in blood vessels and promote clotting. Platelets only survive about one week, but they are constantly replaced and at any given time millions are circulating in the bloodstream.

Blood red

Blood is a reddish blend of plasma, cells and platelets, but the shade of red changes as blood circulates. Blood that has freshly passed through lung capillaries is bright red because the hemoglobin in its red blood cells is fully saturated with oxygen. As red blood cells release oxygen to tissues and far less is bound to hemoglobin, the color of blood darkens—so visible veins in areas such as the wrists look blue.

BLOOD CLOTTING

A sudden, massive blood clot is an obvious medical
emergency, but every day less dramatic, often hidden
breaches threaten the circulatory system. The body's
small blood vessels are exceedingly delicate, and cuts,
scrapes, blows, strenuous exercise and even normal
daily activities rip or tear them. These seemingly minor
injuries are threats as well, for if the body loses more than
a small amount of blood, tissues and organs may be
damaged or die and the whole circulatory system may
break down. Fortunately, several built-in mechanisms known
collectively as hemostasis act quickly to staunch bleeding
from small vessels, whether inside the body or at its surface.
They slow or stop bleeding, and if necessary, form the
natural dam known as a blood clot. When large or numerous
blood vessels rupture, clotting generally cannot stop blood
from flowing. Then stitches and dressings control bleeding
while longer-term repair mechanisms heal the wound.

Why blood clots

A blood clot is the end result of an intricately coordinated series of chemical steps.
Proteins called clotting factors circulate in blood or are released by injured cells.
When a small vessel is torn or punctured, a cascade of clotting factors produces an
interaction between an enzyme called thrombin and fibrinogen, a blood protein,
which forms a clot. People with the inherited disorder hemophilia lack one of the
usual clotting factors, so their blood does not clot normally. Administering the
missing factor, often by injection, can avert potentially lethal bleeding.

Blood clotting steps

When a small vessel ruptures, its walls constrict to reduce the flow of blood
and platelets form a plug. Next, the enzyme thrombin acts on the blood
protein fibrinogen. Fibrinogen molecules form a net that snares platelets
and blood cells in a thick, sticky clump.

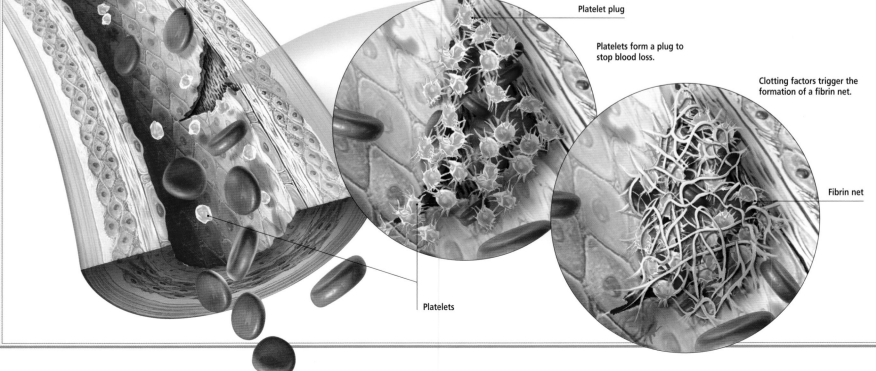

Red blood cell

The clotting process
begins when platelets
become sticky.

Platelet plug

Platelets form a plug to
stop blood loss.

Clotting factors trigger the
formation of a fibrin net.

Fibrin net

Platelets

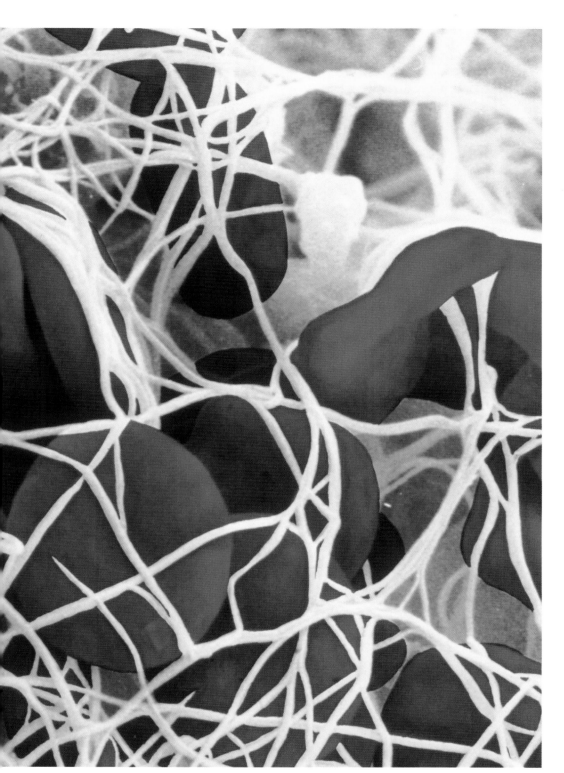

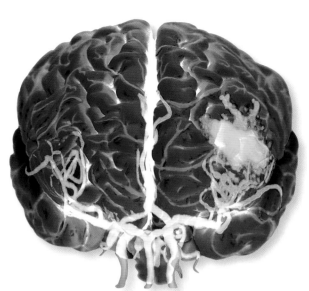

Bleeding in the brain
A broken vessel in the brain may trigger a hemorrhage, as shown here in the left hemisphere of a patient's brain. A hemorrhage or its opposite—an abnormal blood clot in the brain—both can cause a "brain attack" or stroke.

Vitamin K
Liver cells use vitamin K to produce several clotting factors. Helpful intestinal bacteria normally make enough vitamin K to meet body needs, but supplements may be prescribed for people with liver disease, hemophilia or other health issues. Green vegetables such as broccoli also contain this vitamin.

Thrombosis
A clot that forms in an intact blood vessel, called a thrombus, may cause a dangerous blockage called a thrombosis. Limited circulation may cause the affected tissue to malfunction or die. Many heart attacks are due to a thrombosis in one or more vessels serving the heart muscle.

BLOOD DISORDERS

Blood circulates throughout the body, carrying oxygen, nutrients and other substances. When red blood cells cannot function normally, it is inevitable that all body tissues and organs will suffer. Two insidious blood disorders are iron deficiency anemia and pernicious anemia, a condition due to inadequate vitamin B_{12} in the diet. These disorders and sickle-cell anemia, an inherited disease, all reduce the blood's capacity to transport oxygen, sometimes dangerously so. Some diseases afflict the whole array of blood cells, as well as the platelets required for normal clotting. Without prompt treatment, the group of cancers called leukemias, which can destroy the capacity of bone marrow to produce adequate numbers of healthy blood cells, are invariably fatal. Death may be an even more imminent threat with septicemia, commonly known as "blood poisoning." Septicemia results when pathogenic bacteria enter the bloodstream and then very rapidly multiply there.

SICKLE-CELL ANEMIA

In sickle-cell anemia the blood's hemoglobin is abnormal. Affected red blood cells take on a sickle shape and die prematurely. People with the full-blown disease inherit a faulty gene from both parents and may suffer greatly from anemia and painful damage to major organs. Symptoms are much milder for those who inherit only one copy of the gene—a heritage that also confers resistance to malaria. The sickle-cell gene is most common among people of West African, Mediterranean and tropical Asian descent—regions where malaria is most prevalent.

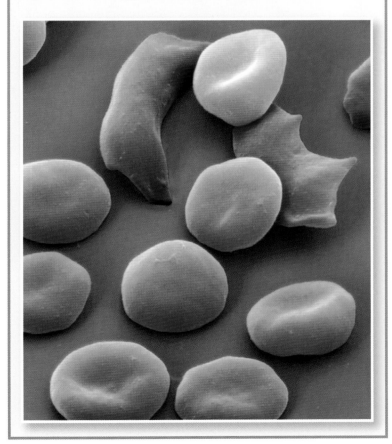

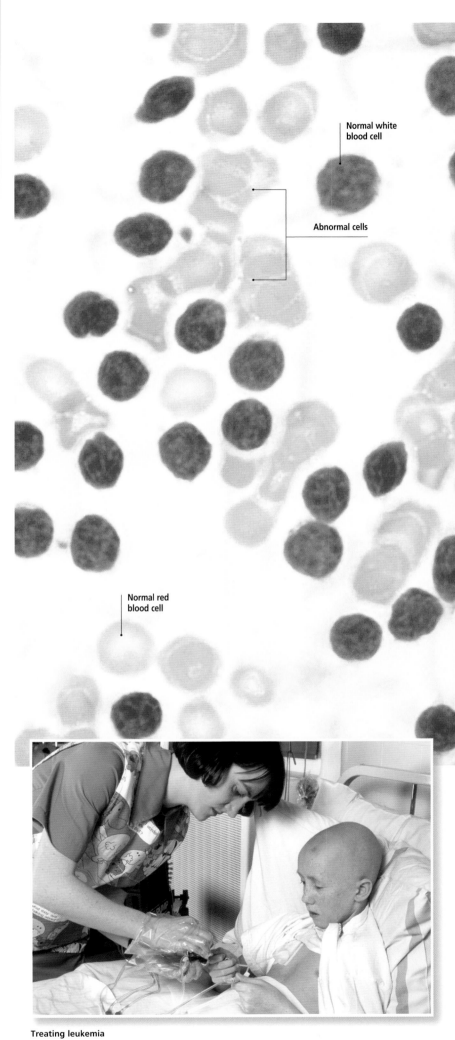

Normal white blood cell

Abnormal cells

Normal red blood cell

Treating leukemia
Leukemia treatments range from chemotherapy and radiation to transplanting bone marrow and administering therapeutic agents designed to boost the patient's immune responses. Some of the factors a physician considers in treatment are the patient's age, the type of leukemia and whether it has spread to the cerebrospinal fluid.

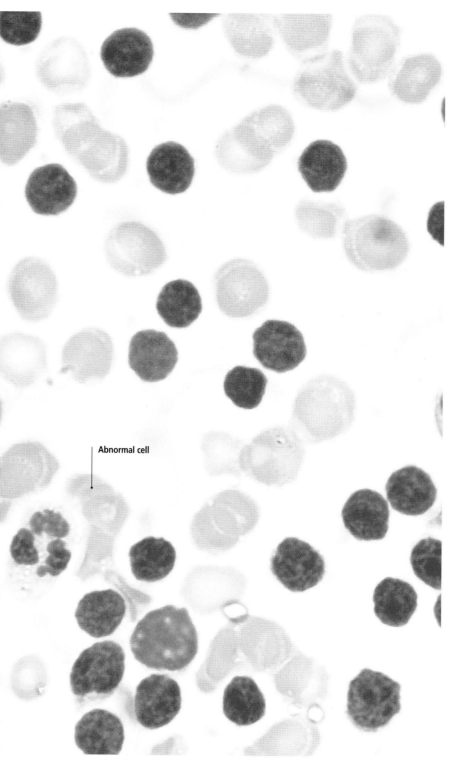

Abnormal cell

Leukemia cells

In leukemias, white blood cells become cancerous. Cells called myeloblasts are affected in myelocytic leukemia, and lymphocytes in lymphocytic leukemia. Abnormal cells overwhelm healthy ones as they multiply uncontrolled in bone marrow. Lacking enough normal white blood cells and platelets, the person is susceptible to infections and internal bleeding. A dwindling supply of red blood cells triggers anemia and other problems. Acute leukemia develops quickly, causing symptoms such as night sweats and extreme fatigue. In other cases the disease is chronic and progresses only slowly.

Malaria
Mosquitoes transmit the pathogen that causes malaria, which strikes more than 100 million people annually. The protozoan inhabits and finally destroys red blood cells, causing symptoms including shaking, fever, heavy sweating and chills. Drug treatments can be erratic and too costly for many patients. Common complications include anemia and lifelong recurrence. Increased use of antimalarial pills and mosquito nets can help reduce outbreaks of this disease.

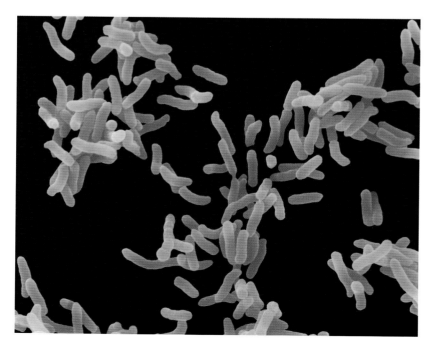

Bacteria in the blood
Bacteria like those pictured here may cause septicemia when they enter the blood from a wound or infection such as bacterial meningitis. The microbes or their toxins trigger sepsis, an immune response involving rampant inflammation and blood clotting in capillaries. Fortunate patients are treated with powerful intravenous antibiotics.

DAMAGE TO BLOOD VESSELS

Ailments that clog or impair the body's blood transport channels prevent blood from flowing efficiently to tissues and organs. This negative shift in normal blood circulation, known as peripheral vessel disease (PVD), is often painful and deprives body parts of the blood supply they require for good health and normal functioning.

The most common source of PVD is "hardening of the arteries" or atherosclerosis. Arteries narrow as fatty plaques develop in their walls. Over time, scarlike, calcified lesions develop, making the arterial wall much less elastic. Plaques may affect vessels in the heart, brain and elsewhere, and the reduced blood supply starves cells of oxygen. In cases where leg vessels are seriously affected, so much tissue may die that only amputation can save the patient's life. Many changes associated with aging, such as declining blood flow to the brain, reflect the progress of PVD.

The stealthy killer

Chronic high blood pressure, or hypertension, is a stealthy killer. Besides having symptoms such as a dull headache, many hypertensive people are unaware of their condition. Yet over time the walls of blood vessels, the kidneys and the heart muscle all may be damaged. Hypertension is a major cause of hemorrhagic stroke, in which a vessel bursts in the brain. Usually no single factor is responsible, but excess weight, smoking, stress and a family history of the condition increase the risk.

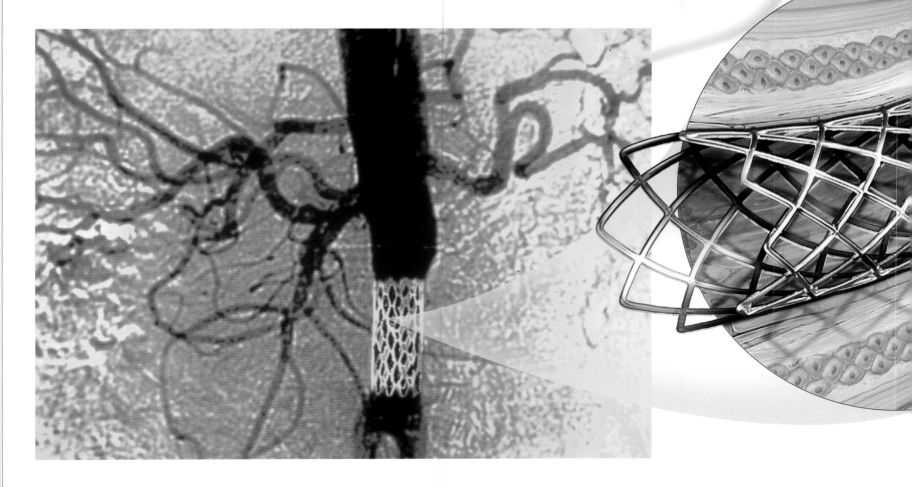

Angioplasty
Laser angioplasty uses a high-energy light beam to vaporize small plaques. In balloon angioplasty, a small balloon is threaded through a catheter into a blocked vessel and inflated to flatten a plaque.

Artery
A healthy artery's thick, multilayered wall is resilient, but becomes much less so as atherosclerosis advances.

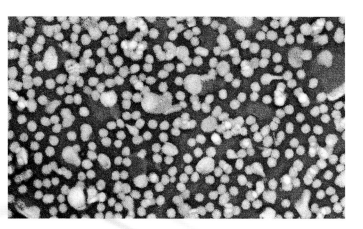

Good vs. bad cholesterol
The proteins called low-density lipoproteins (LDLs), captured in this image as blue-green particles, are termed "bad" cholesterol because they transport cholesterol throughout the bloodstream. High-density lipoproteins (HDLs) are "good" cholesterol because they ferry cholesterol to the liver, which moves it into the bowel to be eliminated.

Atherosclerosis
In an atherosclerotic plaque, deposits of excess blood cholesterol infiltrate scar tissue and create a bulging obstruction. Studies suggest that vessel scarring results from chronic low-level inflammation, possibly triggered by genetic factors or viral infection.

Blood
As inflammation develops at the plaque site, white blood cells arrive via the bloodstream. Ironically, this defense response causes changes that spur the growth of the plaque.

Plaque
Plaque begins to develop as excess LDL, or "bad" cholesterol, builds up in an artery's wall, triggering inflammation and eventually resulting in a bulging mass.

Lumen
The lumen, or space, inside an artery often remains sufficiently open for adequate blood flow until atherosclerosis reaches an advanced stage.

Stent
A small wire cylinder called a stent may be inserted by an angioplasty procedure to help keep a vessel open. So-called "drug-eluting stents" are coated with a chemical to inhibit the development of scar tissue that might otherwise form a new blockage.

HEART DISEASE

A diseased or damaged heart cannot pump blood efficiently. This fact has major implications for other organs and tissues, all of which rely on circulating blood to deliver oxygen, nutrients, hormones and other substances. Blood circulated by the heart also functions as a crucial waste carrier, transporting substances such as carbon dioxide and urea from protein digestion to the lungs, kidneys or other disposal sites. Because these are in constant demand, a malfunctioning heart is one of the most serious and frightening health problems a person can experience. In a heart attack or myocardial infarction, part of the heart dies when its blood supply is blocked. Other common heart ailments include faulty heart valves and disorders such as heart failure that arise as complications of other disease states.

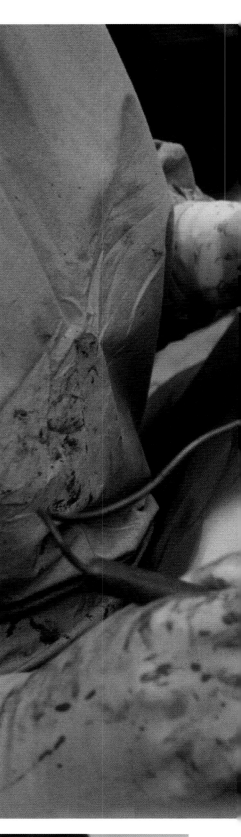

FAULTY HEART VALVES

Heart attack damage, infections and inborn or acquired defects can prevent heart valves from functioning properly. An "incompetent" valve fails to close fully, so blood leaks back into the chamber that pumped it. Calcium deposits or other factors can cause stenosis, the abnormal narrowing of a valve. Such defects usually require medical or surgical treatment because they force the heart to work overtime in order to pump sufficient blood.

Prosthetic tricuspid heart valves

Replacement valves
The most commonly replaced heart valves are the mitral or bicuspid valve between the left atrium and left ventricle and the valve leading from the left ventricle to the aorta.

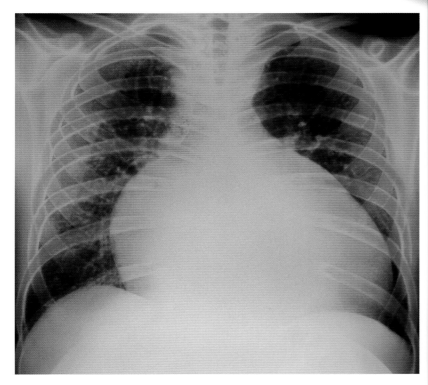

Heart failure
Heart failure is a condition in which some underlying factor, such as obesity, lung disease, chronic hypertension or a heart attack has so weakened the heart muscle that it no longer pumps blood efficiently. The overstressed heart may enlarge, as in this colored X-ray image which shows it as a swollen area on the right.

Congenital heart defects
Defective valves or a "hole" in some part of the heart wall are the most common birth defects. The resulting "murmur" of the heart can be detected with a stethoscope. Some have little negative impact, but a hole in the wall between the heart ventricles requires surgical repair.

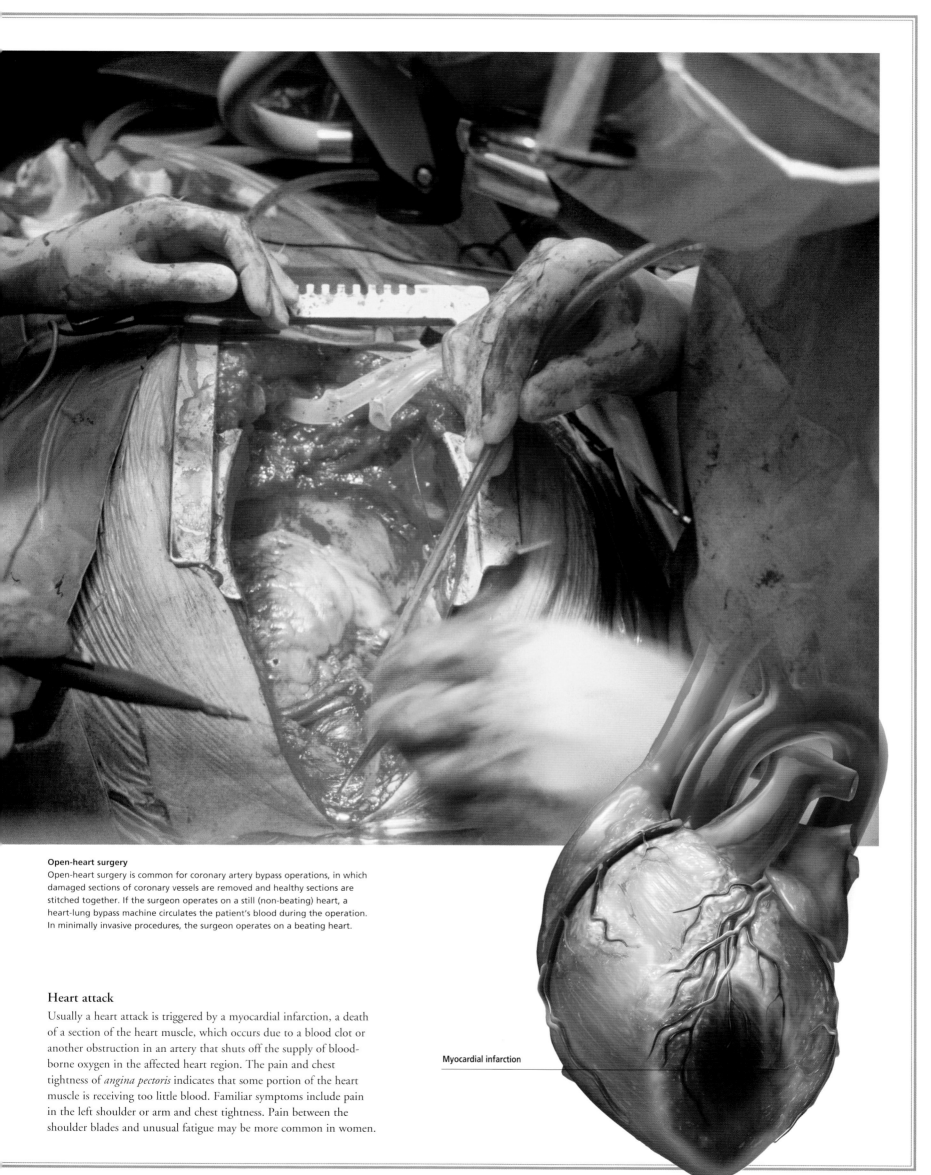

Open-heart surgery
Open-heart surgery is common for coronary artery bypass operations, in which damaged sections of coronary vessels are removed and healthy sections are stitched together. If the surgeon operates on a still (non-beating) heart, a heart-lung bypass machine circulates the patient's blood during the operation. In minimally invasive procedures, the surgeon operates on a beating heart.

Myocardial infarction

Heart attack

Usually a heart attack is triggered by a myocardial infarction, a death of a section of the heart muscle, which occurs due to a blood clot or another obstruction in an artery that shuts off the supply of blood-borne oxygen in the affected heart region. The pain and chest tightness of *angina pectoris* indicates that some portion of the heart muscle is receiving too little blood. Familiar symptoms include pain in the left shoulder or arm and chest tightness. Pain between the shoulder blades and unusual fatigue may be more common in women.

RESPIRATORY SYSTEM

The respiratory system exists to fill our spongy, expandable lungs with air and to provide a site where oxygen will move into the bloodstream and where carbon dioxide, a major metabolic waste, will be expelled. This function of gas exchange is so crucial that permanent brain damage usually occurs within minutes if it stops, and death follows quickly unless breathing resumes. Upper parts of the system, the nasal passages, pharynx and larynx, mainly provide a route for air to reach the trachea, or windpipe. Held open by rings of cartilage, the trachea funnels air to the point where large branches, the bronchi, diverge. At this fork in the respiratory road, air reaches its destination, the lungs. From this point onward, the so-called "respiratory tree" branches repeatedly into ever-narrower passages leading to clusters of microscopic sacs. In these alveoli, oxygen crosses into the blood, carbon dioxide comes out to be exhaled and life goes on.

Eight Main Components of the Resiratory System and Their Functions	
Nasal Cavity	Receives inhaled air
Pharynx	Funnels inhaled air toward the trachea/food toward the esophagus
Larynx	Site where speech sounds are produced
Trachea	Airway to the bronchi
Main Bronchi	Two, each of which carry air into one of the two lungs
Bronchiole	Small airway branches within the lungs
Lungs	Organs where oxygen and carbon dioxide are exchanged
Alveoli	Sacs where oxygen moves into the blood and carbon dioxide exits

Gases exchanged
Like tiny bunches of hollow grapes, alveoli are clusters of sacs surrounded by a lacework of blood vessels. Carbon dioxide diffuses from venules into the sacs, while inhaled oxygen crosses outward, into blood capillaries.

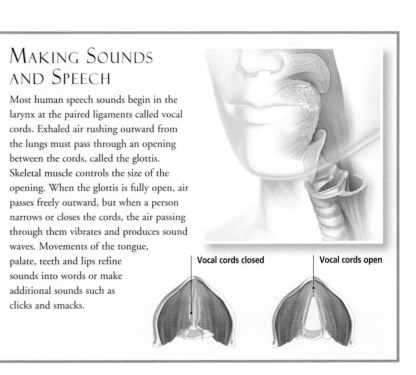

Alveoli

Venule

Arteriole

CO_2

Carbon dioxide entering from blood

O_2

Oxygen moving into blood

The multifaceted diaphragm
The diaphragm is a dome-shaped skeletal muscle that separates the pleural and abdominal cavities. Its rhythmic cycle of contraction and relaxation is partly responsible for the normal in-out rhythm of quiet breathing. Diaphragm contractions also force the stomach contents up and out during vomiting and sometimes help void feces and urine.

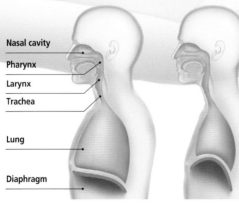

Nasal cavity

Pharynx

Larynx

Trachea

Lung

Diaphragm

Inhalation   Exhalation

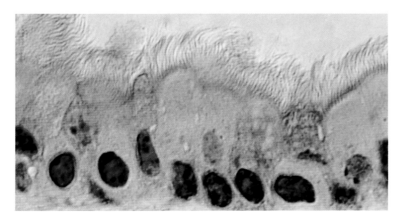

Airway housekeeping
The airways are lined with epithelium that includes cells with minute hairlike projections called cilia. This image shows cilia-bearing cells in the bronchi.

MAKING SOUNDS AND SPEECH

Most human speech sounds begin in the larynx at the paired ligaments called vocal cords. Exhaled air rushing outward from the lungs must pass through an opening between the cords, called the glottis. Skeletal muscle controls the size of the opening. When the glottis is fully open, air passes freely outward, but when a person narrows or closes the cords, the air passing through them vibrates and produces sound waves. Movements of the tongue, palate, teeth and lips refine sounds into words or make additional sounds such as clicks and smacks.

Vocal cords closed   Vocal cords open

Smooth muscle

Healthy airways

The human respiratory system is exposed to all manner of airborne debris and toxic substances, including dust and particles emitted from automobiles, factories and products such as house paint, pesticides and carpets. The system's primary defense against these environmental assaults is mucus produced by cells or glands in the epithelium lining the airways. Larger particles become trapped in the sticky mucus, which is swept upward by beating cilia. When this material reaches the throat, it may be expelled or swallowed and eliminated from the body either way. Certain small foreign particles, such as asbestos fibers, may not be removed, but instead can enter the lungs and cause serious disease.

Nasal passages
Inhaled air warms and takes on moisture as it moves through the nasal cavity. Mucus-coated hairs may trap dust and debris.

Oral cavity
The interior of the mouth is an alternate breathing route during heavy exertion or when nasal passages are clogged.

Pharynx
The pharynx or throat is a transit point for air moving into or out of the lungs and for swallowed food moving into the esophagus.

Epiglottis
During swallowing, this flap of tissue moves downward over the larynx to prevent food from entering the airways beyond.

Trachea
This tube connects the larynx with the two bronchi, the major airways leading to the lungs. Rings of cartilage help prop it open.

Larynx
This short passageway, also called the voice box, contains the vocal cords.

Bronchus
Each bronchus branches into ever-smaller air passages. This inverted branching network is often called the respiratory tree.

Bifurcation of trachea (carina)

Bronchiole
Bronchioles are the narrowest passages of the respiratory tree. They end at alveoli, the microscopic sacs where oxygen moves into the blood and carbon dioxide moves out.

Lungs
Each lung is a spongy elastic organ with several lobes. The lungs jointly contain an estimated 300 million alveoli.

Pleural membrane
This double membrane surrounds the lungs and lines the pleural cavity. Fluid between the layers prevents friction with the cavity's inner wall as the lungs repeatedly expand and contract.

Diaphragm
This sheet of skeletal muscle separates the pleural and abdominal cavities below. Its contractions are part of the breathing sequence.

GAS EXCHANGE

In just one minute of normal breathing, about 1 gallon (7.5 L) of fresh air flows into the lungs and a similar quantity of air containing carbon dioxide rushes outward. Most people will take more than half a billion breaths during their lifetime, each one an exercise in gas exchange—oxygen in, carbon dioxide out. To accomplish gas exchange, the respiratory system exploits a simple physical rule. Gases move when pressure changes pull them from place to place. When the lungs expand, pressure inside them falls, so fresh air rushes in. Carbon dioxide is flushed out when the elastic lungs recoil. Differences in pressure within the lungs also move oxygen into the bloodstream and draw waste carbon dioxide out. This step requires that each gas dissolves in water, which coats the thin walls of an estimated 300 million microscopic air chambers called alveoli.

Gaining altitude
At sea level, air is 21 percent oxygen, but rise higher than 8,000 feet (2,500 m) above sea level and the percentage drops drastically. Without supplemental oxygen high-altitude climbers risk hypoxia—an oxygen shortage that may cause altitude sickness including headache, vomiting and dangerous accumulation of fluid in the lungs and brain.

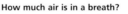

How much air is in a breath?
With a normal breath, the lungs inhale about 2 cups (475 ml) of air and exhale a similar amount of carbon dioxide. You can forcibly increase these amounts, as when you deliberately exhale a large amount of air to inflate a balloon.

Alveolus

Oxygen

Red blood cells

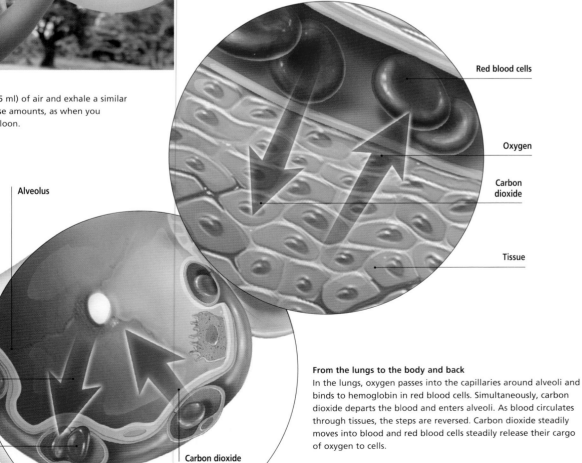

Red blood cells

Oxygen

Carbon dioxide

Tissue

Carbon dioxide

From the lungs to the body and back
In the lungs, oxygen passes into the capillaries around alveoli and binds to hemoglobin in red blood cells. Simultaneously, carbon dioxide departs the blood and enters alveoli. As blood circulates through tissues, the steps are reversed. Carbon dioxide steadily moves into blood and red blood cells steadily release their cargo of oxygen to cells.

Gas exchange in alveoli

Air entering the lungs contains more oxygen, and much less carbon dioxide, than are present in blood flowing in the capillaries that hug alveoli. The differences make simple work of gas exchange, because oxygen and carbon dioxide need only follow their natural pressure gradients. Oxygen's gradient pulls it from inhaled air into lung capillaries where it binds to hemoglobin in red blood cells. The gradient of CO_2 draws it out of the bloodstream and into the lungs, where it is exhaled.

Bronchioles, the tiniest air passages
Starting at the base of the trachea, the airways branch repeatedly in an inverted "respiratory tree." Deep within the lungs are the narrowest, most delicate branches, the bronchioles that funnel air into alveoli. A thin layer of smooth muscle in bronchiole walls can contract or relax, adjusting how much air will flow through them.

Alveoli
With their moist, gossamer-thin walls, alveoli make up most of the lungs and are the main sites of gas exchange.

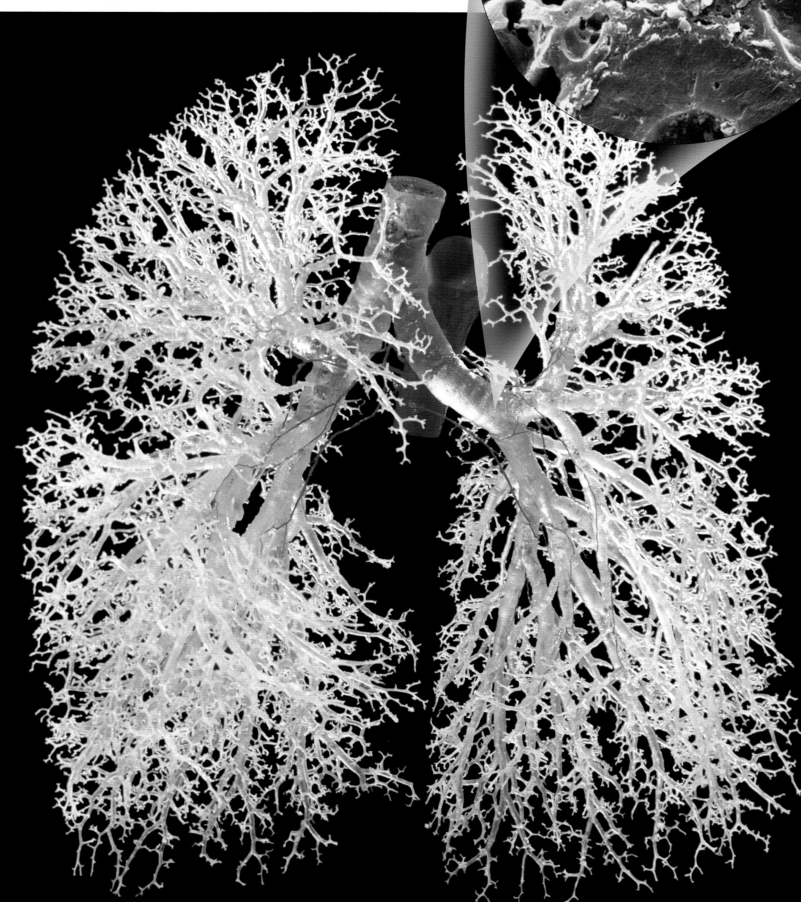

BREATHING CONTROLS

Inhale, exhale and repeat—for as long as we live the incessant rhythm of breathing depends on controls that operate in the brain, the lungs and elsewhere. Generally speaking, people do not have to consciously remember to breathe. Instead, automatic commands that issue from the brain stem regulate inhalation and exhalation. And while it might seem that the impulse to breathe comes from falling oxygen in the blood, in fact the body monitors carbon dioxide.

Sensors in the aorta and the carotid arteries in the neck track the amount of carbon dioxide it contains. The lungs themselves also are sensitive to shifting carbon dioxide levels. If too little is being exhaled, the muscular walls of bronchioles dilate so that more air can flow through them. Blood capillaries of the lungs also dilate or constrict to help match the moment-to-moment flow of blood to the amount of oxygen in inhaled air.

Muscles moving air

When the diaphragm and rib cage muscles expand, the chest cavity and lungs also expand. The increased volume lowers pressure in the lungs, so outside air rushes in. When the muscles contract again, the chest cavity contracts, pressure increases and carbon dioxide is flushed out from the lungs. When a person laughs or sobs, inhalation is followed by a series of short exhalations. Hiccups are intermittent spasms of the diaphragm muscle.

BREATHING AND THE BRAIN

People who suffer brain stem damage may suffocate without the aid of a respirator. This is because respiratory centers in the medulla and pons manage the mechanics of breathing, sending a steady stream of nerve impulses to the diaphragm and rib cage muscles. The result is the in-and-out flow of air physiologists call ventilation. The brain also monitors carbon dioxide in cerebrospinal fluid and increases the rate and depth of breathing if necessary to reduce CO_2 levels.

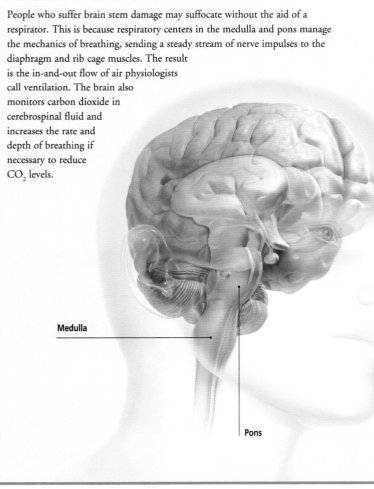

Medulla

Pons

Inhalation

Breathing on hold
At best, most people can only hold their breath for a minute or two. As the brain's respiratory centers detect dangerously increasing carbon dioxide in the blood, their neural commands to inhale become irresistible.

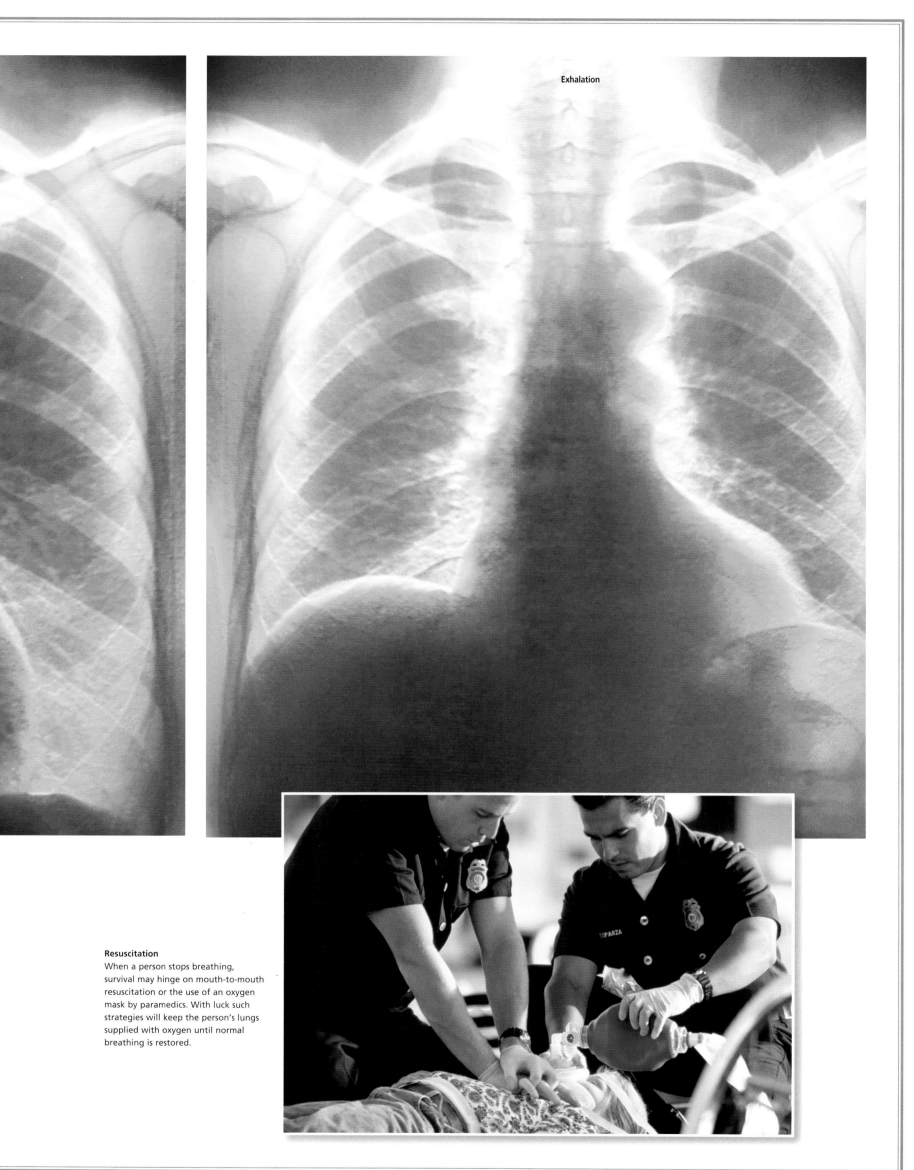

Exhalation

Resuscitation
When a person stops breathing, survival may hinge on mouth-to-mouth resuscitation or the use of an oxygen mask by paramedics. With luck such strategies will keep the person's lungs supplied with oxygen until normal breathing is restored.

RESPIRATORY DISEASES AND DISORDERS

Under normal circumstances, 12 to 15 times each minute fresh air is inhaled into the airways as the lungs expand, and then stale air is exhaled out. Humans take this sequence for granted until an infection or respiratory disease interferes with it. Defensive responses to viruses and bacteria produce the congested, swollen nasal passages of the common cold, the irritation of laryngitis and the coughing and wheezing of bronchitis. In cigarette smokers, bronchial inflammation can become chronic, causing a near-constant cough and breathing problems. Even more serious is asthma, an allergic response to air pollutants or stress that can bring a lifetime of small crises and occasional emergencies in which patients are in danger of suffocation. Like some other airway disorders, asthma disrupts the functioning of the bronchi, the wide, cartilage-supported airways that normally transport large volumes of air into and out of the lungs.

The common cold

The mild respiratory infection coryza, or the common cold, originates with hundreds of different viral pathogens. Roughly half of colds are caused by rhinoviruses, coronaviruses and their relatives. Other unidentified viruses are probably responsible for many more. Most colds last about seven days and produce a familiar list of symptoms, including congestion, sore throat and headache. Cold viruses are notoriously contagious, moving easily from person to person via sneezing, coughing and contaminated objects like tissues.

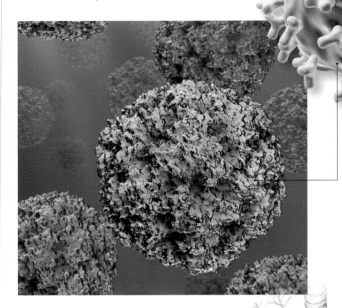

Cellular receptor

A typical rhinovirus

Bronchitis
This light micrograph shows a section of lung tissue affected by chronic bronchitis, an inflammation of the airways. The bronchi and bronchiole connecting the trachea to the lungs can become inflamed due to an infection or smoking and produce thick mucus that triggers coughing spasms. Antibiotics are prescribed to prevent bacterial infections from spreading to the lungs.

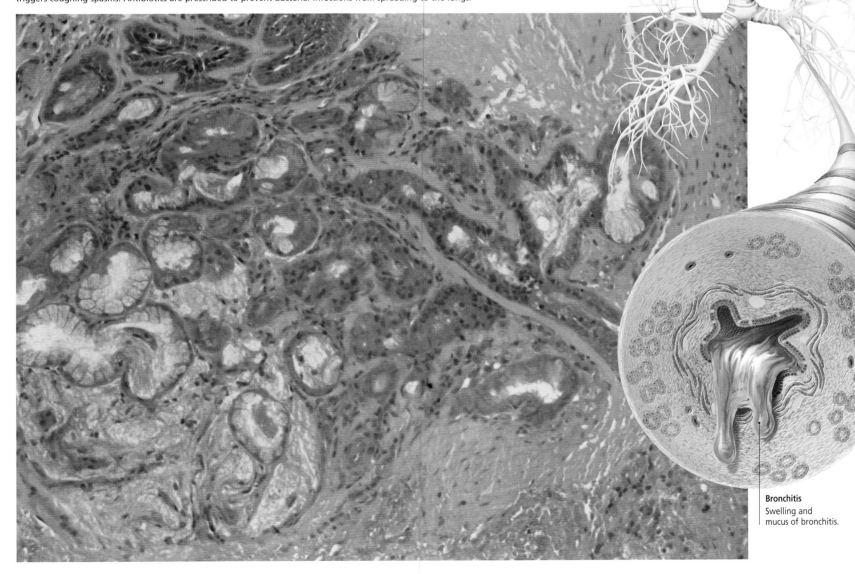

Bronchitis
Swelling and mucus of bronchitis.

Upper respiratory infections
Viral infections develop in the upper respiratory tract when virus particles penetrate mucus covering the surface epithelium and enter cells there. This process usually takes two to four days, the incubation period of an impending cold.

Tonsillitis
The tonsils contain cells that intercept microbes but which can be overwhelmed and become infected and inflamed.

Pharyngitis (sore throat)
Viruses cause most sore throats, but a bacterium, *Streptococcus pyogenes,* causes the illness commonly called "strep throat."

Laryngitis
Inflammation due to viral or bacterial infection of the larynx (voice box) prevents the vocal cords from vibrating as usual.

CYSTIC FIBROSIS

Cystic fibrosis (CF) is an inherited disorder that is most common among people of European descent. Among other effects, cells that produce mucus malfunction and thick, dry mucus clogs the airways. Severe lung infections develop when bacteria colonize the mucus. CF is incurable and eventually destroys the lungs, but antibiotics can help control infections and experimental treatments are under development. Patients may also undergo physiotherapy that includes thumping on the back and chest to loosen mucus so it can be expelled.

Cystic fibrosis
This young cystic fibrosis patient is participating in an experiment to test whether a protein called alpha 1 can safely reduce inflammation that injures lung tissues.

Inflammation of bronchiole

Asthma
For patients with asthma, the mist of medication delivered by an aerosol inhaler may literally be the breath of life. An untreated attack may abruptly close the bronchial passages and prevent the person from breathing.

THREATS TO THE LUNGS

Diseased alveolus

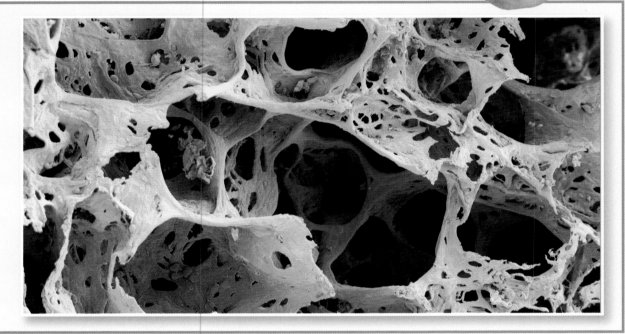

Roughly 17,000 times a day, outside air fills tens of millions of alveoli, the tiny air sacs in the lungs. In addition to oxygen, nitrogen and other gases in air, each inhaled breath may contain an array of bacteria, viruses, fungal pathogens, industrial pollutants, toxins from cigarette smoke and the like. All of these inhaled irritants have the potential to, acutely or chronically, drastically reduce the number of healthy alveoli. This decrease may in turn severely limit the lungs' capacity to take in oxygen, transfer it to the bloodstream and expel carbon dioxide. Lung diseases and disorders range from curable pneumonias and tuberculosis to potentially deadly cancers and crippling emphysema and mesothelioma. Emphysema and chronic bronchitis may blend in an increasingly prevalent disorder, chronic obstructive pulmonary disease (COPD).

DANGERS OF SMOKING

Cigarette smoke contains a blend of known carcinogens and toxins. Inhaled directly or secondhand in a smoky environment, it is a major cause of or contributor to lung cancer and several other malignancies, emphysema, heart disease, chronic bronchitis and chronic obstructive pulmonary disorder (COPD). Inhaled smoke also impairs immunity and slows normal healing processes. Health authorities estimate that by 2030, smoking-related illnesses will kill ten million people each year worldwide.

Emphysema
This scanning electron micrograph shows lung tissue that has been damaged due to emphysema. In this disease, the alveoli become enlarged, which can deteriorate the walls surrounding them.

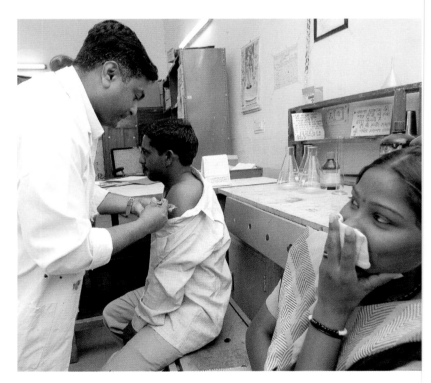

Tuberculosis
Tuberculosis (TB) is a communicable disease caused by the bacterium *Mycobacterium tuberculosis*. Antibiotics once used to treat TB patients can no longer kill certain highly virulent strains. TB is reemerging as a major health threat on every continent.

Iron lungs
"Iron lungs" once saved the lives of polio patients with paralyzed respiratory muscles. Air pressure in the closed device was manipulated to force the lungs to expand and recoil as in normal breathing. Ventilators later mostly replaced the technology.

Lung cancer

Lung cancer is a leading killer worldwide—only a minority of patients survive more than two to three years from diagnosis. Lung cancer usually begins in the bronchial tubes and may spread aggressively to the lungs, lymph nodes, bones and other sites. The red area in the accompanying image shows a large lung tumor. Early symptoms mimic those of other respiratory disorders, so the cancer often is well advanced before it is detected.

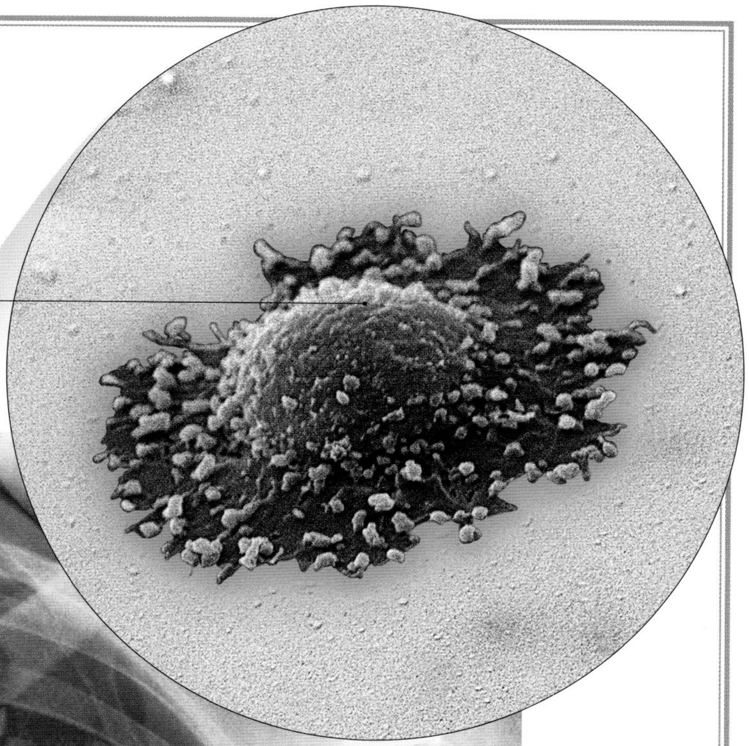

Cancerous lung cell
This image of a lung cancer cell reveals the characteristic extensions that allow the cell to move and the cancer to spread.

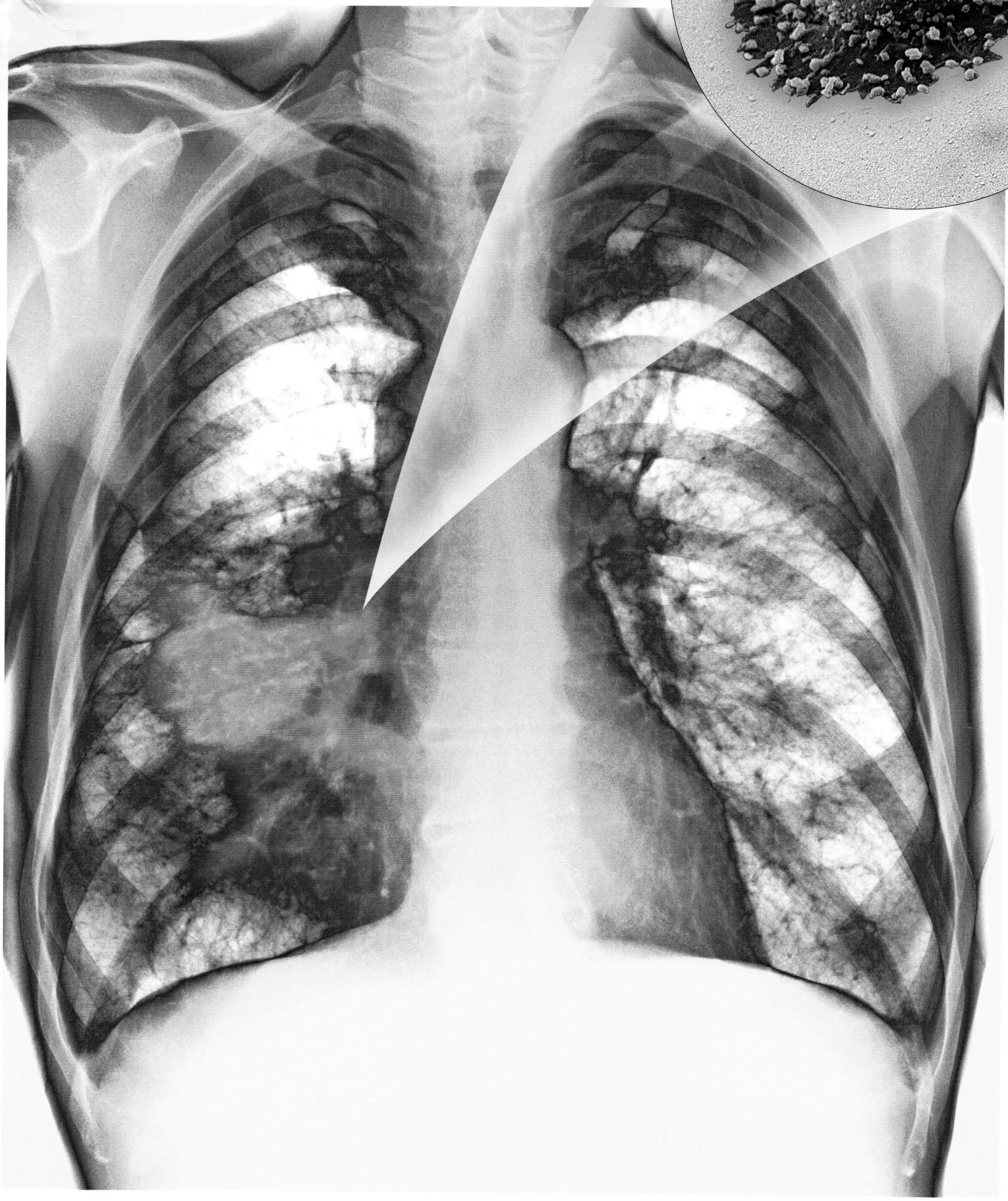

DEFENSE AND LYMPHATIC SYSTEM

A far-flung network of lymphatic vessels threads through tissues everywhere in the body except the central nervous system, bones, bone marrow and teeth. These vessels drain through some of the body's less familiar organs—lymph nodes, the spleen, the tonsils, the thymus and even clumps of lymphatic tissue in the small intestine and appendix. This network of vessels, organs and tissue patches, called the lymphatic system, serves two distinct but essential functions. Lymphatic vessels pick up needed fluid and proteins that have leaked out of blood capillaries and return them, as the clear fluid called lymph, back to the bloodstream. Before that happens, however, the lymphatic organs serve as a bodywide staging area for defense. Lymph en route to the great veins trickles through lymph nodes and other lymphoid tissues, where white blood cells, including macrophages and lymphocytes, may intercept microbes and other threats and launch the immune system's defensive counterattack.

Thymus
In this gland, T cells mature and acquire the capacity to mount the type of immune response known as cell-mediated immunity.

Lacteals
These lymphatic capillaries in the small intestine absorb digested dietary fats and shunt them into the bloodstream.

Peyer's patches
Clusters of lymphoid tissue in the lower small intestine, these patches house defensive cells that respond to pathogens in the gastrointestinal tract.

Appendix
The appendix is a lymphoid organ with a downside. Its unique structure is an ideal place for bacteria to collect and potentially cause inflammation.

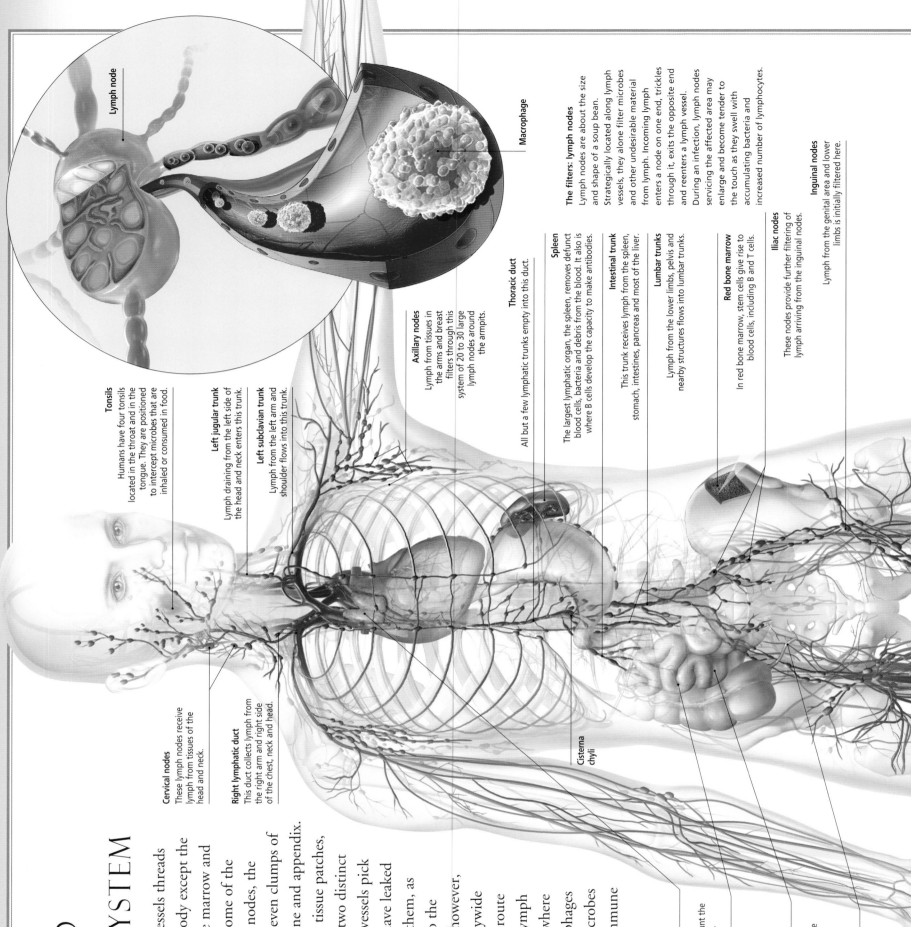

Lymph node

Macrophage

Tonsils
Humans have four tonsils located in the throat and in the tongue. They are positioned to intercept microbes that are inhaled or consumed in food.

Left jugular trunk
Lymph draining from the left side of the head and neck enters this trunk.

Left subclavian trunk
Lymph from the left arm and shoulder flows into this trunk.

Cervical nodes
These lymph nodes receive lymph from tissues of the head and neck.

Right lymphatic duct
This duct collects lymph from the right arm and right side of the chest, neck and head.

Axillary nodes
Lymph from tissues in the arms and breast filters through this system of 20 to 30 large lymph nodes around the armpits.

Thoracic duct
All but a few lymphatic trunks empty into this duct.

Spleen
The largest lymphatic organ, the spleen, removes defunct blood cells, bacteria and debris from the blood. It also is where B cells develop the capacity to make antibodies.

Intestinal trunk
This trunk receives lymph from the spleen, stomach, intestines, pancreas and most of the liver.

Lumbar trunks
Lymph from the lower limbs, pelvis and nearby structures flows into lumbar trunks.

Red bone marrow
In red bone marrow, stem cells give rise to blood cells, including B and T cells.

Iliac nodes
These nodes provide further filtering of lymph arriving from the inguinal nodes.

Cisterna chyli

The filters: lymph nodes
Lymph nodes are about the size and shape of a soup bean. Strategically located along lymph vessels, they alone filter microbes and other undesirable material from lymph. Incoming lymph enters a node on one end, trickles through it, exits the opposite end and reenters a lymph vessel. During an infection, lymph nodes servicing the affected area may enlarge and become tender to the touch as they swell with accumulating bacteria and increased number of lymphocytes.

Inguinal nodes
Lymph from the genital area and lower limbs is initially filtered here.

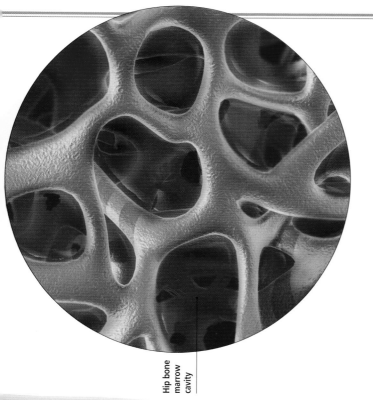

Hip bone marrow cavity

Recognizing Non-self

To function properly, the immune system must be able to distinguish between cells and substances that belong in the body and those that are foreign and potentially dangerous. Lymphocytes such as T cells, B cells and macrophages can detect gene-coded chemical features on the surface of a cell that signify "self" or "nonself" and respond accordingly. Self markers, called MHC proteins, are normally ignored. Nonself markers, termed antigens, normally trigger an immune response. Autoimmune disorders usually develop when the immune system mistakes normal body cells for foreign material.

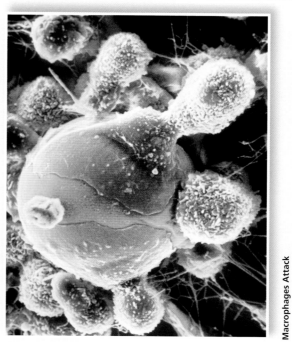

Macrophages Attack
Macrophages (in blue) surround and digest a foreign body. After destroying the pathogen, the macrophages "presents" an antigen to help the immune system identify and fight the pathogen now or in the future.

Popliteal nodes

Lymphatic vessel
Many miles of lymphatic vessels collect lymph from lymph capillaries and channel it onward.

Lymph's route through the body

Tiny lymph capillaries take up fluid from the spaces between cells in a tissue. The lymph passes next into larger lymph vessels and is filtered in a succession of lymph nodes. Vessels that receive cleansed lymph converge into lymph trunks that deliver their fluid cargo into ducts that return the lymph to large veins near the heart.

Lymph vessels

Lymphatic capillaries are positioned close to the blood capillaries and venules in tissues. The blind-ended capillaries converge to form lymphatic vessels, in which valves prevent lymph from flowing backward. As a result of this architecture, unlike blood in the circulatory system, lymph flows in only one direction, toward the heart. Lymphatic vessels close to the skin generally follow veins, while those deeper in the body typically follow the paths of arteries.

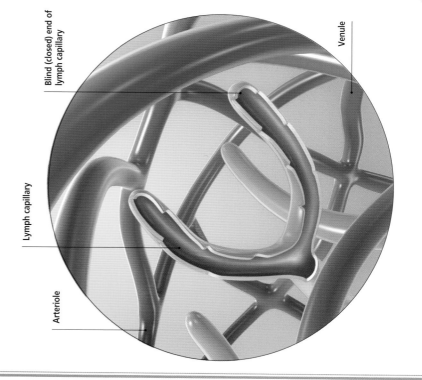

Blind (closed) end of lymph capillary

Venule

Lymph capillary

Arteriole

IMMUNE RESPONSES

The defensive strategies, called immunity, utilize lymphocytes. These are the specialized white blood cells that develop in parts of the lymphatic system, including red bone marrow and the thymus. Among these cells are T and B lymphocytes, which are located within lymph nodes and other lymphatic tissues. T cells are the catalysts of cellular immunity. They launch and support the activities of other cells that can detect and destroy infected or abnormal body cells. B cells, by contrast, produce antibodies—defensive proteins that counteract threats yet to enter cells, including bacteria, viruses, protozoa and toxins circulating in tissues or body fluids such as blood. Their protective action is known as humoral (blood-borne) immunity. Together, antibody-based responses by B cells and cell-based responses mounted by T cells provide the body's system of adaptive immunity—defenses that are tailored to a specific pathogen or abnormal body cell.

Self and non-self

All body cells have proteins, or markers, on their surface that flag them as self—that is, something that belongs in one's own body. Cells and most substances that are not normal body constituents are non-self. This "non-self" designation is the definition of a foreign antigen—a substance that is not tolerated and provokes an immune response. Healthy body defenses depend on the ability of lymphocytes and other defenders to distinguish between normal body constituents and foreign or otherwise abnormal ones.

Macrophage

Red blood cells

Lymphocytes

Macrophages
Macrophages (blue) are white blood cells that engulf and destroy invading bacteria and other pathogens. They also consume dead body cells and other debris. Most macrophages operate in lymph nodes or tissues, using long, arm-like extensions to gather in material. Specialized macrophages in brain tissue remove undesirable material there.

Inside a lymph node
A lymph node consists of clusters of white blood cells, including lymphocytes and macrophages. As lymph passes through small lymph vessels, these defenders attack and destroy bacteria or other antigen-bearing material they detect in it. Lymph nodes are strategically clustered along lymph vessels in the groin, abdomen, armpits, neck and elsewhere.

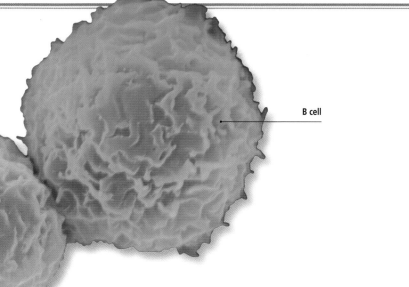

B cell

Helper T cell

Lymphocytes

Like other white blood cells, lymphocytes arise from stem cells in bone marrow. B and T cells play the major role in adaptive immune responses, which target specific invaders. A third type of lymphocyte, natural killer (NK) cells, is most active in inborn responses that destroy body cells that are cancerous or infected by a virus.

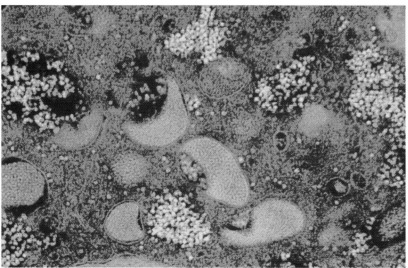

Basophils and eosinophils

Basophils, the rarest white blood cells, release histamine to promote inflammation. They circulate in the blood stream, but function in connective tissue, and have granules (shown in blue) that contain histamine and other chemicals.

Neutrophils

Neutrophils (green) are the most abundant white blood cells. Like macrophages, they are phagocytes ("cell eaters") that chemically attack and digest foreign material. They converge on inflamed, infected or damaged tissues by following chemical trails exuded by injured cells.

INFLAMMATION RESPONSES

The adaptive immunity conferred by T cells and antibodies provides a potent arsenal of weapons against specific sorts of threats, but these counterattacks take time to develop. The body also has a system of inborn or innate immunity—general but fast-acting responses that are deployed as soon as tissues are damaged, regardless of the source. Leading the list of general responses is inflammation, which mobilizes blood-borne substances and white blood cells to mount an immediate counterattack to injury. Although aspects of the process produce discomfort, acute or sudden inflammatory response to tissue damage is essential to healing. Without it, wounds would not heal and even the most minor infections would advance unchecked. Equally crucial are internal mechanisms that normally regulate inflammation and bring it to a close. Uncontrolled, chronic inflammation is the foundation for many cases of coronary artery disease and a host of other illnesses.

Increased blood flow

After circulating cytokines get inflammation underway, the resulting flood of defensive chemicals, especially histamine, dilates small blood vessels and loosens connections between cells in their walls so that the vessels become "leaky." As more blood flows to the affected area, it brings various types of white blood cells that can squeeze out of the leaky vessels and into damaged tissues. There, the defensive cells, including neutrophils and macrophages, detect, bind and destroy bacteria and begin consuming debris.

HARMFUL INFLAMMATIONS

Inflammation has long been a high-profile factor in various forms of arthritis and some other conditions. Recent studies suggest that chronic inflammation may underlie or promote a host of diseases and disorders, including the development of atherosclerotic plaques that block coronary arteries, the brain deterioration of Alzheimer's disease and the disabling of insulin-producing cells in type 1 diabetes. One research focus is the role of body fat (particularly in the abdomen) in the process, since fat cells produce the cytokines that trigger inflammation.

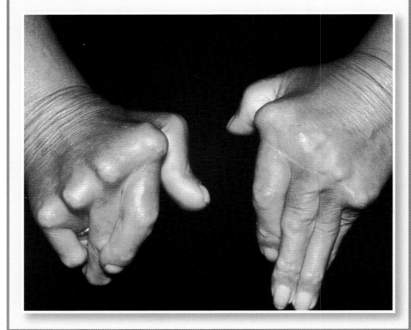

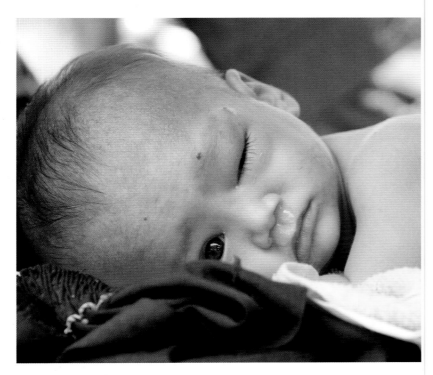

Signs of inflammation
The four indicators of acute inflammation are redness, warmth, swelling and pain. Vascular changes of inflammation cause these classic signs: increased blood flow makes affected tissues turn reddish and warm; the leaking of fluid from blood vessels produces edema (swelling), which in turn causes pain.

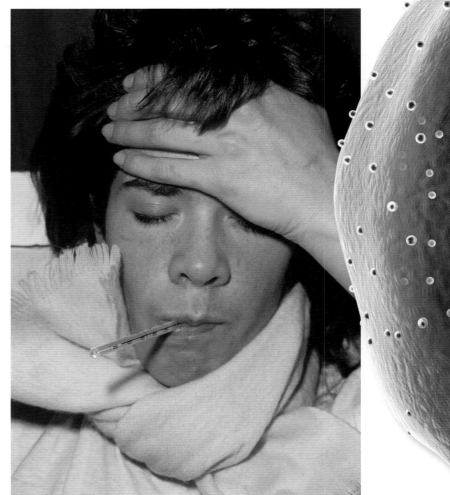

Fever
An infection may result in a fever, an abnormally elevated core temperature. Fever develops when macrophages and other white blood cells release pyrogens, chemicals that stimulate the hypothalamus to shift the activity of brain centers that regulate body temperature. Mild to moderate fever speeds tissue repair processes.

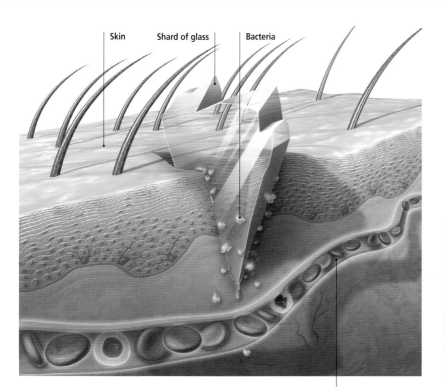

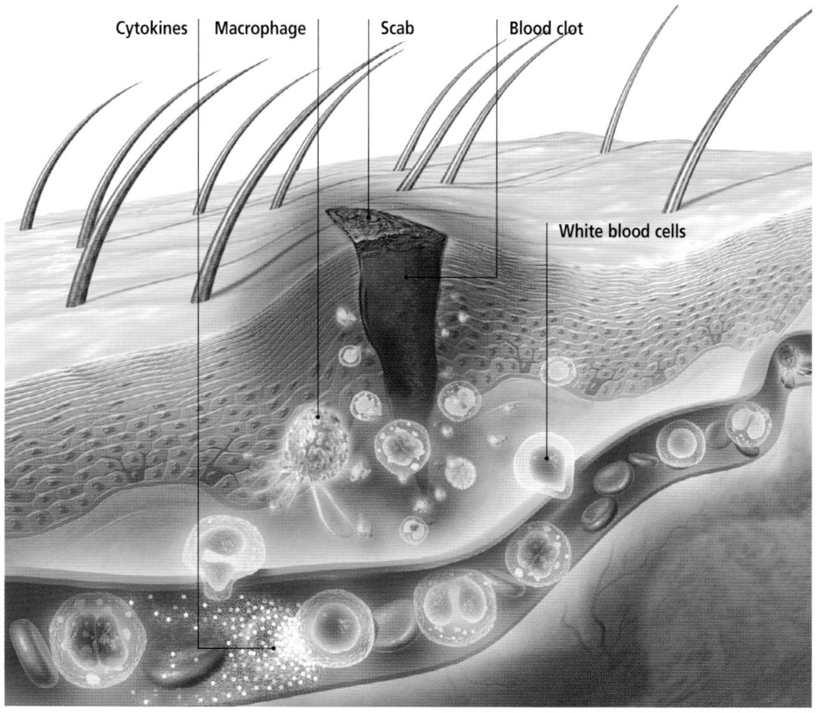

Skin | Shard of glass | Bacteria

Cytokines | Macrophage | Scab | Blood clot

White blood cells

Blood capillary

Launching inflammation
Tissue damage stimulates macrophages and healthy cells near an injury site to release cytokines—"cell movers" that circulate in the blood and trigger the cascade of ensuing inflammation responses.

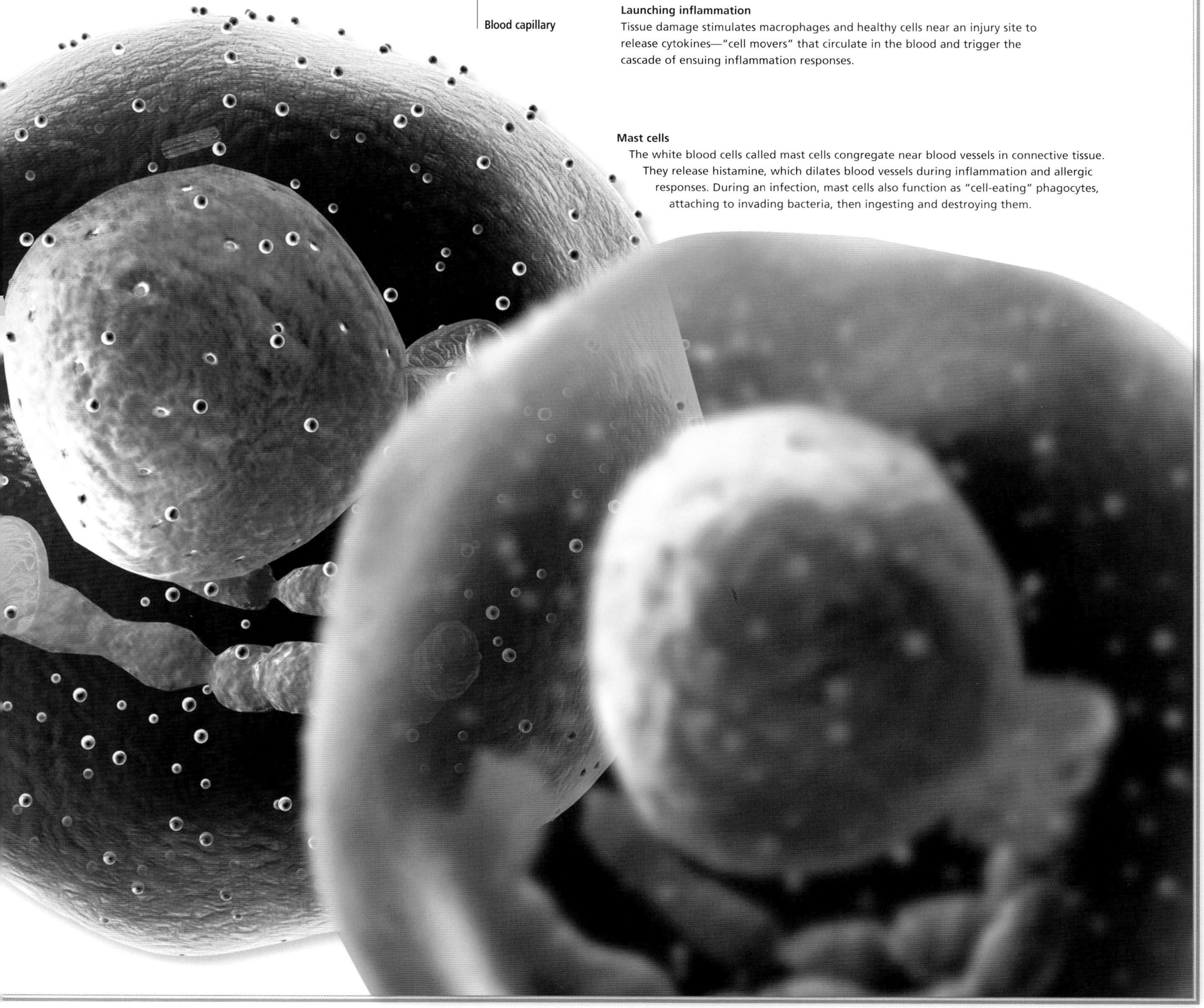

Mast cells
The white blood cells called mast cells congregate near blood vessels in connective tissue. They release histamine, which dilates blood vessels during inflammation and allergic responses. During an infection, mast cells also function as "cell-eating" phagocytes, attaching to invading bacteria, then ingesting and destroying them.

IMMUNE RESPONSES IN ACTION

When T and B lymphocytes have reached maturity, they move into lymph nodes, the spleen and other lymphatic tissues where they monitor lymph for bacteria, viruses, defective or cancerous body cells or anything else chemically recognizable as foreign. If invading bacteria are not destroyed by the inflammatory response, T cells, B cells or both will be activated and begin to mobilize. Helper T cells release cytokines that stimulate cytotoxic T cells and natural killer cells to multiply, forming armies of defenders primed to destroy infected body cells. Activated B cells also may produce legions of plasma cells that release a flood of antibodies—defensive proteins that target pathogens still circulating in the blood or tissues. The ranks of T cells and B cells also include memory cells that remain in the bloodstream and are available to mount a more rapid counterattack if the same pathogen enters the body again.

Exercise and immunity

Exercise may give immunity a boost. In one study, people who regularly engaged in moderate exercise tended to have more circulating antibodies sensitive to viruses that cause common respiratory infections. In another study, moderate exercisers had more of certain types of T cells. Subjects who exercised more heavily had fewer of both types of defenses, possibly because extreme physical exertion triggers the release of cortisol, a hormone that suppresses immune responses.

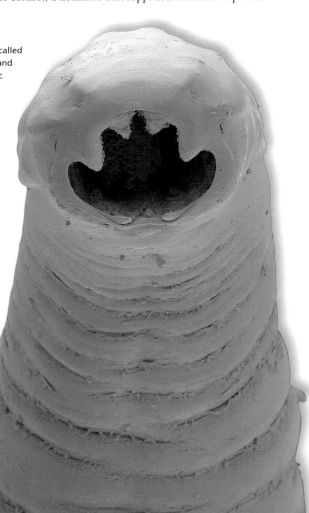

Parasites
The white blood cells called eosinophils attach to and chemically kill parasitic worms in the body. This image shows the head of a hookworm, which attaches in the small intestine where adult worms suck blood and breed. Millions of people in tropical areas have hookworm infections.

When viruses attack
When a virus infects a cell, it quickly multiplies and destroys its host. Immune defenders called dendritic cells display remains of the dead cell to T cells in the lymph nodes or spleen. This interaction stimulates the multiplication of cytotoxic "cell-killing" T cells that enter the blood and kill body cells infected with the same virus.

Virus injecting DNA into cell

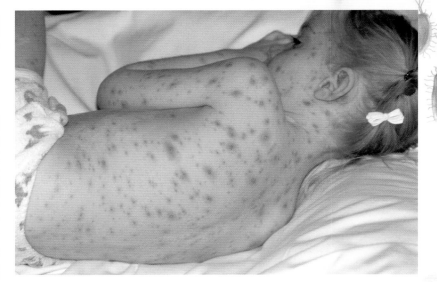

Chicken pox
Chicken pox, caused by the varicella zoster virus, once was a common childhood illness. Children in many regions today are vaccinated against the disease. Because vaccination produces memory cytotoxic T cells, chicken pox is a once-in-a-lifetime illness.

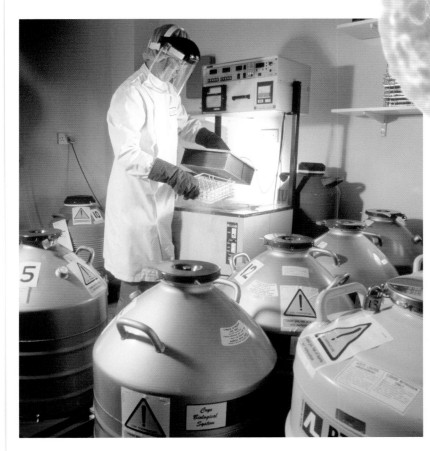

Interleukins and interferons
Proteins called interleukins and interferons aid immunity after an infection has begun. Interleukins promote the proliferation of T cells and B cells. Dying virus-infected cells release interferons, which help healthy cells mount chemical barriers to viral multiplication. Laboratory-made interferons are both research and treatment tools.

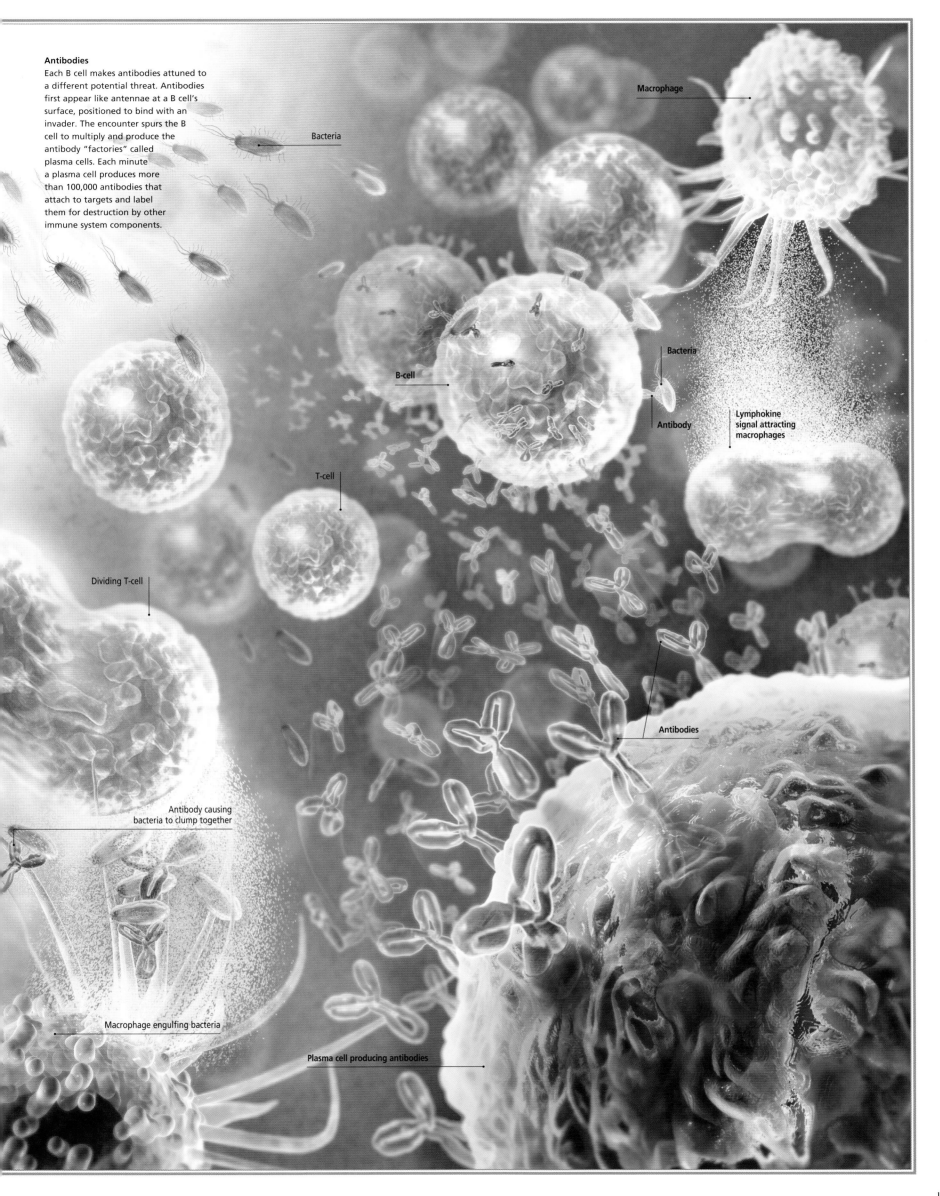

Antibodies
Each B cell makes antibodies attuned to a different potential threat. Antibodies first appear like antennae at a B cell's surface, positioned to bind with an invader. The encounter spurs the B cell to multiply and produce the antibody "factories" called plasma cells. Each minute a plasma cell produces more than 100,000 antibodies that attach to targets and label them for destruction by other immune system components.

Macrophage

Bacteria

Bacteria

B-cell

Antibody

Lymphokine signal attracting macrophages

T-cell

Dividing T-cell

Antibodies

Antibody causing bacteria to clump together

Macrophage engulfing bacteria

Plasma cell producing antibodies

ALLERGIES AND ALLERGIC RESPONSES

Immune defenses are based on constant surveillance of blood and tissue fluids for signs of potentially dangerous infection. Hypersensitivities, known as allergies, can sometimes confuse these defense mechanisms. Allergic reactions are immune responses launched against normally harmless substances, often particles or chemicals in the air or in food. The nasal drip and itching eyes associated with rhinitis can be triggered by encounters with a host of materials including the house mites that live virtually everywhere humans do, plant pollen, mold spores and pet dander. Millions of people suffer allergies to foods, certain antibiotics, bee and wasp venom, latex and even their own sweat. The physiological impact of such allergic responses is highly personal, with symptoms ranging from minor gastric upsets, rashes, hives or wheezing to full-blown anaphylactic shock—a life-threatening condition in which blood pressure plummets, airways constrict and the heart may fail.

ANAPHYLAXIS

Anaphylaxis is a severe and sometimes life-threatening allergic response. It occurs when an allergen triggers the massive release of histamine and other inflammatory chemicals. As blood vessels throughout the body suddenly dilate, fluid may flood the bronchial passages, blood pressure may plummet and the heart may stop. Single dose shots of epinephrine can get an anaphalactic reaction under control. People who suffer from potentially lethal allergies must constantly carry emergency treatment in the form of epinephrine injections. The one worn by the girl below has an auto-injector and can be self-administered.

Shellfish

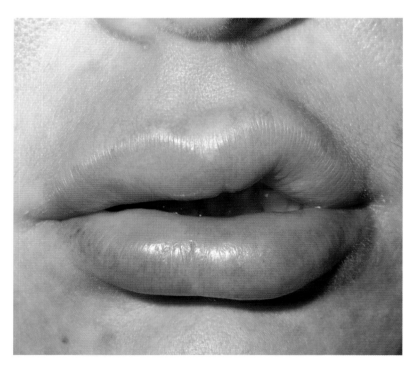

Angioedema

In angioedema, a hives-like swelling occurs deep beneath the skin. Although usually short-lived, angioedema can cause uncomfortable puffiness and tightness in the skin almost anywhere on the human body, as well as in the mouth and throat. Edema occurring there can close off the upper airways, creating a medical emergency.

Rhinitis

In rhinitis (hay fever), plant pollen or some other substance triggers allergic symptoms in the nasal passages and eyes. Once a person becomes sensitized to a given allergen, B cells produce IgE antibodies against it. When the allergen challenges the immune system, these antibodies stimulate mast cells, which in turn stimulate the common rhinitis symptoms—sneezing, congestion, the secretion of copious mucus in the nasal passages and tearing or itching in the eyes.

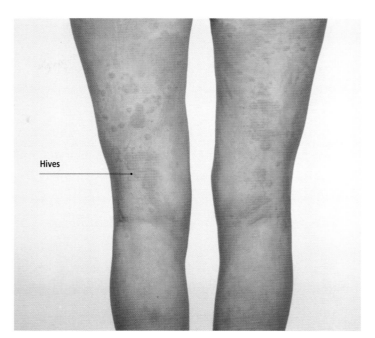

Hives

Hives

Skin eruptions called hives can appear within moments of contact with an allergen. They are common with food allergies or allergic responses to insect venom and drugs, such as those in the penicillin family. Hives may be mere spots or quite extensive and can develop almost anywhere on the skin or in the mouth. They form when an inflammatory response produces histamine-triggered changes in skin capillaries. Depending on individual circumstances, hives can last for minutes, days or weeks.

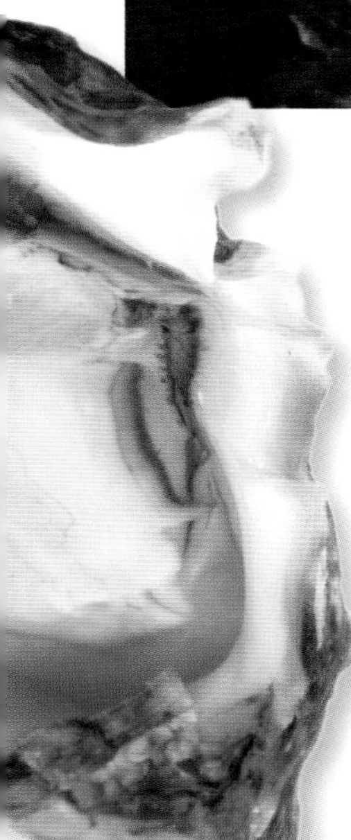

Dust mite

Common allergens

A number of everyday items can trigger allergic responses. Dander, or material shed from animals, contains dead skin, hair or feathers and is a common allergen. Pollen from trees, grasses and other plants is the source of seasonal allergies. Secreted wastes of microscopic dust mites can bring on allergy attacks inside the home. Many people are also allergic to foods such as eggs, milk, nuts, strawberries and shellfish.

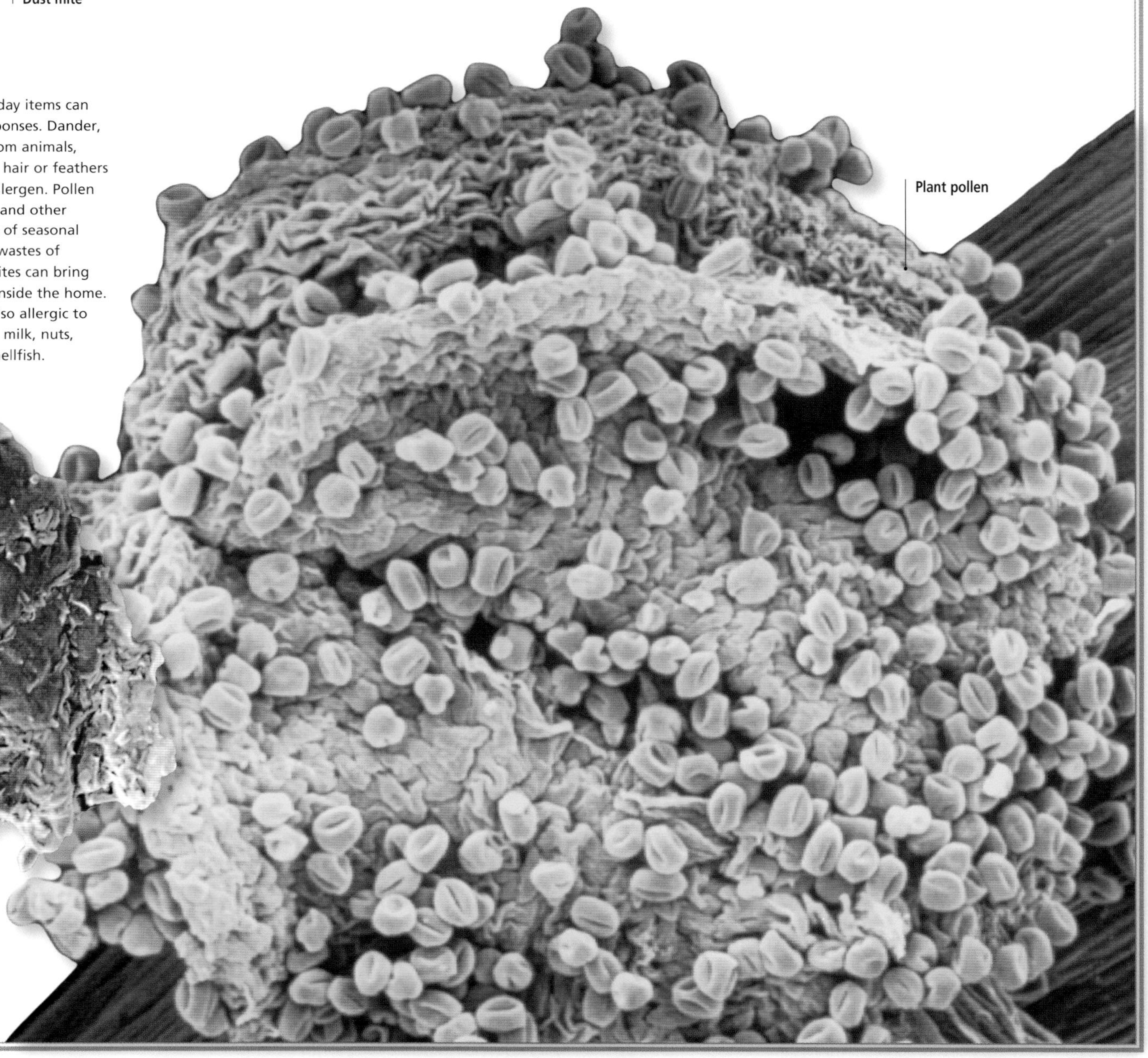

Plant pollen

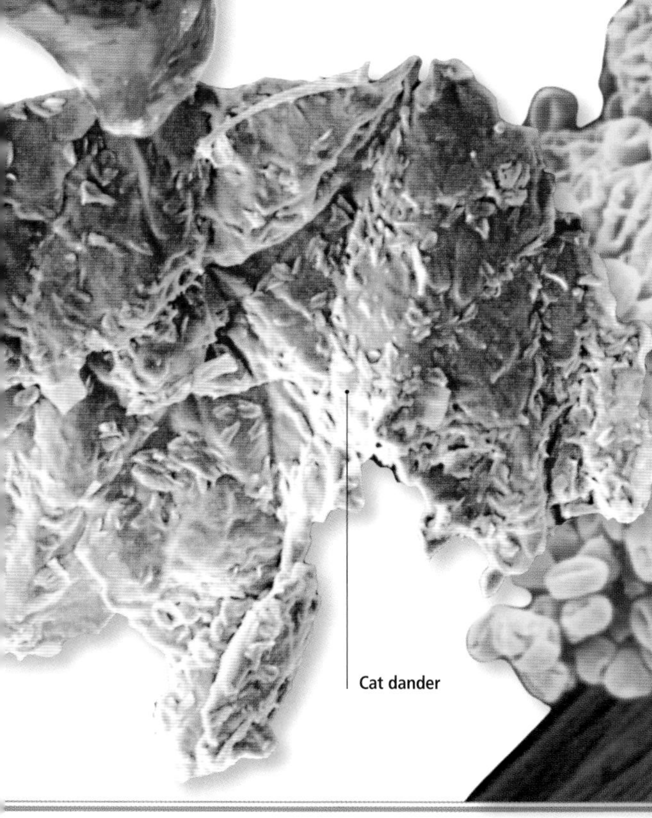

Cat dander

Other General Defenses

The body's defenses include specialized mechanisms known mostly by immunologists and more general defenses familiar to the public. In the first category are some 20 proteins that form a "complement system," which enhances other defenses. These circulate in the bloodstream, killing bacteria they encounter and leaving a chemical trail that leads white blood cells to sites where damage has occurred. The body's surface contains more conspicuous barriers to infection: intact skin and the mucous membranes that line body cavities that open to the outside—the entire digestive tract, respiratory airways and urogenital openings, such as the vagina and urethra. Urine, vaginal secretions, tears and saliva also contain protective substances, while the thousands of types of usually harmless bacteria that colonize human tissues may prevent potential pathogens from gaining a foothold. Together, these structures and mechanisms serve as a remarkably effective biological armor.

Bacteria pro and con
These pink rods are E. coli bacteria. The type that normally inhabits the intestine produces vitamin K, which is important in blood clotting. In other circumstances E. coli cause disease.

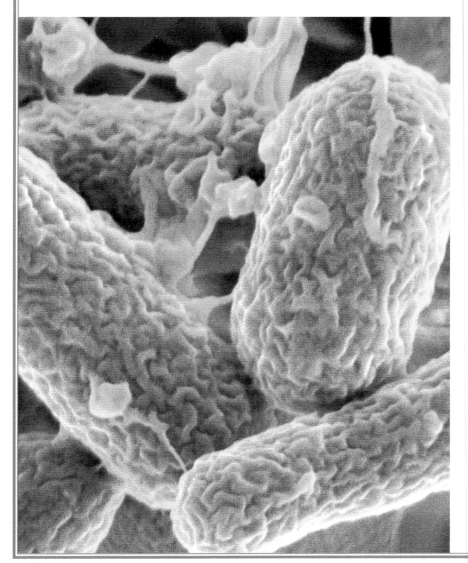

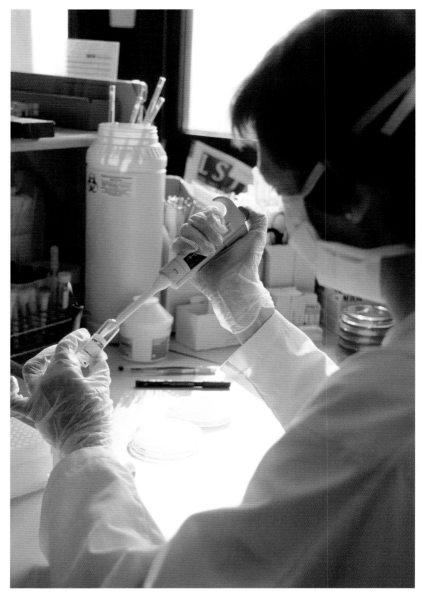

Supplementing immunity
Antibiotics cannot kill viruses, but they have saved untold lives by augmenting natural defenses that counteract bacteria, fungi and parasites. Unfortunately, their overuse has contributed to the troubling phenomenon of antibiotic resistance.

Flushing Out the Enemy

Tears contain antimicrobial substances such as lysozyme that act defensively to protect the exposed surface of the eyeball. Like gastric fluid, urine is normally highly acidic and therefore inhospitable to most microorganisms. Urination also physically flushes microbes out of the urinary tract. Diarrhea is equally beneficial for removing intestinal microbes and physicians often recommend allowing moderate diarrhea to take its course.

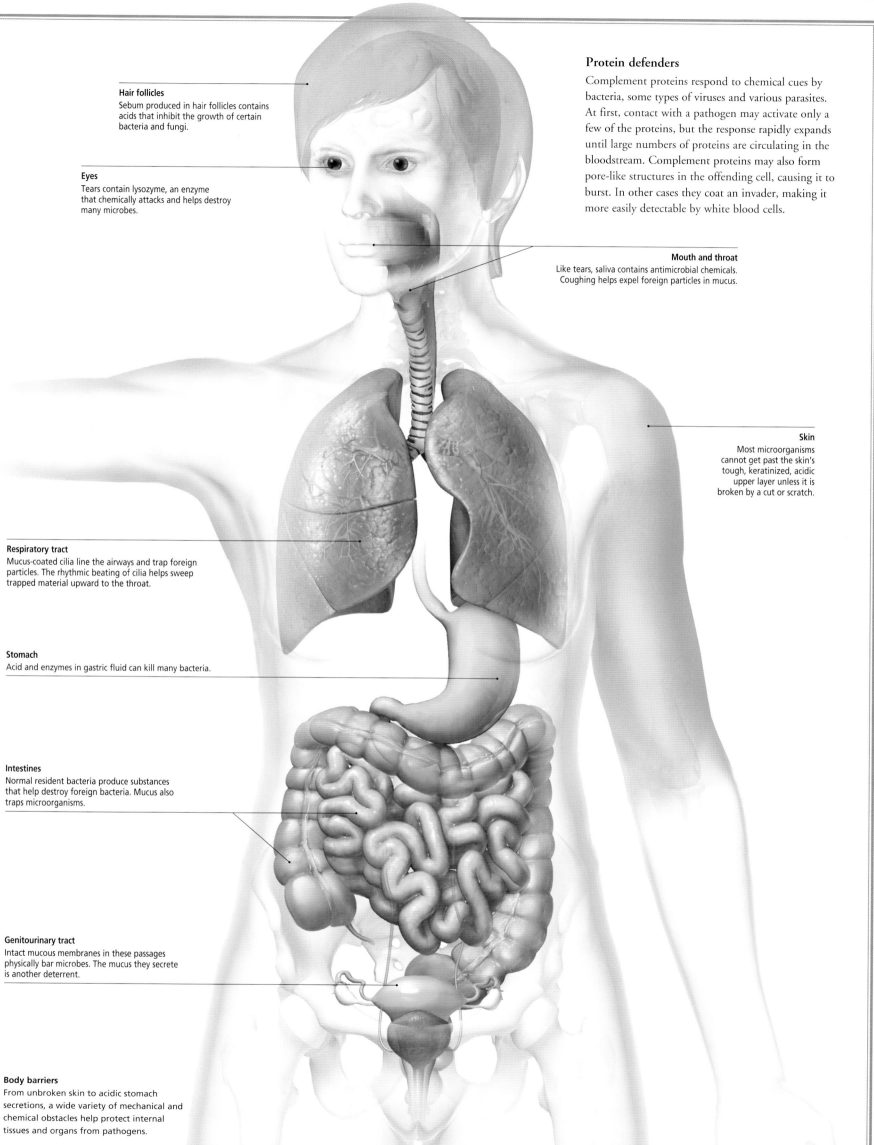

Hair follicles
Sebum produced in hair follicles contains acids that inhibit the growth of certain bacteria and fungi.

Eyes
Tears contain lysozyme, an enzyme that chemically attacks and helps destroy many microbes.

Protein defenders

Complement proteins respond to chemical cues by bacteria, some types of viruses and various parasites. At first, contact with a pathogen may activate only a few of the proteins, but the response rapidly expands until large numbers of proteins are circulating in the bloodstream. Complement proteins may also form pore-like structures in the offending cell, causing it to burst. In other cases they coat an invader, making it more easily detectable by white blood cells.

Mouth and throat
Like tears, saliva contains antimicrobial chemicals. Coughing helps expel foreign particles in mucus.

Skin
Most microorganisms cannot get past the skin's tough, keratinized, acidic upper layer unless it is broken by a cut or scratch.

Respiratory tract
Mucus-coated cilia line the airways and trap foreign particles. The rhythmic beating of cilia helps sweep trapped material upward to the throat.

Stomach
Acid and enzymes in gastric fluid can kill many bacteria.

Intestines
Normal resident bacteria produce substances that help destroy foreign bacteria. Mucus also traps microorganisms.

Genitourinary tract
Intact mucous membranes in these passages physically bar microbes. The mucus they secrete is another deterrent.

Body barriers
From unbroken skin to acidic stomach secretions, a wide variety of mechanical and chemical obstacles help protect internal tissues and organs from pathogens.

IMMUNE DISEASES

Infection, cancer and malfunctions of lymphatic defenses underlie a wide array of difficult and disabling health challenges. Young adults are particularly susceptible to infectious mononucleosis, an illness caused when Epstein-Barr virus invades B cells. Mononucleosis often lasts for a month or longer. Hodgkin's disease, a rather rare cancer of the lymph nodes, is often curable, but non-Hodgkin's lymphoma, in which many parts of the lymphatic system are besieged by cancerous lymphocytes, is more dangerous. Autoimmune diseases unleash body defenses against normal tissues. Type 1 diabetes, which typically strikes in childhood or adolescence, develops when autoimmune responses kill the insulin-producing beta cells of the pancreas. In many other autoimmune disorders, including rheumatoid arthritis, unchecked and misdirected inflammation causes the damage. Medications that suppress the immune system, including some commonly prescribed steroids, can help relieve symptoms of autoimmune disorders, although they also increase a patient's risk of infections.

Autoimmune disorders

In autoimmune diseases, inflammation, misguided T cells or antibodies from B cells, or a combination of these factors, injure or destroy healthy tissues. Two common autoimmune conditions are Graves' disease and rheumatoid arthritis. In Graves' disease, antibodies stimulate overproduction of thyroid hormone. Rheumatoid arthritis is caused when the membrane lining the joints in the hands, limbs and spine becomes inflamed. Abnormal inflammation is also at work in systemic lupus erythematosus (SLE), known simply as "lupus."

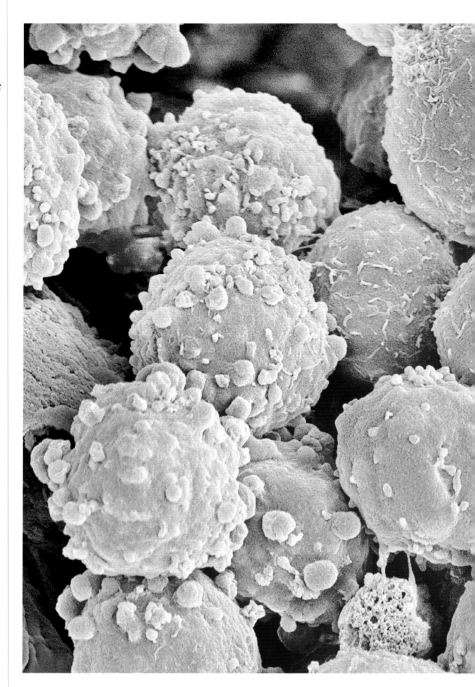

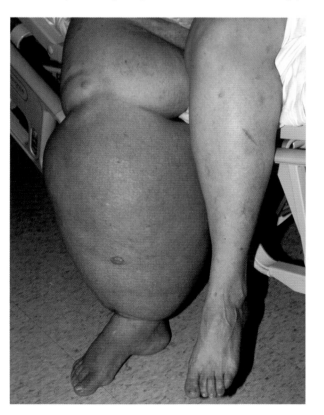

Filariasis
In filariasis, worms transmitted by mosquitos cause inflammation and blockage of lymphatic ducts in limbs and other regions, building up tissue fluid usually in the legs. Some infected people develop elephantitis, a hardening and thickening of the skin and connective tissue.

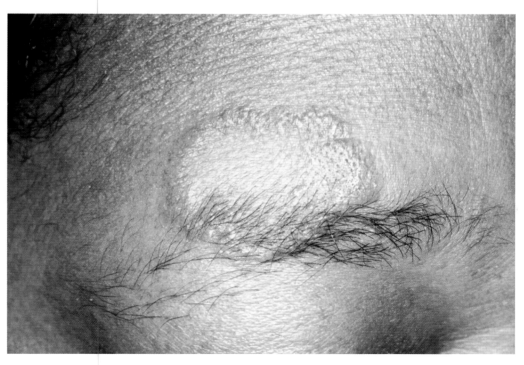

Sarcoidosis
Tissue damage from inflammation marks sarcoidosis, which begins in the lungs but may spread through the body. Reddish skin bumps are one obvious symptom. The disorder may disappear as mysteriously as it arose. There is currently no cure.

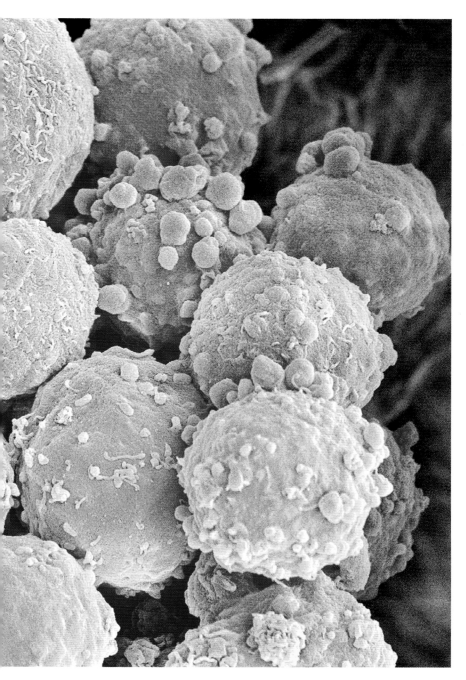

Lymphomas

The cancer called non-Hodgkin's lymphoma is much more common than Hodgkin's disease and may develop in either B cells (shown above) or T cells. Early symptoms mimic those of Hodgkin's or a severe bout of flu. Treatment options include chemotherapy and radiation.

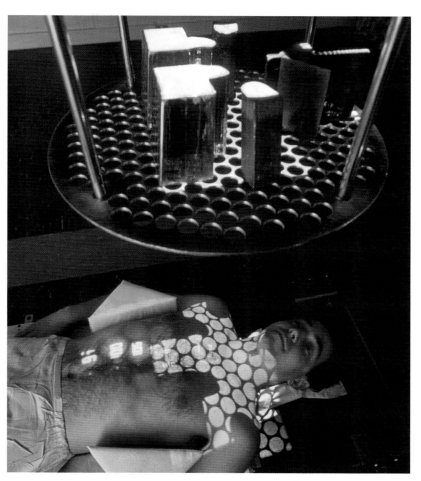

Hodgkin's disease

In Hodgkin's disease, B cells become cancerous. Swollen lymph nodes may be the first sign, although untreated disease often spreads. This patient is receiving radiation, the preferred treatment for early stages of the cancer.

Lupus

In lupus, inflammation developing in blood vessels causes body-wide damage that is most severe in the kidneys, heart, lungs and skin. Patients also experience fatigue and may develop heart and kidney disease.

Hair loss

Headaches

Restricted blood circulation

Pale skin

Kidney failure

Swollen joints

Muscle fatigue

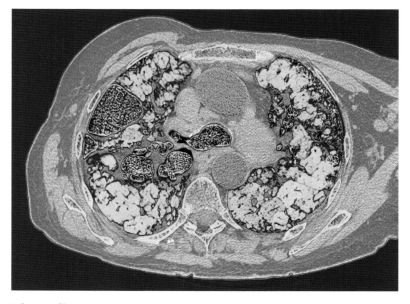

Pulmonary fibrosis

Orange areas in this CT scan show where inflammation associated with lung disorders has produced scar tissue in alveoli, the tiny lung air sacs (yellow). The resulting disease, pulmonary fibrosis, is incurable and eventually fatal.

IMMUNE DEFICIENCY DISEASES

Immune deficiency is an inborn or acquired disorder in which the immune system becomes weakened or disabled and therefore provides little or no defense against harmful organisms or abnormal body cells. The best known acquired immune deficiency disease is AIDS (acquired immunodeficiency syndrome), caused by infection by the human immunodeficiency virus (HIV). The HIV/AIDS epidemic has spurred intensive educational efforts and an ongoing search for an effective vaccine, and patients who receive advanced drug treatments now can live with AIDS in relative good health for many years. A well-known congenital immune deficiency is SCID, severe combined immunodeficiency syndrome. The term covers several genetic disorders that cause a sharp drop in the numbers of T cells and B cells in affected children, so even minor infections are life-threatening. Recent medical advances including gene therapy have begun to offer hope of effective SCID treatments.

The spread of HIV

Since HIV/AIDS was first recognized in the early 1980s, it has taken millions of lives and continues to infect tens of millions of people globally. Most cases have resulted from unsafe sexual contact or use of a shared needle for intravenous drugs. Until a safe and effective vaccine becomes available, prevention is the sole option for halting HIV's spread. In many countries, educational programs are producing modest success: the number of reported new HIV infections is dropping, if only slowly.

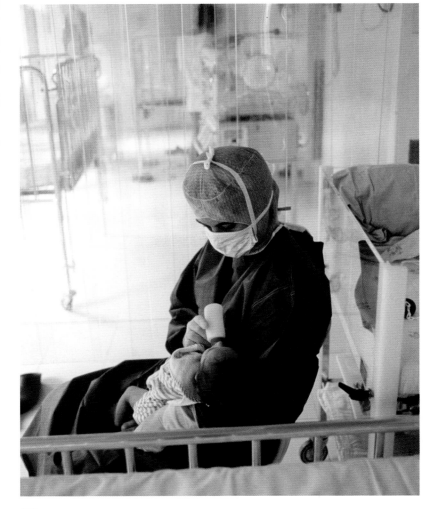

SCID
At one time, children with SCID were confined to a sterile "bubble" in order to prevent infections. Today, bone marrow transplants help rebuild the immune systems of some patients, while children with a form of the disease called ADA-SCID, which is characterized by a lack of the enzyme adenosine deaminase, may receive gene therapy successfully.

How HIV replicates
When an HIV particle infects a T lymphocyte, it inserts its genetic material (RNA) into the cell. An enzyme converts the RNA to DNA, which then directs the formation of new HIV particles that will exit the dying cell.

Infected T cell

HIV particle

Dying T cell

New HIV particle

Antibody

Viral RNA

Nucleus

Viral DNA

T cell DNA

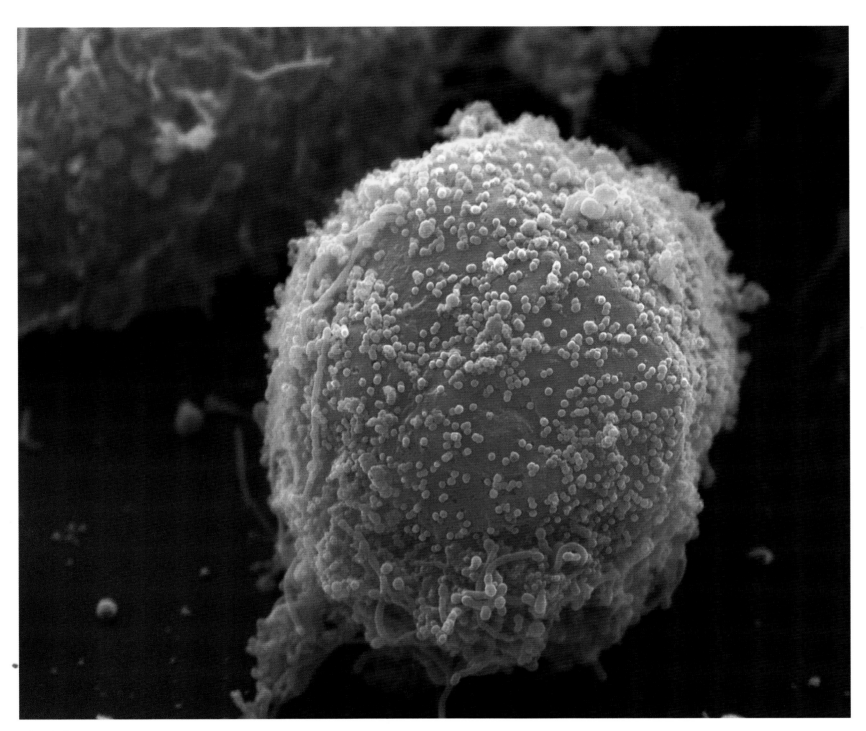

Infected cell
HIV particles appear as blue specks on the surface of a human T cell. The virus particles are budding from the infected cell, entering lymph nodes or the bloodstream to renew the infection cycle.

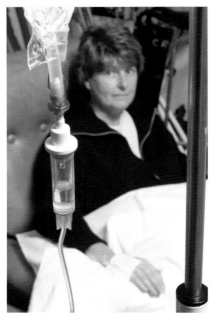

Chemotherapy
Chemotherapy often seriously disables the immune system. The potent drugs target cancer cells, but also kill other naturally dividing cells, including the stem cells in bone marrow that produce lymphocytes, important in immunity.

AIDS AROUND THE WORLD

In many affluent nations HIV infection rates are dropping and patients live longer with drug treatments that slow the disease. But an estimated 60 to 70 percent of global HIV/AIDS cases are in sub-Saharan Africa, where treatment and prevention resources are limited. Worldwide, women and children account for an increasing number of new infections.

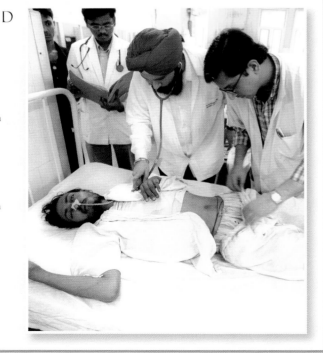

ORGAN TRANSPLANTS

For patients with severely impaired organs such as heart, kidneys, lungs or liver, a transplant may be the only hope for survival. Where disease or injury has damaged tissues such as the cornea, bone marrow, tendons, heart valves, bones or large areas of skin, replacements can dramatically improve the quality of life. With the exception of corneal transplants, the body's powerful immune responses force organ recipients and their physicians to confront the prospect of rejection. Therefore, the price for success may be a lifelong commitment to treatment with immunosuppressive drugs that prevent the patient's immune system from destroying the transplanted organ. From early days when all organ transplants were risky experimental procedures, the success rates for transplant surgery have improved tremendously. In many nations computerized registries help match donors and recipients. Even so, the need for donor organs far outstrips the supply.

Transplants and the immune response

In transplant rejection, T cells, macrophages and B cells respond to the foreign "self" proteins, called MHC markers, on donor cells as antigens and launch a swift attack to rid the tissue from the body. Most transplants are allografts, or grafts of tissue donated from one human to another. Xenografts are tissue donations from one species to another. Allografts are screened to ensure that the donors share the patient's blood type and a majority of markers. To meet this demanding standard, close relatives are usually the best sources for donated organs.

TRANSPLANT FRONTIERS

Improved microsurgery methods, tissue compatibility tests such as the one shown below, simple blood tests for impending rejection and advances in post-surgical care are rapidly opening new vistas for organ and tissue transplants. Multiple organ transplants, such as heart-lungs-liver and heart-liver-kidney, are becoming much more common and successful. In new procedures, a patient may receive multiple deceased-donor organs, simultaneously donating a healthy "duplicate" organ to someone else. In 2005, the first known partial face transplant restored a woman's nose, cheeks and lips.

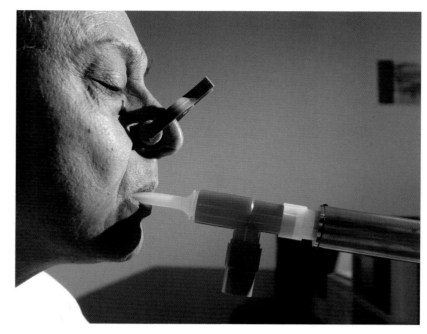

Managing rejection
The recipient of a transplanted organ receives antirejection drugs and is periodically tested for signs of rejection. One or more biopsies may be conducted to monitor how well the new organ is being tolerated.

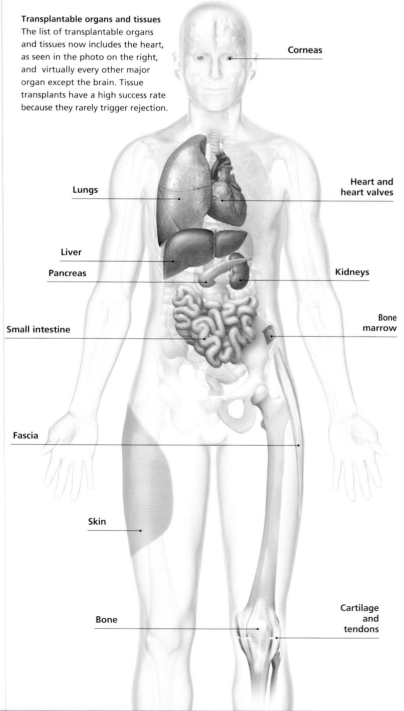

Transplantable organs and tissues
The list of transplantable organs and tissues now includes the heart, as seen in the photo on the right, and virtually every other major organ except the brain. Tissue transplants have a high success rate because they rarely trigger rejection.

Corneas

Heart and heart valves

Lungs

Liver

Pancreas

Kidneys

Small intestine

Bone marrow

Fascia

Skin

Bone

Cartilage and tendons

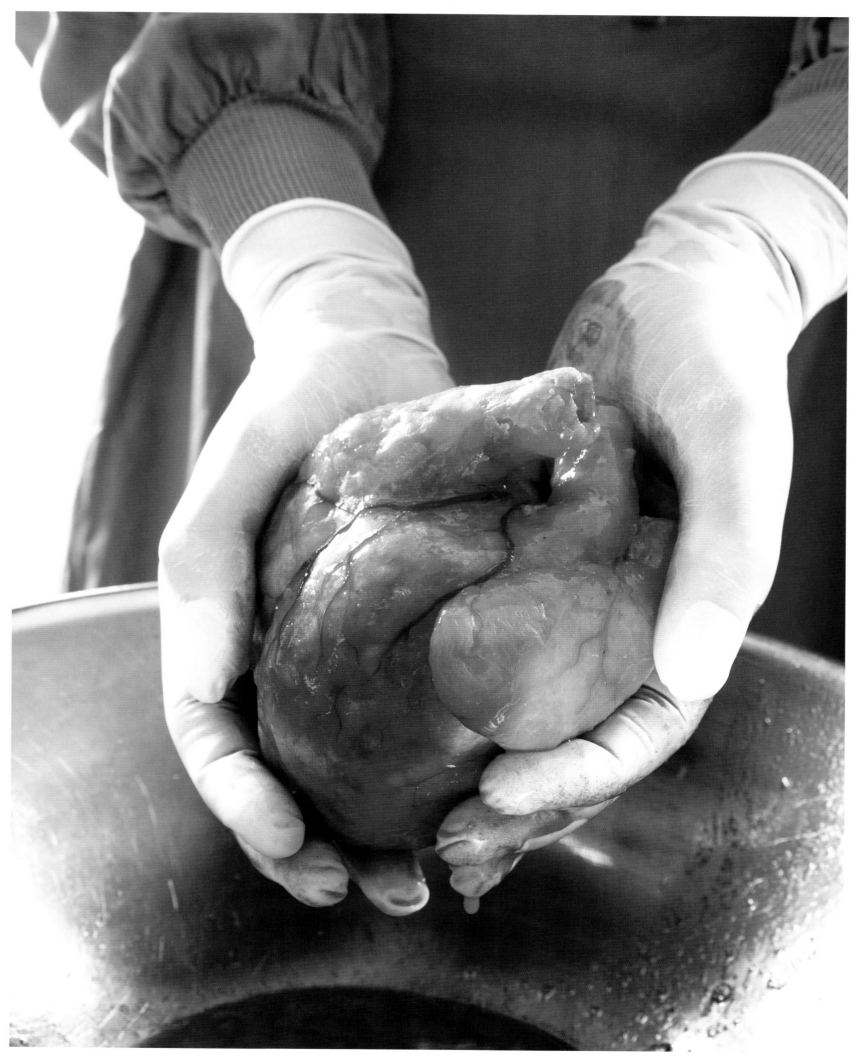

Transplant surgery
Organ transplantation requires securing a compatible organ from a living or deceased donor, using blood type, age and weight to achieve a close match to the recipient. Surgeries to harvest and transplant the organ are scheduled closely to limit deterioration of the harvested organ.

IMMUNIZATION AND IMMUNOTHERAPY

For centuries humans have sought to increase their defenses against disease. Active immunity develops the first time a given pathogen challenges a person's immune system and B cells produce both antibodies and memory cells against it. Often this so-called primary response involves a bout of illness. Immunization, by contrast, confers *acquired* immunity by introducing into the body a dead or weakened pathogen that provokes a mild, and perhaps even unnoticeable response, that also triggers the formation of memory cells.

Although immunization is not risk-free, today it protects hundreds of millions of people from once-common childhood ills, such as measles, polio, tetanus, diphtheria and whooping cough. Travelers are routinely vaccinated against infectious diseases, such as typhoid fever and yellow fever. Medical immunotherapies utilize various immune system components to treat cancers and other diseases. Among these are commercially prepared antibodies used in consumer products and to diagnose or treat illness.

Harnessing the immune system

The components of natural immunity are making major contributions to clinical advances and even consumer products. For example, monoclonal antibodies (MAbs), are used to diagnose allergies, rabies and hepatitis and to screen for prostate cancer and other malignancies. Some augment or replace the immunosuppression drugs prescribed for transplant patients. MAbs can also identify drug residues in a person's bloodstream and are used in pregnancy tests. Therapeutic immunotoxins join toxic proteins with MAbs to deliver the poison to cancer cells.

ERADICATING POLIO

Poliomyelitis, or polio, was a dreaded disease for several centuries and became epidemic in the United States and Europe in the early 1900s. Poliovirus infection causes nerve damage that results in various degrees of paralysis, often in the legs. The first polio vaccines began to be administered worldwide in the 1950s and 1960s. Ongoing efforts to eradicate the disease have met with considerable success and today cases are increasingly rare.

Making monoclonal antibodies
One method for making monoclonal antibodies is injecting a mouse, rat or rabbit with an antigen to trigger the formation of B cells, producers of natural antibodies. The B cells are then fused with modified cancer cells, yielding hybrid cells that produce antibodies and multiply rapidly.

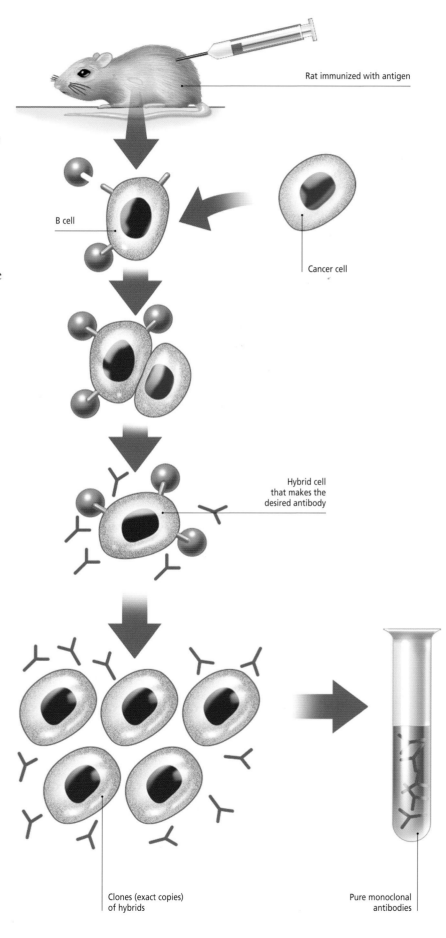

Rat immunized with antigen

B cell

Cancer cell

Hybrid cell that makes the desired antibody

Clones (exact copies) of hybrids

Pure monoclonal antibodies

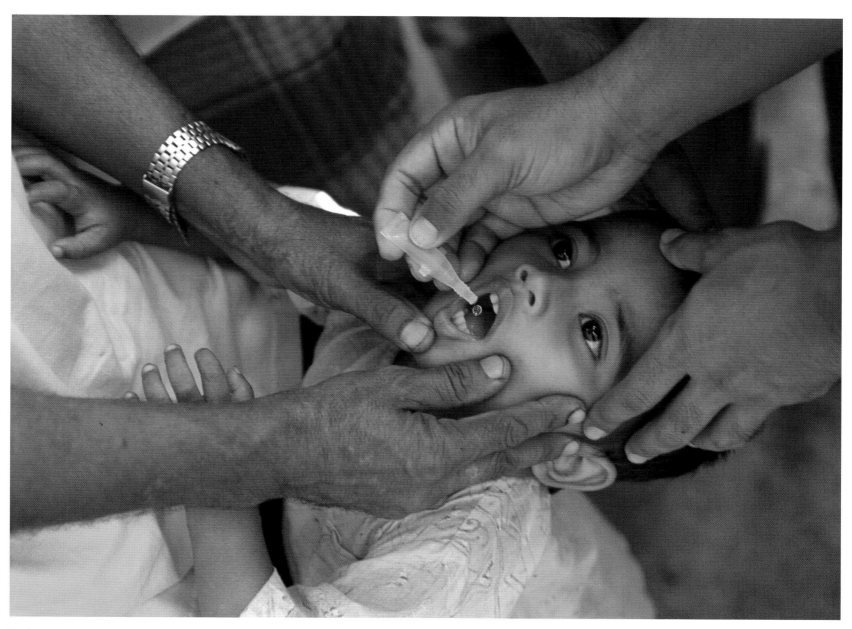

Vaccines

A vaccine contains an antigen, such as part of a bacterium or virus. This attenuated, or weakened, version of the pathogen triggers an immune response and results in the production of antibodies, even though the disease never develops. Most vaccinations provide 7 to 10 years of immunity. Booster shots administered later extend the protection period.

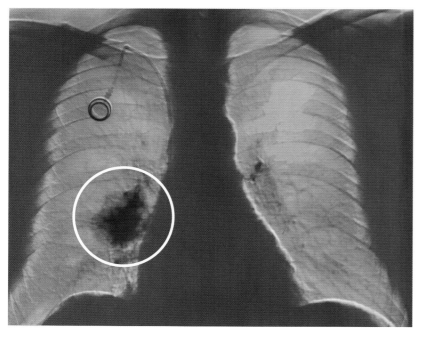

Cancer immunotherapy

Monoclonal antibodies are available or under development for use against malignancies, such as colorectal cancer and breast cancer. Other anticarrier immunotherapies employ cytokines, including interferons and interleukins, which boost a patient's immune responses. This X-ray shows a lung cancer tumor which is being treated with interleukin-2 via an implant.

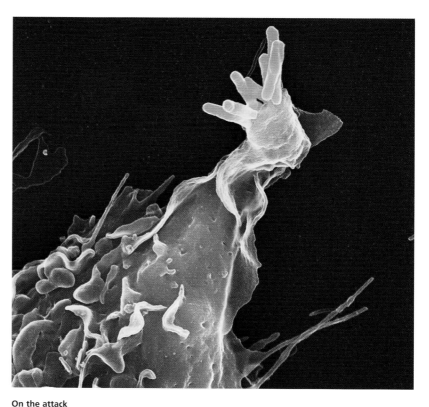

On the attack

Many vaccines contain attenuated (weakened) bacteria or viruses. This photograph shows a macrophage (yellow) engulfing a weakened bacteria (orange). The macrophage later "presents" bacterial fragments to B cells, the first step toward generating antibodies and memory cells.

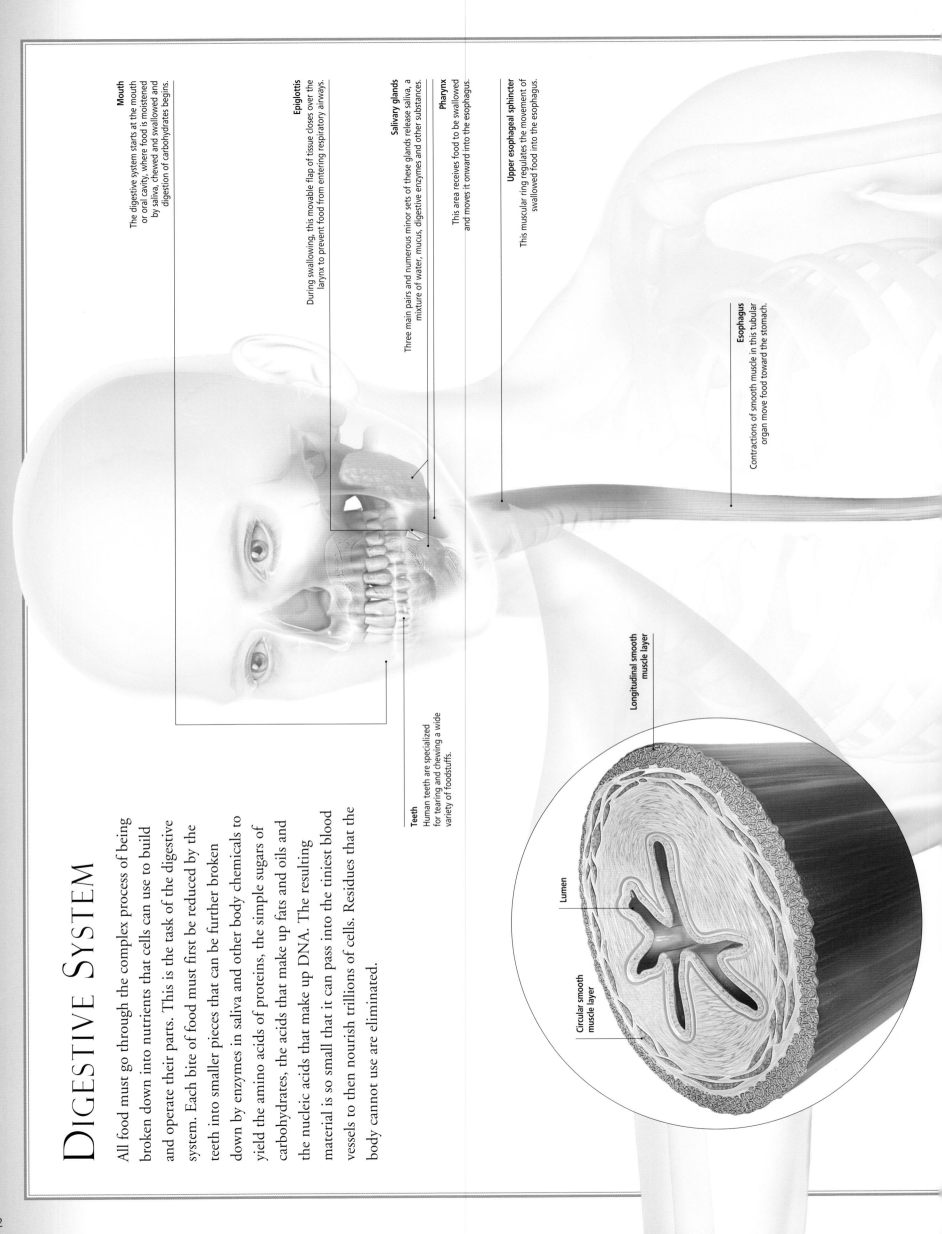

DIGESTIVE SYSTEM

All food must go through the complex process of being broken down into nutrients that cells can use to build and operate their parts. This is the task of the digestive system. Each bite of food must first be reduced by the teeth into smaller pieces that can be further broken down by enzymes in saliva and other body chemicals to yield the amino acids of proteins, the simple sugars of carbohydrates, the acids that make up fats and oils and the nucleic acids that make up DNA. The resulting material is so small that it can pass into the tiniest blood vessels to then nourish trillions of cells. Residues that the body cannot use are eliminated.

Mouth
The digestive system starts at the mouth or oral cavity, where food is moistened by saliva, chewed and swallowed and digestion of carbohydrates begins.

Epiglottis
During swallowing, this movable flap of tissue closes over the larynx to prevent food from entering respiratory airways.

Salivary glands
Three main pairs and numerous minor sets of these glands release saliva, a mixture of water, mucus, digestive enzymes and other substances.

Pharynx
This area receives food to be swallowed and moves it onward into the esophagus.

Upper esophageal sphincter
This muscular ring regulates the movement of swallowed food into the esophagus.

Teeth
Human teeth are specialized for tearing and chewing a wide variety of foodstuffs.

Esophagus
Contractions of smooth muscle in this tubular organ move food toward the stomach.

Longitudinal smooth muscle layer

Lumen

Circular smooth muscle layer

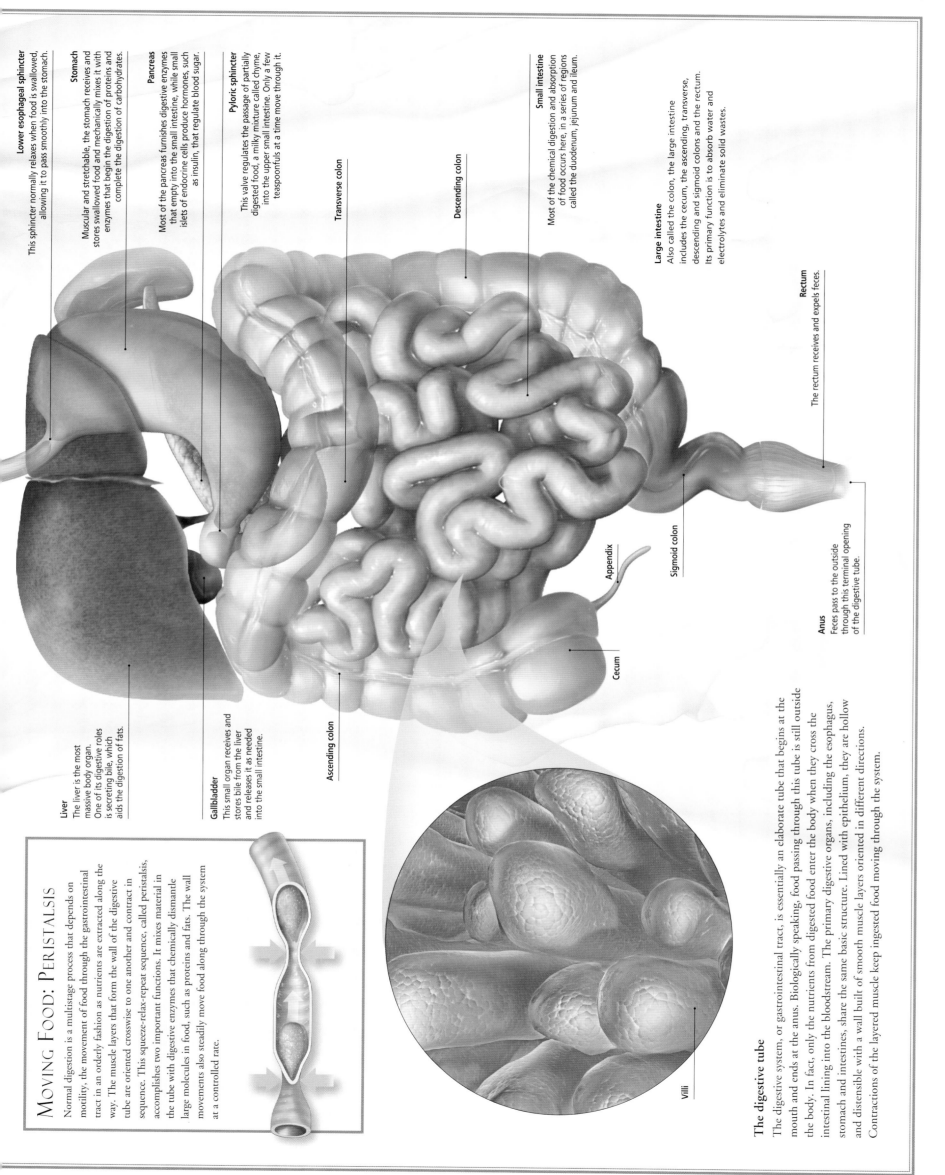

Lower esophageal sphincter
This sphincter normally relaxes when food is swallowed, allowing it to pass smoothly into the stomach.

Stomach
Muscular and stretchable, the stomach receives and stores swallowed food and mechanically mixes it with enzymes that begin the digestion of proteins and complete the digestion of carbohydrates.

Pancreas
Most of the pancreas furnishes digestive enzymes that empty into the small intestine, while small islets of endocrine cells produce hormones, such as insulin, that regulate blood sugar.

Pyloric sphincter
This valve regulates the passage of partially digested food, a milky mixture called chyme, into the upper small intestine. Only a few teaspoonfuls at a time move through it.

Transverse colon

Descending colon

Small intestine
Most of the chemical digestion and absorption of food occurs here, in a series of regions called the duodenum, jejunum and ileum.

Large intestine
Also called the colon, the large intestine includes the cecum, the ascending, transverse, descending and sigmoid colons and the rectum. Its primary function is to absorb water and electrolytes and eliminate solid wastes.

Rectum
The rectum receives and expels feces.

Liver
The liver is the most massive body organ. One of its digestive roles is secreting bile, which aids the digestion of fats.

Gallbladder
This small organ receives and stores bile from the liver and releases it as needed into the small intestine.

Ascending colon

Appendix

Sigmoid colon

Cecum

Anus
Feces pass to the outside through this terminal opening of the digestive tube.

Villi

Moving Food: Peristalsis

Normal digestion is a multistage process that depends on motility, the movement of food through the gastrointestinal tract in an orderly fashion as nutrients are extracted along the way. The muscle layers that form the wall of the digestive tube are oriented crosswise to one another and contract in sequence. This squeeze-relax-repeat sequence, called peristalsis, accomplishes two important functions. It mixes material in the tube with digestive enzymes that chemically dismantle large molecules in food, such as proteins and fats. The wall movements also steadily move food along through the system at a controlled rate.

The digestive tube

The digestive system, or gastrointestinal tract, is essentially an elaborate tube that begins at the mouth and ends at the anus. Biologically speaking, food passing through this tube is still outside the body. In fact, only the nutrients from digested food enter the body when they cross the intestinal lining into the bloodstream. The primary digestive organs, including the esophagus, stomach and intestines, share the same basic structure. Lined with epithelium, they are hollow and distensible with a wall built of smooth muscle layers oriented in different directions. Contractions of the layered muscle keep ingested food moving through the system.

Food Processing Begins

The digestive system obtains nutrients from food by dismantling ingested material mechanically and chemically, and both of these processes begin in the mouth. For solid food, biting and chewing are the initial steps. Chewing also moistens and mixes food with saliva that enters from the salivary glands. This mix of substances contains water, sticky proteins called mucins that help bind bits of chewed food into a ball or bolus, and salivary amylase, which begins the chemical breakdown of starchy carbohydrates. Salivary amylase is only the first of many enzymes that act on various types of substances in food, including proteins and fats, as it travels onward through the digestive system. As the tongue manipulates food in the mouth, it eventually forces each bolus up against the hard palate and back into the throat for swallowing—the start of the digestive process.

The movement of food

During swallowing, a series of voluntary and involuntary muscle contractions moves food into the esophagus. Muscles there then begin to contract and relax, a mechanism called peristalsis, forcing the bolus downward. A sphincter at the base of the esophagus allows small amounts of food into the stomach, where the muscles of the stomach wall grind it. At the base of the stomach the pyloric sphincter periodically squeezes some stomach contents into the small intestine. Continuing peristalsis steadily advances digesting food through the system.

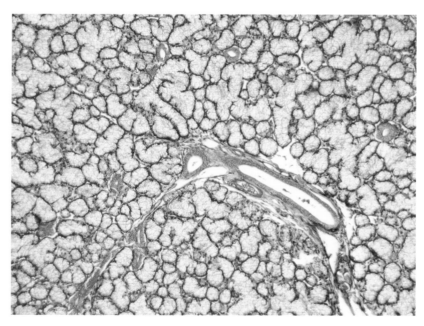

Digesting carbohydrates
The digestion of simple carbohydrates begins as soon as a bite of starchy food enters the mouth. Foods high in carbohydrates begin to dissolve in the mouth as salivary amylase breaks chemical bonds that hold starch molecules together.

Swallowing

Swallowing, or deglutition, involves a number of muscles. The tip of the tongue first pushes the bolus, or chewed food, toward the throat. The uvula and pharynx then move up, forcing the bolus down. Muscles in the pharynx contract, which closes off the larynx and prevents the food from going "the wrong way" into the larynx and trachea. The bolus then slides into the esophagus and continues its journey to the stomach.

Pharynx	Uvula

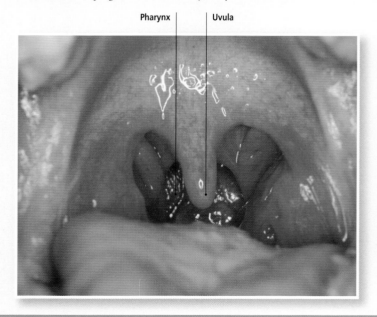

Salivary glands
This image shows a salivary gland. The three main types are the parotid glands, located roughly in front of the ears, the sublingual glands, under the tongue, and the submandibular glands, in the floor of the mouth below the mandible.

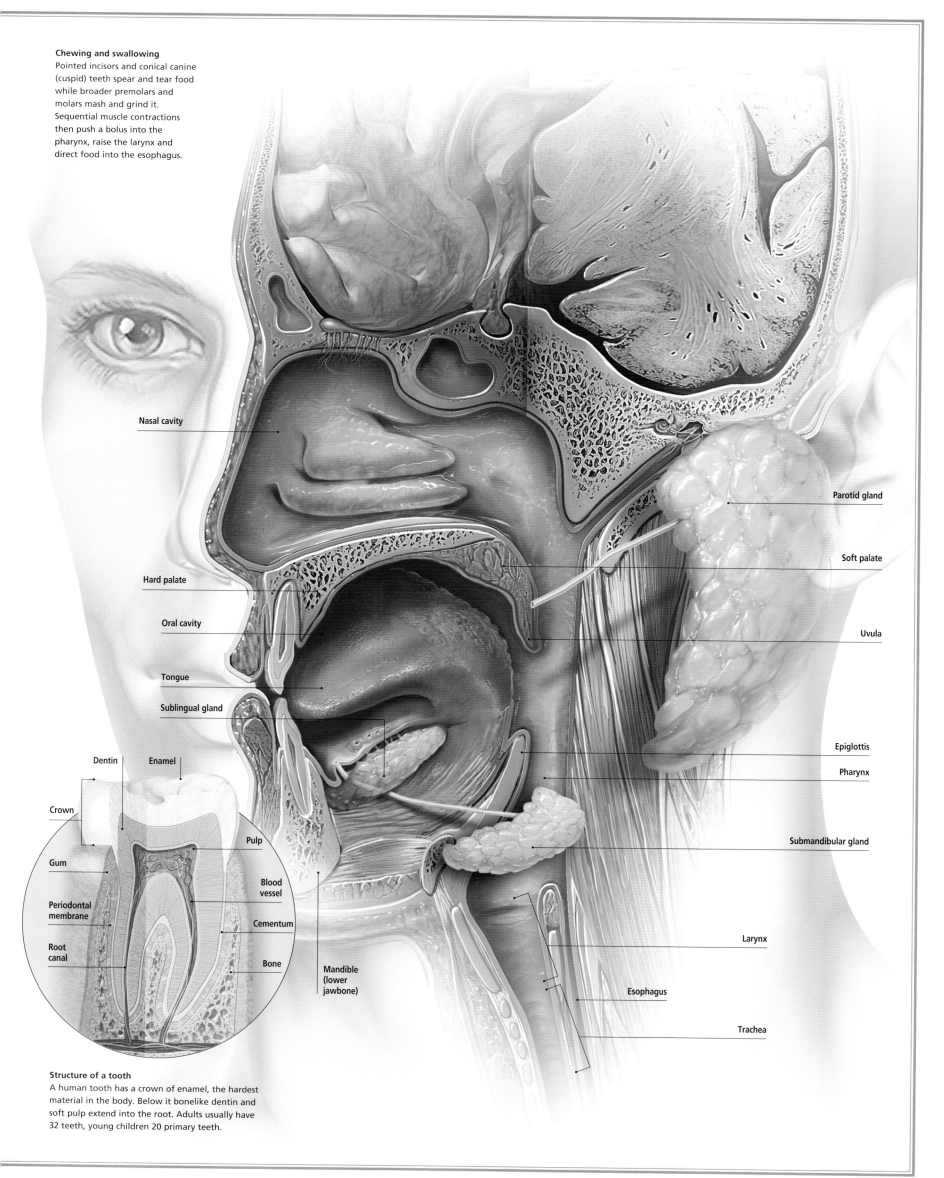

Chewing and swallowing
Pointed incisors and conical canine (cuspid) teeth spear and tear food while broader premolars and molars mash and grind it. Sequential muscle contractions then push a bolus into the pharynx, raise the larynx and direct food into the esophagus.

Nasal cavity

Hard palate

Oral cavity

Tongue

Sublingual gland

Dentin   Enamel

Crown

Gum

Periodontal membrane

Root canal

Pulp

Blood vessel

Cementum

Bone

Mandible (lower jawbone)

Parotid gland

Soft palate

Uvula

Epiglottis

Pharynx

Submandibular gland

Larynx

Esophagus

Trachea

Structure of a tooth
A human tooth has a crown of enamel, the hardest material in the body. Below it bonelike dentin and soft pulp extend into the root. Adults usually have 32 teeth, young children 20 primary teeth.

THE STOMACH

The human stomach is a hollow, J-shaped, expandable, ten-inch (25-cm) muscular organ that briefly stores food, mixes it with enzymes and other secretions and regulates its transmission to the small intestine. The sheets of smooth muscle in its walls contract in waves, churning food boluses to continue the mechanical process of digestion. Secretions of gastric juices, which include hydrochloric acid, water and the building blocks of enzymes, called pepsins, accompany this wave of peristalsis. The acid kills many food-borne microbes and helps transform ingested food into chyme. Pepsins begin to chemically cleave large proteins in the chyme into fragments. Peristalsis gradually forces chyme through the pyloric sphincter in amounts that the small intestine can process without being overburdened.

HOW THE STOMACH MANAGES FOOD

An average adult's stomach can easily hold about one quart (1L), but its capacity can distend to as much as four quarts (4.2L), or about 20 times its volume when empty. As food enters, the rugae of the stomach wall smooth out. It can take four hours or longer for a completely full stomach to empty via the pyloric sphincter.

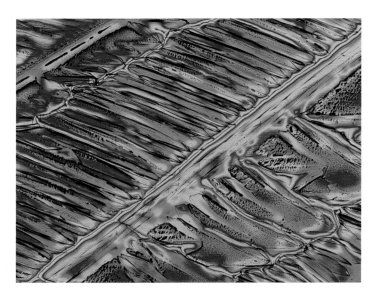

Stomach enzymes
Two major enzymes form part of the gastric juices. Pepsin begins the digestion of proteins while gastric lipase breaks down fat molecules into smaller fragments. This image shows stomach enzymes that have formed luminous crystals.

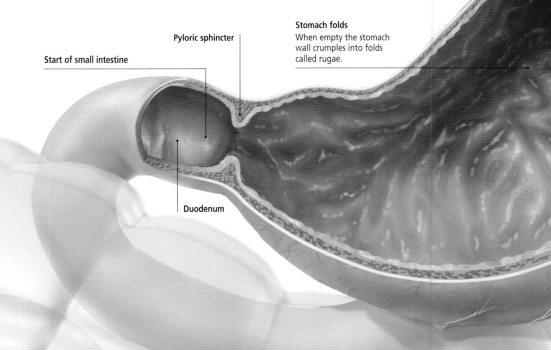

Serosa (outer covering)

Longitudinal layer

Circular layer

Oblique layer

Start of small intestine

Pyloric sphincter

Duodenum

Stomach folds
When empty the stomach wall crumples into folds called rugae.

Absorption in the stomach

Although enzymes begin to chemically digest carbohydrates, proteins and fats in the stomach, only a few substances are actually absorbed into the bloodstream because cells of the stomach lining cannot absorb most nutrients. Exceptions are the lining's mucus-secreting cells: they can absorb some water, alcohol, a few drugs, such as aspirin, and some mineral ions and fragments from dismantled fat molecules. Other nutrients and substances in food are absorbed in the small and large intestines.

The stomach's inner surface
In the stomach's inner surface, clusters of glands release enzymes and other substances that form digestive juices. Thousands of gastric glands, the deep pits shown here, line the stomach wall.

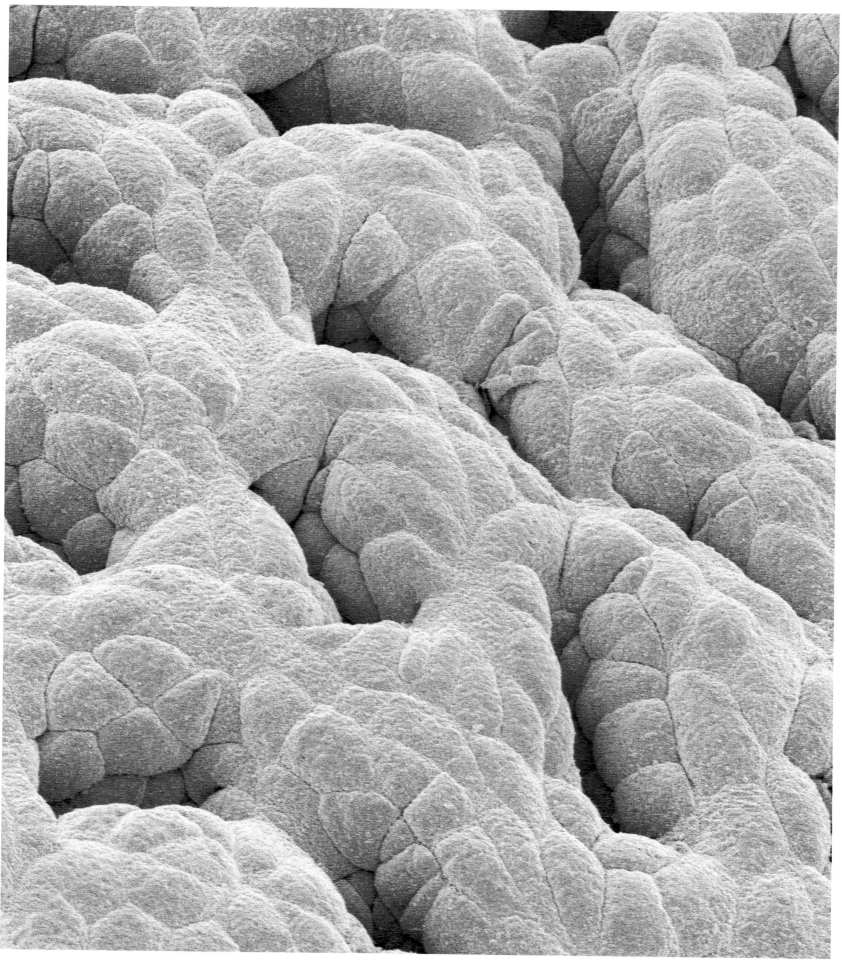

THE SMALL AND LARGE INTESTINES

The intestines are divided into two major sections: the small intestine, where most food digestion occurs, and the large intestine, or colon, where processing concludes, water is absorbed and food residues are stored for elimination. The small intestine is approximately 20 feet (6m) long. It consists of three sections: the duodenum, jejunum and ileum.

This coiled tube contains roughly 2700 square feet (300m²) of surface area for absorbing nutrients into the bloodstream. The large intestine (colon) functions as a receptacle where water and electrolytes can be reabsorbed into the bloodstream and undigested material is compacted and stored as feces. About 30 percent of the dry weight of feces consists of bacteria that normally inhabit the gastrointestinal tract, living on food residues and manufacturing vitamin K and some other useful substances in return. The common brown color of human solid waste comes from bile salts that are excreted in it.

Absorbing fats

Fats are never absorbed directly into the bloodstream. First, intestinal peristalsis breaks apart large fat molecules (triglycerides), which pancreatic enzymes then digest into smaller fragments. Bile formed in the liver keeps the fragments from separating out of the watery chyme. The fragments eventually enter villi, absorptive cells of the intestinal lining. They recombine into large globules and are channeled into lymphatic vessels that finally deliver them to the general circulation.

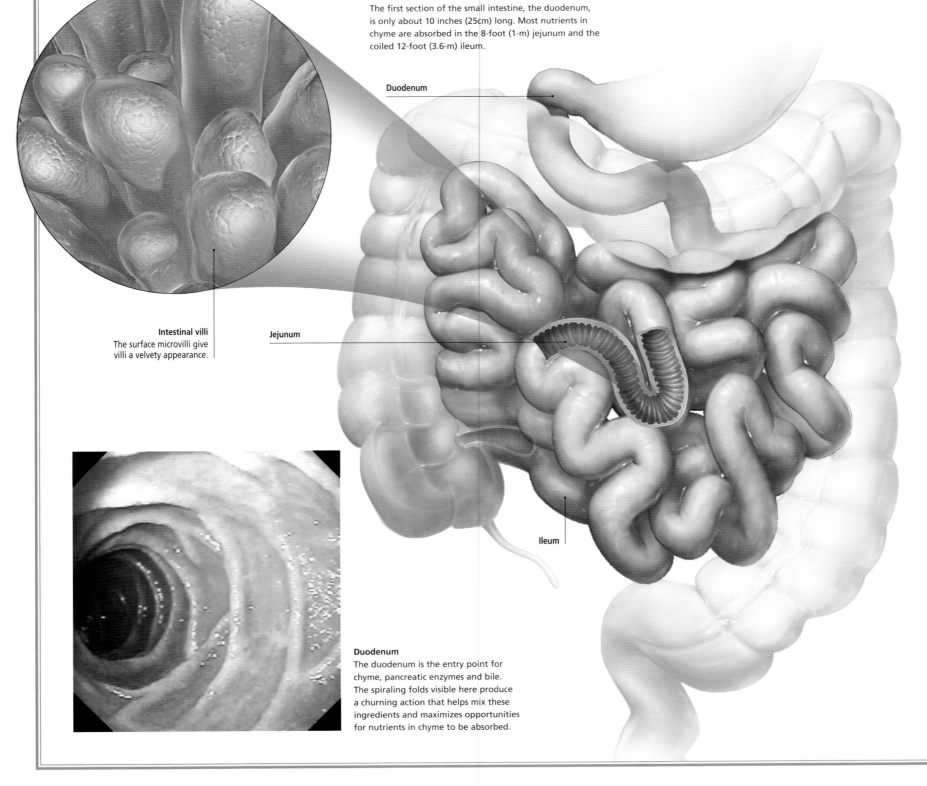

The small intestine
The first section of the small intestine, the duodenum, is only about 10 inches (25cm) long. Most nutrients in chyme are absorbed in the 8-foot (1-m) jejunum and the coiled 12-foot (3.6-m) ileum.

Duodenum

Intestinal villi
The surface microvilli give villi a velvety appearance.

Jejunum

Ileum

Duodenum
The duodenum is the entry point for chyme, pancreatic enzymes and bile. The spiraling folds visible here produce a churning action that helps mix these ingredients and maximizes opportunities for nutrients in chyme to be absorbed.

Millions of villi
Villi form millions of absorptive "fingers" on the lining of the small intestine. Each contains blood vessels and a lymph vessel and is covered with minute microvilli. Simple sugar molecules and most amino acids move into the blood vessels; some fats enter the lymph vessel.

THE APPENDIX

Because the appendix can be removed with no ill effects, it was long considered a vestigial organ with no apparent function. The recent discovery of populations of beneficial bacteria in appendix tissue suggests to some that this fingerlike structure may help restock the intestines with "good" bacteria when they are flushed out by severe diarrhea.

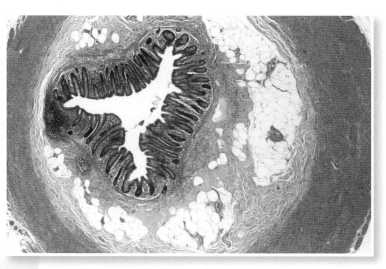

Inside the appendix
Blue regions in this image are areas in the appendix wall containing lymphatic tissues that may help defend against intestinal infection.

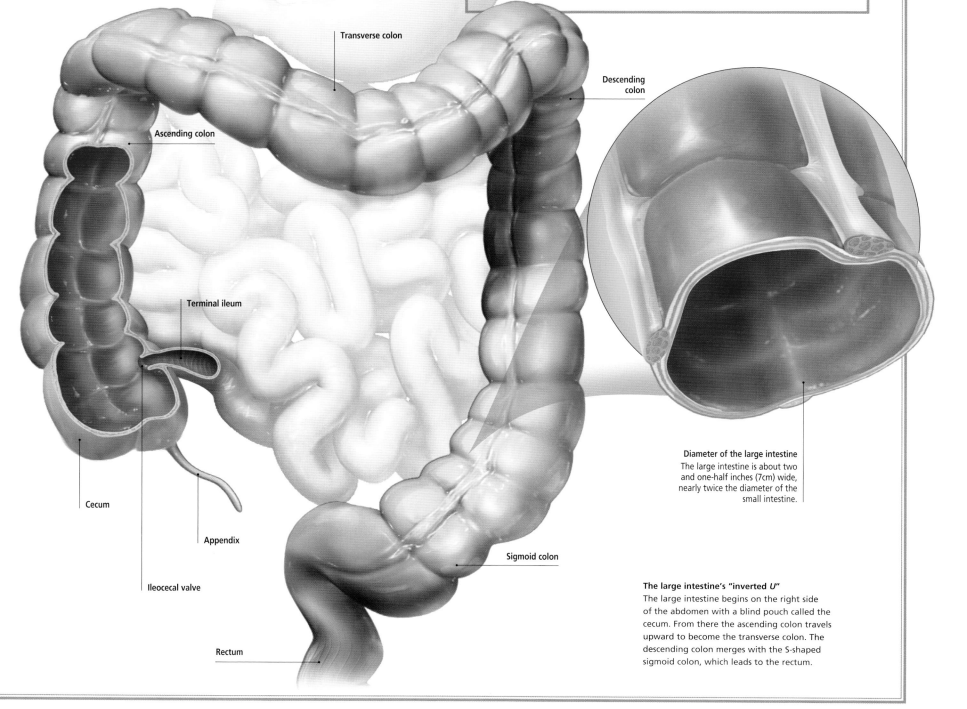

Transverse colon

Descending colon

Ascending colon

Terminal ileum

Cecum

Appendix

Ileocecal valve

Rectum

Sigmoid colon

Diameter of the large intestine
The large intestine is about two and one-half inches (7cm) wide, nearly twice the diameter of the small intestine.

The large intestine's "inverted U"
The large intestine begins on the right side of the abdomen with a blind pouch called the cecum. From there the ascending colon travels upward to become the transverse colon. The descending colon merges with the S-shaped sigmoid colon, which leads to the rectum.

ACCESSORY ORGANS OF DIGESTION

Several organs provide support for food processing and human nutrition. The pancreas contains islands of endocrine cells that secrete hormones that regulate blood sugar. The pancreas also produces enzymes that can break down all major types of food molecules including complex carbohydrates, proteins, fats and the nucleic acids that make up DNA. As food moves through the small intestine, pancreatic enzymes ensure that the majority of nutrient molecules it contains are released. The liver secretes bile, a greenish substance containing chemical salts derived from cholesterol. Bile salts assist fat digestion and their manufacture is one way the body removes excess cholesterol from the blood. The gallbladder stores bile from the liver and releases it into the small intestine as needed.

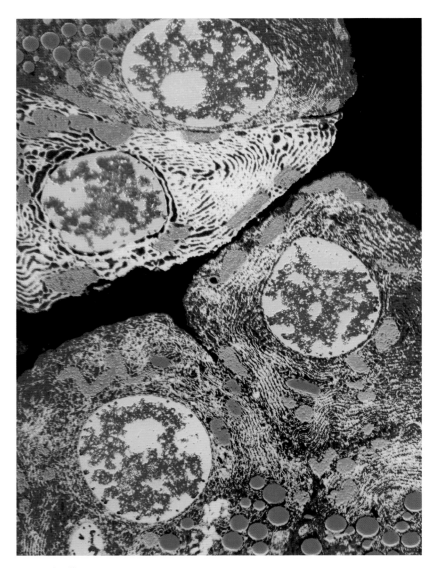

Pancreatic cells
The pale, threadlike masses in these pancreas cells are rough endoplasmic reticulum where enzymes are manufactured. Once they have been synthesized, the enzymes are stored in granules, which appear as red dots in this micrograph.

LIVER DISORDERS

Hepatitis, an inflammation of the liver, is caused by several viruses. Type B hepatitis brings an increased risk of liver cancer and type C hepatitis can be fatal without prompt treatment. Chronic inflammation due to viral infection or to routine heavy alcohol consumption can lead to cirrhosis, in which scar tissue and abnormal fat deposits replace much of the liver's healthy tissue. Often, the only hope for long-term survival is a liver transplant.

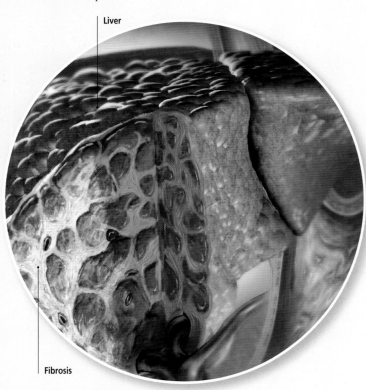

Liver

Fibrosis

Cirrhosis of the liver
Fibrosis, or scar formation in the liver, plus fatty deposits and impaired blood circulation are all characteristics of cirrhosis. Symptoms include jaundice, bleeding and fluid buildup (edema) in the lower legs.

Gallstones
Most gallstones mainly consist of crystallized cholesterol. Even small stones may cause severe pain in the upper right side of the abdomen, especially if one lodges in the bile duct. Standard treatments include gallbladder removal.

The multifunctional liver

In addition to secreting bile, the liver also processes the blood that flows through it. The hepatic portal vein transports blood from the small intestine into and through the liver. There, cells remove and store excess sugar and process other nutrient molecules into needed substances such as blood plasma proteins. The liver also cleanses the blood of hormones and residues of alcohol and other drugs, and converts ammonia from the breakdown of proteins into less toxic urea that is excreted in urine.

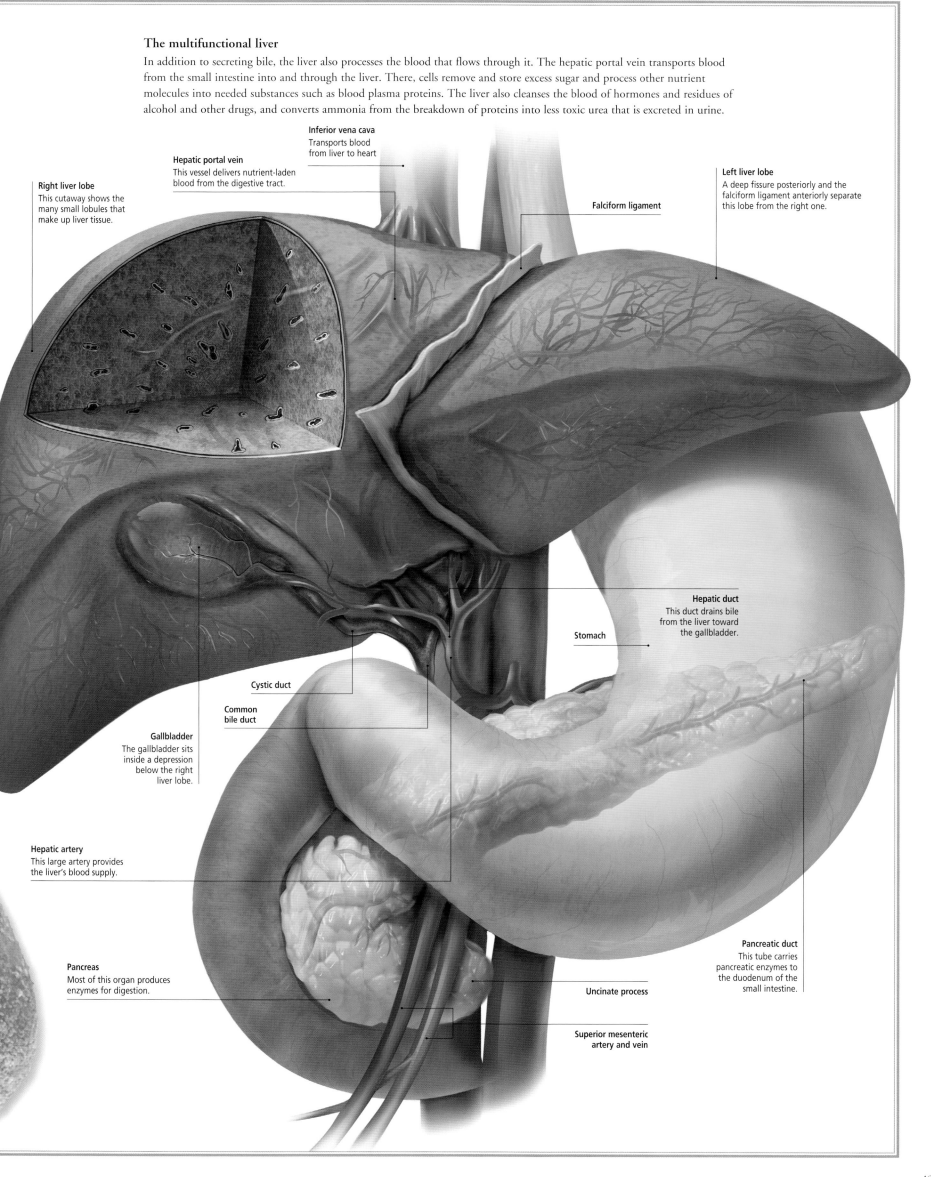

Inferior vena cava
Transports blood from liver to heart

Hepatic portal vein
This vessel delivers nutrient-laden blood from the digestive tract.

Right liver lobe
This cutaway shows the many small lobules that make up liver tissue.

Falciform ligament

Left liver lobe
A deep fissure posteriorly and the falciform ligament anteriorly separate this lobe from the right one.

Hepatic duct
This duct drains bile from the liver toward the gallbladder.

Stomach

Cystic duct

Common bile duct

Gallbladder
The gallbladder sits inside a depression below the right liver lobe.

Hepatic artery
This large artery provides the liver's blood supply.

Pancreatic duct
This tube carries pancreatic enzymes to the duodenum of the small intestine.

Pancreas
Most of this organ produces enzymes for digestion.

Uncinate process

Superior mesenteric artery and vein

ORAL DISORDERS

Dental plaque is a pale film of cells, food particles and bacteria that thrive in the mouth. Plaque not removed by daily brushing and flossing can cause cavities, or dental caries, areas where bacteria break down a tooth's enamel and dentin. If plaque hardens into tartar or calculus, a mild infection called gingivitis may make gums tender and prone to bleeding. Worldwide, nine out of ten people over 40 have some form of periodontal disease, a more serious infection that develops when bacteria move deeper and break down the bony tooth sockets. This is the most common cause of adult tooth loss and may cause some forms of heart disease due to bacteria entering the bloodstream and contributing to clot formation in coronary arteries. Oral cancers, frequently related to tobacco use, may require disfiguring surgery and can potentially spread elsewhere in the body.

Risk factors

Major factors that correlate with an individual's risk of developing disorders of the mouth and teeth include: poor oral hygiene, a diet that includes too many sugary and processed foods, tobacco use and excessive alcohol consumption. According to the World Health Organization, these factors are also on the list of risky lifestyle choices that contribute to the four most common global chronic diseases: cancer, cardiovascular disease and chronic respiratory diseases, such as emphysema and type 2 diabetes.

FINDING A QUEEN

Some 3500 years ago, the Egyptian Queen Hatshepsut died and monuments erected during her reign were destroyed. In 2007, Egyptian archeologists used a CAT scan to match a tooth preserved in a box bearing the queen's name with an empty tooth socket in the mouth of a long-unidentified mummy. DNA evidence supports the conclusion that the mummy is none other than Queen Hatshepsut herself.

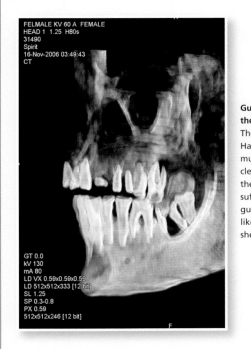

Gum disease and the mummy
The CT scan of Hatshepsut's mummy shows clear signs that the queen suffered from gum disease—the likely reason that she lost her tooth.

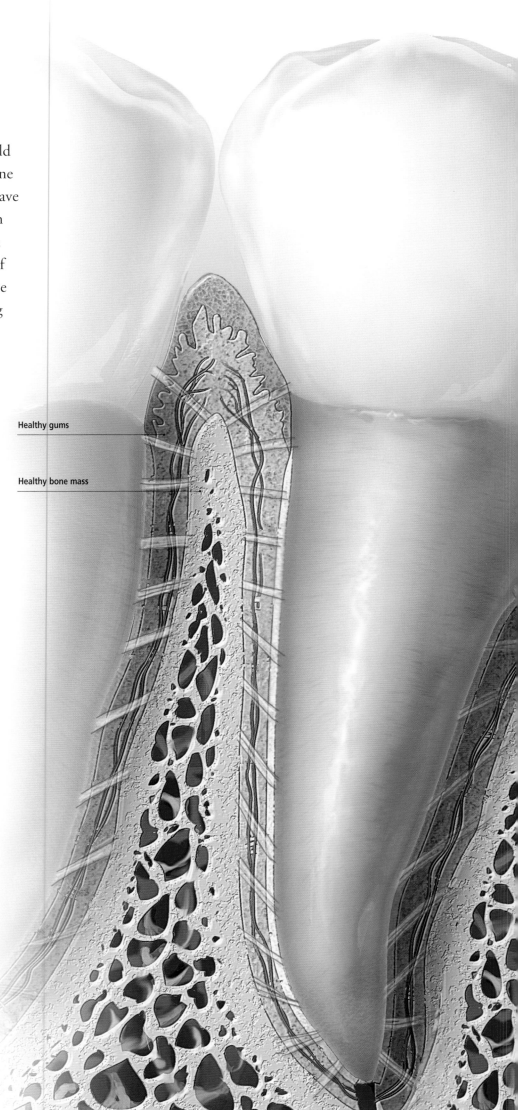

Healthy gums

Healthy bone mass

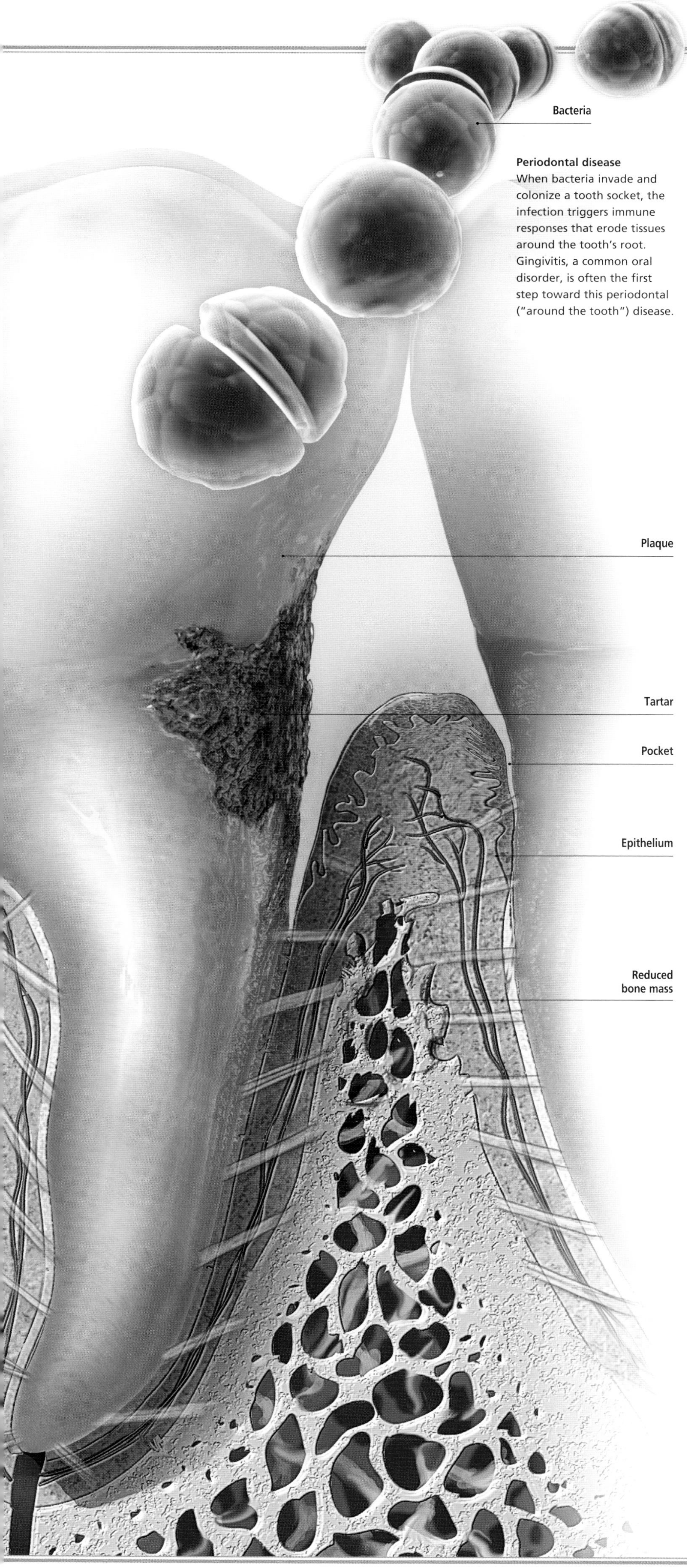

Bacteria

Periodontal disease
When bacteria invade and colonize a tooth socket, the infection triggers immune responses that erode tissues around the tooth's root. Gingivitis, a common oral disorder, is often the first step toward this periodontal ("around the tooth") disease.

Plaque

Tartar

Pocket

Epithelium

Reduced bone mass

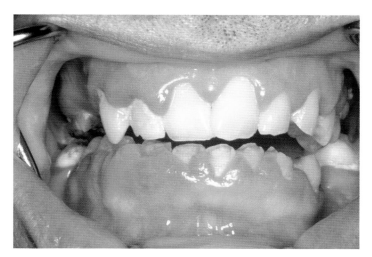

Gingivitis
Inflammation of the gums, called gingivitis, is a common complication when bacteria not removed by proper flossing or brushing infect gum tissue. It may progress to full-blown periodontal disease that can destroy the tooth socket.

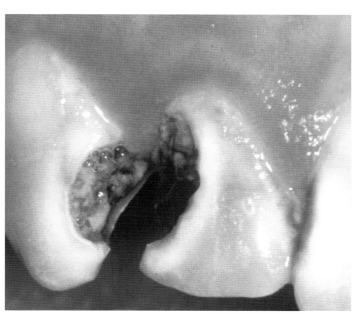

Dental caries
Tooth decay, or dental caries, develops as bacteria that metabolize food residues produce acids that eat away tooth enamel and the dentine and pulp. Untreated, the resulting cavity may deepen until the infection destroys the pulp, crown or root.

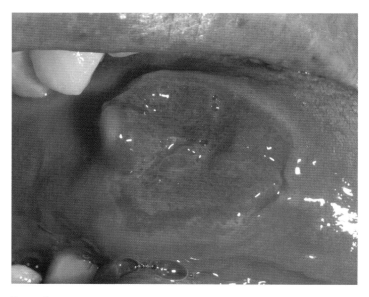

Tongue tumors
Cancerous tongue tumors are the most common oral cancers, and most develop in patients who use tobacco or chew material, such as betel nuts, which irritate tongue tissue. Treatment options include radiation and surgical removal of the affected area.

Gastric and Esophageal Diseases and Disorders

As the passageway for food that people eat, the esophagus is prone to damage from digestive upsets. The most common problem is caused when acidic, irritating stomach contents back up through the gastroesophageal sphincter, which normally closes after food enters the stomach. The result of this reflux is the familiar sensation of heartburn, or acid indigestion. Reflux affects nearly everyone from time to time, but in some people it is severe enough to be known as gastroesophageal reflux disease (GERD). Another ailment, peptic ulcer, is a painful, often bleeding sore that develops in the lining of the stomach or upper small intestine. About 90 percent of peptic ulcers are caused by the bacterium *Helicobacter pylori*. Excessive use of non-steroidal anti-inflammatory drugs (NSAIDs) may also trigger the damage. Risk factors for stomach cancer include consuming large amounts of salted, pickled or smoked food, genetic factors and tobacco use.

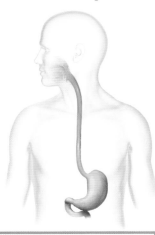

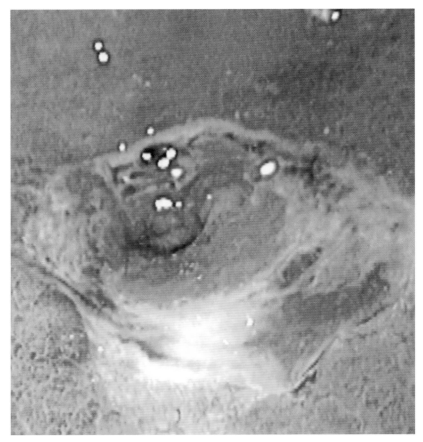

Stomach ulcers
Examination using an endoscope reveals the whitish ulcerated stomach lining around a patient's pyloric sphincter. Such ulcers may be caused by excess stomach acid but are usually due to infection by *Helicobacter pylori* bacteria.

A Dangerous Bacterium

The bacterium *Helicobacter pylori* is linked to several major digestive disorders. Both the stomach and duodenum, the upper portion of the small intestine, may become inflamed if *H. pylori* bacteria are present. The inflammation may be mild, or severe enough to cause significant pain. *H. pylori* has also been identified as a factor in many, and perhaps the majority of, stomach cancers. Worldwide, *H. pylori* infection is present in nearly 90 percent of people diagnosed with the disease.

Helicobacter pylori bacteria

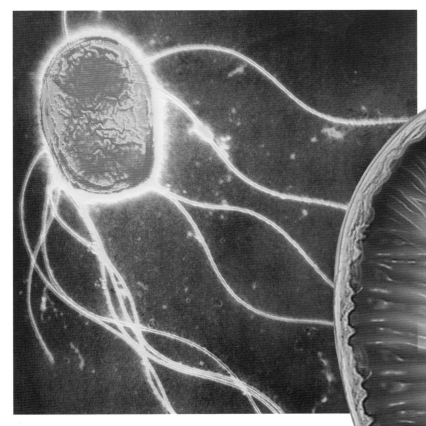

Food poisoning
Eggs, milk, meat and other foods contaminated by *Salmonella* bacteria cause infection when a bacterial toxin is released in the gastrointestinal tract. The *Salmonella* cell in this electron microscope image moves with its hairlike flagella.

Esophageal cancer
This illustration shows a cancerous tumor large enough to nearly close off the patient's esophagus. Esophageal cancer is often a complication of excessive tobacco or alcohol use. Most cases occur in older men.

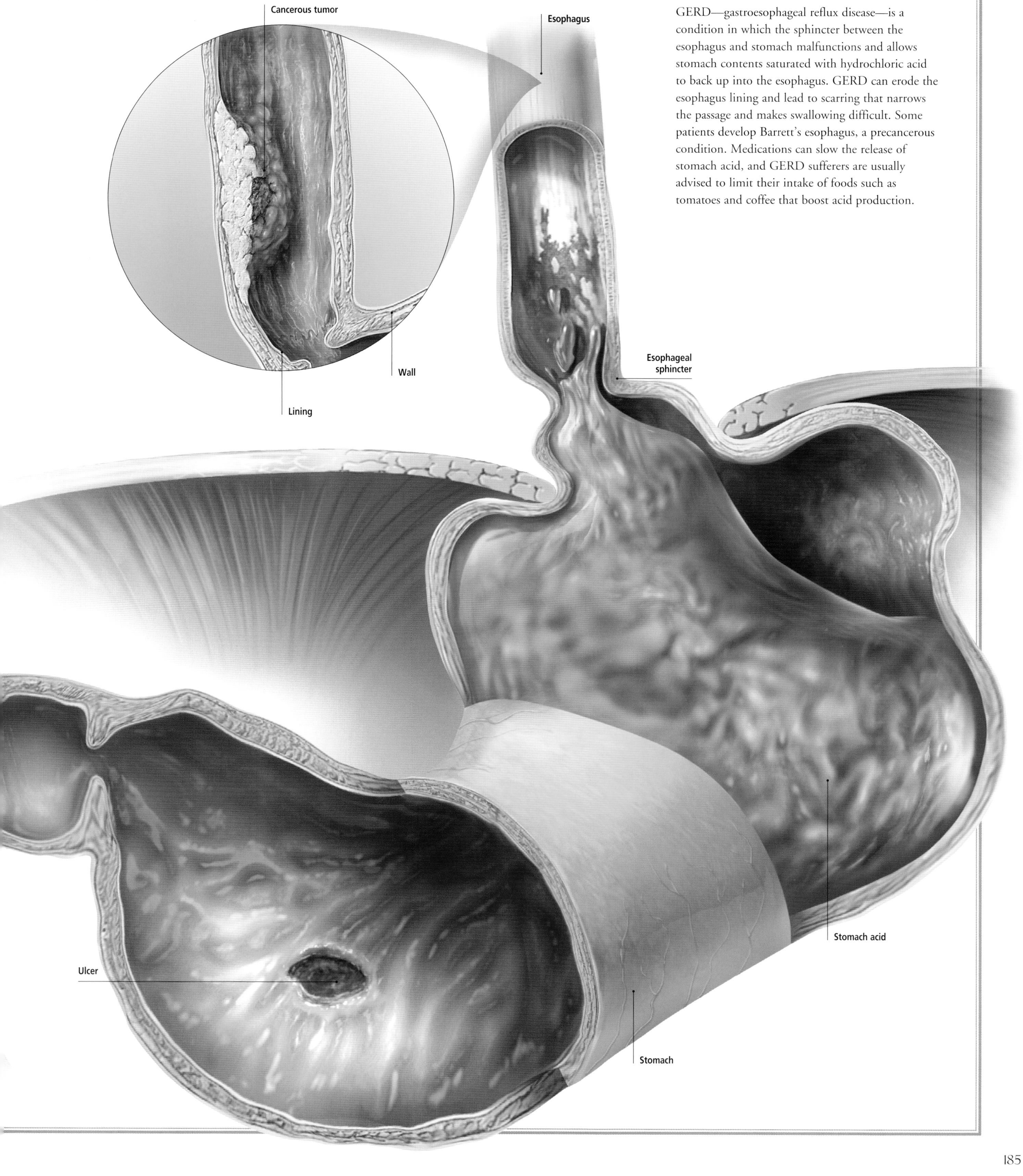

Cancerous tumor

Esophagus

Wall

Lining

GERD

GERD—gastroesophageal reflux disease—is a condition in which the sphincter between the esophagus and stomach malfunctions and allows stomach contents saturated with hydrochloric acid to back up into the esophagus. GERD can erode the esophagus lining and lead to scarring that narrows the passage and makes swallowing difficult. Some patients develop Barrett's esophagus, a precancerous condition. Medications can slow the release of stomach acid, and GERD sufferers are usually advised to limit their intake of foods such as tomatoes and coffee that boost acid production.

Esophageal sphincter

Stomach acid

Ulcer

Stomach

Intestinal Diseases and Disorders

The small and large intestines are vulnerable to ailments that affect core processes of digestion, including the flow of nutrients into the bloodstream. Inflammatory diseases can cause severe problems in the intestines. In the small intestine, where most nutrients are absorbed, an autoimmune condition called Crohn's disease causes inflammation and ulcers in the intestinal wall. Patients can become dangerously malnourished and in severe cases large portions of the small intestine must be removed. Inflammation, ulcers and bleeding in the colon are the main symptoms of ulcerative colitis. Most people over age 50 have at least some diverticula, small protruding pouches at weak spots in the wall of the large intestine. Painful diverticulitis develops if the pouches become infected. Aging or a genetic predisposition can lead to the development of fleshy polyps in the colon that may be precursors to colorectal cancer—one of the most common cancers worldwide.

Colorectal cancer

In developed regions of the world, colorectal cancer is among the top-diagnosed malignancies and accounts for a significant percentage of cancer deaths. This cancer often begins with a concave patch of abnormal cells or a growth called a polyp on the colon wall. The tendency to develop precancerous growths and colon cancer can run in families, but most often there is no apparent genetic link. Tumors and precancerous tissues are usually easily diagnosed during a colonoscopy.

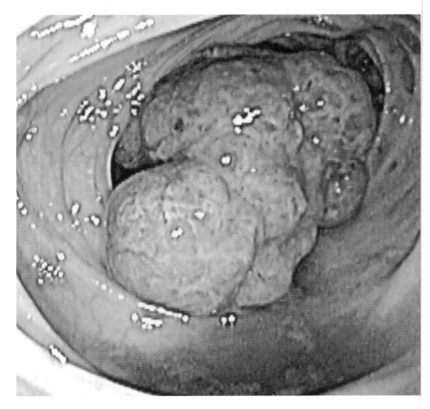

Colon cancer
This image shows a large, malignant tumor in a patient's colon. Like cancerous tumors generally, this one secretes substances that promote vascularization of the abnormal tissue—the development of blood vessels that nourish its rapid growth.

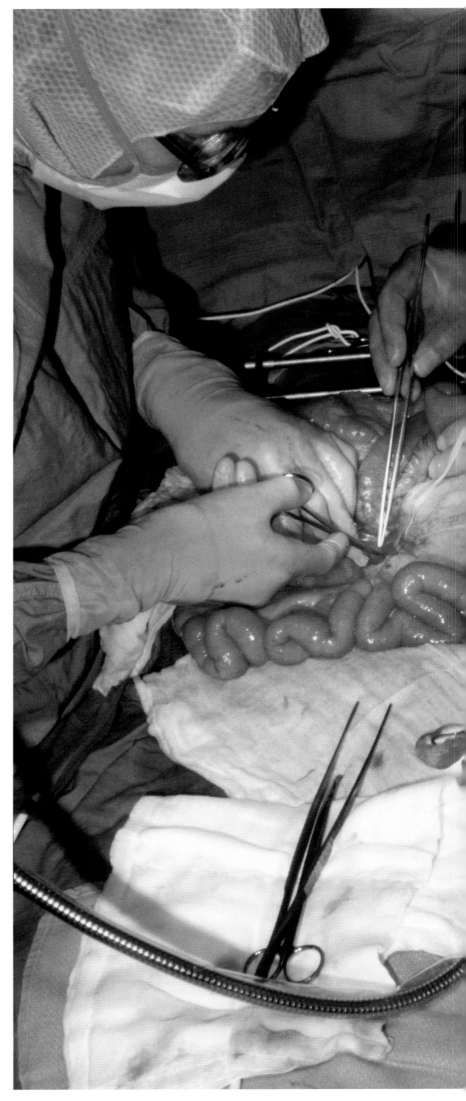

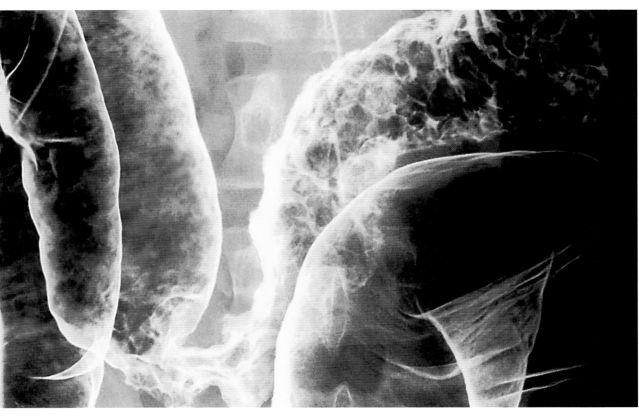

Crohn's disease
A colored barium X-ray shows a portion of a colon damaged by Crohn's disease. Ulcers have formed in the mottled area at the upper right. Spinal vertebrae are visible in the background.

DIARRHEA

Diarrhea, or watery feces, often indicates a mild to serious intestinal infection. Infectious bacteria produce toxins that cause the intestinal lining to flood the colon with more water than it can absorb in a short time. Other causes include the failure of the digestive organs to intake water from the bolus or from food residue rushing through the large intestine too rapidly. Especially dangerous for children, diarrheal diseases may deplete the body of water and electrolytes—chemical salts that nerves and muscles require to function properly.

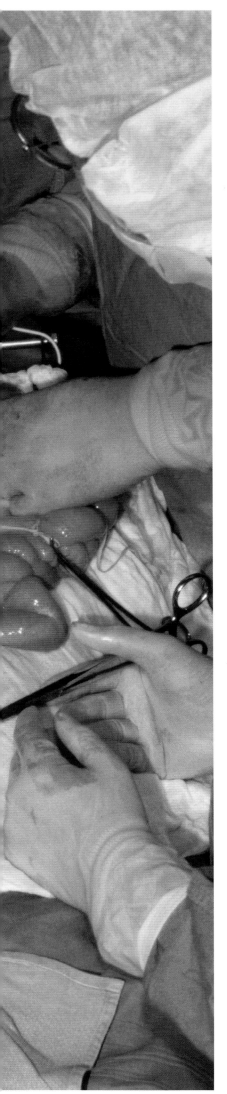

Colostomy
When a diseased section of the colon is removed, a procedure called colostomy is used to bring the remaining end of the intestine out through an opening in the abdominal wall, where a bag for receiving feces can be attached.

Intestinal surgery
A surgery patient's abdomen has been opened to expose the coiled intestine. When the treatment plan permits, many such surgeries are now performed using the much less invasive technique called laparoscopy.

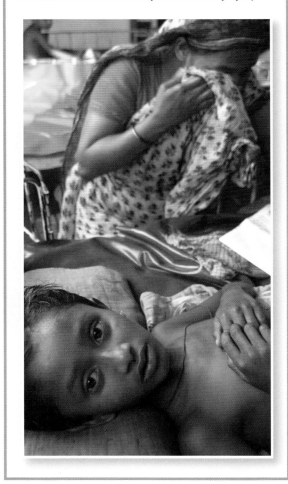

OBESITY ON THE GLOBAL STAGE

In developed nations especially, increasing numbers of people are obese. Clinical obesity is defined as a weight that greatly exceeds a range considered healthy for a person's height—generally by more than 20 percent. Research shows how lifestyle habits, and for some, genetics, promote obesity. Scientists are also investigating the role of obesity in chronic diseases, such as type 2 diabetes, heart disease, chronic hypertension and other ailments. High-profile surgical procedures dramatically reduce the stomach's food capacity and yield equally dramatic weight loss and a reduction in obesity-related disease. However, these strategies come with the risk of complications and are available only to relative few patients. Scientists are researching therapeutic drugs or other approaches that can expand treatments to millions more.

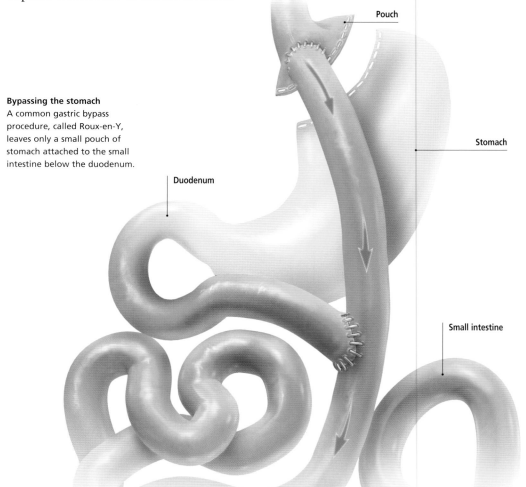

Pouch

Bypassing the stomach
A common gastric bypass procedure, called Roux-en-Y, leaves only a small pouch of stomach attached to the small intestine below the duodenum.

Stomach

Duodenum

Small intestine

Gastric bypass surgery
Today, gastric bypass surgery is often minimally invasive. Here the surgical team has inserted several hollow, lighted cylinders into the patient's abdomen through small incisions. Instruments used in the operation pass through the cylinders.

Body mass index

Body mass index, or BMI, is a rough indicator of weight-related health risk. To determine an adult's BMI, a value for weight is divided by a value for height. Formulas for calculating BMI using either English or metric units are available from many public health organizations. As a rule of thumb, a BMI of 25 to 30 indicates that a person is overweight, while a BMI greater than 30 indicates obesity.

CHILDHOOD OBESITY

Because obesity correlates with serious chronic diseases, the rise in obesity among children and adolescents is a high-profile global concern. Even in nations where many people lack adequate food, public health statistics show that large numbers of children are medically obese. Key factors in this epidemic are lack of physical exercise and increasing availability of low-cost, high-calorie processed foods and beverages.

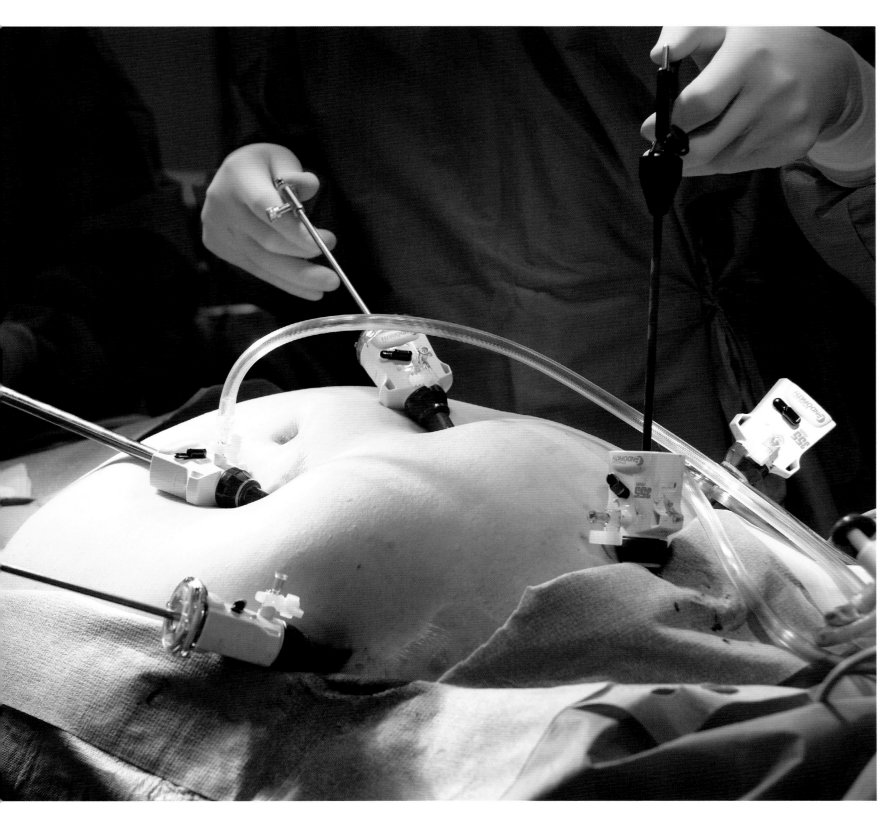

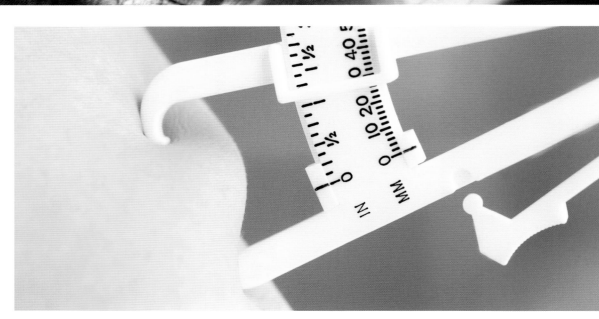

BODY MASS INDEX CATEGORIES	
BMI	**CATEGORY**
Under 18.5	Underweight
18.5–24.9	Normal weight
25–29.9	Overweight
30–39.9	Obese
40 or above	Extremely obese

Skinfold measurements
These measurements can provide a rough assessment of the relative amounts of fat and lean muscle in a person's body. Actual calculations take into account a person's age and gender.

MALNUTRITION AND UNDERNUTRITION

Malnutrition and disorders that hamper the absorption of food nutrients are problems for millions of people. Malnutrition can be caused by a lack of one or more key nutrients, consuming too little food energy or both. In people with a malabsorption disorder, the digestive system cannot properly absorb one or more nutrients. Tens of millions of people suffer from lactose intolerance, an inability to break down the sugar in milk and milk products due the lack of the enzyme lactase. Similarly, cystic fibrosis patients lack pancreatic enzymes that allow normal digestion and absorption of fats and other nutrients. Undernutrition of impoverished children is a worldwide plight. Inadequate protein, iron, B vitamins or an overall shortage of food energy can cause irreversible physical and mental impairments.

Starvation

Starvation is a state of extreme malnutrition in which a person's intake of food energy and essential nutrients is severely limited. To keep the nervous system and heart functioning in this state, cells obtain energy first by drawing down the body's reserves of stored fat and then by breaking down muscle. A simultaneous deficiency of vitamins and minerals may trigger diseases such as scurvy and anemia, with symptoms that include diarrhea, extreme fatigue, tooth loss and, eventually, heart failure.

Starvation's effects
The limbs of a 54-year-old woman with severe malnutrition show the wasting that occurs when the body dismantles muscle to use its protein as fuel. Starving people also often suffer mental confusion and kidney disorders.

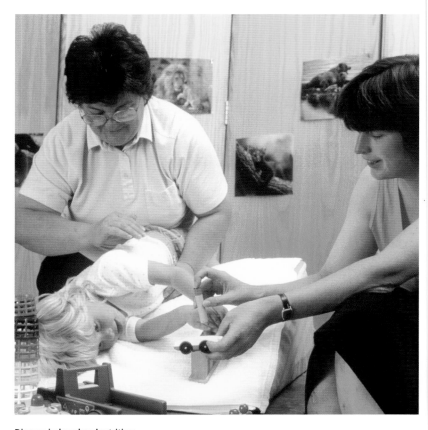

Disease-induced malnutrition
Cystic fibrosis (CF) patients like the child shown here, who is receiving percussion therapy, risk nutrient deficiencies because abnormal mucus can clog ducts carrying digestive enzymes. CF patients generally take enzyme and vitamin supplements.

Food pyramid
A food pyramid shows the proportions of different food groups in a healthful diet. Complex carbohydrates, including whole grain products, vegetables and fruits, make up most of the recommended diet, with less protein, fats and sugars.

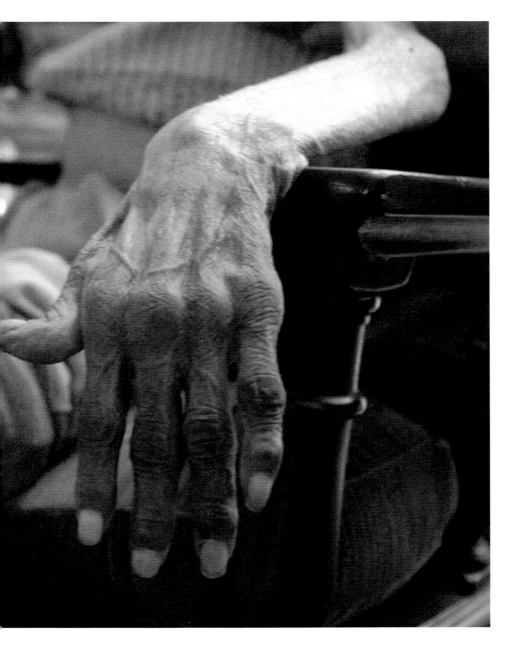

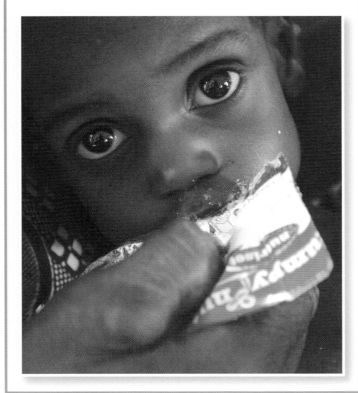

FILLING THE HUNGER GAP

Each year in the developing world, malnutrition kills an estimated five million children under the age of five. To help hungry children in places where clean water, refrigeration and cooking fuel are luxuries, the aid organization Doctors Without Borders distributes ready-to-eat nutritional supplements called Plumpynut and Plumpydoz. Both consist of ground peanuts enriched with vitamins and protein. One serving provides about one-third of a child's daily nutritional needs.

Other factors
Chronic abusers of narcotics, amphetamines and alcohol are at risk for malnutrition. They not only eat poorly, but chronic damage to the liver and other organs also reduces their ability to absorb nutrients.

EATING DISORDERS

In some otherwise healthy people with access to plenty of nutritious food, psychological issues trigger an eating disorder, such as anorexia nervosa or bulimia. Affected people—usually adolescent girls or young, single women—chronically use drastic measures to reduce their body's supply of energy in order to lose or avoid gaining weight. Driven by a distorted view of "normal" body weight, a person with anorexia nervosa is fixated on consuming as little food as possible regardless of hunger and may use a combination of self-starvation and laxatives to deprive the body of food energy. Bulimia is a binge-purge syndrome in which the individual drastically overeats several times a week, then uses vomiting, extreme exercise, laxatives or other strategies to purge food from the digestive tract. Bulimia is typically associated with intense fear of being perceived as overweight, depression or stress.

Anorexia's unintended consequences

Anorexia nervosa has physiological effects that collectively make it a devastating and ultimately life-threatening disorder. Common consequences include not only drastic weight loss but osteoporosis and the cessation of menstruation. Self-starvation and laxative abuse also severely upset the balance of fluid and electrolytes required for nerve impulses and muscle contraction. The lack of nutrients and the breakdown of muscle tissue eventually triggers lethal heart failure—the sad fate of an estimated 10 to 20 percent of anorexia nervosa victims.

Overexercising
Exercising obsessively in order to lose weight fast can be dangerous. Muscles and joints do not rest adequately and are prone to injury. Strenuous exercise also depletes electrolytes crucial to the heart's functioning through sweat.

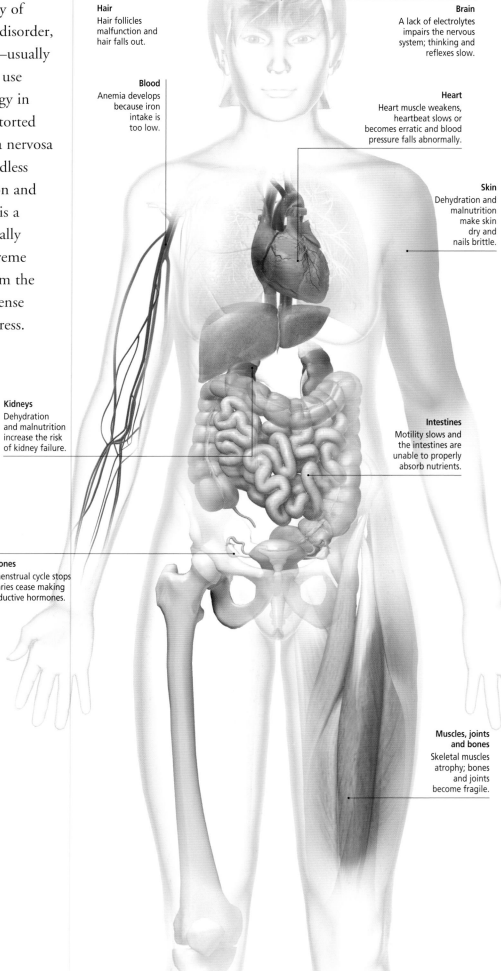

Hair
Hair follicles malfunction and hair falls out.

Blood
Anemia develops because iron intake is too low.

Kidneys
Dehydration and malnutrition increase the risk of kidney failure.

Hormones
The menstrual cycle stops as ovaries cease making reproductive hormones.

Brain
A lack of electrolytes impairs the nervous system; thinking and reflexes slow.

Heart
Heart muscle weakens, heartbeat slows or becomes erratic and blood pressure falls abnormally.

Skin
Dehydration and malnutrition make skin dry and nails brittle.

Intestines
Motility slows and the intestines are unable to properly absorb nutrients.

Muscles, joints and bones
Skeletal muscles atrophy; bones and joints become fragile.

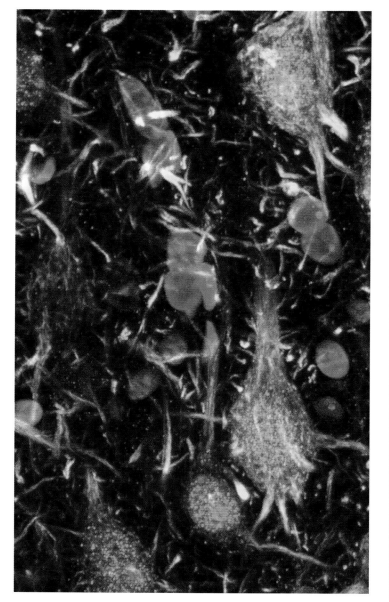

Hunger hormone receptors
This light micrograph shows orexin receptors (red) in the brain. New research suggests the hypothalamus secretes the hormone orexin to stimulate appetite. People with eating disorders ignore these and other signals urging them to eat.

Anorexia nervosa
Anorexia nervosa has classic physical and psychological symptoms. In addition to persistent, dramatic weight loss, signs include lack of menstruation for three months or more (in non-pregnant women) and intense fear of gaining weight.

TREATING EATING DISORDERS

Addressed in time, eating disorders can be successfully reversed and the patient restored to physical and psychological health. Intensive psychotherapy to deal with feelings of shame and self-loathing, antidepressant drugs and careful management of the person's diet all are part of the treatment regimen. When a physical cause is identified, such as a tumor that affects centers in the hypothalamus that regulate eating behavior, surgery may be required.

Eating disorder deaths
Comparing death rates from different countries suggests that social and cultural factors play a role in eating disorders. Research indicates that anorexia nervosa and bulimia are most common in societies where thinness is equated with personal worth.

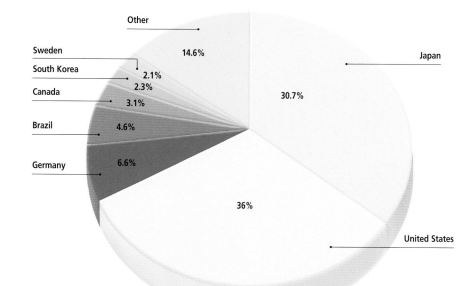

Other 14.6%
Sweden 2.1%
South Korea 2.3%
Canada 3.1%
Brazil 4.6%
Germany 6.6%
Japan 30.7%
United States 36%

URINARY SYSTEM

Like some other organ systems, the urinary system is multipurpose: it functions as a combination blood cleanser and chemical-balancing apparatus. Around the clock, millions of microscopic structures in the system's two bean-shaped kidneys filter the blood of water, impurities, metabolic byproducts and other substances. This freshly filtered fluid is called filtrate, and it is the starting point for fine-tuned chemical adjustments. As it moves through nephrons, the operational units of kidneys, these filters remove excess salt, acid from cell metabolism and other potential toxins, and unneeded substances such as drug residues. At the same time, nephrons retrieve needed materials from the filtrate and either remove or retain water so that when filtered blood eventually leaves the kidneys, it contains enough water for adequate blood pressure. The end result of these adjustments is the yellowish fluid called urine, which eventually is eliminated even while the kidneys are continuing their vital filtering task.

Bodily balance

Complex interactions link the urinary system with other body systems. Renal arteries and veins deliver and pick up blood the kidneys process, but an entirely different set of vessels service the requirements of kidney cells for obtaining oxygen and removing wastes. The digestive system both supplies kidney cells with nutrients and delivers a wide variety of other substances that demand a swift physiological response from the kidneys in order to maintain the blood's chemical balance. Only the urinary system can permanently remove from the blood excess acid that would otherwise prove lethal.

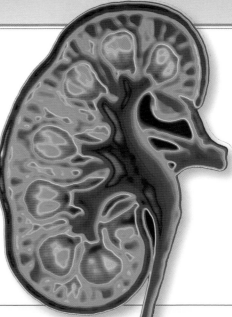

Blood filter
This functional magnetic resonance image shows a kidney with its active blood-filtering regions lit up a bright orange.

COMMON URINE TESTS		
	NORMAL RANGE	**WHY TESTED**
COLOR	Pale to dark yellow	Gives indication of how much water is in the urine. Certain foods, vitamins and medicines can change color of urine.
CLARITY	Clear	Cloudy urine may contain bacteria, mucous or other substances.
ODOR	Slightly "nutty" odor to fresh urine	Some foods or medicines may alter the odor; bad smelling urine may indicate an infection; diabetes or starvation can make it smell "fruity."
pH	4.6-8.0	Indicates how acid or basic (alkaline) the urine is. The pH may be affected by certain foods, medications or disorders.
PROTEIN	Not present	Protein in the urine may be a sign of kidney disorders but can also happen with fever, pregnancy or strenuous exercise.
GLUCOSE	Not present	Most common cause of glucose ("sugar") in the urine is diabetes. May also be caused by kidney disease.
KETONES	Not usually present	Ketones, formed when the body breaks down fat for energy, may be caused by starvation, low-carbohydrate diets, diabetic acidosis or sometimes alcohol toxicity.
BLOOD	Not present	Red or white blood cells in the urine may be a sign of urinary tract infection (UTI) or injury.
BACTERIA	Not present	Bacteria in the urine indicates infection. Bacteria may also show as nitrates in the urine.

VITAL WATER

By weight, an average young female is about 50 percent water, an average young male about 60 percent, a difference due mainly to the amounts of skeletal muscle in their bodies. For muscle fibers and all other cells, water is essential for the chemical reactions that sustain life. Water is also a major component of whole blood, making up 90 percent of the total blood volume.

Dynamic duo

Operations of the whole urinary system may shift in response to sudden changes in the composition of blood. For example, drinking a large quantity of water in a short time spurs the kidney filters to quickly remove the excess as dilute urine lest it remain in the bloodstream and raise blood pressure.

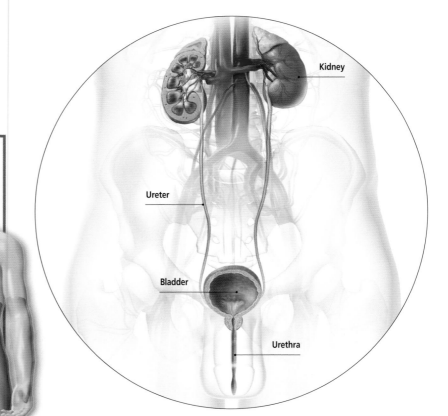

The male and female urinary systems
Males and females have identical urinary systems except for the urethra. In males this channel is about nine inches (23cm) long, while a female's urethra extends only about two inches (5cm) before it opens to the outside. This shorter length helps explain why females are more likely to get bladder infections, because infectious bacteria from the urogenital area have a much shorter distance to travel to reach the protected environment of the bladder.

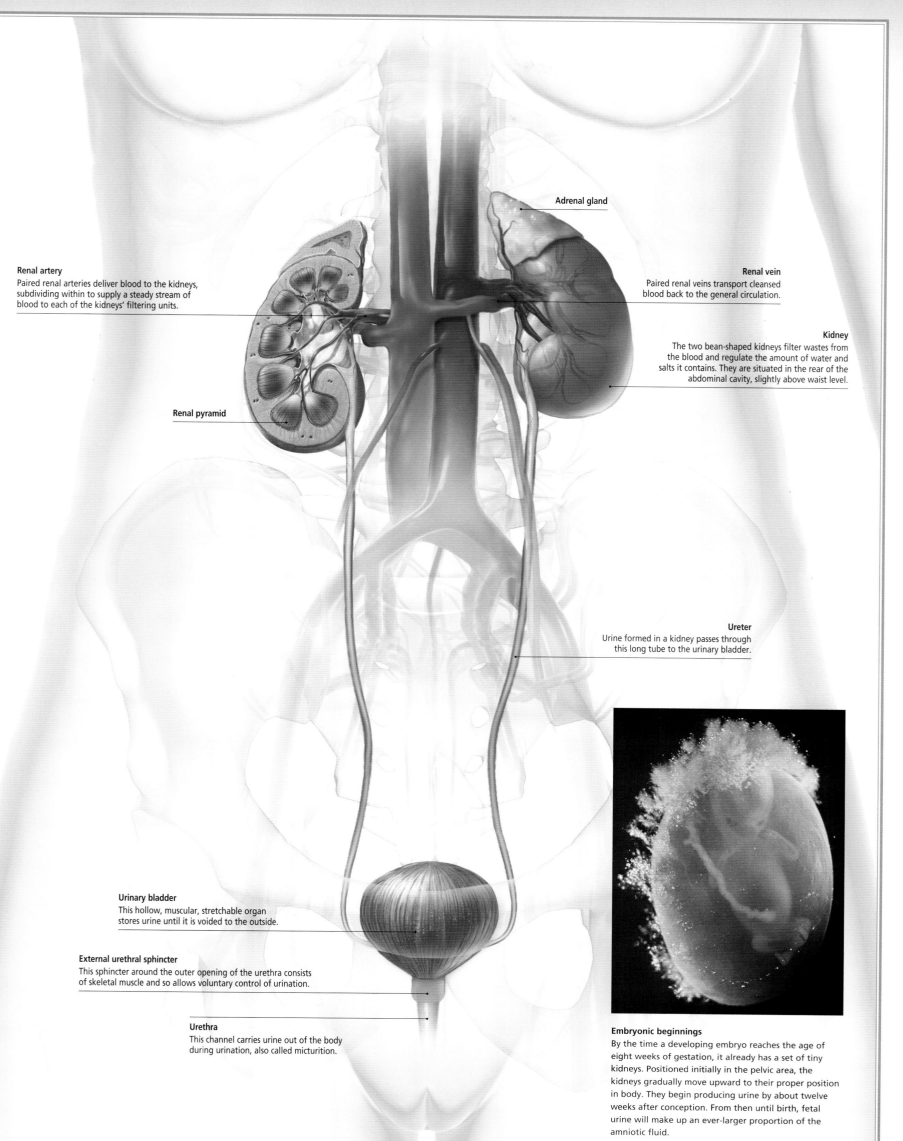

Renal artery
Paired renal arteries deliver blood to the kidneys, subdividing within to supply a steady stream of blood to each of the kidneys' filtering units.

Renal pyramid

Adrenal gland

Renal vein
Paired renal veins transport cleansed blood back to the general circulation.

Kidney
The two bean-shaped kidneys filter wastes from the blood and regulate the amount of water and salts it contains. They are situated in the rear of the abdominal cavity, slightly above waist level.

Ureter
Urine formed in a kidney passes through this long tube to the urinary bladder.

Urinary bladder
This hollow, muscular, stretchable organ stores urine until it is voided to the outside.

External urethral sphincter
This sphincter around the outer opening of the urethra consists of skeletal muscle and so allows voluntary control of urination.

Urethra
This channel carries urine out of the body during urination, also called micturition.

Embryonic beginnings
By the time a developing embryo reaches the age of eight weeks of gestation, it already has a set of tiny kidneys. Positioned initially in the pelvic area, the kidneys gradually move upward to their proper position in body. They begin producing urine by about twelve weeks after conception. From then until birth, fetal urine will make up an ever-larger proportion of the amniotic fluid.

INTERNAL ENVIRONMENT

The human body is composed largely of fluids. Organelles, working parts within each cell, are suspended in fluid that contains enzymes and other molecules needed for, or produced by, life-sustaining chemical reactions. Fluid also fills the microscopic spaces between cells. This tissue fluid and blood plasma together form extracellular fluid, or ECF, which accounts for half or more of body weight. The chemical makeup of ECF constantly shifts as cells remove nutrients, oxygen, hormones and other substances and simultaneously add metabolic products or wastes. Strategically located sensors in the brain, blood vessels and kidneys monitor blood chemistry and make adjustments that collectively maintain the appropriate balance of water, salts and other materials.

ELECTROLYTES

One role of the kidneys is to ensure that ECF contains enough of certain salts, including sodium, calcium, potassium and phosphate, which serve as electrolytes—ions that enable a solution to conduct an electric current. Neurons cannot transmit nerve impulses without electrolytes. The kidneys also manage the amounts of acidic and basic, or alkaline, substances in the ECF. Metabolic activity forms acids and bases, which can be toxic to the body if levels rise too high.

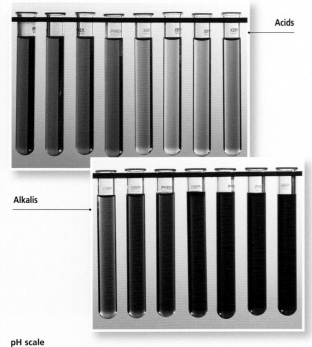

Acids

Alkalis

pH scale
In these test tubes, color reflects the pH values of various fluids. pH (potential of Hydrogen) measures acidity on a scale from 0 to 14. Acids increase in strength from pH 6 down to pH 0. Alkalis, or bases, increase in strength from pH 8 to pH 14, with pH 7 being neutral. The kidneys help adjust blood's chemical makeup to maintain a nearly neutral pH of 7.3–7.5.

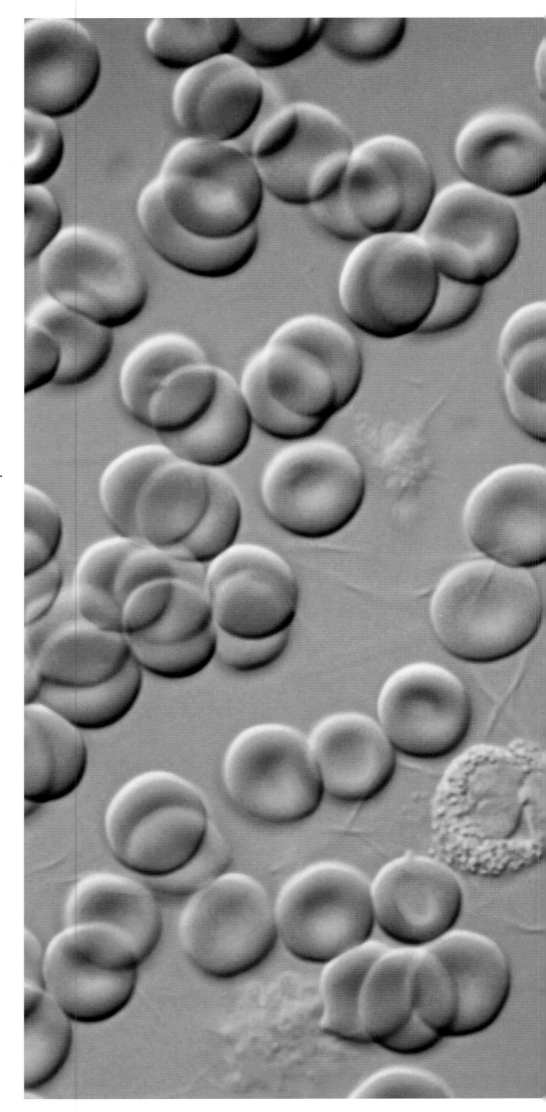

Balanced gains and losses

Assisted by the nervous system, the urinary system is responsible for water and salt balance in the body. Each day, the body gains about 2.75 quarts (2.6L) of extracellular fluid, the same amount of water as the body loses in urine, feces, sweat and evaporation from the lungs and skin. A thirst center in the brain helps ensure that food and liquids provide sufficient water to supplement water-producing metabolic reactions in cells, while one of the kidneys' main functions is to ensure that no water needed by the body is excreted in urine.

Watery surroundings
Water is an essential ingredient of body fluids in part because most of the chemical reactions required for life occur in water-based solutions. This image (left) shows blood cells immersed in the watery solution called blood plasma.

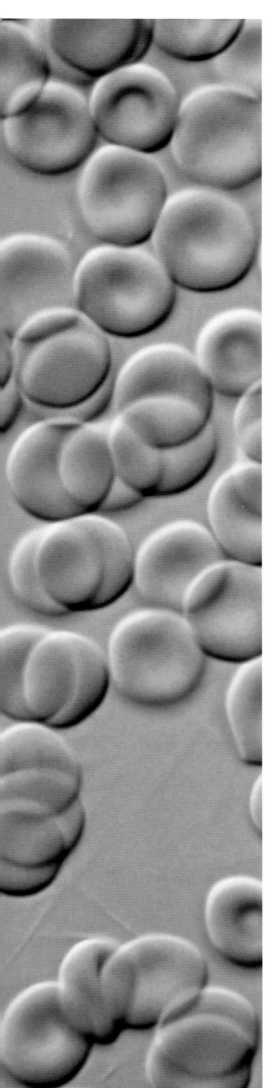

Water vapor
The body's water balance shifts constantly as water enters or leaves the internal environment. About one-third of daily water losses occur in the form of evaporating water vapor, such as in exhaled air.

Perspiration
A key property of water is its capacity to absorb heat. Sweat is about 99 percent water. When the body becomes overheated, sweat exits the body via the skin and then evaporates, cooling the body in the process.

Drinking fluids
Drinking fluids accounts for about half of the water that enters the internal environment each day. A brain-based thirst mechanism generally prompts a person to drink enough fluid to avoid dehydration, although strenuous exercise increases the demand.

THE KIDNEYS

The two kidneys are the body's main blood filters. Each is only about four inches (10cm) long and two inches (5.5cm) thick, but is packed with roughly one million microscopic filtering units called nephrons. This huge supply of filters correlates with the main function of kidneys—to remove metabolic wastes from the blood and adjust the balance of water, salt and other substances.

The hormone erythropoietin, which stimulates the production of red blood cells, is produced by the kidneys, and they convert vitamin D to a form required for the absorption of dietary calcium. The kidneys also make an enzyme, renin, that helps regulate blood pressure. Healthy kidneys are amazingly efficient. Although humans are born with two, one kidney will do almost as well. People who lose a kidney to disease or injury or who donate a kidney to someone with kidney failure suffer no major ill effects.

KIDNEY ENZYMES AND HORMONES	
NAME	**WHAT IT DOES**
Renin	Enzyme that helps regulate blood pressure; triggers reactions that produce angiotensin II when the body needs to retain water
Angiotensin II	Protein that stimulates adrenal cortex to secrete the hormone aldosterone (ADH), which signals kidney nephrons to excrete less water (and salt)
Erythropoietin	Hormone that stimulates production of red blood cells in bone marrow

KIDNEY TRANSPLANTS

When a donor and an otherwise-healthy recipient have compatible blood and tissue types, kidney transplants have a high success rate. Recipients typically have advanced disease that has rendered both kidneys nearly or totally nonfunctional. After surgery, the lone healthy kidney remaining in the donor, as well as the one transplanted into the recipient, gradually enlarge so that the filtering capacity equals about 80 percent of the capacity of two kidneys. The greatest long-term success comes with kidneys from living donors, although cadaver organs also save many lives.

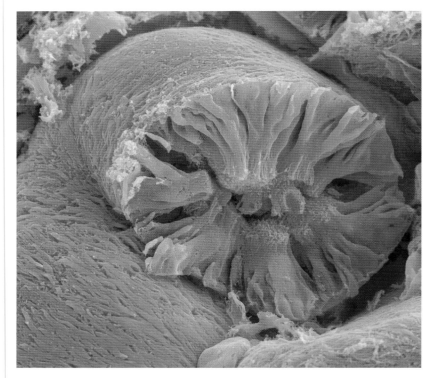

Nephrons
This colored image shows the interior of a curving nephron tubule, where urine forms. A steady drip of urine flows into collecting ducts that carry it to the kidney's central cavity, the renal pelvis.

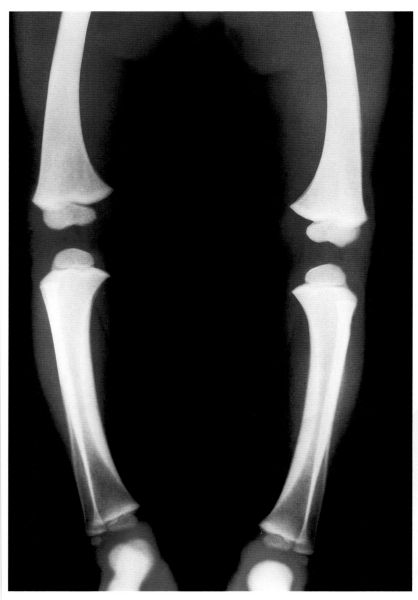

Absorbing calcium
A deficiency of calcium, vitamin D or phosphate causes the bone-weakening disease rickets, which can lead to bowed legs as seen in this X-ray. Renal rickets may develop when a genetic disorder prevents kidney nephrons from reabsorbing the phosphate needed for bone growth and strength previously filtered out of the blood.

Efficient filters

At rest, up to 25 percent of blood pumped by the heart enters the kidneys. Every 24 hours, the nephrons in a male's kidneys filter and process about 100 gallons (378L) of fluid from this incoming blood and a female's kidneys filter and process about 83 gallons (314L). The filtered fluid, or filtrate, contains no blood cells or whole proteins. It consists of water and substances such as sugar, amino acids, sodium and urea, a potentially toxic byproduct of the body's protein use.

Anatomy of a kidney
Blood-filtering parts of nephron tubules are located in the cortex of each internal lobe, while the lower loop, where needed water is reabsorbed, is in the medulla below. Urine flows via the calyx to the renal pelvis, then into the ureter.

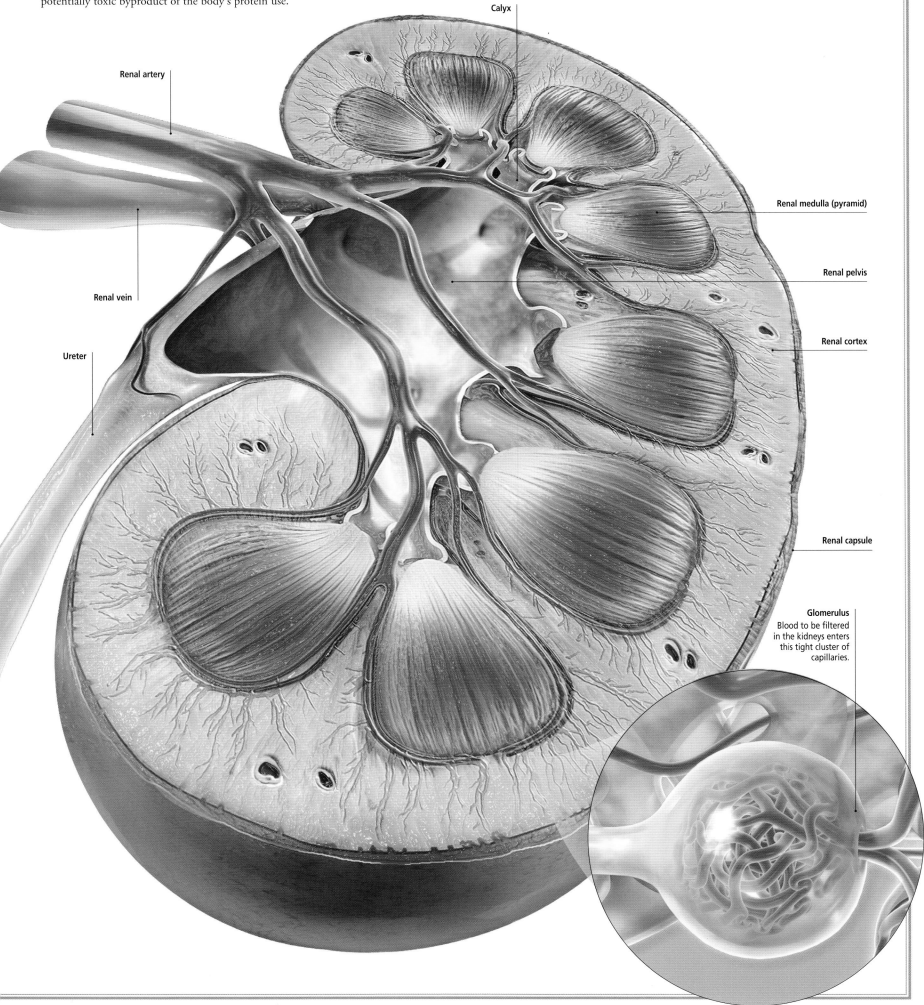

Calyx

Renal artery

Renal medulla (pyramid)

Renal vein

Renal pelvis

Ureter

Renal cortex

Renal capsule

Glomerulus
Blood to be filtered in the kidneys enters this tight cluster of capillaries.

URINE FORMATION

The urine production process reveals the work the kidneys do to cleanse the body of wastes, toxins and foreign substances, such as antibiotics, while retaining needed water and salts. Urine forms in a sequence of three steps that begins when kidney nephrons filter out water and dissolved materials from the blood. The sequence ends when all essential substances have been returned to blood flowing out of the kidneys, leaving what the body does not need to be excreted in the urine. Whether urine is dark yellow or pale depends on how much water it contains, which is controlled by the kidneys to compensate for changes in the amount of dietary water and to regulate blood volume and pressure. Generally, at least 70 percent of the water and salts filtered from blood, and often more, are retained by the body at the end of this process.

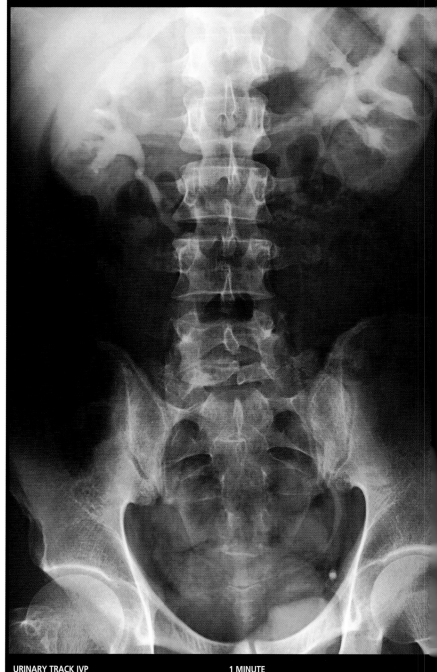

URINARY TRACK IVP   1 MINUTE

Diuretics
Diuretics reduce the amount of water nephrons reabsorb, so the kidneys produce more urine. Physicians sometimes prescribe diuretics to reduce blood volume in patients with high blood pressure. Alcohol and the caffeine in tea, coffee and cola drinks are diuretics. So are herbs such as dandelion root, which can be infused to make tea.

URINALYSIS

Urinalysis can provide important information about a person's health. The presence of pus—dead white blood cells—suggests a urinary tract infection, while red blood cells may be a sign of other infection, trauma, kidney stones or another problem. Urine's yellow color comes from excreted bile salts, and high levels of these compounds may indicate liver or gallbladder disease. Excessive sugar in urine may be linked to diabetes, and excessive proteins to severe hypertension or other circulatory disease.

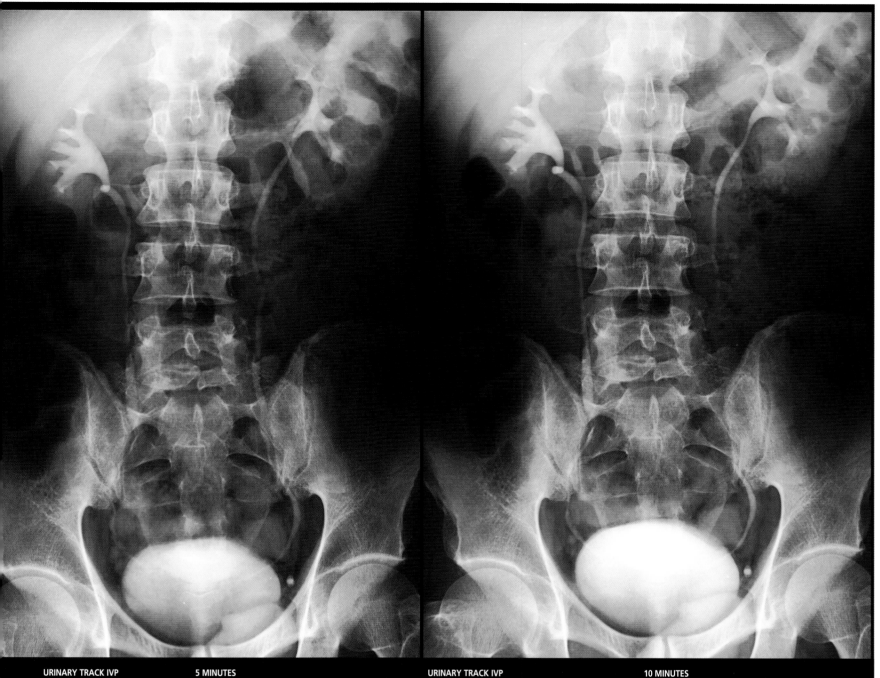

| URINARY TRACK IVP | 5 MINUTES | URINARY TRACK IVP | 10 MINUTES |

Visualizing the bladder

Diagnosing a urinary tract disorder may involve assessing how the bladder fills with and retains urine. When X-rays are used for such urodynamic tests, the patient's bladder is filled with a solution containing a contrast medium, such as barium, which makes the urinary system clearly visible.

Ridding the body of toxic nitrogen

Urine gets its name from nitrogen-containing byproducts, including urea and uric acid, that are released when cells break down proteins and the nucleic acids DNA and RNA. Skeletal muscle produces a third nitrogenous compound, creatinine, as it forms energy-rich fuel molecules from creatine. Nephrons filter these potentially toxic substances from the blood. Some urea and uric acid are reabsorbed as the forming urine moves through the nephron loop. The remainder, and all filtered creatinine, is eliminated in urine.

Forming urine

Urine forms in the tubules of the nephron, which normally retain or excrete water as required to maintain the necessary volume of extracellular fluid, including circulating blood. Two hormones, ADH and aldosterone, stimulate water conservation in time of need. Otherwise the kidneys automatically produce dilute urine.

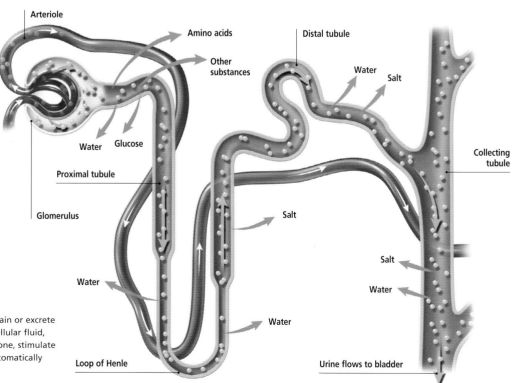

Arteriole
Amino acids
Other substances
Distal tubule
Water
Salt
Water
Glucose
Proximal tubule
Collecting tubule
Glomerulus
Salt
Salt
Water
Water
Water
Loop of Henle
Urine flows to bladder

URINARY TRACT DISORDERS

Virtually all of the urinary system is vulnerable to infection by microbes, including bacteria spread by sexual activity. Symptoms often include frequent urination and pain in the affected organ or tissue, and infections can usually be cured with antibiotics. The anatomy of the urinary system fosters traveling infections from pathogens that enter the lower urethra and move upward. Urethritis is an infection limited to the urethra. If it moves on to the bladder, the result is a urinary tract infection, or UTI. If inflammation develops, the condition becomes cystitis. UTIs often result when intestinal bacteria find their way into the urethra. A suspected UTI requires prompt diagnosis as the symptoms can also be signs of bladder cancer. Readily treatable in its early stages, bladder cancer is most common in men and is associated with exposure to carcinogens in tobacco smoke and certain industrial chemicals.

Urinary tract infections

Because the female urethra is only about 2 inches (5cm) or so long, UTIs are much more common in women. Beyond frequent, burning or painful urination, patients may develop low back pain and distressing minor incontinence. For patients who suffer repeated UTIs, physicians sometimes recommend drinking cranberry juice, which hinders the growth of harmful bacteria in the bladder. Males can also develop UTIs, and untreated infection may spread to the prostate gland.

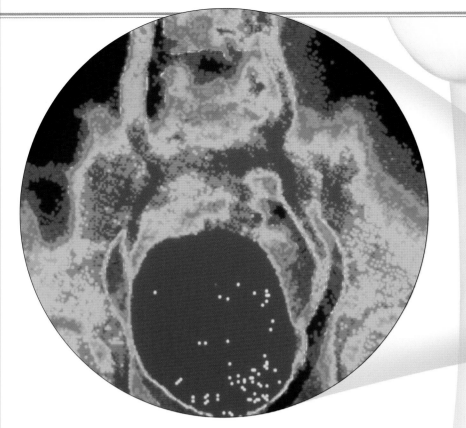

Urinary reflux
Blockage in the urethra or contractions in the bladder can cause urine to back up, which leads to infection. This X-ray urogram shows a buildup of urine (red) in the bladder flowing up to the kidneys (top right and left).

INTERSTITIAL CYSTITIS

Interstitial cystitis, or painful bladder syndrome (PBS), can be diagnosed with a urine sample such as the one shown below, but this disorder is not well understood. Most common in women, it has not been traced to infection, and symptoms vary widely. Most patients report aching or discomfort in the bladder and a frequent urge to urinate. There is currently no cure, but some sufferers are helped by therapeutic drugs and treatments that fill the bladder with fluid, sometimes containing medication.

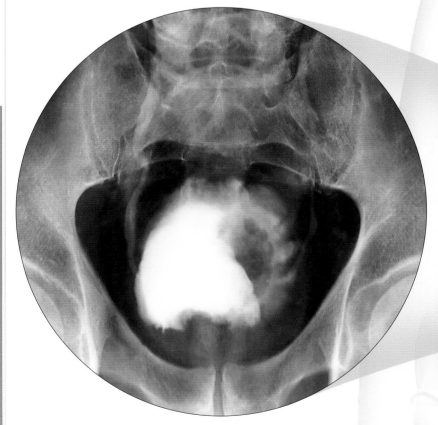

Bladder cancer
A colored X-ray shows a cancerous bladder tumor. Bladder cancer is fairly common, especially among smokers. Early symptoms include blood in the urine and pressure as the mass enlarges.

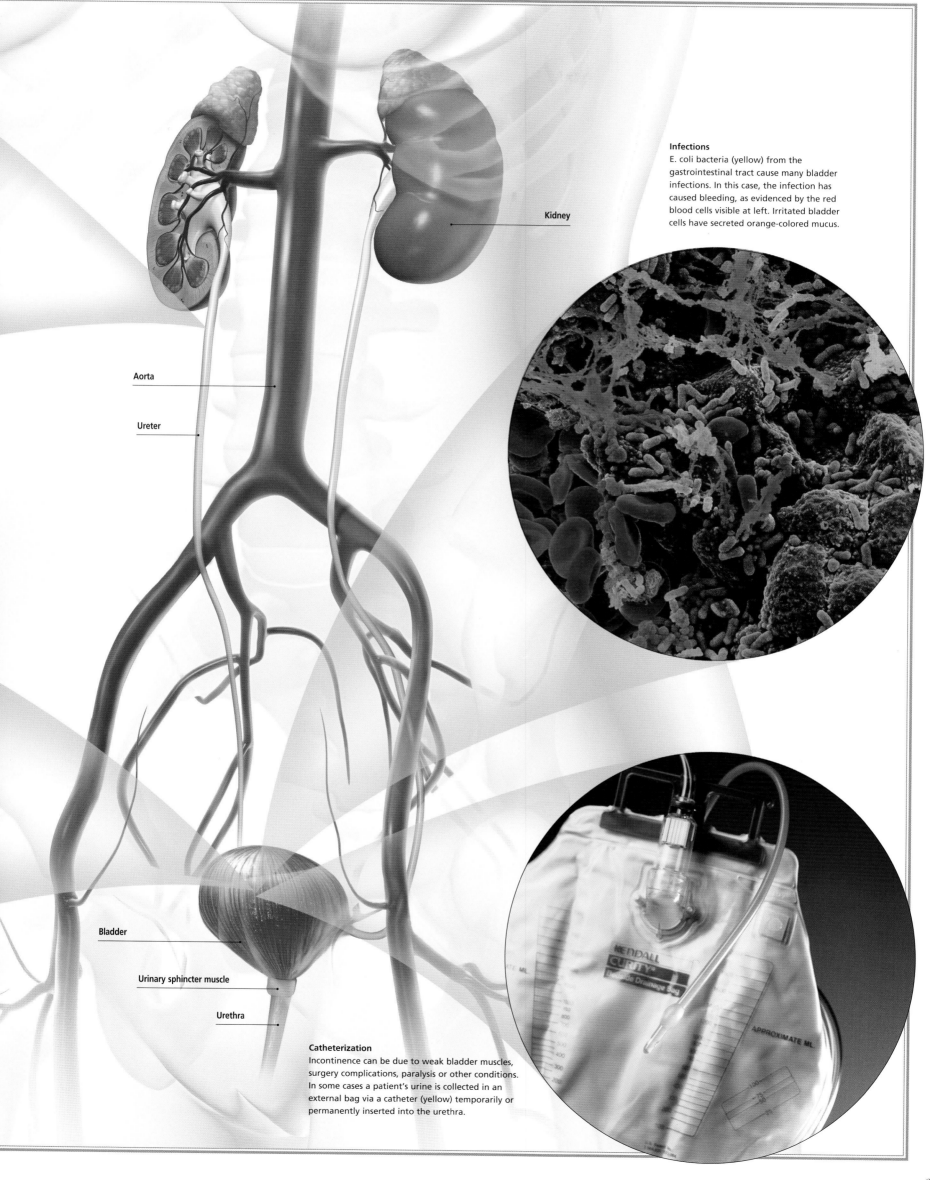

Kidney

Aorta

Ureter

Bladder

Urinary sphincter muscle

Urethra

Infections
E. coli bacteria (yellow) from the gastrointestinal tract cause many bladder infections. In this case, the infection has caused bleeding, as evidenced by the red blood cells visible at left. Irritated bladder cells have secreted orange-colored mucus.

Catheterization
Incontinence can be due to weak bladder muscles, surgery complications, paralysis or other conditions. In some cases a patient's urine is collected in an external bag via a catheter (yellow) temporarily or permanently inserted into the urethra.

KIDNEY DISEASES AND DISORDERS

Some kidney disorders are merely a nuisance, others bothersome and painful but not life-threatening and still others are health emergencies. Kidney stones are hard, often jagged deposits formed from a mix of calcium compounds, uric acid and other substances. Stones form in the kidney's interior cavity, the renal pelvis. Small stones may pass out in urine with little or no trouble, but larger ones can cause excruciating pain when they enter or block a ureter, the bladder or the urethra. An untreated urinary tract infection may eventually take hold in the kidneys and trigger the condition known as pyelonephritis, a serious disorder with symptoms of abdominal pain, fever and mental confusion. Bacterial infections, diabetes or autoimmune disorders can trigger inflammation or other damage that seriously disrupts or destroys the kidneys' ability to cleanse the blood. Hemodialysis or a transplant may be the only long-term solution.

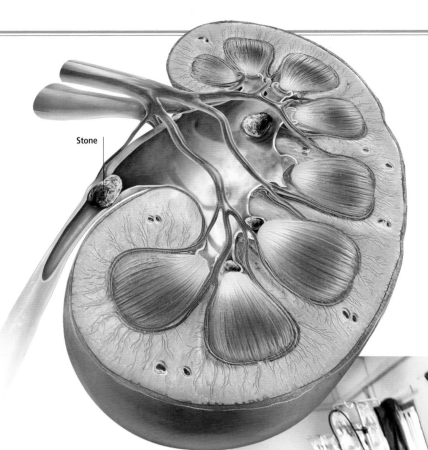

Stone

Kidney stones
Kidney stones consist of calcium salts, uric acid or other material that collects in the renal pelvis, and in rare cases the renal tubules, and may cause excruciating pain as a stone travels through a ureter. The treatment, called lithotripsy, uses high-energy sound waves to fragment the stones.

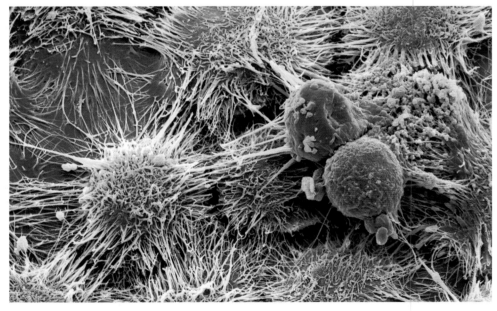

Kidney cancer
Colored pink-purple by a laboratory staining chemical, these cells from a kidney tumor have extended slender pseudopodia (false feet) that enable them to break away from the parent tumor—the first step in metastasis.

POLYCYSTIC KIDNEY DISEASE

Polycystic kidney disease is one of the most common human genetic disorders. Often signaled initially by frequent, severe urinary tract infections, the disease progressively destroys kidney function as fluid-filled cysts develop in millions of nephron tubules. Limiting protein intake and other measures can help most patients remain active until midlife, when accumulating damage requires dialysis and ultimately leads to kidney failure. A kidney transplant is the only cure for this disease.

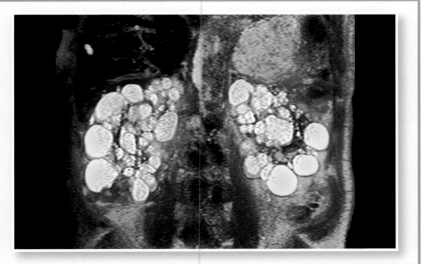

Blood-cleansing dialysis

In hemodialysis, a dialysis machine is most commonly connected to an arteriovenous graft or fistula implanted inside the body. Both are created by connecting an artery to a vein, bypassing capillaries and tissues. Blood is then diverted through tubes made of a permeable membrane-like material. Water around the tubes contains a solution that draws impurities across the membrane and out of the blood, which then flows back into the patient's bloodstream. Patients typically undergo dialysis several times a week, and the procedure usually is considered a temporary measure until a reversible kidney disorder improves or the patient receives a transplant.

Dialysis treatment
In Gaza City, a patient with kidney failure waits to be hooked up to a dialysis machine. Treatment usually takes three to five hours and is repeated three times a week.

Nephritis
The light brown areas of this kidney clearly show damage from inflammation, or nephritis, which may be triggered by an infection or toxin. Unaffected tissue is dark red. Most patients recover once the cause is treated.

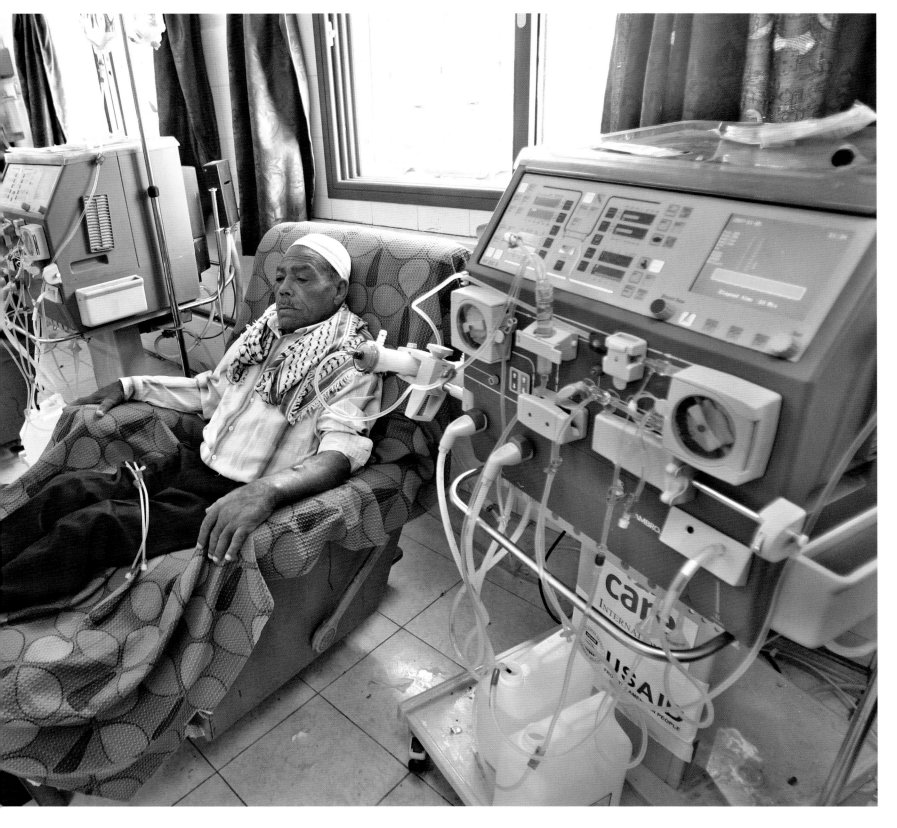

SENSORY SYSTEM

The body's survival depends on a steady stream of sensory input to the brain and spinal cord. Sensory systems are crucial in allowing the central nervous system to receive, manage and respond to changes within and outside the body. The body's sensory apparatus includes millions of sensory receptors of varying complexity and arrangement. There are two categories of human senses: general senses (temperature, touch, pressure and pain) and special senses (vision, hearing, smell, taste and balance). Sensory receptors also fall into groups. Exteroceptors detect external stimuli, such as touch, temperature, sound and light. Interoceptors detect stimuli that arise in internal organs. Proprioceptors, located mostly in muscles, tendons, joints and ligaments, inform the brain about the body's position and movement. All sensory receptors operate alike. They detect a stimulus, such as light, mechanical pressure or a stretching muscle and convert it to a nerve impulse that speeds along sensory neurons to the central nervous system.

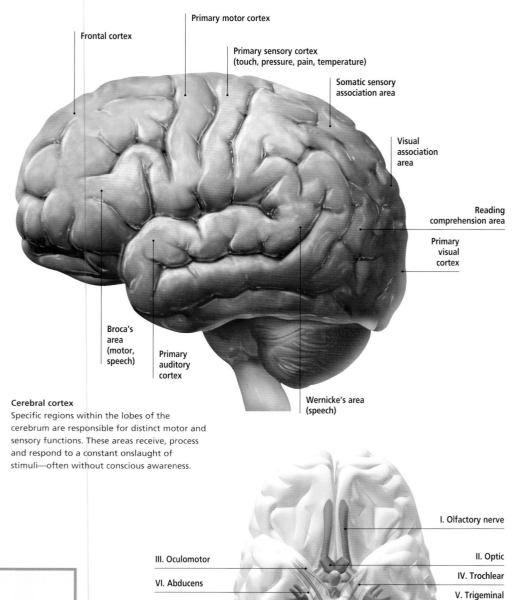

Frontal cortex

Primary motor cortex

Primary sensory cortex
(touch, pressure, pain, temperature)

Somatic sensory association area

Visual association area

Reading comprehension area

Primary visual cortex

Broca's area (motor, speech)

Primary auditory cortex

Wernicke's area (speech)

Cerebral cortex
Specific regions within the lobes of the cerebrum are responsible for distinct motor and sensory functions. These areas receive, process and respond to a constant onslaught of stimuli—often without conscious awareness.

PERCEPTION AND RESPONSE

Sense receptors send nerve impulses speeding along sensory nerves to the brain. There, the appropriate centers interpret incoming signals. You experience a visual image of an apple when brain vision centers process signals from the optic nerves. An initial response is the simple perception "I see an apple." The brain may then issue commands via motor pathways to your arm and hand muscles to pick up the apple.

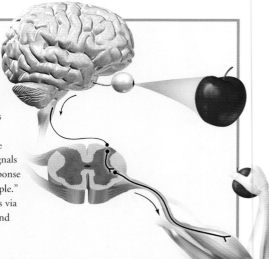

I. Olfactory nerve

III. Oculomotor

VI. Abducens

VIII. Vestibulocochlear

X. Vagus

XI. Accessory

II. Optic

IV. Trochlear

V. Trigeminal

VII. Facial

IX. Glossopharyngeal

XII. Hypoglossal

Cranial nerves
Twelve pairs of nerves convey signals into the brain. Some, like the optic nerve, carry only inputs from sensory receptors in the head; most carry a mix of sensory and motor signals. In addition to muscle contraction signals, these "mixed nerves" also convey information about the body's position, balance and movements from proprioceptors in the muscles.

CRANIAL NERVE	TYPE	FUNCTION
I Olfactory nerve	Sensory	Smell (olfaction)
II Optic nerve	Sensory	Vision
III Oculomotor nerve	Primarily motor	Moves eyeball up, down and inward; raises eyelid; changes lens shape; constricts pupil
IV Trochlear nerve	Primarily motor	Moves eyeball
V Trigeminal nerve	Mixed	Sensory input about touch, temperature, pain in the face, mouth and scalp; movement of muscles of mastication
VI Abducens	Primarily motor	Moves eye laterally (outward)
VII Facial nerve	Mixed	Sensory input from some taste buds; moves facial muscles; increases tear and saliva secretions
VIII Vestibulocochlear nerve	Sensory	Hearing, balance
IX Glossopharyngeal nerve	Mixed	Sensory input from other taste buds; swallowing
X Vagus nerve	Mixed	Parasympathetic sensory innervation to various organs of the chest and abdomen; involved in swallowing, heartbeat, breathing, stomach secretions
XI Accessory nerve	Primarily motor	Moves some neck muscles and some pharynx muscles
XII Hypoglossal nerve	Primarily motor	Moves tongue muscles

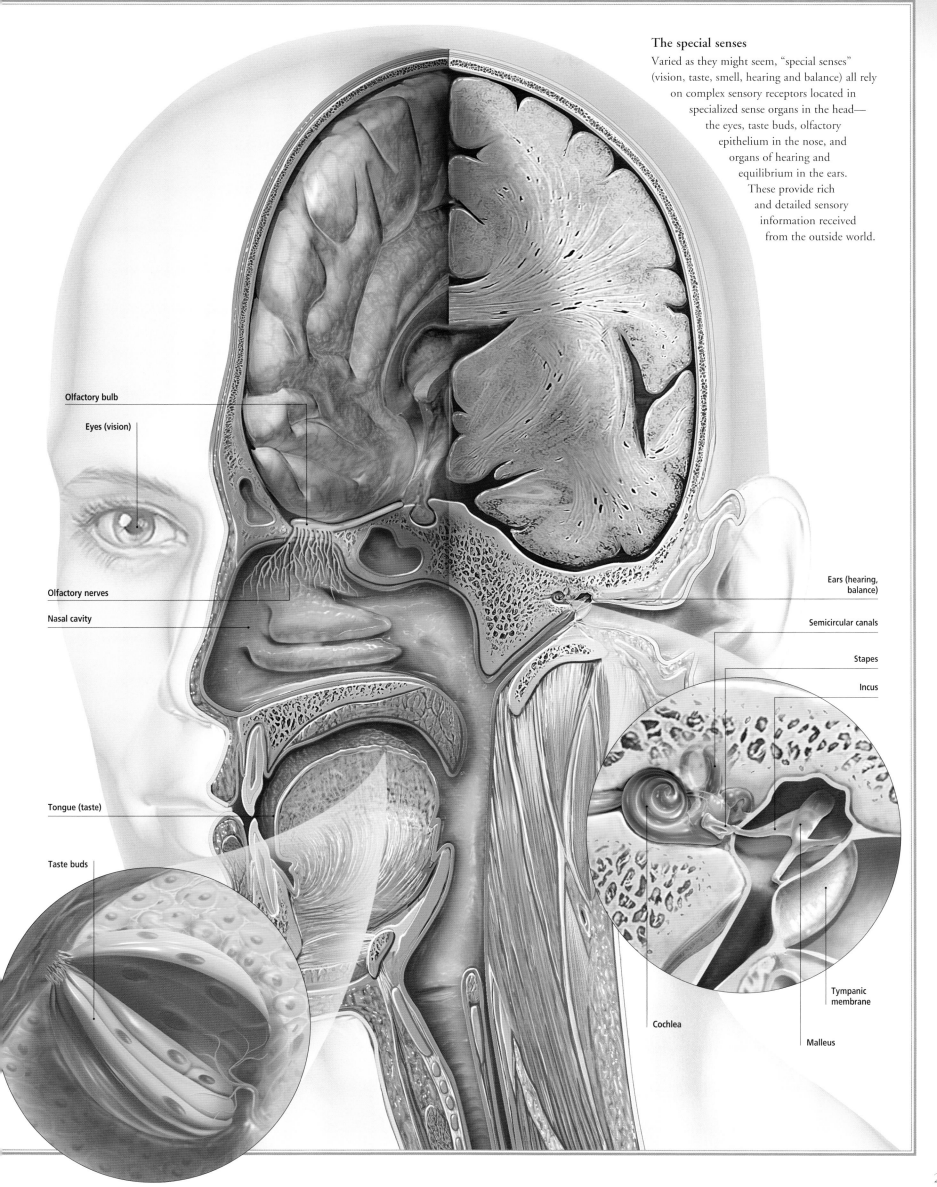

The special senses
Varied as they might seem, "special senses" (vision, taste, smell, hearing and balance) all rely on complex sensory receptors located in specialized sense organs in the head— the eyes, taste buds, olfactory epithelium in the nose, and organs of hearing and equilibrium in the ears. These provide rich and detailed sensory information received from the outside world.

Olfactory bulb

Eyes (vision)

Olfactory nerves

Nasal cavity

Tongue (taste)

Taste buds

Ears (hearing, balance)

Semicircular canals

Stapes

Incus

Tympanic membrane

Cochlea

Malleus

VISION

The three-layered architecture of the eye makes sight possible. The outer layer includes the cornea and the white sclera, a tough, fibrous structure that protects the more delicate parts within. The middle layer includes blood vessels and muscles that move the lens, which focuses light at the back of the eyeball on the third, innermost layer, the retina. The retina contains more than 125 million photoreceptors and support neurons. Axons from some of these neurons form the optic nerve, which carries impulses that enable for vision. Extremely sensitive to light, the photoreceptors consist of tapered cone cells that respond to bright light and blunt-ended rod cells that respond to dim light. Both types of photoreceptors contain photopigments, proteins that absorb different wavelengths, or colors, of light, which ultimately makes for human vision.

Focusing images

Minute changes in the shape or position of the lens can focus visual stimuli on the retina with great precision. A narrow ciliary muscle encircles each lens and is attached to it with ligaments. If light is initially focused behind the retina, the muscle contracts so the lens bulges and the focal point moves forward. If light is focused too far forward, the muscle relaxes and shifts the focal point farther back. These adjustments are known as visual accommodation.

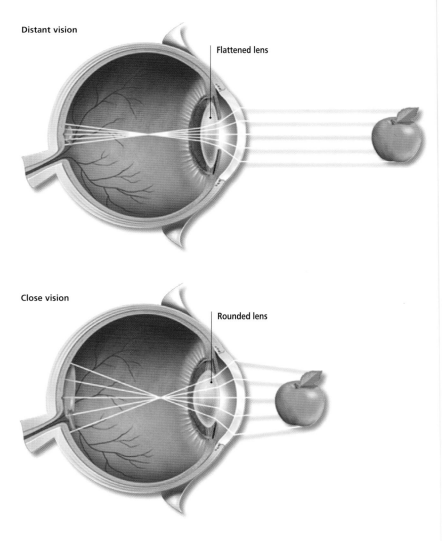

Distant vision

Flattened lens

Close vision

Rounded lens

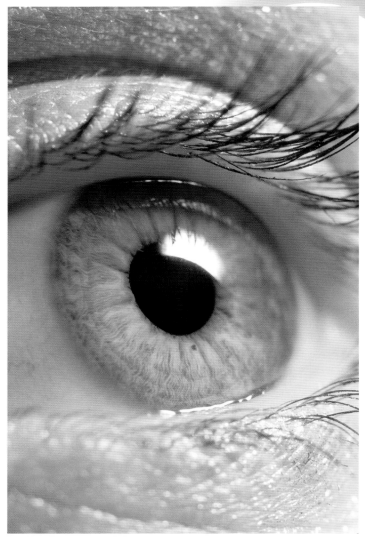

Iris
Smooth muscle fibers in the eye's iris radiate outward in a pattern that is unique to each person. This feature makes the iris an excellent personal identifier, and iris scanning is now used in some security systems.

CURVE OF THE CORNEA

Light rays entering the eye strike the curved surface of the cornea at different angles. As they pass through the cornea their paths bend, then converge at the back of the eyeball. These trajectory changes cause the light rays to stimulate photoreceptors in a pattern that is reversed right to left and upside-down relative to the rays' source. Visual processing in the brain corrects positioning to its normal orientation.

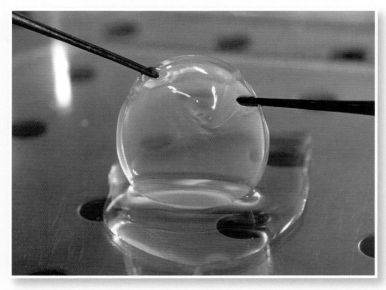

Corneal strip
This strip of transparent tissue has been grown from cells removed from a human cornea and cultured in the laboratory. The tissue can be used to replace a defective cornea.

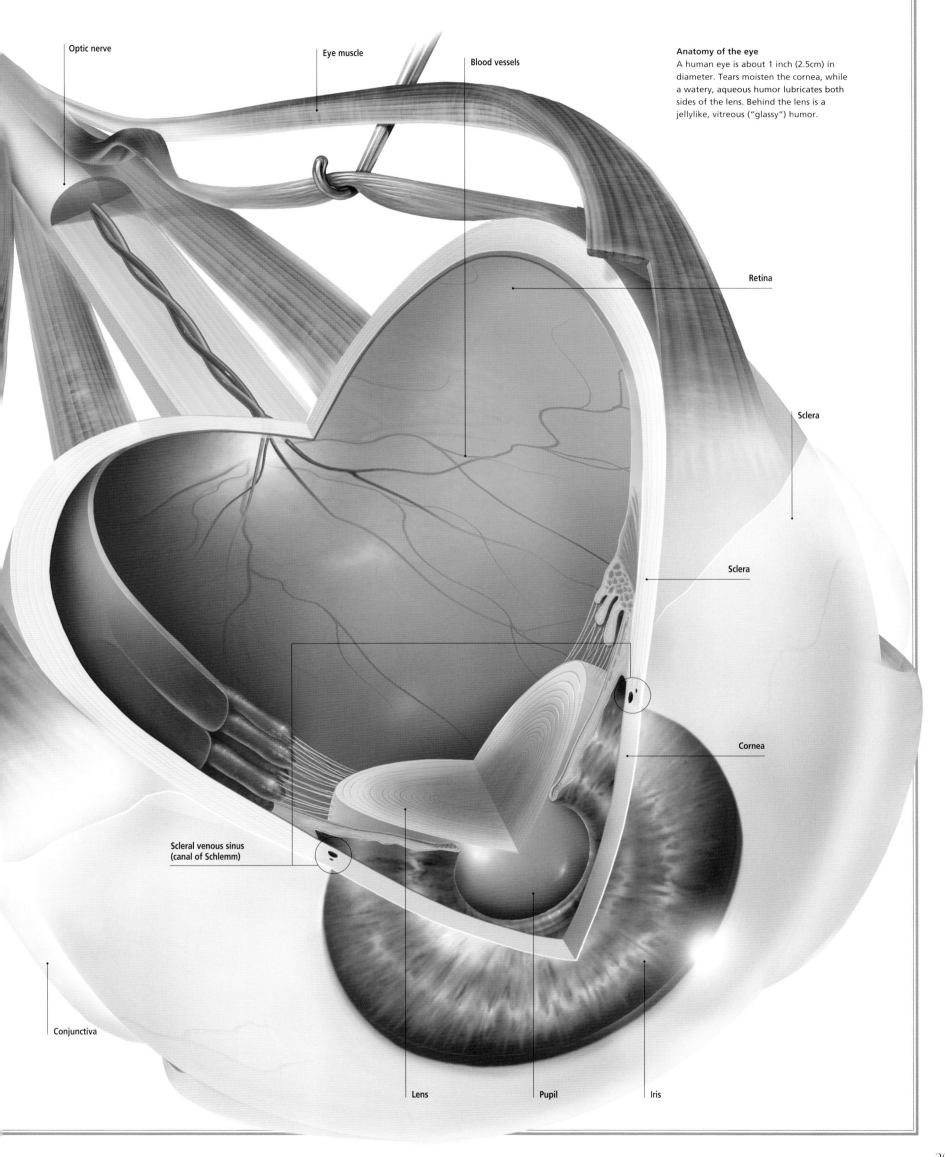

Optic nerve

Eye muscle

Blood vessels

Anatomy of the eye
A human eye is about 1 inch (2.5cm) in diameter. Tears moisten the cornea, while a watery, aqueous humor lubricates both sides of the lens. Behind the lens is a jellylike, vitreous ("glassy") humor.

Retina

Sclera

Sclera

Cornea

Scleral venous sinus (canal of Schlemm)

Conjunctiva

Lens

Pupil

Iris

Visual Processing

Seeing is a complex process that requires chemical reactions to convert light into nerve impulses. The process begins in rods and cones where photopigments intercept light focused on the retina by the lens. The light energy temporarily reconfigures these colored proteins, molding them into a new shape. The change quickly reverses, but it allows the neurons next to the photoreceptors to fire. These newly generated visual signals converge onto a number of other neurons, called ganglion cells. Processing the arriving signals in complex ways, ganglion cells ultimately send nerve impulses speeding along their axons, which converge to form the optic nerve. Arriving first in the primary visual cortex, the signals move swiftly to nearby association centers where raw visual data is processed to form our perception of specific images.

Visual pigments

Without the visual pigments in rods and cones, the human eye would be unable to send nerve impulses along the optic nerves. Each cone contains one of three pigments sensitive to blue, green or red light, while rods contain the pigment rhodopsin, which absorbs blue-green light wavelengths typical of dim environments. A rhodopsin molecule is a combination of the proteins opsin and cis-retinal, a compound formed from vitamin A. Consuming too little vitamin A can impair a person's vision, especially at night.

Bending light
Light rays refract, or bend, when they pass from air to water which is why the swimmer's arms appear bent and distorted in this photo. Light entering the fluid-filled interior of the eye is bent toward a focal point at the back of the retina.

Like Night and Day

The rhodopsin in rods responds when even a small amount of light enters the eye, so rods are crucial for vision in poorly lit surroundings. Collectively, the three cone pigments are the basis for sharp, vibrant daytime vision. The nature of available light wavelengths can thus alter our perception of visual phenomena. Objects viewed at night, when cone pigments are inactive, always seem a bit fuzzier than they do during the day.

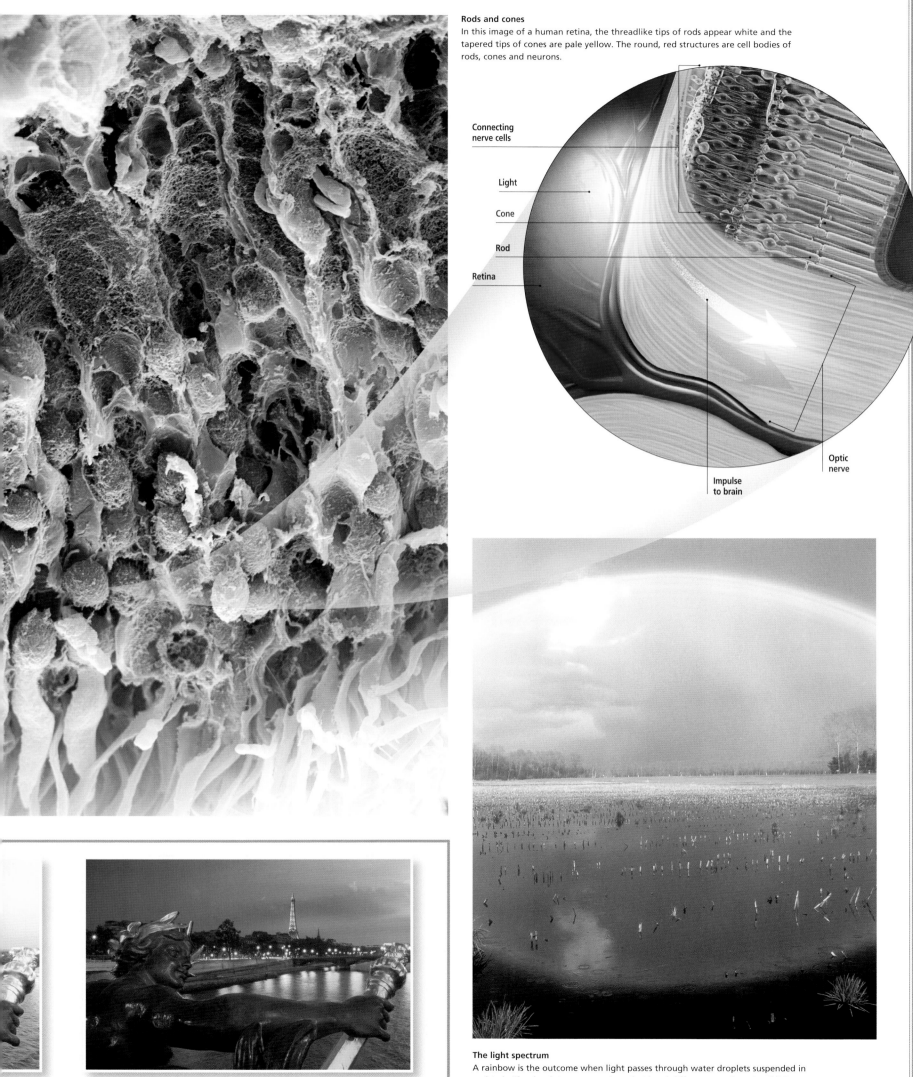

Rods and cones
In this image of a human retina, the threadlike tips of rods appear white and the tapered tips of cones are pale yellow. The round, red structures are cell bodies of rods, cones and neurons.

Connecting nerve cells

Light

Cone

Rod

Retina

Impulse to brain

Optic nerve

The light spectrum
A rainbow is the outcome when light passes through water droplets suspended in moist air. The droplets serve as prisms that bend different wavelengths of light at different angles, producing a band of colors.

OPTICAL ILLUSIONS

Even worms are able to detect light, but human vision is a sophisticated sense that can determine the shape and position of visual stimuli as well as their brightness, movement and distance from the viewer. This versatility comes from different fields in the retina, where photoreceptors supply signals to various groups of impulse-firing neurons. Each group responds best to a specific category of stimuli: spots of light ringed with dark, hard-edged lines, motion or some other attribute. Optical illusions result from the brain's efforts to sort confusing or unusual visual stimuli into these pre-programmed categories—to make the visual input fit patterns the brain commonly encounters. Although optical illusions may seem like faulty visual processing, in reality they provide a window into the brain's resources for interpreting a lifelong string of unpredictable visual stimuli.

Sorting sights

The brain's preset visual patterns include broad classes, such as "shadow," "sharp edge" and "tilted line," and many intriguing optical illusions exploit neurological processes geared to fit visual phenomena into one of these standard groupings. Neural processing also equalizes any perceived size differences between shapes that are close to each other, such as a circle inside a square.

DIAGNOSTIC ILLUSIONS

Some illusions are brought on by diseases and disorders. Migraine headaches and some forms of epilepsy share a variety of symptoms, including visual phenomena called auras. Characteristics of the aura can help a physician distinguish between the two disorders. Neural impulses that are stimulated at the onset of a migraine frequently trigger images of zig-zagging black and white patterns that may last up to 20 minutes. Epileptic auras often feature multicolored circles and usually last only a minute or two.

Micropsia and macropsia
In Alice-in-Wonderland syndrome, or micropsia, swelling around the cornea results in objects appearing much smaller than they are. In macropsia the reverse occurs, and objects appear much bigger than they are. Both disorders are associated with brain tumors, migraine headaches and in rare cases, epilepsy.

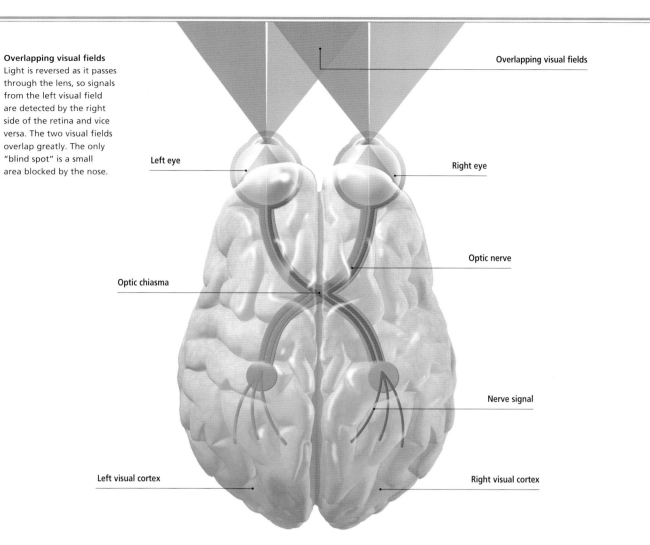

Overlapping visual fields

Light is reversed as it passes through the lens, so signals from the left visual field are detected by the right side of the retina and vice versa. The two visual fields overlap greatly. The only "blind spot" is a small area blocked by the nose.

Overlapping visual fields

Left eye

Right eye

Optic nerve

Optic chiasma

Nerve signal

Left visual cortex

Right visual cortex

What do you see?

Given two possible interpretations of an image—here a goblet or two faces in profile—the brain may switch between the two. Below, contrasting tiles produce visual signals of contrasting intensity. The lines between the tiles are parallel, but the brain's effort to manage the contrasting inputs makes them appear jagged.

Mirror tricks

Mirror tricks resemble optical illusions. A mirror placed at a right angle to the centerline of this boy's body reflects the side facing it, making it appear as if the boy's entire body is facing the viewer.

HEARING

The ears detect sound waves and convert them to nerve impulses that travel to the brain. The ear's outer flap, the pinna, receives sound waves and channels them to the middle ear, where tiny interlocking bones amplify the wave energy and transfer it to fluid in the inner ear. The waves literally have a ripple effect that is the force behind hearing. In the tiny, curling cochlea, the waves create vibrations in a membrane that presses on the ear's mechanoreceptors—cells with delicate hairlike structures called stereocilia protruding from them. As incoming vibrations bend the stereocilia, the hairs generate volleys of nerve impulses that move to the brain via the cochlear nerve. When the pressure ceases, the hairs straighten and nerve impulses stop. Although vibrating fluid is the direct trigger for auditory signals, the vibrations physically track those of the original sound waves—so a person perceives sounds as they were produced in air.

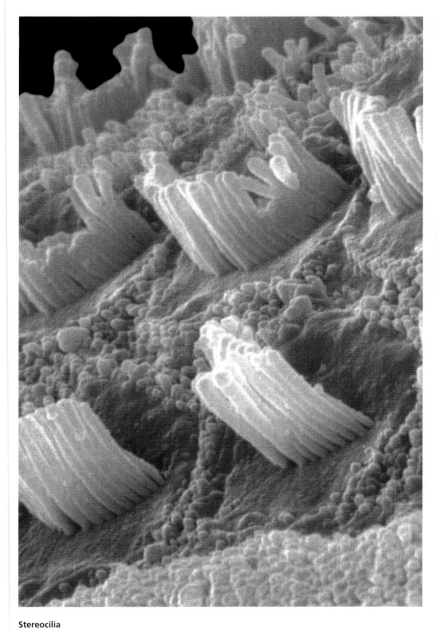

Cochlear nerve

Organ of Corti

The ear's sensors
The coiled cochlea contains the ear's sound sensors—rows of hair cells in a ribbon of tissue called the organ of Corti.

MIDDLE EAR INFECTION

To equalize changes in external air pressure, air enters or exits the middle ear—often with a "pop"—via the Eustachian tubes, which lead to the upper throat. Unrelieved pressure due to congestion or some other cause can be quite painful and can even cause hearing damage. Microbes in the nose or throat can also travel up the Eustachian tubes to the middle ears. The resulting infection, called otitis media, is the most common ear ailment in children and can lead to earaches and fluid or pus secretion.

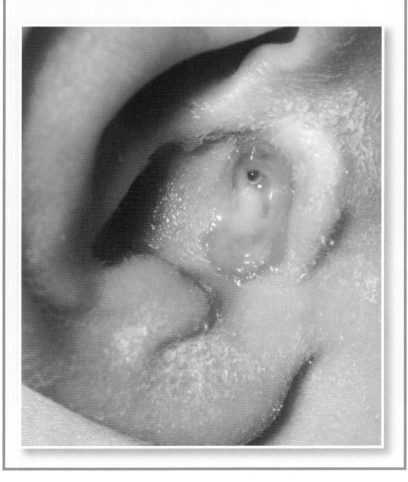

Stereocilia
The cochlea's 16,000 hair cells each have about 100 stereocilia protruding from them. When pressure waves traveling in the cochlear fluid push a membrane against stereocilia, it stimulates a hair cell to fire nerve impulses.

Sound waves

Hearing is the result of a biological domino effect. When you clap your hands, the air between them forms invisible sound waves. Speeding through air at about 1000 feet (305m) per second, the waves provide the force that makes inner ear fluid vibrate. Those vibrations set up pressure waves that bend the ear's sensory hairs. A sound's frequency reflects the number of waves produced in a given time; the faster that waves are generated, the higher a sound's pitch.

A sound transfer system
The body's smallest bones are the interlocking malleus, incus and stapes. When sound waves vibrate the eardrum, the malleus begins vibrating at the same frequency. Its motion transfers to the incus, stapes and finally to the oval window, creating pressure waves in the cochlear fluid.

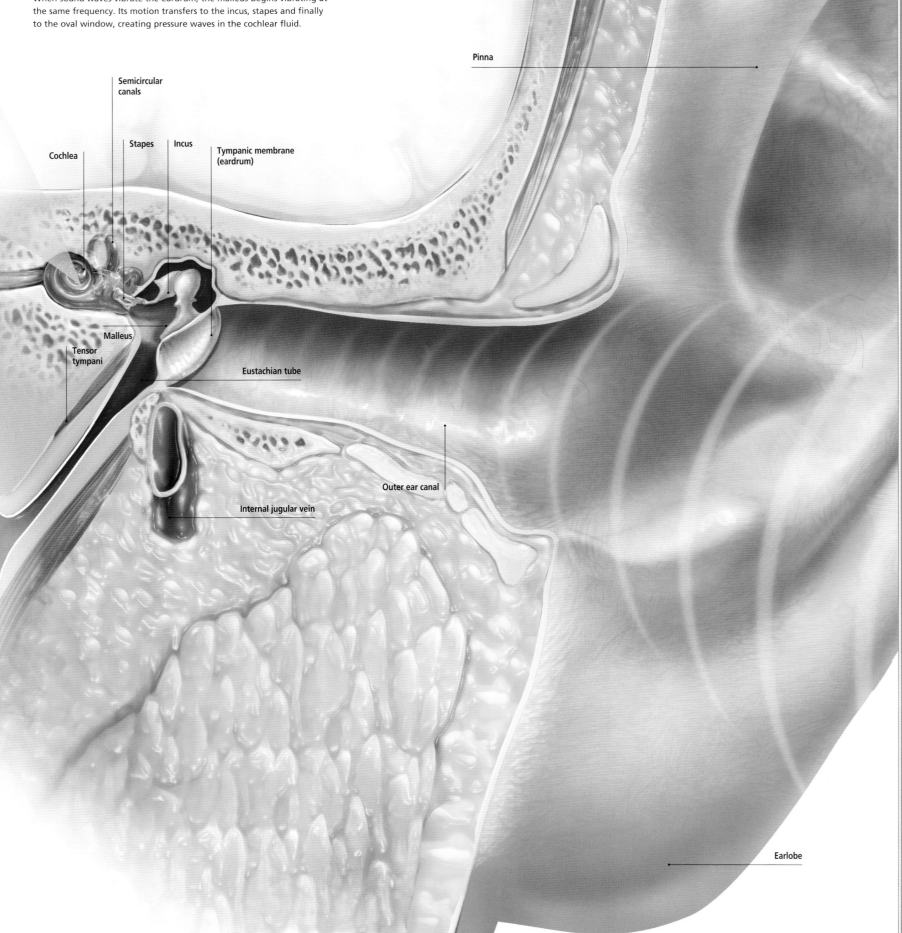

Pinna

Semicircular canals

Stapes

Incus

Cochlea

Tympanic membrane (eardrum)

Malleus

Tensor tympani

Eustachian tube

Outer ear canal

Internal jugular vein

Earlobe

BALANCE

Stand straight and the body's position feels stable, but when riding in a rollercoaster the body instantly senses when the car drops sharply or achieves great speed.

The sense of natural body position is called equilibrium or balance. Our organs of equilibrium are located in the inner ear in a system of fluid-filled sacs and looping channels called the vestibular apparatus. There, sensory hair cells register changes in the head's position including linear movements, as in normal walking, and complex motions, such as twirling across a dance floor, that combine acceleration or deceleration with rotation. The brain gathers input from other sensory systems as it monitors the body's position. The eyes provide visual cues about the direction of movements and proprioceptors in skeletal muscles, joints, tendons and ligaments convey information about the degree of stretching in those tissues—sensory feedback that assists the brain in its task of maintaining equilibrium.

Stay balanced!
Balancing on a surfboard challenges the brain to integrate an influx of sensory signals from the inner ear, eye and muscle proprioceptors. The resulting muscle activity seeks to maintain upright posture despite gravity's downward pull.

PROPRIORECEPTORS

Proprioceptors are sensors in synovial joints, skeletal muscles and connections between muscles and tendons. Those known as muscle spindles detect the length or "stretch" of skeletal muscles, allowing the brain to adjust and coordinate muscle contractions to match the demands of the activity involved. The receptors in joints convey information about the positions and movement of our arms, legs, fingers and other parts while those associated with tendons register muscle tension.

Balance organs

The orientation of the semicircular canals corresponds to the three planes of space. Their hair cells respond to movement in fluid in the canals from vertical or horizontal rotation of the head. Receptors in sacs called the utricle and saccule assess static equilibrium, the head's position relative to the ground (the pull of gravity). Chambers in the sacs contain otoliths, shards of calcium carbonate that slide when the head tilts, bending hair cells that trigger nerve impulses.

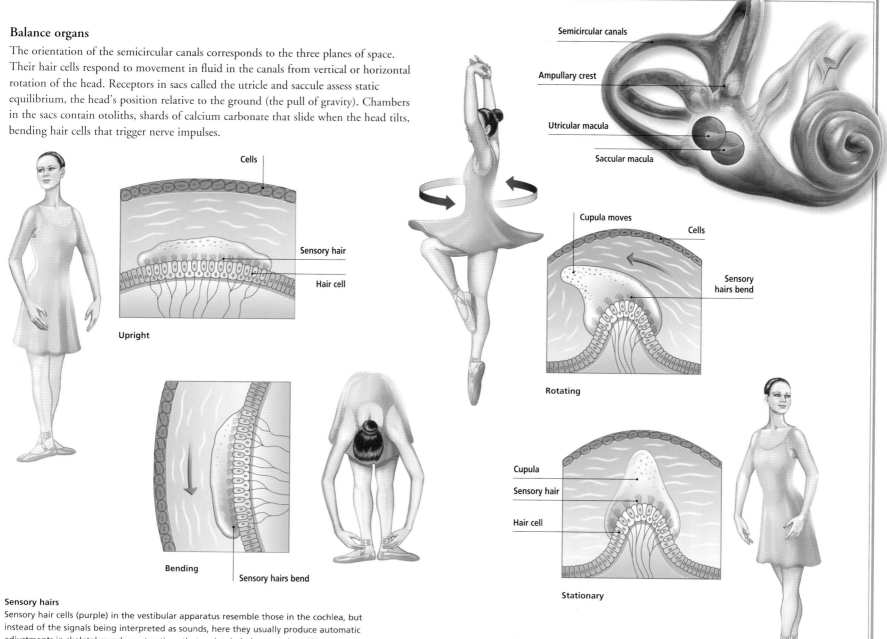

Semicircular canals

Ampullary crest

Utricular macula

Saccular macula

Cells

Sensory hair

Hair cell

Upright

Cupula moves

Cells

Sensory hairs bend

Rotating

Bending

Sensory hairs bend

Cupula

Sensory hair

Hair cell

Stationary

Sensory hairs

Sensory hair cells (purple) in the vestibular apparatus resemble those in the cochlea, but instead of the signals being interpreted as sounds, here they usually produce automatic adjustments in skeletal muscle contractions that maintain balance and equilibrium.

TASTE

Taste, or gustation, is one of the body's two chemical senses. Taste is the province of the estimated 10,000 taste buds clustered in different areas of the tongue's surface and scattered across the palate and throat. Within taste buds are chemoreceptors that are sensitive to chemicals from substances that dissolve in saliva. This sensory ability has survival value. For example, when a person first tastes (and smells) food, the digestive system increases its secretion of digestive enzymes required to break down ingested food and extract its nutrients. In addition, many toxic substances taste bitter, and spoiled food often has a telltale flavor that flags it as potentially harmful. Research shows that individual taste preferences are shaped by genetic variations in taste bud receptors, and by the particular flavors people are exposed to during infancy and childhood. Those differences help explain why some people prefer or strongly dislike certain foods.

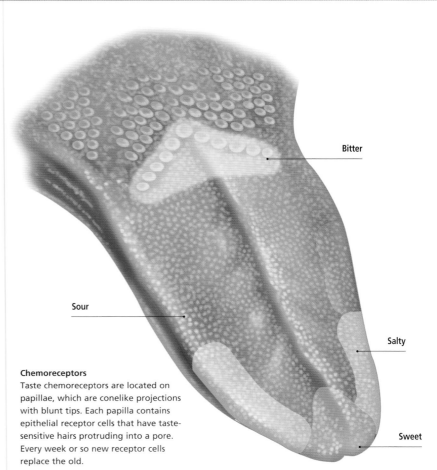

Chemoreceptors
Taste chemoreceptors are located on papillae, which are conelike projections with blunt tips. Each papilla contains epithelial receptor cells that have taste-sensitive hairs protruding into a pore. Every week or so new receptor cells replace the old.

SUPERTASTERS

Genes determine the capacity of taste receptors in taste buds to detect particular chemicals. As a result, people who inherit certain forms of genes, especially those coding for bitter tastes, are especially sensitive to some tastants. Common examples are PTC (phenylthiocarbamate), a chemical in cruciferous vegetables such as cabbage and broccoli, and naringin, a bitter-tasting component of grapefruit juice. Overall, humans can detect more than 100 different bitter-tasting substances.

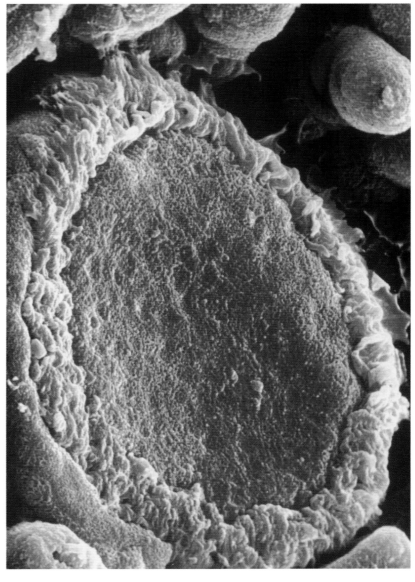

Taste buds
This taste bud sits on a large papilla along the tongue. Taste buds are mainly located in this spot, but can also be scattered across other areas, such as the palate, pharynx and epiglottis. No matter their location, taste buds all have the same structure.

Categories of taste

Physiologists recognize five primary tastes: sweet, sour, salty, bitter and umami, the savory taste associated with protein-rich foods, such as meat and pungent cheeses. Each category is associated with particular tastant chemicals, such as the sodium that stimulates salt-sensitive receptors, and sugars, amino acids and alcohols that stimulate sweet-sensitive receptors. All of these chemoreceptors steadily wear out and are replaced. This turnover slows with age, perhaps helping to explain why some older adults perceive that certain foods have "lost their flavor."

A world of tastes
The variety of a spice market reflects ancient practices of using pungent spices to mask the "off" flavors and odors of meats and other fresh foods that had to be stored without the benefit of refrigeration.

Vallate papilla
These raised, fleshy areas at the back of the tongue contain clusters of taste buds.

Hard palate
The membrane covering this bony roof of the mouth also contains some taste receptors.

Vallate papillae
These large papillae toward the rear of the tongue are readily visible.

Filiform papillae
Most tongue papillae are this type, which do not contain taste buds.

Fungiform papillae
Mushroom-shaped fungiform papillae are located mainly on the tongue's sides and tip.

SMELL

Humans possess an estimated five million olfactory receptors of various types that are sensitive to thousands of odor molecules. This diverse array of receptors associated with the sense of smell may be responsible for as much as 80 percent of the experience of taste. Perceived flavors are generally a blend of the five primary tastes, the texture of a food and cues from odor molecules that make their way into the nasal passages. A head cold makes food taste bland due to a thicker than usual coating of mucus in the olfactory epithelium. Signals related to both taste and smell are split when they reach the brain. Some taste signals are relayed to centers in the parietal lobe while others travel to the "emotional brain" in the limbic system. Likewise, processing in the olfactory bulbs provides our immediate perception of odors, but neural connections with the limbic system can link particular odors with lifelong memories and emotions.

The ancient chemical sense

The ability to sense chemicals may be as old as life itself. Neurobiologists hypothesize that the primitive brains in ancient insects and similar creatures were devoted almost entirely to processing information about environmental chemicals. The early vertebrates of 400 million years ago had brains with massive olfactory bulbs, a reflection of the survival value of a keen sense of smell. Although humans and other primates evolved sophisticated vision, modern mammals such as dogs retain a highly refined sense of smell with hundreds of millions of olfactory receptors.

SENSING PHEROMONES

A pheromone is a distinctive chemical used to influence the behavior of others of the same species. For many animals, pheromone signals are essential in locating mates or communicating danger or the presence of food. Although definitive evidence of human pheromones has been elusive, the synchronization of menstrual cycles among women sharing living quarters suggests to some researchers that humans also may be sensitive to pheromone-like odorants. New studies are exploring the intriguing possibility that pheromones help influence sexual attraction.

Nasal cavity lining
This scanning electron micrograph shows nasal cavity lining cells. The lining also has cells that secrete moisture and mucus, which traps bacteria, dust and other particles and keeps them from entering the lungs.

Take a sniff
Like some other mammals, humans sniff foods and other substances. Sniffing draws odor molecules into the upper nasal passages more rapidly than they would arrive during normal breathing. Inside the nasal cavity, olfactory hairs (left) collect chemical information from the circulating molecules.

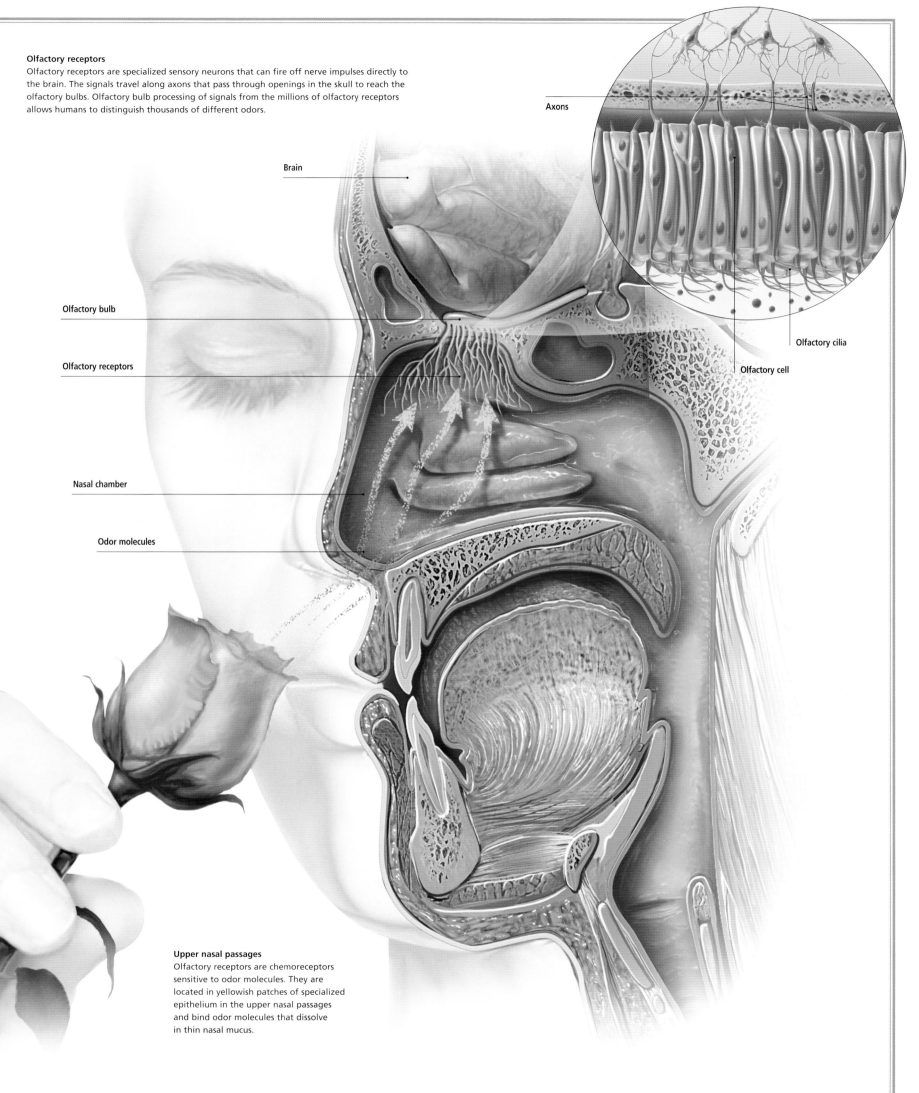

Olfactory receptors

Olfactory receptors are specialized sensory neurons that can fire off nerve impulses directly to the brain. The signals travel along axons that pass through openings in the skull to reach the olfactory bulbs. Olfactory bulb processing of signals from the millions of olfactory receptors allows humans to distinguish thousands of different odors.

Axons

Olfactory cilia

Olfactory cell

Brain

Olfactory bulb

Olfactory receptors

Nasal chamber

Odor molecules

Upper nasal passages

Olfactory receptors are chemoreceptors sensitive to odor molecules. They are located in yellowish patches of specialized epithelium in the upper nasal passages and bind odor molecules that dissolve in thin nasal mucus.

TOUCH

The somatic, or "body," senses of touch, pressure and vibration depend on receptors in and just below the skin and in mucous membranes. Some of these sensors are free nerve endings, such as those that wrap the base of a hair follicle and fire impulses when something moves the hair shaft—be it a gust of wind or a crawling bug. Others are more elaborate mechanoreceptors embedded in a capsule. When tactile receptors are activated, the brain receives information about the location, shape, size and texture of what has touched the skin. Such signals convey the tactile difference between a rubber ball in the hand and a drop of water dribbling down the arm. Most tactile receptors adapt, either rapidly or slowly, and gradually become less sensitive to stimuli. Fast adaptation of sensors that detect fine touch and skin pressure explains why people quickly become less aware of wearing eyeglasses or clothing.

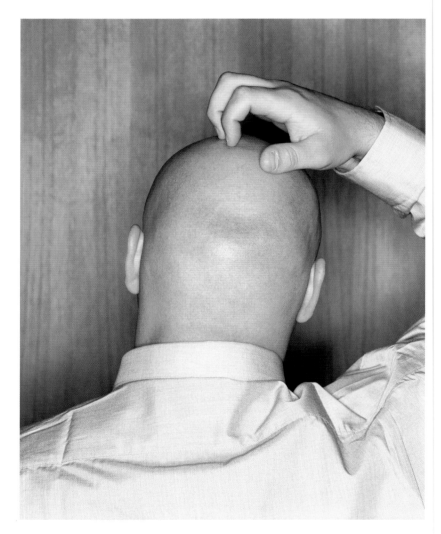

Heat, cold and itching

Free nerve endings detect most stimuli responsible for itchiness, tickles and sensations of heat and cold. Itching often is due to inflammation caused by chemicals such as the protein bradykinin. Receptors in the dermis, the second layer of skin, are sensitive to warmth and generally register thermal stimuli between 90° and 118°F (32–48°C). Receptors for cold lie closer to the skin surface and respond to stimuli ranging from 50° to 105°F (10–40°C). Colder temperatures activate pain sensors.

INTERNAL SENSATIONS

Blood vessels and many internal organs contain interoceptors, which are sensors that respond to events below the body surface, such as the stretching of tissue or a chemical change. Usually the brain monitors these signals below the level of consciousness, so often people are not aware of such internal sensations. At times, however, as when a large meal distends the stomach or accumulating urine stretches the bladder, interoceptor signals are perceived as internal pressure or pain.

Meissner's corpuscle
Hairless skin contains these sensors attuned to vibration and light pressure.

Dermis
This layer contains free nerve endings around hair follicles and receptors sensitive to skin stretching and deep pressure.

Ruffini's corpuscle
This sensor is located in the dermis and subcutaneous tissue, where it detects deep, sustained pressure.

Basal cell layer
In this lower epidermal layer are Merkel disks, which respond to light pressure.

Pacinian corpuscle
Rapid vibrations and deep pressure stimulate this sensor in dermis and subcutaneous ligaments and elsewhere.

Receptors are not drawn to scale.
Meissner = 5.9 inches (150mm) long
Ruffini = 0.039–0.078 inches (1–2mm) long
Pacinian = 0.039 inches (1mm) long

Subcutaneous layer
Also called the hypodermis, this fat-rich layer loosely anchors the skin to underlying tissue.

Sensory receptors

Various types of sensory receptors are distributed widely in the body, but familiar touch sensations rely on those in the skin's epidermis, the dermis below it and even in subcutaneous tissue. Free nerve endings are the most common. The receptors shown in the illustration below, such as Ruffini's corpuscle, are not drawn to scale.

Epidermis
This uppermost skin layer is supplied with several types of free nerve endings.

Free nerve endings
Pain, heat and cold stimulate these exposed endings of sensory neurons.

Tactile signals
Human fingertips are extremely well supplied with touch sensors. Like other tactile signals, the nerve impulses they generate travel to the spinal cord, where interneurons relay them to brain processing centers that produce conscious perceptions of the sensations.

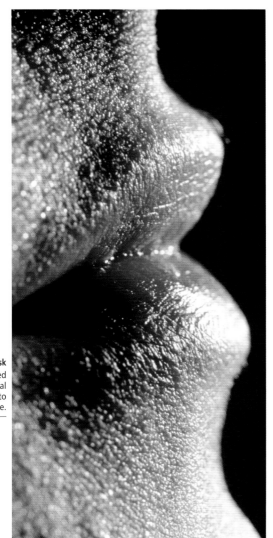

Merkel disk
These flattened structures in the basal cell layer respond to sustained light pressure.

Lips and tongue
The lips and tongue are sensitive to heat and cold as well as to pressure. Per unit of area, they have more free nerve endings and other sensory receptors than any other body part.

PAIN

Pain is a sign of bodily damage and information that is crucial to avoiding or combating injuries. Not surprisingly, the body's pain detectors, millions of free nerve endings called nociceptors, are present everywhere except the brain. Nociceptors produce two general forms of pain—sharp "fast" pain, such as a pin prick or shaving nick that is felt within a tenth of a second after damage occurs, and the aching or throbbing "slow" pain that takes longer to register and lasts longer as well. The stimulus for pain signals may be an injury, chafing or chemical irritation of a tissue, over-stretching, reduced blood flow, muscle spasms or intense heat or cold. Whatever the insult, affected cells release prostaglandins and other chemicals involved in inflammation. Neurons in the central nervous system that receive incoming pain signals release substance P, a chemical that strengthens the brain's responses to pain.

Pain tolerance
Everyone's pain receptors have the same sensory threshold—the stimulus intensity that triggers a nerve impulse. Individuals do differ, however, in their tolerance and ability to cope with pain. Cultural norms, emotional states, age and other factors all shape responses to painful episodes. When pain is prolonged, however, even a high degree of tolerance fades.

NATURAL PAIN RELIEF

The body produces several chemicals that help make pain more bearable. These natural painkillers, endorphins and enkephalins, work by slowing the release of substance P in the brain. Endorphins also function in the brain's "pleasure responses," producing the euphoria some people experience during extended strenuous exercise. Narcotics that produce euphoria, such as morphine and heroin, bind to endorphin receptors in the brain. Consuming alcohol also triggers the endorphin system.

Crystals of beta-endorphin

Referred pain

A quirk in the body's pain signaling system causes "referred pain." In this phenomenon, the brain ascribes pain sensations from an internal organ to some region of the skin. The classic example is pain from a heart attack that is felt in the skin of the left arm or shoulder or between the shoulder blades. Similarly, pain from the ovaries may be felt in skin of the upper abdomen and from the bladder in skin of the buttocks.

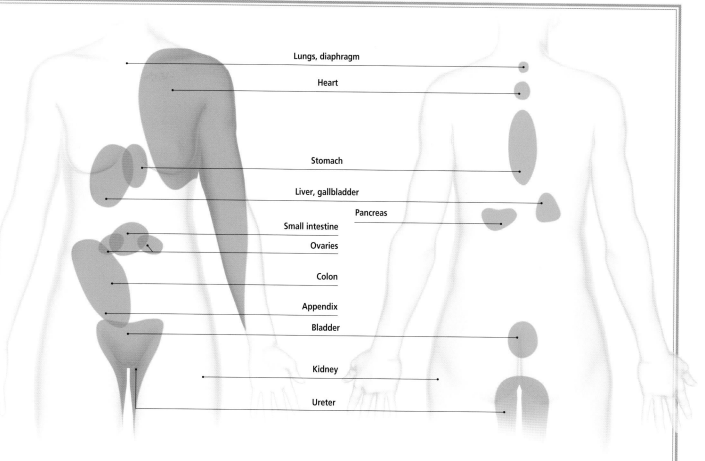

Lungs, diaphragm
Heart
Stomach
Liver, gallbladder
Pancreas
Small intestine
Ovaries
Colon
Appendix
Bladder
Kidney
Ureter

Acupuncture

The ancient Chinese practice of acupuncture employs slender needles to relieve pain by stimulating certain body "pressure points." The points correspond to different body organs and are situated along specific pathways, or channels. There are six primary yin and yang channels on each arm, and six on each leg.

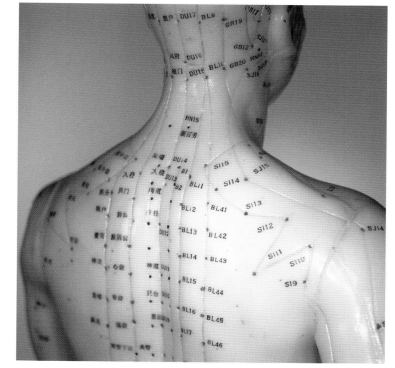

Nociceptors

This visualization shows a nociceptor nerve ending, a sensory receptor that triggers the pain response. Nociceptors are found in any area of the body that can sense pain either externally or internally.

ACUPUNCTURE CHANNEL	LOCATION	AFFECTED BODY AREAS
Three yin channels of the arm	Begin on the chest and travel along the inner surface of the arm to the hand	Lung, pericardium, heart
Three yang channels of the arm	Begin on the hand and travel along the outer surface of the arm to the head	Large intestine, lymphatic system and small intestine
Three yin channels of the leg	Begin on the foot and travel along the inner surface of the leg to the chest	Kidney, liver, spleen
Three yang channels of the leg	Begin on the face near the eye and travel down the body, along the outer surface, to the foot	Bladder, gallbladder, stomach

Eye Diseases and Disorders

Eye ailments have an impact on daily life that ranges from inconvenient to calamitous. The most common and easily treatable eye conditions include myopia (nearsightedness), hyperopia (farsightedness) and astigmatism, in which the cornea is misshapen and does not bend light rays properly. Red-green color blindness is a genetic abnormality in which the eyes lack a normal supply of cone cells with pigments that respond to red and green light. Babies also may be born with inherited defects that cause congenital blindness, and about 5 in every 100,000 are born with retinoblastoma, a cancer of the retina that usually requires removal of the affected eye. A physical blow can detach the retina from the underlying tissue, leading to blindness if the damage is not corrected surgically. Infectious eye diseases such as conjunctivitis afflict millions. Other common eye problems, including glaucoma, cataracts and macular degeneration, often develop as people age.

Cataract Surgery

The lens clouding known as a cataract causes progressive vision loss in millions of people and is the major cause of blindness worldwide. In addition to simple aging, the most common causes include damaging sun exposure, eye injuries, tobacco use and diabetes. With modern treatment advances, cataracts can be removed before they become severe, often using pulses of ultrasound to break up clouded areas of the lens. Surgical replacement of the lens, or intraocular lens implantation, is another common option.

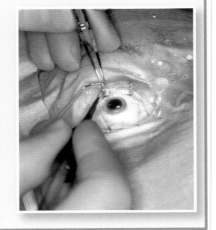

Correcting common vision problems

Myopia and hyperopia can be corrected by adjusting how light rays are bent in the eye. Prescription eyeglasses and contact lenses are the simplest, least expensive strategies. An alternative for mild to moderate nearsightedness is the intracorneal ring, a removable plastic insert that slightly flattens the cornea so that light focuses on the retina. Eye surgeons can use a tiny laser to reshape the cornea. For patients with extreme refractive defects, the lens may be replaced with an implant.

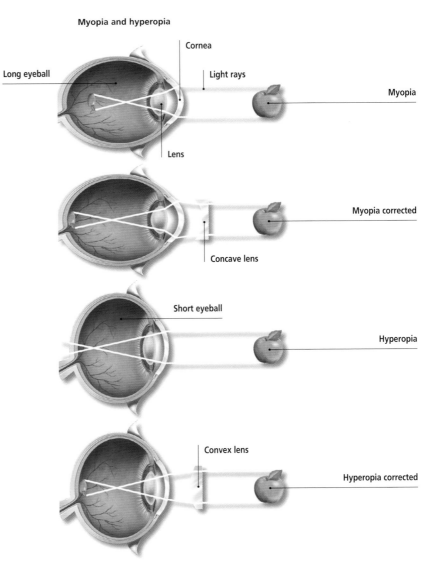

Myopia and hyperopia

Long eyeball — Cornea — Light rays — Myopia — Lens

Myopia corrected — Concave lens

Short eyeball — Hyperopia

Convex lens — Hyperopia corrected

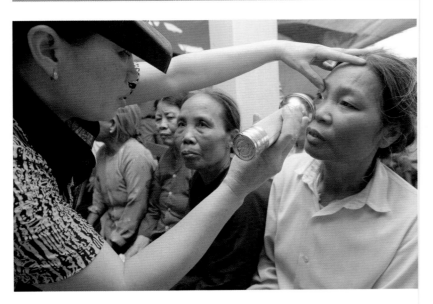

Trachoma
Trachoma is a contagious bacterial infection of the cornea and conjunctiva.
Patients lose their sight unless the infection is treated with antibiotics.
Trachoma is a leading cause of blindness in parts of Africa and Asia.

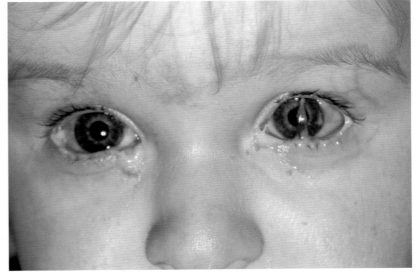

Conjunctivitis
This child has bacterial conjunctivitis, a pus-producing infection of the conjunctiva—the clear mucous membrane lining the eyelids and covering the white of the eye. Antibiotic eye drops or ointments are the usual cure.

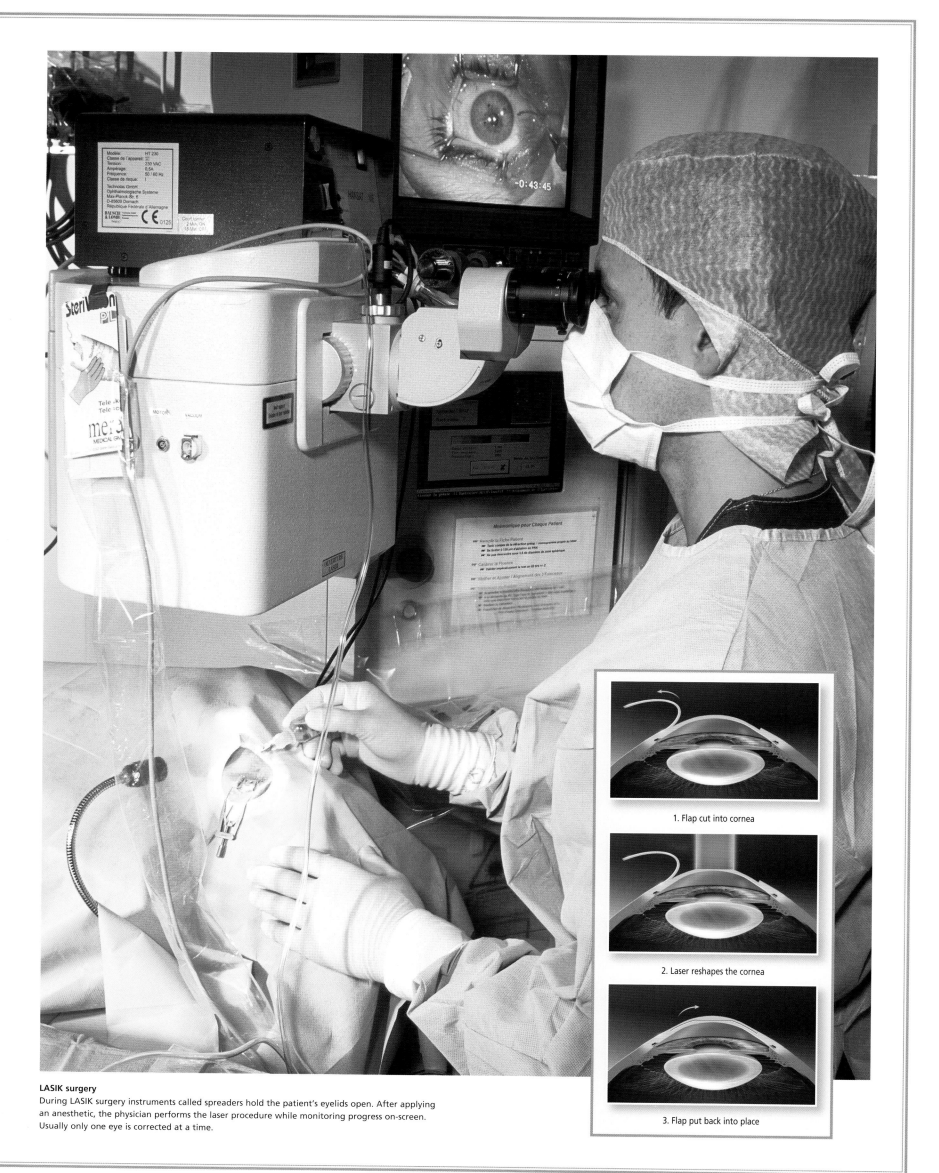

LASIK surgery

During LASIK surgery instruments called spreaders hold the patient's eyelids open. After applying an anesthetic, the physician performs the laser procedure while monitoring progress on-screen. Usually only one eye is corrected at a time.

1. Flap cut into cornea

2. Laser reshapes the cornea

3. Flap put back into place

EAR DISEASES AND DISORDERS

The most notorious ear ailment is otitis media, inflammation of the middle ear. Every ear region is vulnerable to disorders. Inflammation of the outer ear canal, called otitis externa, may be a complication of eczema, the result of over-vigorous efforts to remove earwax or due to excess moisture that provides a breeding ground for bacteria or fungi responsible for "swimmer's ear." Some individuals have a congenital hearing deficit, and others suffer from temporary or long-term conduction deafness in which a ruptured eardrum, an obstruction, such as a plug of earwax, or age-related changes in the tiny middle ear bones prevent normal sound transmission. Millions of adults develop tinnitus, a harmless but often distressing buzzing, whistling or ringing in the ears. Tinnitus can run in families and it is often an early sign of the onset of sensory or sensorineural deafness.

Sensory hearing loss

Sensorineural deafness, the most common form of hearing loss, often results from aging, genetic factors or noise-related damage to the inner ear's hair cells. As their fragile cilia bend or break off, sensory neurons break down and no longer transmit impulses to the cochlear nerve. Hair cells that respond to high sound frequencies are the most vulnerable; many people with sensorineural deafness first notice trouble hearing high-pitched sounds. Sophisticated electronic hearing aids or cochlear implants can offset a significant amount of sensory hearing loss.

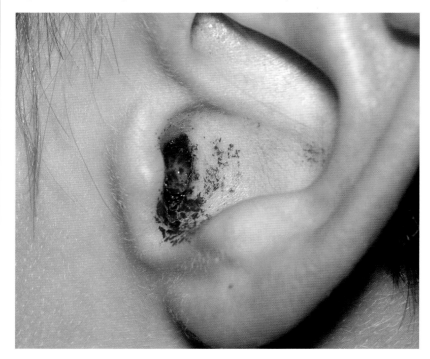

Eardrum disorders
A bloody discharge may signify a perforated eardrum. Such injuries are fairly common because the tympanic membrane is extremely thin and easily ruptured by infection or even a swab inserted to remove earwax. Most cases heal within a few weeks.

Diagnosing hearing loss
This magnetic resonance image (MRI) shows the brain and nerve complexes in an auditory canal. MRIs are often the best method for diagnosing hearing problems. This image shows nerves to the inner ear (vestibulocochlear nerve)—circled—and could reveal any disorders or diseases, such as a tumor, that lead to hearing loss.

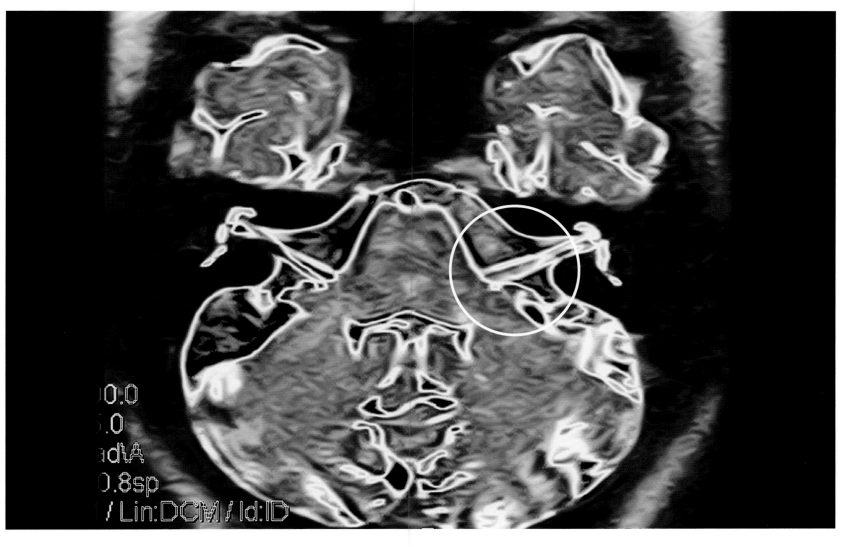

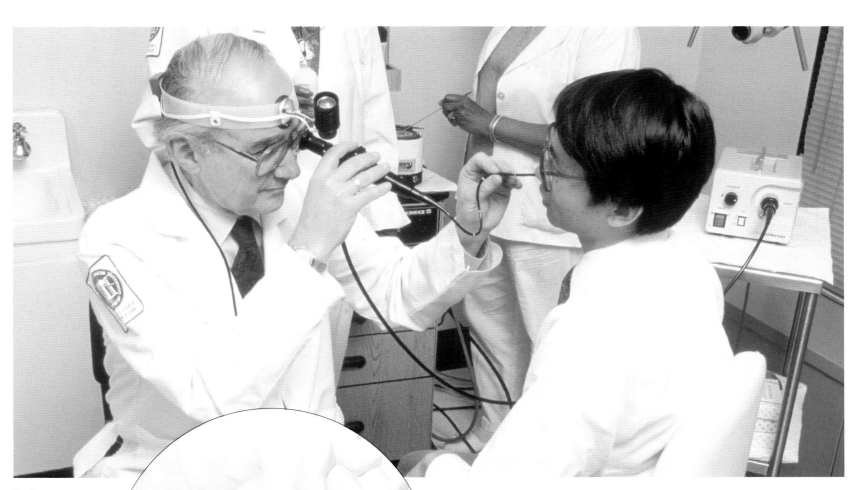

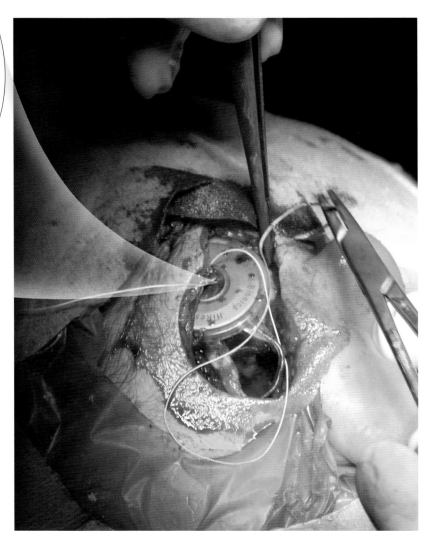

Tinnitus
A physician employs a fiber-optic otoscope to examine a patient with tinnitus, a persistent ringing, clicking or buzzing in the ears. The disorder sometimes runs in families but may have a wide range of causes.

Cochlear implant
Converts sound into electrical signals, which the brain interprets.

NOISE POLLUTION

The increasingly noisy world that surrounds most human beings is a major contributor to sensory hearing loss. The inner ear's hair cells begin to show signs of damage when routinely exposed to sounds louder than 75–80 decibels. Exposure to a single extremely loud sound, such as a shotgun blast or explosion, can cause immediate and permanent injury. Audiologists strongly recommend protective ear wear for people who operate noisy equipment or who work around noisy machines or vehicles.

LOUDNESS OF COMMON SOUNDS	
SOUND	DB
TICKING CLOCK	10
RUSTLING LEAVES	20
NORMAL CONVERSATION	50–60
URBAN STREET NOISE, BUSY RESTAURANT	75–80
KITCHEN BLENDER (HIGH SPEED)	90
BOOM BOX STEREO (HIGH VOLUME)	100+
JET ENGINE ON RUNWAY	110–150
ROCK CONCERT	120–130

Cochlear implant surgery
People with a profound hearing loss due to damage of the cochlea's hair cells may receive a cochlear implant. External parts transduce sounds into electrical impulses, which internal electrodes then transmit to the cochlear nerve.

FEMALE REPRODUCTIVE SYSTEM

A female's reproductive system provides the biological means to produce a new generation. The system consists of ovaries, oviducts, the uterus, cervix and vagina. Of these, the ovaries are the primary reproductive organs, and they may perform their function for 40 years or more. As a girl enters puberty, her ovaries begin to manufacture estrogens, the female sex hormones that influence the development of secondary sexual traits such as adult breasts, hips and buttocks. During a woman's reproductive years, estrogen, progesterone and other hormones from her ovaries and brain ebb and flow, typically in a 28-day cycle. During this menstrual cycle one or more eggs develop and are released, available to be fertilized by a male's sperm and so launch a pregnancy. If no egg is fertilized, the cycle will begin anew, normally repeating over and over until it slows and stops at menopause.

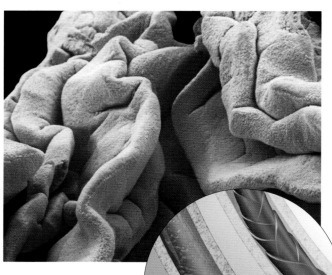

The oviduct
An oviduct is not physically attached to the ovary, so ovulated eggs must cross a narrow gap to enter it. Despite the umbrella-like fimbriae positioned over the entrance to the oviduct, some eggs are lost into the abdominal cavity.

Hair

Oviduct

Inside an oviduct
Fertilization usually occurs while an egg is in an oviduct, a slender channel that is only about the width of a hair. Some cells lining the tube have beating cilia that move the egg toward the uterus.

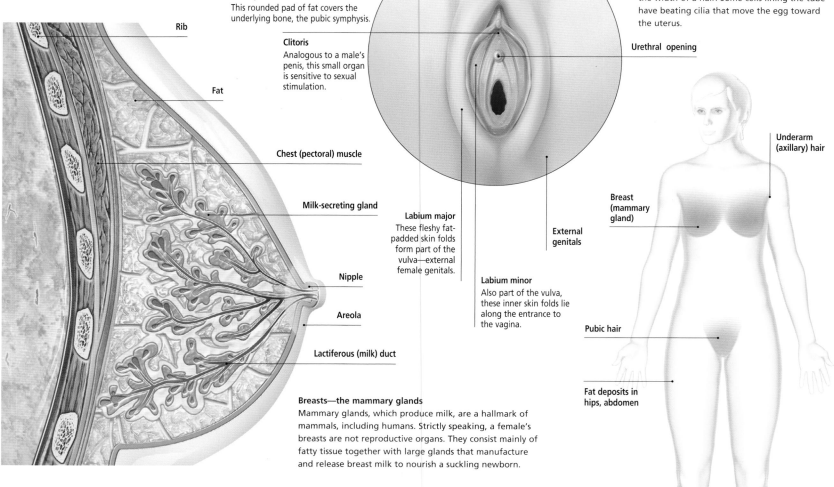

Mons pubis
This rounded pad of fat covers the underlying bone, the pubic symphysis.

Rib

Clitoris
Analogous to a male's penis, this small organ is sensitive to sexual stimulation.

Fat

Urethral opening

Chest (pectoral) muscle

Milk-secreting gland

Labium major
These fleshy fat-padded skin folds form part of the vulva—external female genitals.

External genitals

Underarm (axillary) hair

Breast (mammary gland)

Nipple

Labium minor
Also part of the vulva, these inner skin folds lie along the entrance to the vagina.

Areola

Pubic hair

Lactiferous (milk) duct

Fat deposits in hips, abdomen

Breasts—the mammary glands
Mammary glands, which produce milk, are a hallmark of mammals, including humans. Strictly speaking, a female's breasts are not reproductive organs. They consist mainly of fatty tissue together with large glands that manufacture and release breast milk to nourish a suckling newborn.

FEMALE REPRODUCTIVE ORGANS	
OVARIES	Produce eggs, the female sex cells
OVIDUCTS	Transport ovulated eggs to the uterus
UTERUS	Chamber where an embryo implants and grows
CERVIX	Passageway linking the uterus and vagina
VAGINA	Organ of intercourse, channel for menstrual flow, birth canal

Female secondary sexual characteristics
In response to estrogen, female secondary sexual features develop as a girl passes through puberty. These typically feminine traits include the deposition of fat in the breasts, abdomen and hips and the growth of hair in the armpits and pubic area.

Myometrium
Contractions of the layers of smooth muscle forming this tissue cause menstrual cramps and help expel a fetus during labor.

Oviduct
Each oviduct is about 4 inches (10cm) long and is positioned to receive ovulated eggs and channel them toward the uterus. Oviducts sometimes are called fallopian tubes.

Fimbriae
These fingerlike extensions help direct ovulated eggs into the oviduct.

Uterus
In this hollow, thick-walled organ, a fertilized egg may implant and an embryo may develop.

Ovary
Paired ovaries are a female's primary reproductive organs. These structures produce eggs and reproductive hormones including estrogen and progesterone.

Endometrium
This inner lining of the uterus is where an early embryo implants if conditions are right. It also gives rise to most of the placenta.

Bladder
The bladder is positioned under and slightly forward of the uterus. During pregnancy, pressure from the enlarging uterus triggers frequent urination.

Cervix
Glands in this narrow passage secrete mucus that forms a barrier to microbes and except at midcycle, sperm.

Vagina
This expandable passage plays a triple role as the female organ of sexual intercourse, the channel for menstrual flow and the birth canal.

Urethra
Urine flows from the bladder to outside the body through the urethra.

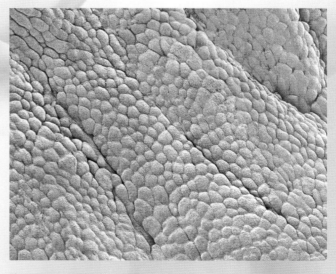

The female reproductive system revealed

A cutaway view shows the muscle layers and linings of the female reproductive system, including the muscular walls of the uterus and the folds of the vaginal wall. In a female who has never been pregnant, the uterus is about 3 inches (7.5cm) long and only about 2 inches (5cm) thick. It enlarges after pregnancy then shrinks at menopause.

The uterus
The major tissues of the uterus are its endometrial lining and the myometrial lining beneath. The endometrium has two layers: an outer permanent one and an inner layer that is built up and then shed with each menstruation. Abundant blood vessels supply the raw materials for this cyclical process. During pregnancy, hormones prevent the lining from sloughing away, allowing a newly formed embryo to implant in it and grow.

MALE REPRODUCTIVE SYSTEM

A male's primary reproductive organs are the testes, each about the size of a small plum. Like a female's ovaries, testes are not essential to a male's personal survival. Yet also like ovaries, testes are crucial organs that exist to help propagate the human species by producing sex hormones and sex cells—sperm—that can unite with an egg and give rise to a new generation. Suspended in the scrotum, each testis is subdivided into 200 or more lobes in which coiled, hair-thin tubules contain sperm cells at different stages of development. A sexually mature male has roughly 1 million sperm maturing within his testes at any given time. Other components of the male reproductive system include the penis and a variety of glands that produce semen that protects and nourishes developing sperm.

Seminiferous tubules
This colored micrograph shows a cross section of seminiferous tubules, the site of sperm production in the testes. Sperm cells, in blue, are shown inside each tubule. Surrounding the tubules is tissue containing Leydig cells, which produce testosterone.

Beard

Chest hair

Testis
Lobes containing the coiled seminiferous tubules make up most of the tissue in a testis. The tubules connect with the epididymis, where maturing sperm are stored. Blood vessels, nerves and a part of the vas deferens run through the spermatic cord.

Male sexual traits
During puberty, testosterone promotes the development of masculine secondary sexual characteristics—growth of a beard, growth of hair in the armpits, pubic area and elsewhere, added muscle mass and a deepening voice.

Pubic hair

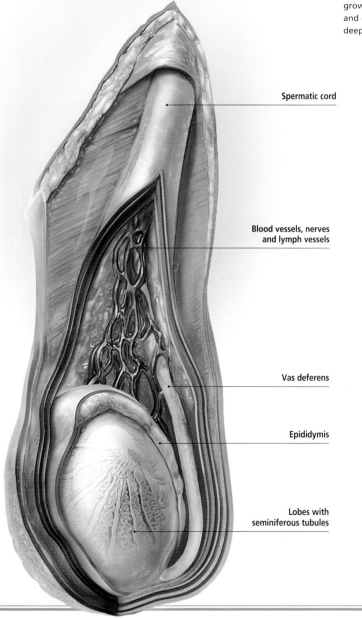

Spermatic cord

Blood vessels, nerves and lymph vessels

Vas deferens

Epididymis

Lobes with seminiferous tubules

CORPORA CAVERNOSA

The two large circular sections in this cross section of a penis are the corpora cavernosa; each surrounds an artery in the penis. During sexual arousal brain signals activate nerves in the penis that relax the arterial smooth muscle. The arteries dilate and the corpora cavernosa fills with blood resulting in an erection.
The corpus spongiosum (smaller circular section) encloses the urethra. It also fills with blood, but remains pliable so the urethra is not pinched shut.

Urethra
The urethra is essential for ejaculation to occur.

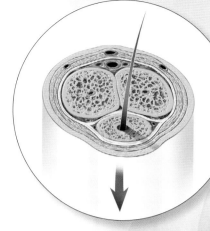

Path of a sperm cell
Rudimentary sperm form in the seminiferous tubules, then pass into the labyrinth of the epididymis. Nutrients there help sperm mature into swimming cells. During sexual arousal, sperm enter the vas deferens, then the ejaculatory duct, where they mix with fluid from the seminal vesicles. Next, secretions from the prostate gland are added and then bulbourethral mucus is added. The muscle contractions of ejaculation finally propel this viscous semen through the urethra and outward.

Ejaculatory duct
During ejaculation a pair of these channels carry sperm from each vas deferens to the urethra.

Prostate gland
The prostate encircles the urethra. It secretes sperm-activating substances that form part of semen.

Seminal vesicle
The two seminal vesicles secrete several substances, including prostaglandins, that become part of semen.

Urethra
In males the urethra serves as a channel for urine and also for the ejaculation of sperm.

Bulbourethral gland
These glands secrete lubricating mucus into the male urethra during sexual arousal.

Penis
The penis is the male organ of copulation. Together with the scrotum it makes up a male's external genitals.

Vas deferens
Sperm stored in the epididymis move through these two thick-walled tubes to the ejaculatory ducts.

Erectile tissue
Erectile tissue contains numerous vascular spaces. During sexual arousal, these spaces fill with blood, creating an erection.

Epididymis
This folded duct system receives and stores sperm prior to ejaculation. Stretched out, the epididymis would be about 20 feet (6m) long.

Glans penis
The tip of the penis is covered with a loosely folding prepuce or foreskin. Circumcision removes the foreskin.

Testis
Paired testes produce sperm and are the primary male reproductive organs.

Scrotum
This external sac at the base of the penis encloses and physically supports the testes.

NEW GENERATIONS

Sexual reproduction—the union of sperm and egg—produces the first cell of a new individual. Sperm and eggs are gametes, sex cells made in the testes and ovaries, and they carry information needed to build and operate the body. This information comes from genes, DNA segments that are organized in chromosomes. All body cells except gametes contain 46 chromosomes, 23 from each parent. In each set of 23 chromosomes, 22 are autosomes, which bear instructions for most body parts and operations. Chromosome 23 is a sex chromosome, X in females and Y in males. Human chromosomes collectively contain about 29,000 genes, a total referred to as the human genome. Because there can be varying forms of genes for a given trait, even close relatives may end up with differently shaped noses, different blood types and other normal variations. Some diseases result when a harmful mutation occurs in one or more genes.

DIVIDING CELLS, ALLOTTING CHROMOSOMES

Cells divide by two different mechanisms that yield different biological outcomes. The mechanism of mitosis duplicates the parts of the parent cell, including its 46 chromosomes, and distributes a full array of these structures to each daughter cell. Gametes result from a division process called meiosis, which allots daughter cells only 23 chromosomes. Meiosis normally ensures that an embryo will receive only half the normal number of chromosomes provided from each parent.

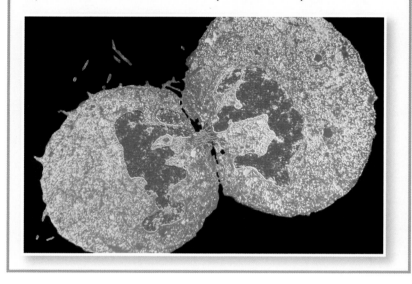

Sex chromosomes

Gametes, such as the egg and sperm cells shown at the right, contain only 23 chromosomes, including the sex chromosome. Unfertilized eggs have only X chromosomes, but sperm cells can have either an X or a Y. The X chromosome carries about 2,350 genes, the smaller Y far fewer. Genes on the Y chromosome code for male reproductive anatomy and functions, but the X chromosome carries genes for a variety of traits. Some are concerned with gender-related features such as the distribution of body fat, but most code for nonsexual traits such as the formation of blood clots and the capacity for color vision. Features controlled by genes on the sex chromosomes are said to be "sex-linked."

Genetic research
Insights about inherited diseases and disorders are emerging from laboratory research on human cells and their DNA. This work includes multinational efforts to identify traits associated with specific genes and to determine how multiple genes may interact.

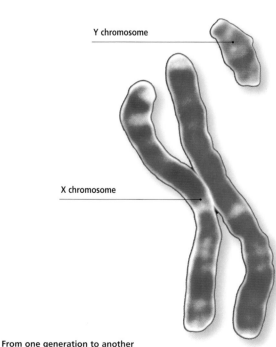

Y chromosome

X chromosome

From one generation to another
Close relatives may show a clear physical likeness, but even among parents and siblings family resemblance is not inevitable. Chance determines the particular mix of facial features and other traits parents pass on to their children.

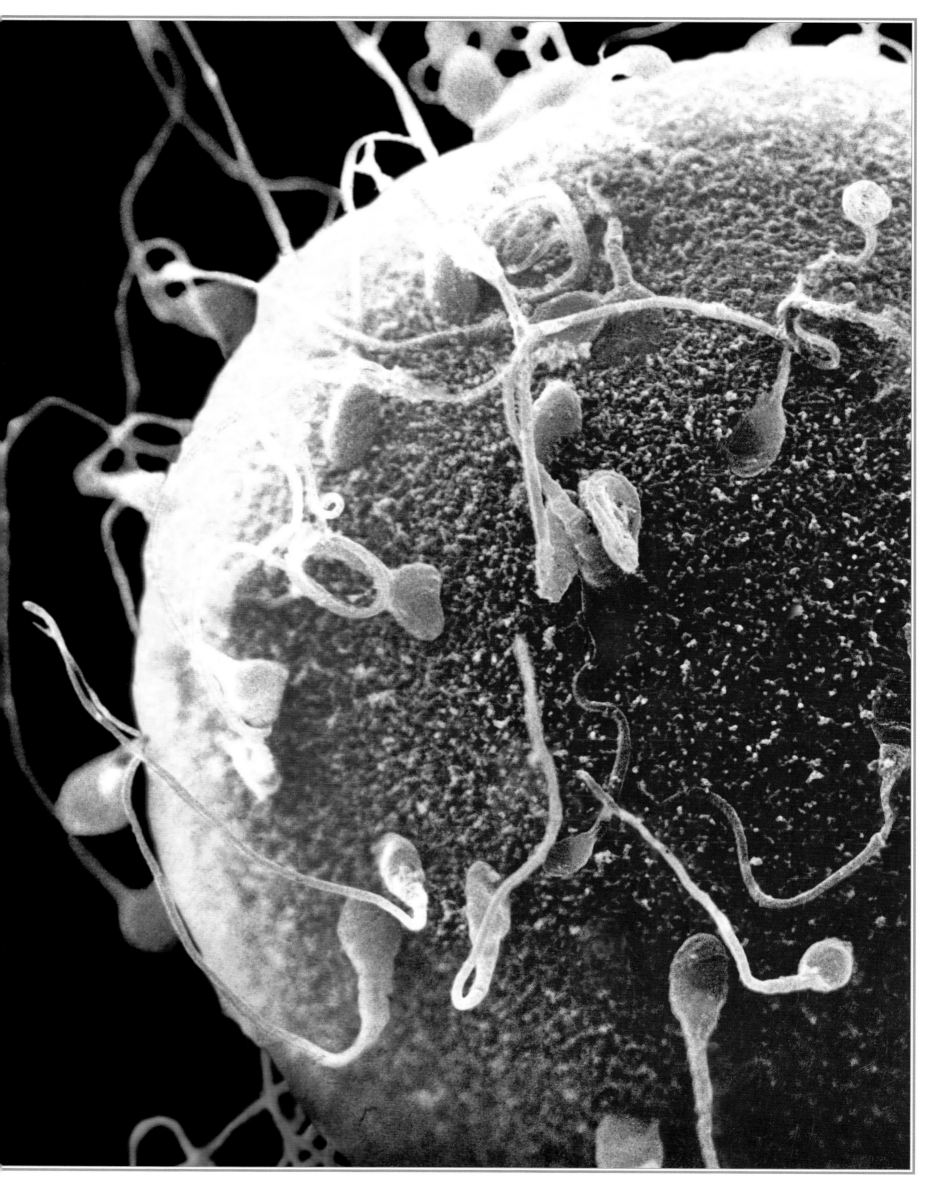

OVARIAN CYCLE

During a female's reproductive years, her menstrual cycle is matched by a complementary cycle in the ovaries, which produces oocytes, or immature ova. The tiny, developing egg is the first step toward pregnancy, since it contains the chromosomes that determine a mother's genetic contribution to her offspring. In the ovarian cycle, estrogen and other hormones guide a sequence of stages in which the egg cell grows larger and develops in ways that prepare it for release from the ovary. If after release the ovulated egg does not successfully cross the gap between the ovary and the infundibulum, the funnel-shaped opening of the oviduct, it will be lost into the abdominal cavity (this is uncommon). If the tiny cell does enter the oviduct, it will then be in the channel where fertilization is most likely to occur. If the egg is not fertilized, menstruation follows and the ovarian and menstrual cycles begin anew.

Hormones control ovulation
LH and FSH hormones from the pituitary gland stimulate follicle development in the ovaries. After ovulation, progesterone and estrogen from the follicle prepare the endometrium for a possible pregnancy.

Inside an ovary
This diagram shows what precedes ovulation. Cells around an oocyte form an enlarging, fluid-filled follicle. After the oocyte is ovulated, the remainder of the follicle forms a corpus luteum (yellow body) that secretes pre-pregnancy hormones.

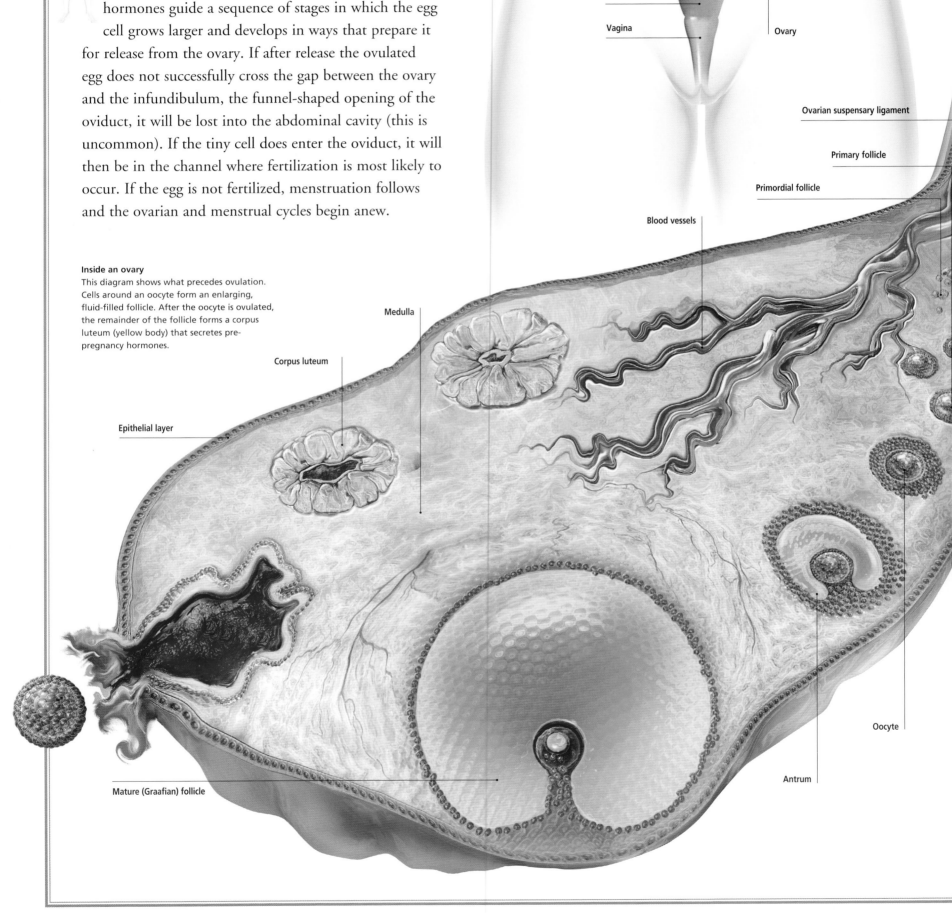

Uterus

Cervix

Vagina

Ovary

Ovarian suspensary ligament

Primary follicle

Primordial follicle

Blood vessels

Medulla

Corpus luteum

Epithelial layer

Oocyte

Antrum

Mature (Graafian) follicle

Coordinated monthly cycles

Coordinated cycles in the ovaries and uterus, each lasting about 28 days, prepare the body for a possible pregnancy. As pituitary hormones stimulate the growth of an ovarian follicle and maturation of an egg, the ovary releases estrogen and progesterone that stimulate thickening of the uterus lining or endometrium. A combination of hormonal signals triggers ovulation in the ovary and maintains the endometrium for about two weeks. If no pregnancy occurs, the production of ovarian hormones stops and part of the endometrium disintegrates, forming the menstrual flow.

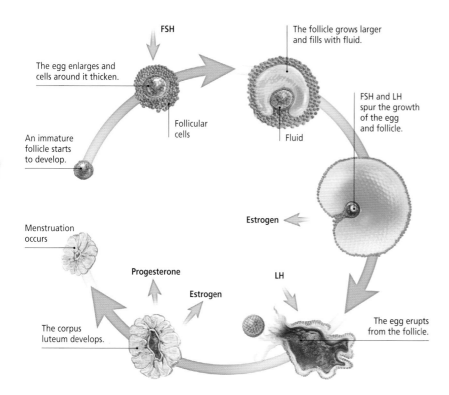

FSH

The egg enlarges and cells around it thicken.

The follicle grows larger and fills with fluid.

Follicular cells

An immature follicle starts to develop.

FSH and LH spur the growth of the egg and follicle.

Fluid

Estrogen

Menstruation occurs

Progesterone

Estrogen

LH

The corpus luteum develops.

The egg erupts from the follicle.

Future egg
The tip of a possible future egg appears green in this colored SEM surrounded by follicular cells (pink). Millions of such cells in a female embryo will develop into primary oocytes, but only a few hundred thousand remain at puberty.

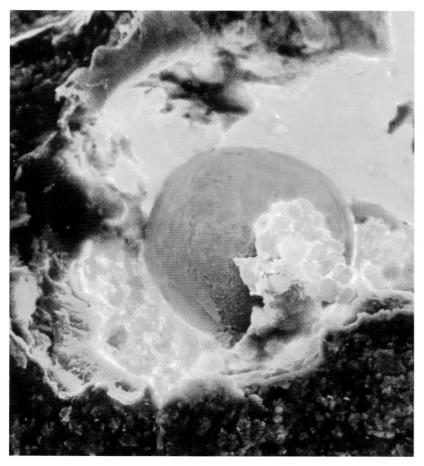

Ovulation
A surge of LH triggers ovulation, when the swollen follicle bursts and releases the oocyte. This image captures the moment at which an oocyte (orange) emerges from an ovary and starts its journey through the fallopian tube to the uterus.

MENARCHE AND MENOPAUSE

Menarche, a female's first menstruation, usually occurs between the ages of 10 and 14. Several decades later, typically in a woman's early to mid 40s, she enters the phase of perimenopause, in which her body's production of reproductive hormones slows and her ovarian and menstrual cycles become increasingly unsettled and irregular. As full menopause arrives, usually in a woman's early to mid 50s, her ovarian and menstrual cycles gradually stop altogether.

Sperm

Spermatozoa, or sperm, are the gametes that carry a male's genes. Over a period of nine to ten weeks, sperm become swimming cells propelled by a whiplike tail called a flagellum. Like oocytes, sperm develop in a process guided by hormones, including testosterone and some of the same hormones that operate during a female's ovarian cycle, such as the follicle-stimulating hormone (FSH). The process starts in seminiferous tubules coiled inside each testis.

Beginning at puberty, a series of genetically determined steps in the tubules transform cells called spermatogonia first into spermatocytes and then into spermatids. The spermatids grow a slender tail and finally become young sperm. During this time, chemical signals from nearby support cells nourish the maturing sperm, which ultimately enter the long, coiled epididymis. Here, the sperm cells complete their development and are stored until they exit the body as part of semen.

Penis

Testis

Flagellum

Parts of a sperm cell

Sperm are specialized to reach and fertilize eggs by swimming through the female reproductive tract. Each has three parts, a head, a midpiece and a flagellum, that support this biological role. The cell's nucleus contains DNA and is located in the head, which is capped by an acrosome. This structure houses enzymes and other proteins that help the sperm attach to and penetrate an egg. Mitochondria in the midpiece produce cellular fuel that powers tail movements as the sperm swims.

Sperm production site
This SEM (scanning electron micrograph) shows a cross-section of a semniferous tubule, the site of sperm production in the testes. Sperm begin their development toward the outer edge of the tubule and gradually move inward as they mature.

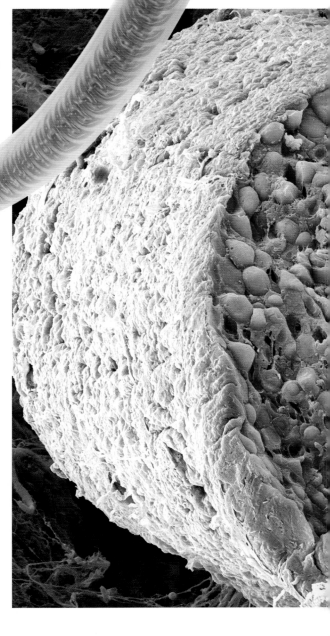

Testosterone

Testosterone is the main human androgen, a type of steroid hormone. Although it is present in both sexes, testosterone is well-known as the predominant sex hormone in males. In an embryo that inherits a Y chromosome, testosterone secreted by the embryonic testes guides the development of other male reproductive organs. Later in life, it is a major shaper of adult male mating behavior and sexual characteristics, including the formation of sperm and the enlargement of skeletal muscles.

Testosterone hormone
This light micrograph shows crystals of the testosterone hormone. It is mainly produced in Leydig cells of the testes.

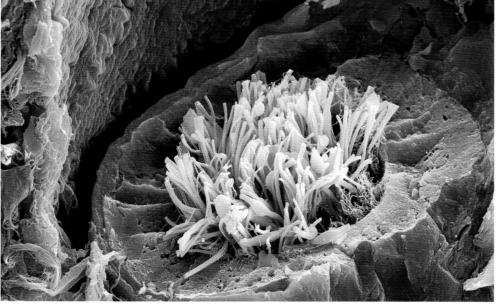

Midpiece   Mitochondria

Neck

Head

Acrosome

Sperm and aging

This SEM (scanning electron micrograph) shows sperm cells in an epididymis, a coiled tube in which sperm mature. As men age, sperm count changes. The number of sperm cells start to taper off around age 40 when testosterone levels decline, but men continue to make sperm well into old age.

Whipping tails

Propelled by its lashing tail, a sperm cell can move toward a possible encounter with an egg only by swimming. As the thick semen is ejaculated, chemical changes make it more watery so sperm can swim more easily.

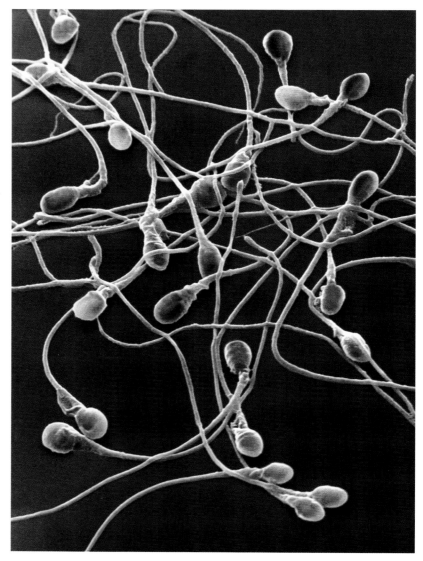

PREGNANCY

Fertilization of an egg by a sperm is by no means guaranteed. Of the millions of sperm a male ejaculates, fewer than a thousand may reach an oviduct. Acidic fluid in the vagina will kill many, and mucus in the cervix may block survivors from the uterus. In the uterus, defensive cells may attack arriving sperm as foreign to the female's body. Ejaculated sperm must also be capacitated, or "made able," by chemical changes that weaken the acrosome covering the sperm's head. This change requires six to eight hours and is a prerequisite for fertilization. Chemical barriers allow only a single sperm to penetrate a human egg. Soon afterward, the genetic material of sperm and egg combine. Implantation of an early embryo in the uterus and the development of a placenta and other support structures occur during pregnancy, the 39-week process that culminates in birth.

Extraembryonic membranes

Four membranes and the placenta help sustain a developing embryo. A yolk sac produces early blood cells, among other functions. The amnion forms the fluid-filled sac that surrounds the embryo. The allantois generates blood vessels linking the embryo to the placenta via the umbilical cord. The chorion surrounds these structures. It secretes hCG (human chorionic gonadotropin), a hormone that prevents the endometrium from eroding until the placenta forms.

MISCARRIAGE

An estimated 20 percent or more of conceptions result in miscarriage, the spontaneous expulsion of an embryo or fetus. An imbalance in pregnancy-related hormones, structural problems in the uterus or cervix and maternal disease such as diabetes can trigger a miscarriage. The risk is also greater if the mother is carrying more than one fetus. In approximately 50 percent of miscarriages, chance genetic disorders prevent the embryo or fetus from developing normally.

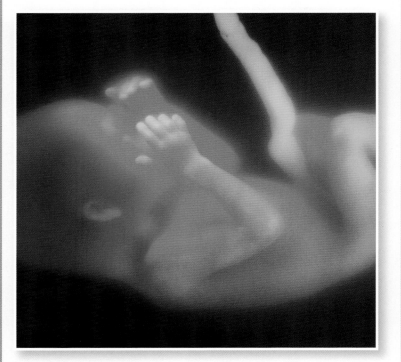

Miscarried 17-week-old fetus

Implantation of the embryo

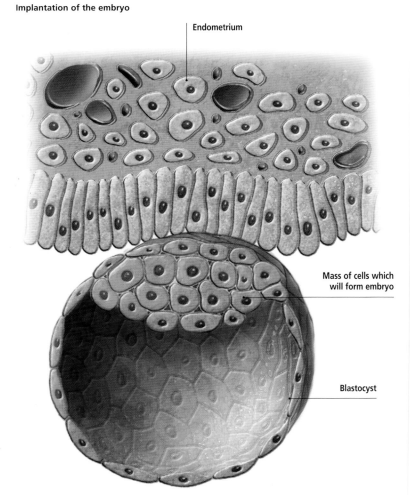

Endometrium

Mass of cells which will form embryo

Blastocyst

Phase 1: Implantation begins
Implantation occurs in three main phases. In the first phase, cells on the blastocyst's surface begin to infiltrate the endometrium. As this takes place the mass of cells from which the embryo will develop is nearest the endometrium.

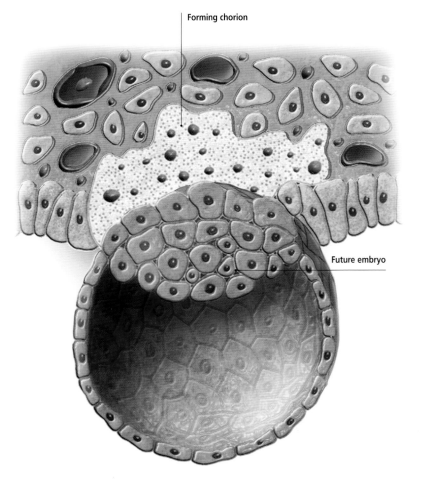

Forming chorion

Future embryo

Phase 2: Implantation deepens
Over the next few days the blastocyst sinks deeper into the endometrium, which eventually closes over it. Meanwhile the embryo has begun to develop, as have extraembryonic membranes. By the third week, the chorion and amniotic cavity have formed.

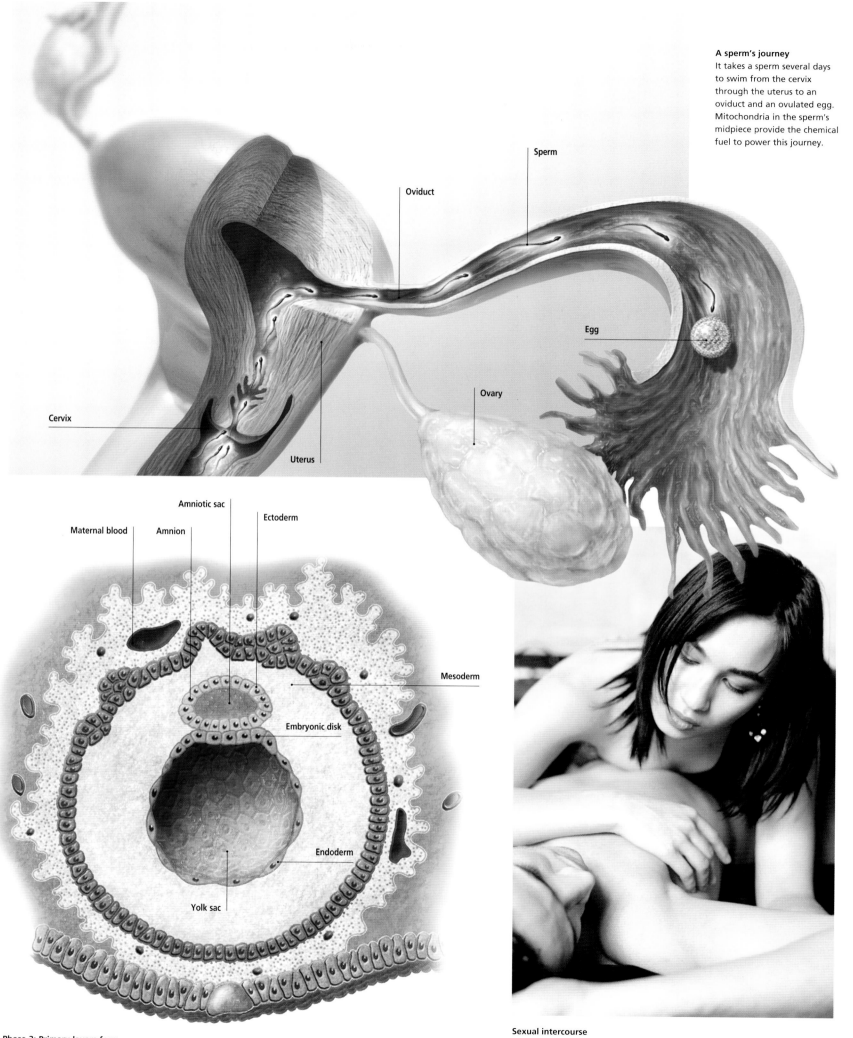

A sperm's journey
It takes a sperm several days to swim from the cervix through the uterus to an oviduct and an ovulated egg. Mitochondria in the sperm's midpiece provide the chemical fuel to power this journey.

Sperm

Oviduct

Egg

Ovary

Cervix

Uterus

Amniotic sac

Maternal blood

Amnion

Ectoderm

Mesoderm

Embryonic disk

Endoderm

Yolk sac

Phase 3: Primary layers form
Phase 3 occurs during the second and third weeks. At this time, the embryonic disk divides into three circular sheets, or layers—the ectoderm, the endoderm and the mesoderm. These three layers will eventually develop into all body tissues and organs.

Sexual intercourse
Reproduction is a powerful biological essential, not only for humans but for all species. Despite technologies that now permit fertilization in the laboratory, amorous encounters fostered by sexual "chemistry" are still the usual first step along this life-affirming pathway.

THE FIRST EIGHT WEEKS

From the moment a blastocyst forms, human development progresses rapidly. The first eight weeks in the womb, the embryonic period, is a time of tremendous growth. During the first four weeks, the placenta and umbilical cord are established and the embryo grows to 500 times its original size. Although it is still only about one-quarter of an inch (0.5cm) long and clearly has a tail, its heart, brain, eyes, limbs and muscles begin to form. Over the following month, the head enlarges as the embryo's brain expands, its tail disappears and limbs, genitals and internal organs take shape. After eight weeks, the embryo is about one inch (2.5cm) long and is designated a fetus. Over the next few weeks, before the end of the first trimester, a fetal monitor will be able to detect its heartbeat.

Five weeks
During week five the embryo continues to elongate. Its head grows rapidly and paddlelike plates presage the development of hands and feet.

Four-week embryo
A four-week embryo has two typical vertebrate features—a tail and pharyngeal arches in the neck region. In humans the tail becomes the coccyx and the pharyngeal arches develop into parts of the face, neck and nasal cavities.

Four weeks
By week four, the heart beats, sending blood through rudimentary vessels.

Three weeks
During week three, the embryo lengthens and a neural tube—the beginning of the brain and spinal cord—begins to form.

Two weeks
At two weeks, the end of implantation, the embryo consists of a two-layered disk attached to a yolk sac.

MATERNAL HEALTH AND NUTRITION

Poor maternal diet, alcohol and tobacco use, disease and even some therapeutic drugs all pose potential serious risk to an unborn child. A mother's meals and any physician-recommended supplements must provide nutrients essential to meet the demands of her rapidly growing offspring. Supplements typically include vitamins, iron and folic acid (folate). Folic acid helps to prevent spina bifida, in which the embryo's neural tube fails to close completely and part of the spinal cord remains exposed.

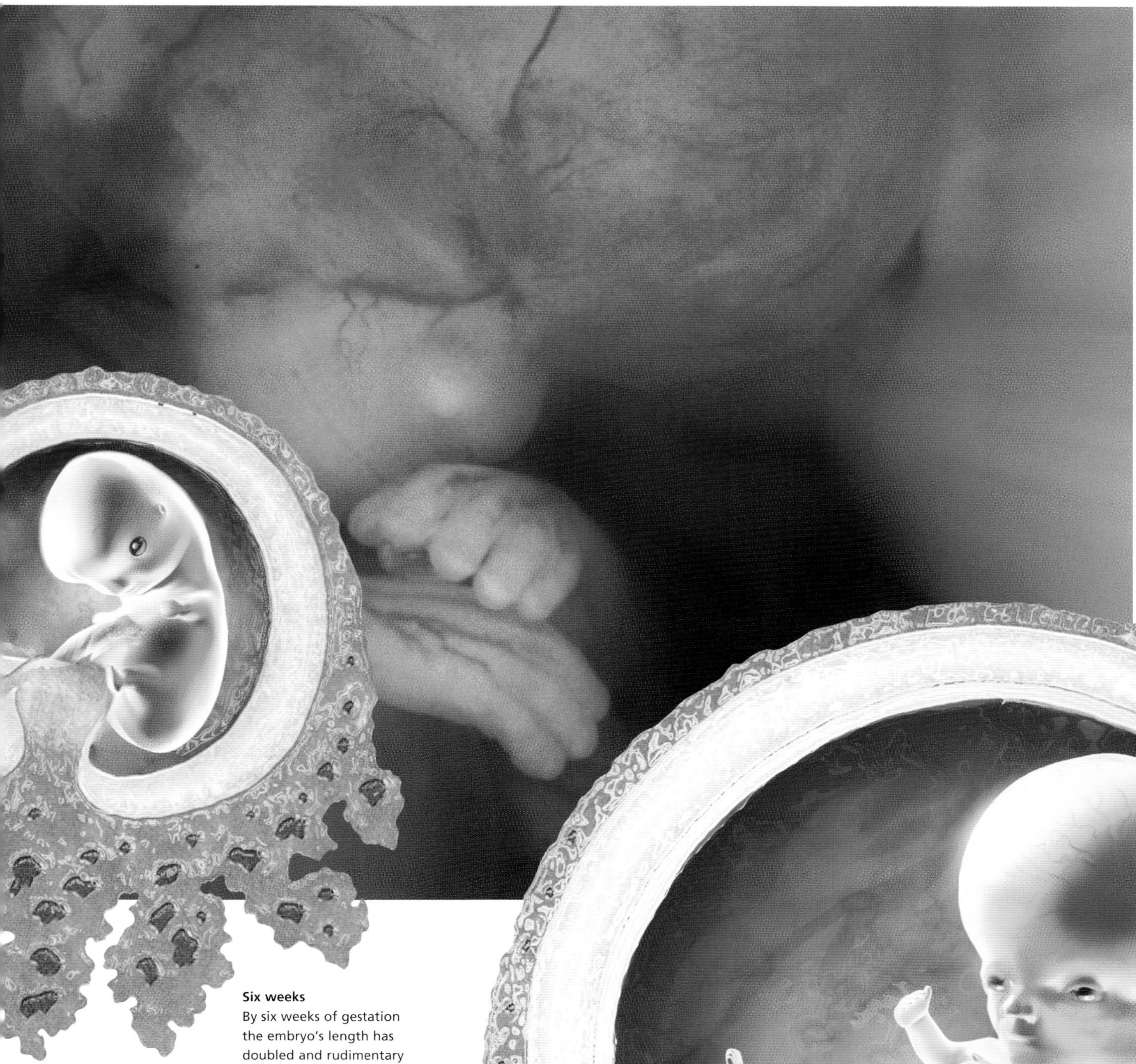

Fingers and toes

In the seventh week of development, paddlelike, webbed hands and feet are present at the ends of an embryo's tiny limbs. Over the following days, a process of genetically programmed cell death normally removes the tissue between the digits, producing five distinct fingers at the end of each hand, as shown on the left, and five toes on each foot. Within them is cartilage that will gradually be replaced by bone over the ensuing weeks.

Six weeks
By six weeks of gestation the embryo's length has doubled and rudimentary eyes and ears are in place.

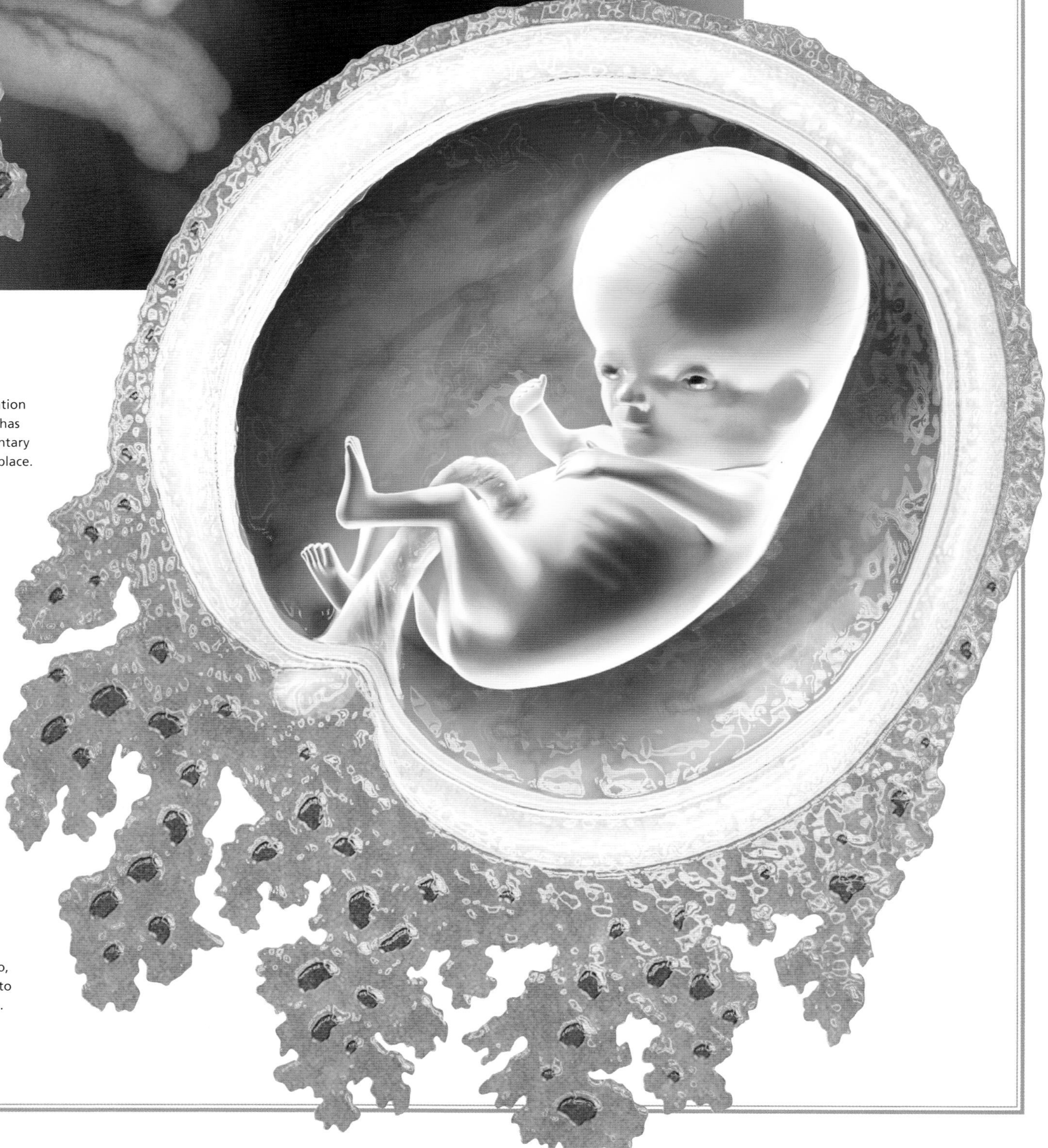

Eight weeks
By eight weeks all the embryo's major organs are developing and the umbilical cord linking it to its mother's bloodstream is fully functional.

Development of the embryo
The first eight weeks of pregnancy bring dramatic changes in the embryo, transforming it from a disk of cells into a tiny but recognizably human figure.

FETAL LIFE

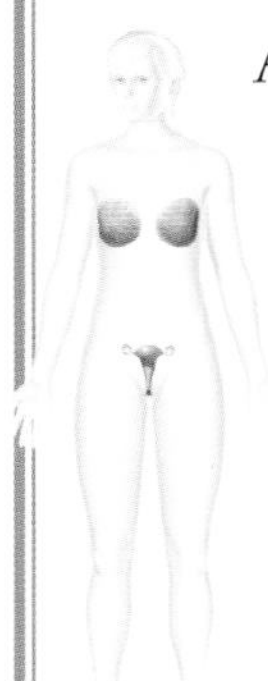

As the fetus ends its first trimester in the womb, it is nearly six inches (15cm) long and its organ systems are formed. A cheesy substance, the vernix caseosa, protects its skin and delicate hairs called lanugo cover its body. The fetal nervous system, with its connections to developing muscles, is becoming established and during the second trimester the mother can easily feel movements of her infant's arms and legs. Although the fetus is nourished via the mother's bloodstream, its mouth makes sucking movements and other facial muscles crinkle its face into frowns and squints. The fetus will soon open its eyes, drink amniotic fluid and urinate while its body systems mature and it grows to birth size. In the final weeks before birth, its lungs and respiratory system become capable of functioning in air. By the ninth month of pregnancy, development of these systems is virtually complete.

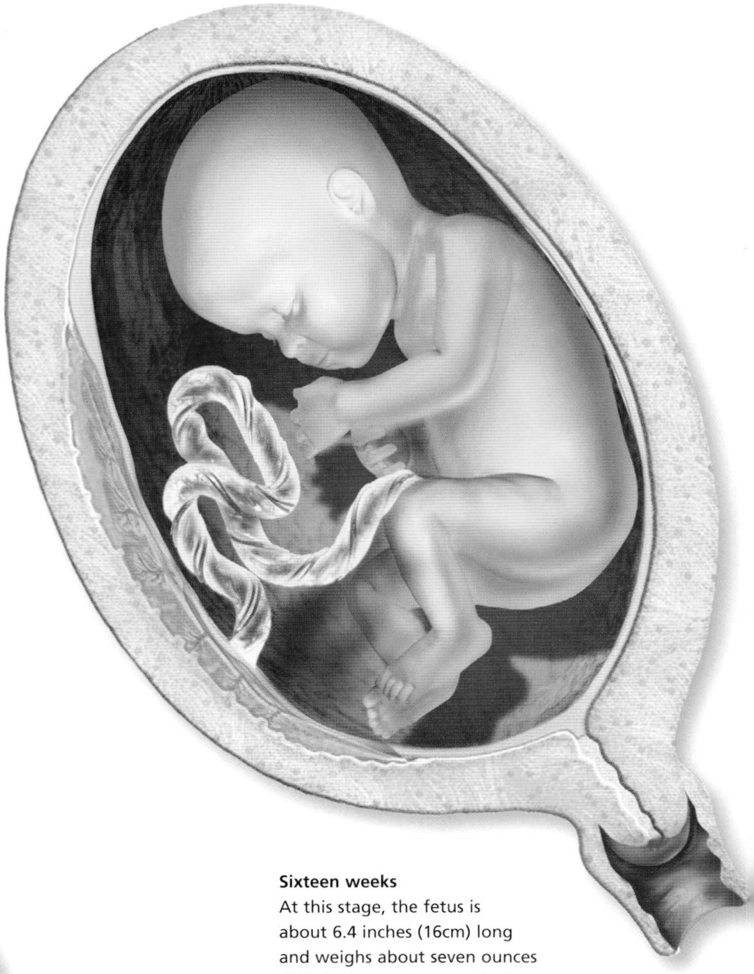

Sixteen weeks
At this stage, the fetus is about 6.4 inches (16cm) long and weighs about seven ounces (200g). The mother may feel it move in her uterus.

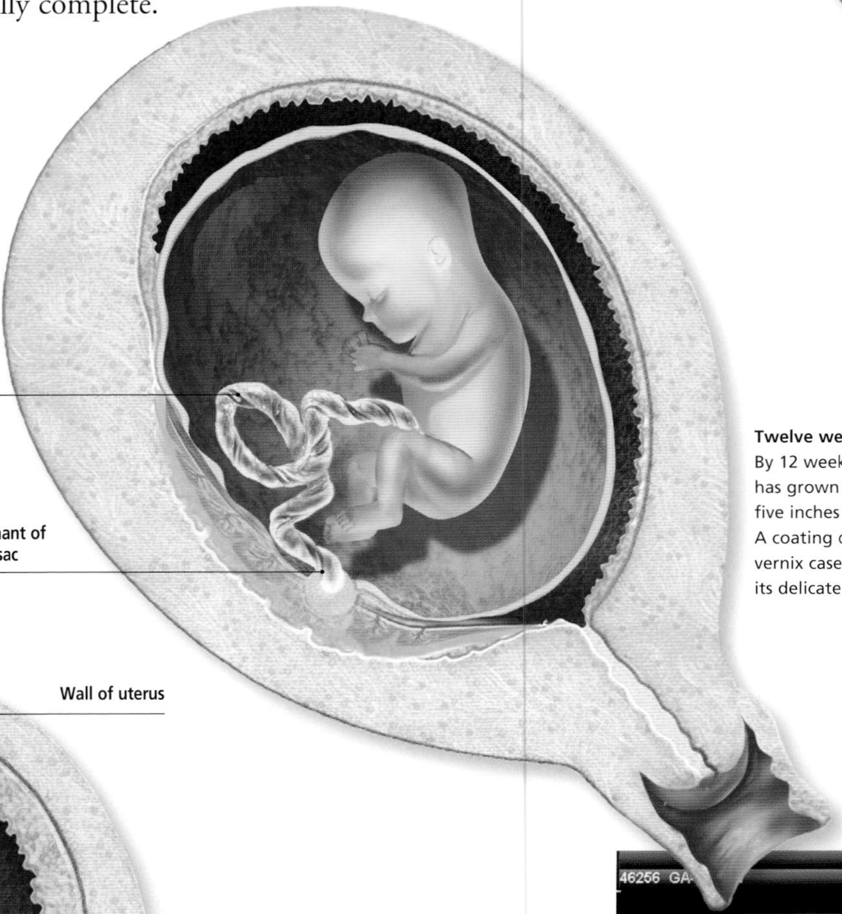

Umbilical cord

Remnant of yolk sac

Wall of uterus

Twelve weeks
By 12 weeks the fetus has grown to nearly five inches (12cm) long. A coating called the vernix caseosa protects its delicate skin.

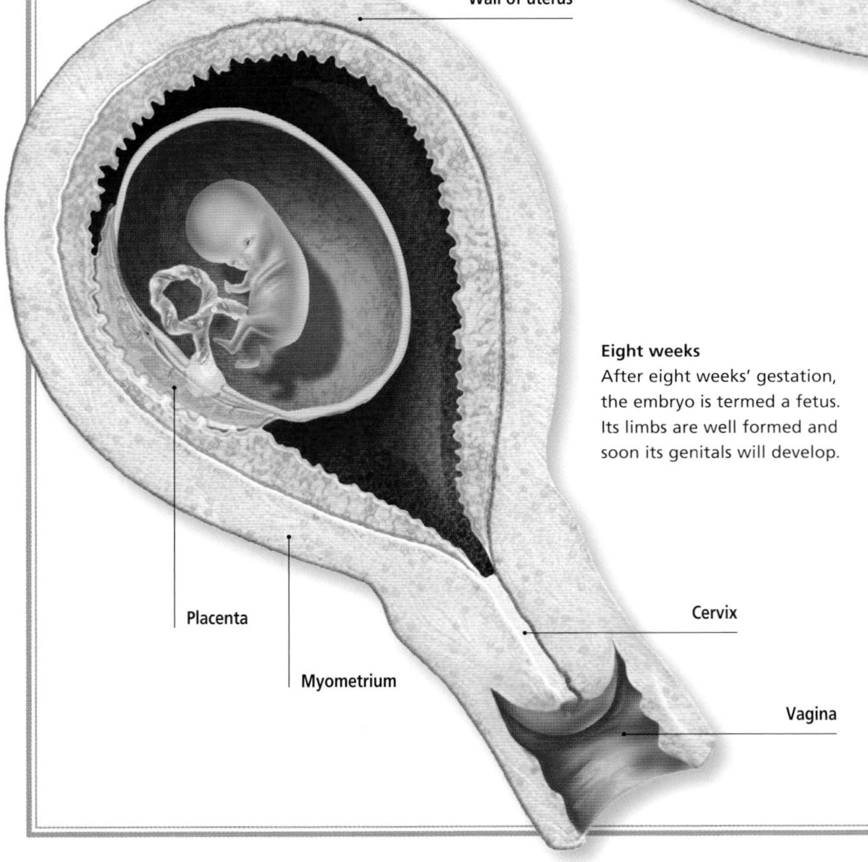

Twins in utero
Due to the limited capacity of the uterus, multiple fetuses often are born before a full term. Twins usually are delivered after about 37 weeks. This 3D ultrasound image shows twins at 12 weeks' gestation.

Eight weeks
After eight weeks' gestation, the embryo is termed a fetus. Its limbs are well formed and soon its genitals will develop.

Placenta

Myometrium

Cervix

Vagina

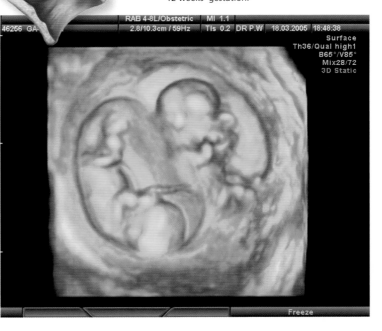

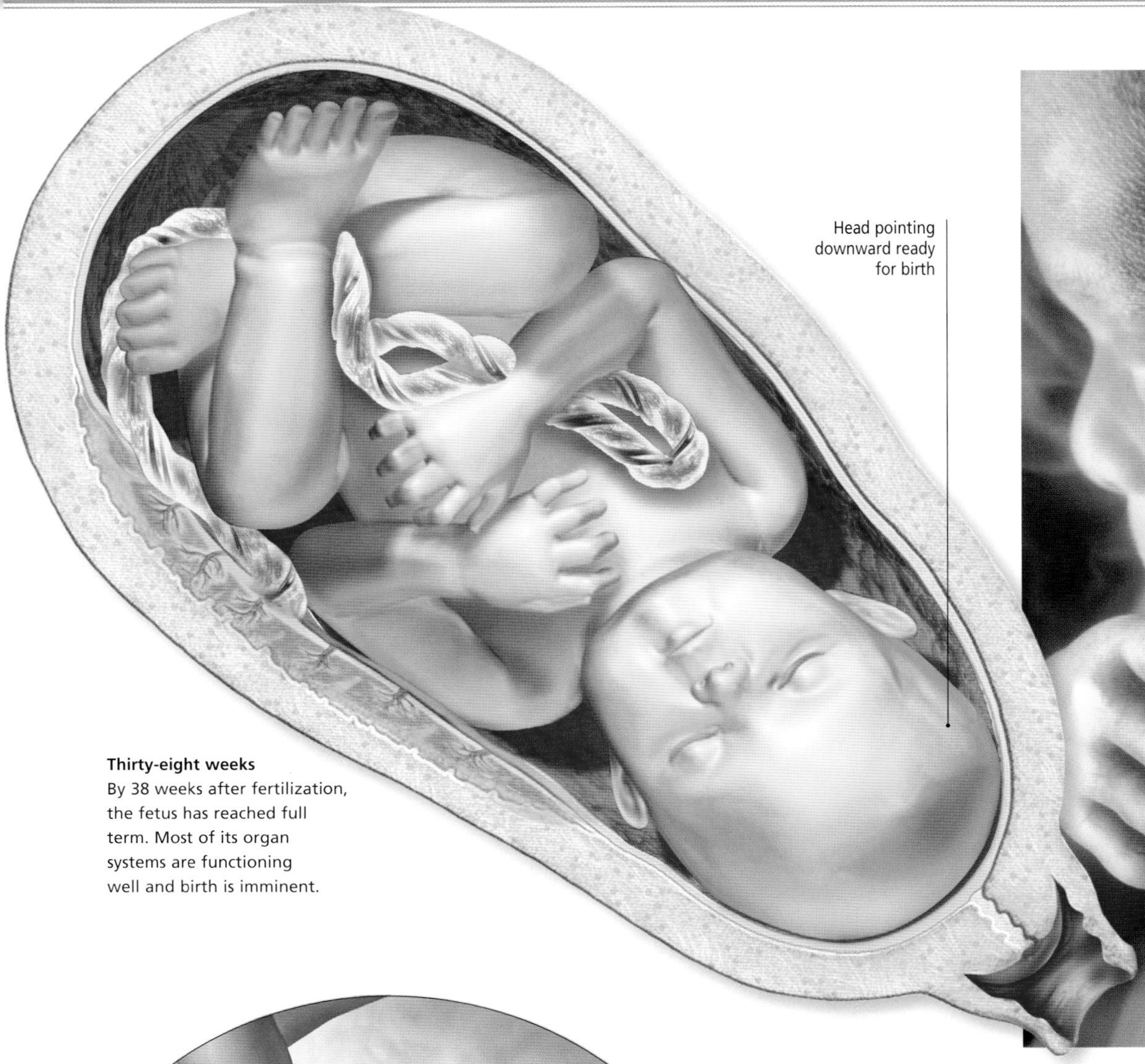

Head pointing downward ready for birth

Thirty-eight weeks
By 38 weeks after fertilization, the fetus has reached full term. Most of its organ systems are functioning well and birth is imminent.

Twenty-week-old fetus
At 20 weeks of gestation a fetus is covered with delicate hair called lanugo. Eyebrows and eyelashes will appear shortly. In the seventh month the fetus will be able to open its eyes.

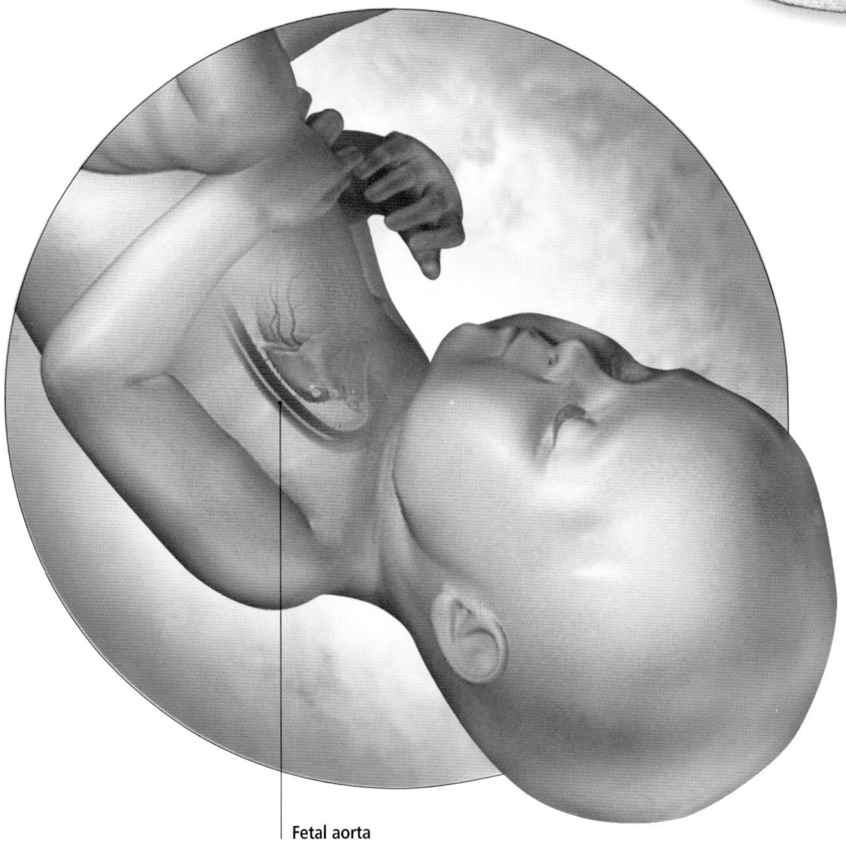

Fetal aorta

Fetal circulation

A fetus' lungs and liver develop more slowly than some other internal organs because the mother's body manages their functions by way of the placenta. The lungs receive a small quantity of blood from the heart, but most circulates through a small hole in the heart called the foramen ovale. A blood vessel called the ductus venosus bypasses the liver. Both these detours normally close down as normal blood circulation is established during the first weeks after birth.

THE DEVELOPING SKELETON

The skeleton develops slowly throughout gestation. Cartilage and other embryonic connective tissue provide a structural model for each bone; bone cells later replace the soft model with mineralized bone tissue. The skull begins to develop during the fourth week, followed by the spinal vertebrae, ribs and pectoral and pelvic girdles. By week six, a cartilage skeleton has begun to form in the limbs.

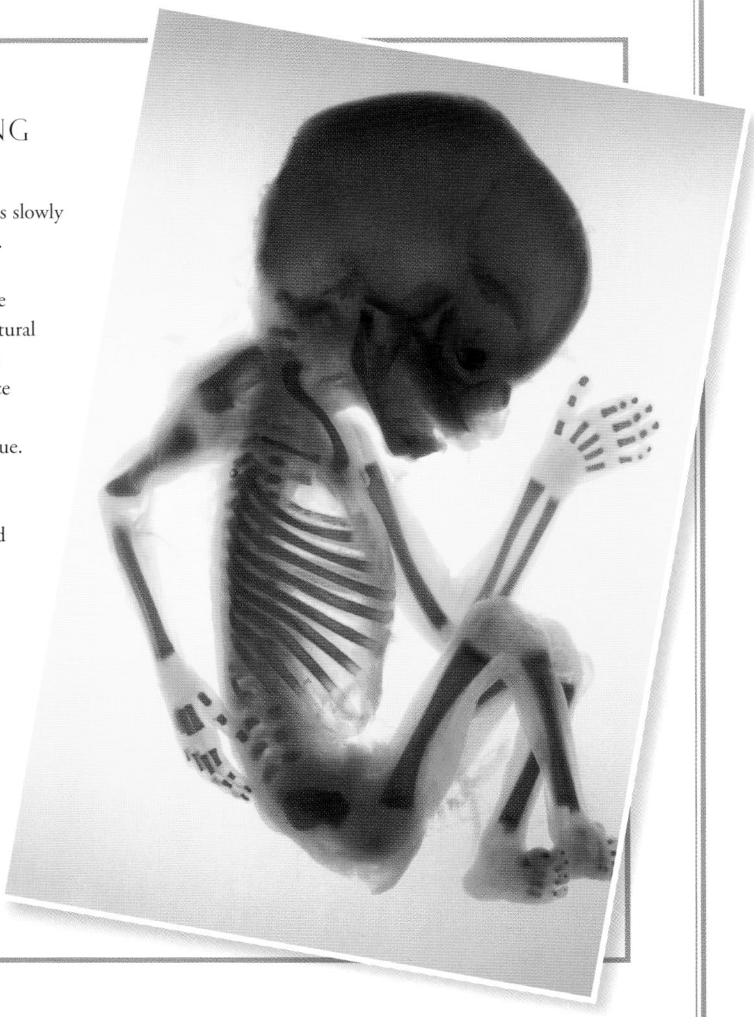

BIRTH

Birth, an infant's abrupt entry into the world, is known technically as parturition. Normally a mother experiences three stages of labor—a pre-birth phase of physical changes that are a prelude to the birth itself; the baby's actual transit out of the uterus and through the birth canal; and a post-birth phase when the placenta or afterbirth is delivered and the umbilical cord is cut. On average, labor takes about 18 hours from the first contraction to the finish, but some births occur in a few hours, while others may take a day or more as the stages slowly advance. When an infant is finally separated from its mother, the placenta can no longer remove carbon dioxide from its blood. This change and other factors stimulate centers in the infant's brain that regulate breathing. As its respiratory system begins to function, the baby takes its first breath.

Birth triggers

Interacting hormones from the placenta and the fetus are chemical triggers for labor. As birth nears, fetal cells produce oxytocin, which causes the placenta to release prostagladins. Both help stimulate the myometrium, the muscular wall of the uterus, bringing on contractions. New research suggests that other hormones also play a part. It is believed the placenta releases CRH (corticotropin-releasing hormone), which seems to stimulate the fetus' adrenal glands to make and release the androgen DHEA (dehydroepiandrosterone). In the placenta, DHEA transforms into estrogen, which in turn contributes to uterine contractions.

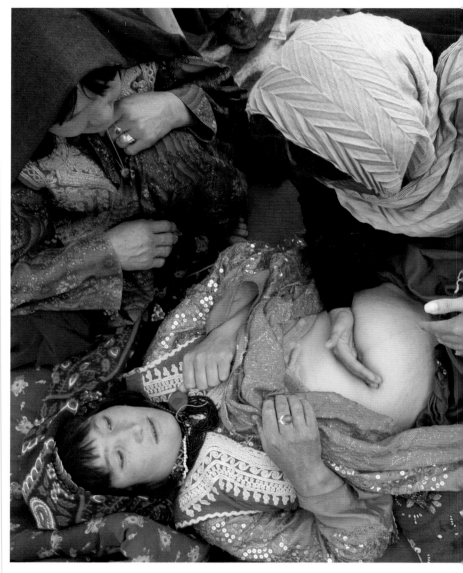

Giving birth
With medical care a rarity in rural Afghanistan, this young woman can be expected to give birth at home assisted by other women of her tribe. Here a midwife checks the progress of her pregnancy.

Stages of birth

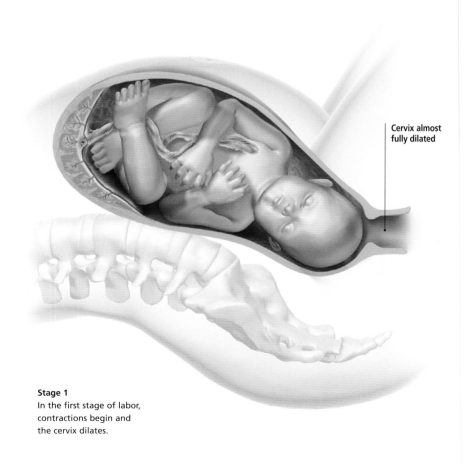

Baby's head turned toward mother's back

Cervix almost fully dilated

Stage 1
In the first stage of labor, contractions begin and the cervix dilates.

Stage 2
Continuing contractions, often over several hours, push the infant's head against the cervix.

246

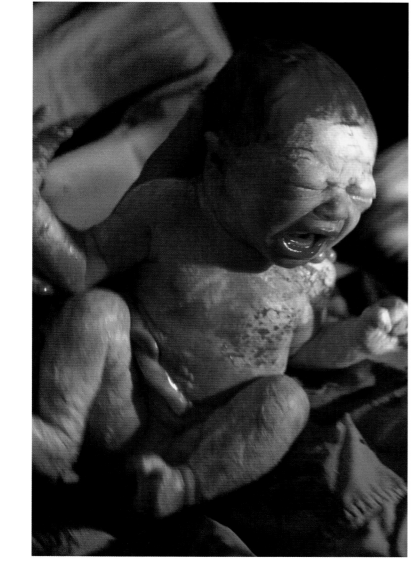

Cutting the cord
Birth is stressful for a newborn, in part because cutting the umbilical cord severs vessels that have provided it with oxygen from the mother's bloodstream. Crying inflates the baby's lungs and it begins breathing on its own.

BORN TOO SOON

A premature infant is one born before 37 weeks of gestation. Premature babies generally weigh much less than full-term babies, and their immature organ systems cannot perform many basic physiological functions. Advanced medical care now ensures the survival of most newborns weighing just under 2 pounds (at least 800g), but premature infants have a much greater chance of childhood learning disorders and other developmental problems. Women with certain health problems, or who are carrying more than one fetus, or who are under age 19 or over age 35 are most likely to give birth prematurely.

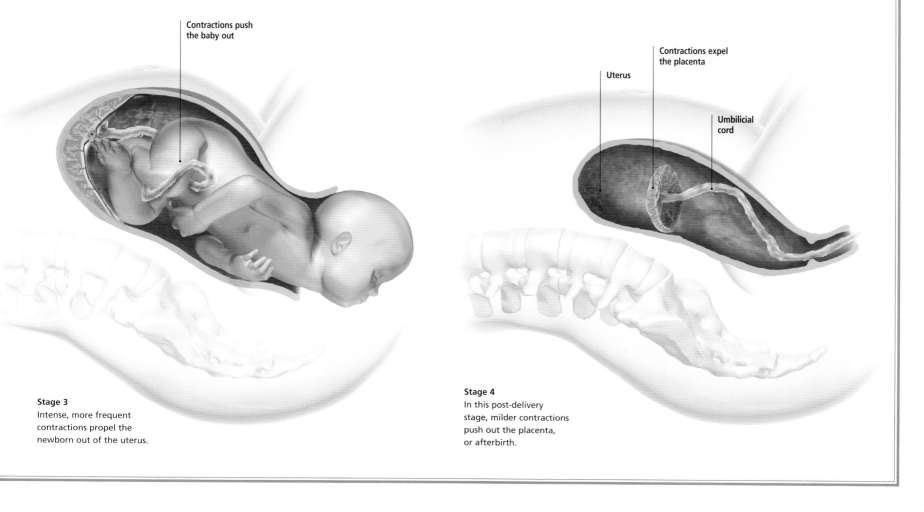

Contractions push
the baby out

Contractions expel
the placenta

Uterus

Umbilicial
cord

Stage 3
Intense, more frequent
contractions propel the
newborn out of the uterus.

Stage 4
In this post-delivery
stage, milder contractions
push out the placenta,
or afterbirth.

CHILDHOOD AND ADOLESCENCE

The human body changes dramatically as a child grows from infancy to adolescence. The changes include major shifts in the physical proportions of the head, trunk and limbs. During infancy and early childhood, steady growth lengthens the body while the head becomes less prominent. Up to about age three, major changes are also taking place in the nervous system. In a newborn, relatively few synapses link brain neurons, but countless new neural connections will form based on gene-guided developmental processes, as well as on a young child's interactions with caregivers and exposure to stimuli in the larger world. As physical growth begins to slow around age four, most children have a solid command of verbal language and are well on the way to having good hand-eye coordination. By about age 12, most youngsters are proportioned much like an adult, although most have not gained their full height. The onset of puberty will reshape their bodies with secondary sexual characteristics, and the brain will continue to change physically and functionally until well into adulthood.

THE CHANGING BRAIN

After its early childhood growth spurt, the brain is relatively stable until shortly before puberty, when its neural wiring again undergoes major changes. In young adolescents, large numbers of synapses form between brain neurons in certain regions. Over the next several years some of these connections are strengthened as nerve cell axons become sheathed in myelin, while others wither. Much of this growth occurs in the prefrontal cortex, the area responsible for abstract thinking, judgment and impulse control. This process, known as myelination, continues to occur into adulthood.

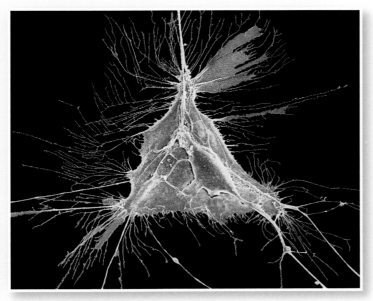

Sheathed brain neurons
The increasing myelination of a teen's brain neurons depends on cells like this one, an oligodendrocyte that can produce enough myelin to sheathe up to 50 neuron axons.

Infancy
For most infants, crawling is the introduction to standing and walking. Infants generally begin crawling between seven and 10 months. Although individual babies differ greatly in their development, by about 14 months many can walk unaided.

Newborn
At this age, the skull and torso are large compared to the limbs.

Three years
The head and torso grow at a slower rate as the limbs lengthen.

Growth spurts

Healthy babies and children grow steadily but not evenly. After the swift gains of early infancy, intervals of more gradual increases in body size and weight are punctuated by growth spurts. During these periods, and sometimes literally overnight, the long bones in a child's limbs lengthen even more rapidly than usual, which can result in achy joints or "growing pains." At puberty, sex hormones trigger the last major growth spurt, marked by speedy growth of the limbs and the development of sexual features.

The teen years
Human adolescence is literally "growth into adulthood." The physical appearance of the teens in this group reflects hormonally driven changes in overall growth and the development of male and female sexual features.

Childhood years
Childhood begins at about age two and lasts until a youngster reaches puberty. During these years, a child's body shape changes markedly and brain development includes extraordinary expansion in the capacity for long-term memory and cognitive skills.

Twenty two years
The brain has reached its full size and forms new synapses less often.

Puberty
Most girls undergo puberty, or the maturation of reproductive organs, from ages 11–16. For most boys, it takes place between ages 12–17.

Ten years
By age 10, the skull and brain have grown to near-adult size.

ADULTHOOD

Far from being biologically "complete," adults can look
forward to—or fret over—decades of steady change in
the form and functioning of their organs and tissues. The
body reaches the peak of its physical potential in early
adulthood. After about age 35, the toll exacted by wear
and tear becomes increasingly obvious as people start to
notice reduced skin tone, weaker muscles and other changes
associated with approaching middle age. Ninety percent of
people over age 40 have some degree of osteoarthritis in
their joints and have a significantly higher ratio of body
fat to muscle than when they were in their 20s. By age
60 or so, virtually all body systems are beginning to
operate at least somewhat less efficiently. Experts
generally recommend a healthful lifestyle that includes
a proper diet, regular moderate exercise, positive social
interactions and stimulating mental activity as the
recipe for graceful aging.

Aging

Structural changes in proteins contribute to the effects of aging. In particular,
collagen molecules become more rigid and less resilient. This affects the structure
and functioning of the skin, blood vessels and most internal organs. As metabolism
slows over the years, fat deposits accumulate. Bone-forming osteoblasts become less
efficient, so bone mass declines, and muscle mass decreases as skeletal muscle fibers
atrophy. Physical activity that includes regular weight-bearing exercise can help
forestall all these changes.

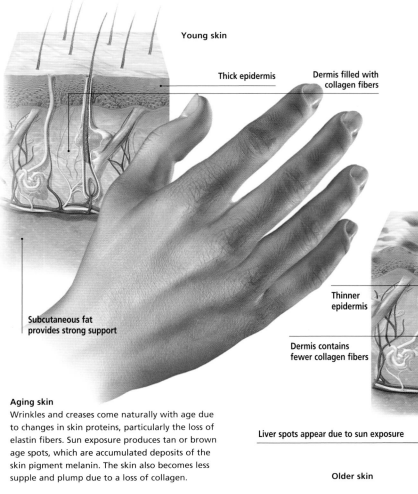

Young skin

Thick epidermis

Dermis filled with
collagen fibers

Subcutaneous fat
provides strong support

Thinner
epidermis

Dermis contains
fewer collagen fibers

Aging skin

Wrinkles and creases come naturally with age due
to changes in skin proteins, particularly the loss of
elastin fibers. Sun exposure produces tan or brown
age spots, which are accumulated deposits of the
skin pigment melanin. The skin also becomes less
supple and plump due to a loss of collagen.

Liver spots appear due to sun exposure

Older skin

Physical peak
Elite athletes in most sports are young, typically in their late teens or 20s when the body is at its natural physical peak and muscles and other organs function with maximum efficiency. Sports performance begins to decline in the early 30s.

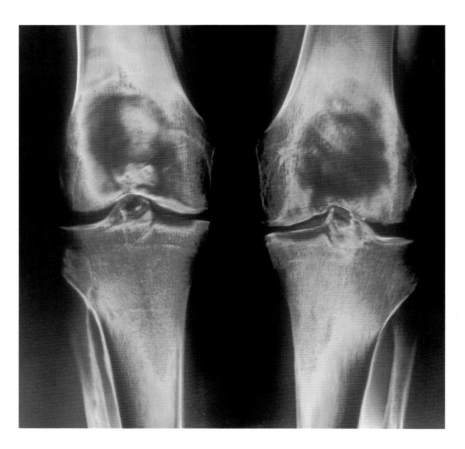

Osteoarthritis
This X-ray of aging knees shows a narrowing of the space between the adjoining bones due to the arthritic erosion of cartilage in the knee joints. Virtually everyone over age 50 has some osteoarthritis.

CALORIE RESTRICTION

Biochemically, aging is complicated. One factor that plays a role in aging is a gene-guided mechanism that limits the number of times a cell can divide—in most human cells, about 80 to 90 times. Intriguing research suggests that consuming only about 30 to 50 percent of the calories that one would otherwise take in (while still obtaining essential nutrients) can dramatically extend lifespan. This effect may be due to a slowdown in the rate at which body cells divide.

FEMALE REPRODUCTIVE SYSTEM DISORDERS

Most if not all women experience some type of reproductive ailment during their lives. Common vaginal yeast infections are uncomfortable but harmless and easily treated. So, usually, are fluid-filled cysts that develop on the ovaries and come and go with a woman's menstrual cycle. Benign uterine tumors called fibroids may develop in as many as 70 percent of women. Hormonal shifts are responsible for premenstrual syndrome (PMS), which can produce cyclic bloating, pelvic cramping, major mood swings and other symptoms. More serious is endometriosis, in which bits of the endometrium lining the uterus begin growing on the ovaries, in the oviducts or elsewhere in the body, triggering inflammation, bleeding and scarring that can leave a woman infertile. Symptoms of ovarian cancer do not appear until the malignancy is well advanced. The cancer has a poor prognosis as it often spreads widely before a woman even knows she is ill.

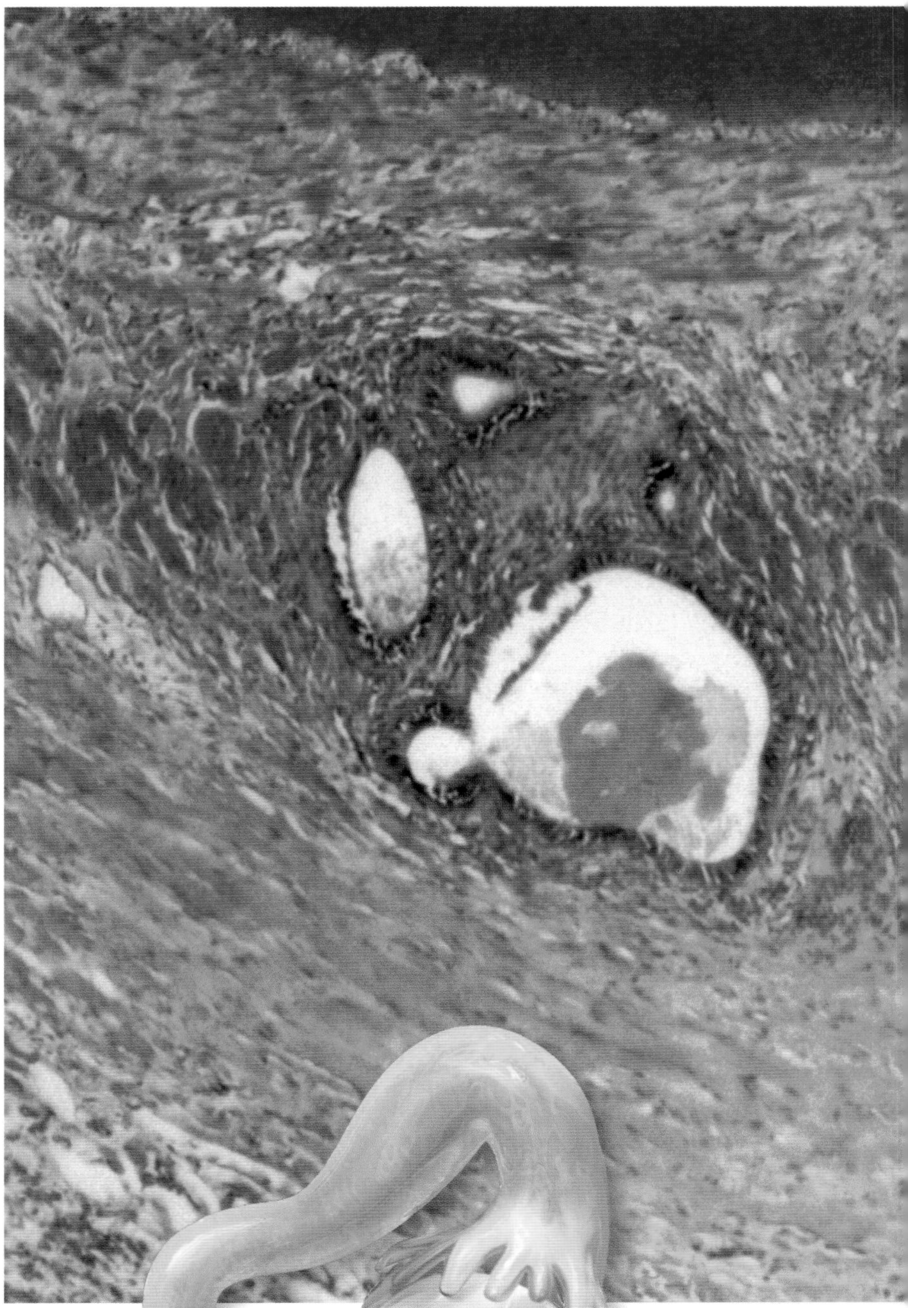

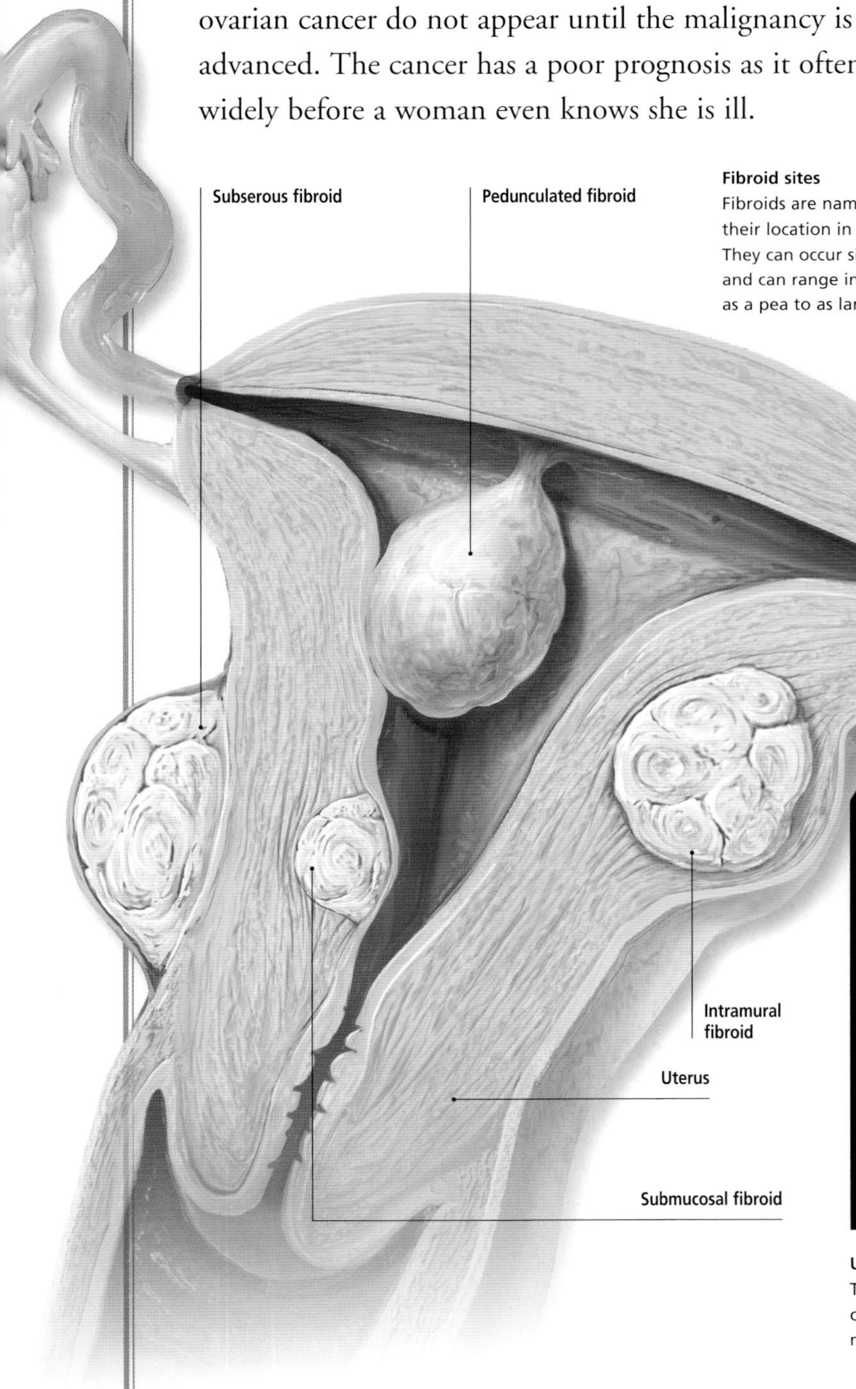

Subserous fibroid

Pedunculated fibroid

Fibroid sites
Fibroids are named according to their location in the uterus or cervix. They can occur singly or in groups and can range in size from as small as a pea to as large as a grapefruit.

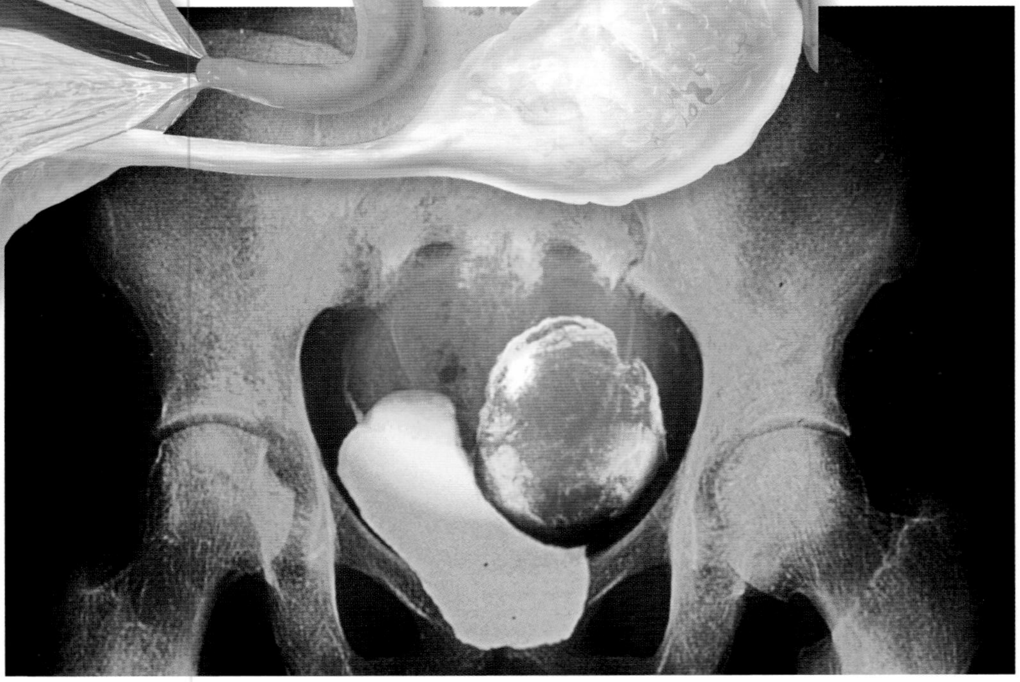

Intramural fibroid

Uterus

Submucosal fibroid

Uterine fibroids
The reddish sphere in this colored urogram is a uterine fibroid, a noncancerous tumor of overgrown muscle and fibrous connective tissue. Very large fibroids such as this one often must be surgically removed. However, smaller ones may require no treatment at all.

Endometriosis

Endometriosis affects approximately ten percent of women, most often during early adulthood. Although no cause is known for certain, one factor may be backflow of menses into and through the oviducts. When endometrial tissue begins to grow outside the uterus, it responds to cyclic hormone fluxes, building up, then disintegrating. The accumulating material causes a variety of symptoms including pelvic pain, especially during menstrual periods and sexual intercourse. Treatment options include medications and surgery, although there is no cure.

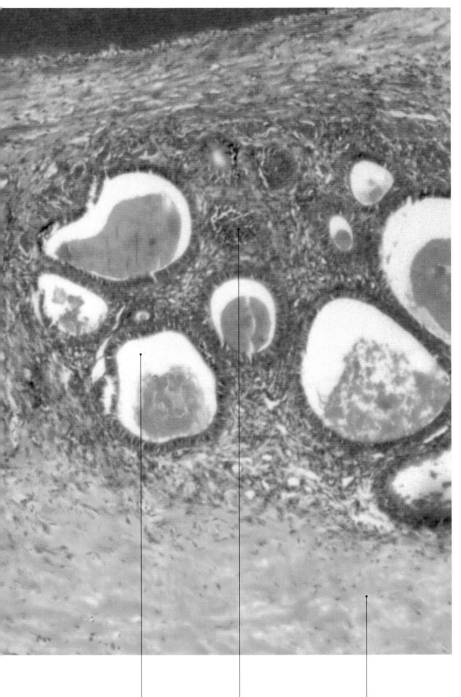

Endometriotic cyst   Bleeding   Vaginal lining

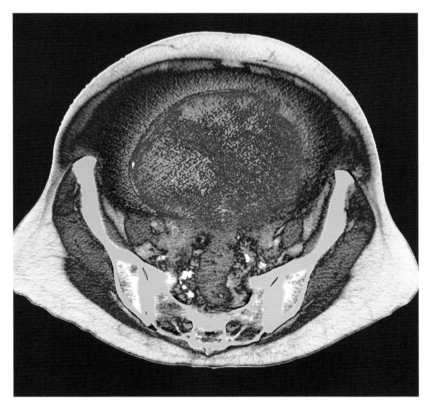

Ovarian cancer
This top-down CT scan reveals the extent of a patient's large ovarian malignancy (purple). Red-colored patches are areas where fluid has accumulated outside the ovaries, a sign the cancer has spread widely into the abdomen.

CERVICAL CANCER

Cancer of the cervix often develops from precancerous cells that have been infected by HPV, the human papilloma virus. Most cervical cancers grow slowly and are easily removed by surgery, which is one reason why physicians recommend regular screening using the Pap test. HPV is typically spread by sexual contact. Many health authorities now encourage young women who are not yet sexually active to be immunized against HPV with one of several newly developed vaccines.

Cervical smear test
Advances in cervical cancer screening include placing cells scraped from a patient's cervix into a preservative solution, as this clinician is doing. Samples prepared in this way yield a much clearer view of individual cells during analysis.

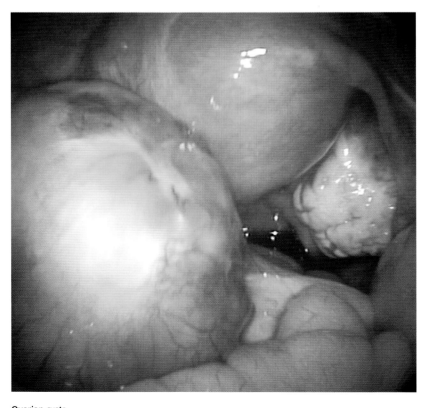

Ovarian cysts
Benign, fluid-filled ovarian cysts are fairly common. The large whitish mass in the foreground of this endoscopic image is a cystic ovary that has swollen to the size of the uterus, the pink structure located just above it.

Male Reproductive System Disorders

Common male reproductive ailments involve the prostate gland and the epididymides, the coiled ducts where sperm complete their development. A disorder known as epididymitis develops when this duct system becomes inflamed, often due to a bacterial infection. Invading bacteria also may trigger prostatitis, a painful prostate inflammation, but often the cause is a frustrating mystery and the inflammation may subside only to reappear later. Testicular cancer, most commonly diagnosed in males aged 15 to 35, is fairly rare. Having an undescended testicle, a condition called cryptorchidism, may increase the risk. In an excruciating condition called testicular torsion, strenuous activity or a physical blow displaces the spermatic cord. The cord wraps around the testicle like a tourniquet and shuts off its blood supply. Emergency surgery is usually the only treatment option.

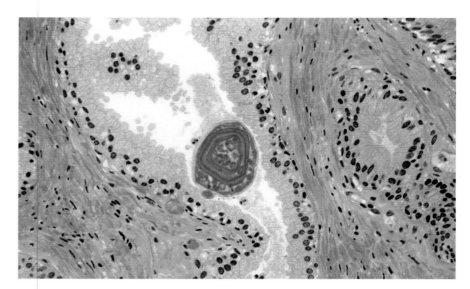

Benign prostatic hyperplasia
After age 50, many men experience enlargement of the prostate gland in a condition known as benign prostatic hyperplasia (BPH). This light micrograph shows a benign nodule (blue, center) in a prostate gland. It can cause the prostate to swell and press against the urethra, leading to an obstructed urine flow. BPH can be treated with medication or surgery in extreme cases.

Undescended testicles

Many premature infant boys and about four percent of full-term male babies are born with one or both testicles still in the abdomen where they first developed, a condition called cryptorchidism. In the majority of these cases, the testicles will descend into the scrotum, but if they have not done so within the first year corrective surgery is the recommended course. If the situation is not corrected, the too-warm environment of the abdomen may prevent normal sperm development and result in sterility and increased risk of testicular cancer.

Erectile Dysfunction

When a man cannot maintain a firm erection at least 25 percent of the time, the diagnosis is erectile dysfunction (ED). ED may be due to psychological issues such as anxiety or stress, but the cause is usually physical and can be related to changing testosterone levels. Certain medications and heavy alcohol use can interfere with having and maintaining an erection. Conditions that hamper blood flow, such as atherosclerosis, diabetes and high blood pressure are other common causes. Oral medications that stimulate an erection temporarily increase blood flow to the penis.

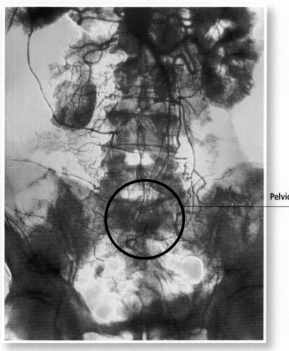

Pelvic blood vessels

Leriche's syndrome
Erectile dysfunction can occur due to Leriche's syndrome, in which fatty deposits block blood flow to the pelvic arteries. This angiograph highlights blood vessels in which blood freely flows and shows fewer arteries than normal in the lower abdominal region.

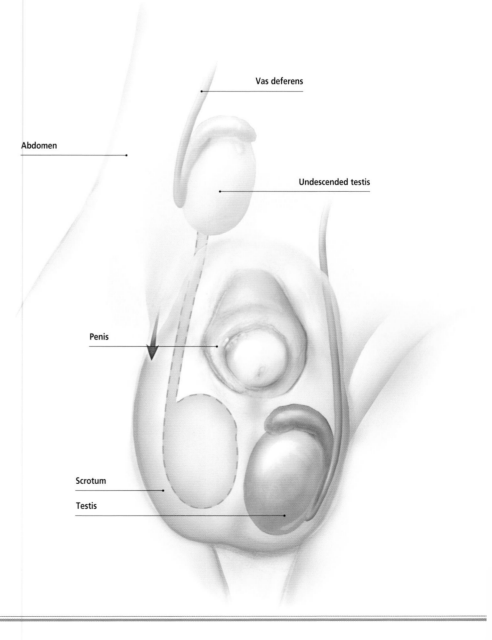

Vas deferens

Abdomen

Undescended testis

Penis

Scrotum

Testis

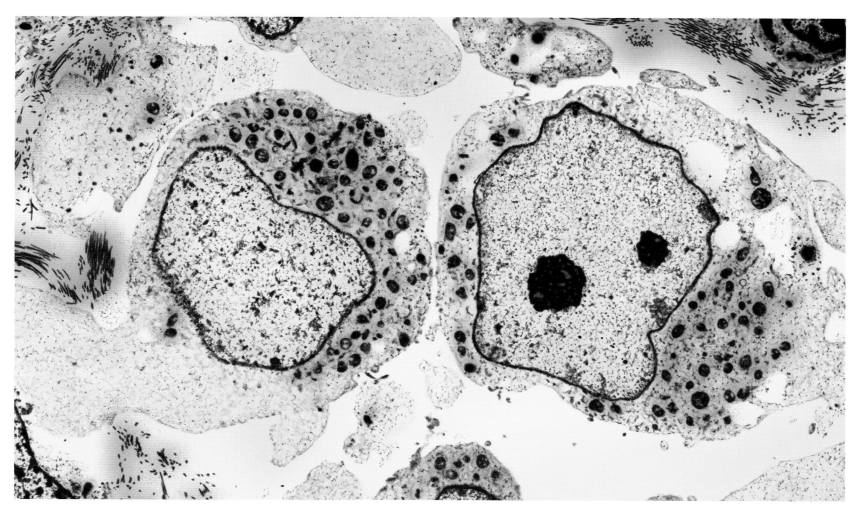

Testicular cancer
This colored transmission electron microscope (TEM) image confirms a case of testicular cancer, revealing abnormally large, irregularly shaped nuclei (yellow-gold) of several malignant cells. Green colored areas are cytoplasm around each nucleus. Early detection and treatment results in remission in the majority of cases.

Epididymis
Coiled tube in which sperm mature.

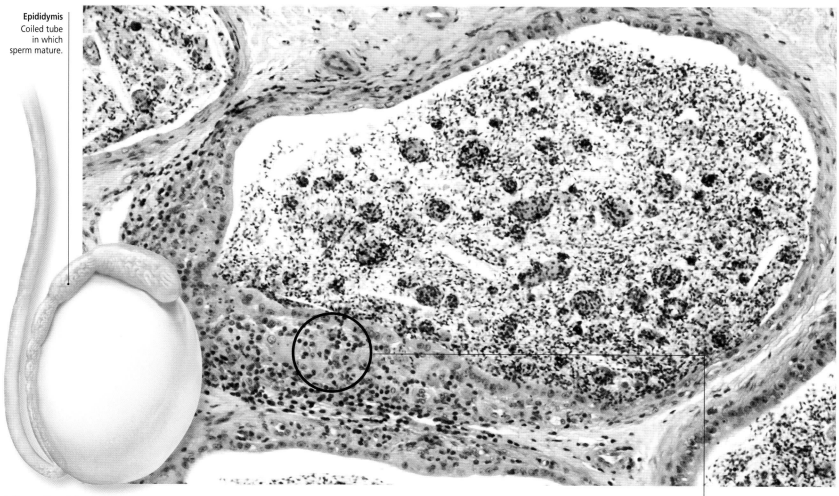

Inflamed area

Inflammation of the epididymis
This light micrograph shows an oval-shaped wall around a section of an epididymis. Part of the wall (left, center) is thicker than normal, which is likely due to inflammation. Infection by bacteria or a virus is the most common cause of this painful ailment, which can occur in males of all ages.

BREAST AND PROSTATE CANCER

Cancers of the breast and prostate are two of the most common reproductive malignancies. One in every nine women will develop breast cancer, and the chances are much greater for those who are genetically susceptible. A cancerous breast tumor contains several types of cells, and depending on its stage may have spread to other organs and tissues. Today, a wide array of treatments, including various types of surgery, radiation and a growing list of chemotherapy options, allow a breast cancer patient and physician to tailor treatment to the specific characteristics of the disease. When detected and treated early, 95 percent of breast cancers are curable. Early detection and a high cure rate are also the norm with prostate cancer. Most prostate tumors grow extremely slowly, improving the chance that a malignancy will be found and treated before it has metastasized.

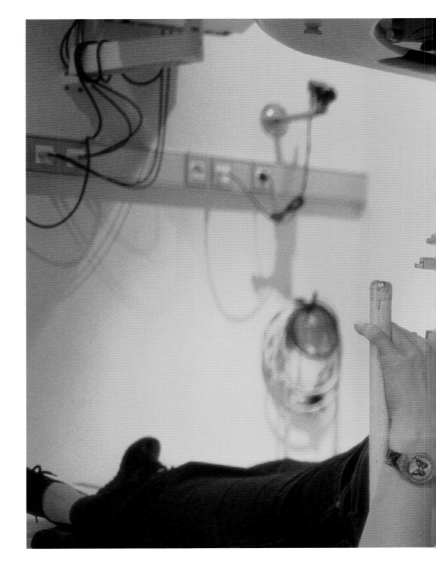

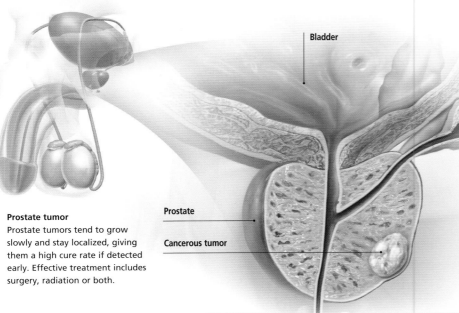

Metastatic prostate cancer
Invasive prostate cancer often spreads first to the bones. White spots in a PET scan reveal a malignancy that has metastasized from the patient's prostate gland to one of his ribs (center and right).

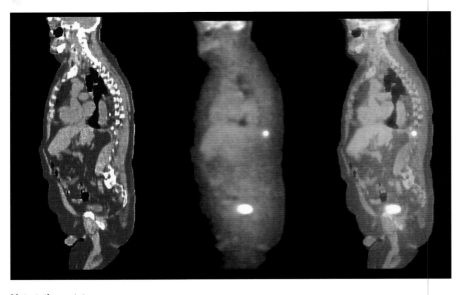

Bladder

Prostate

Cancerous tumor

Prostate tumor
Prostate tumors tend to grow slowly and stay localized, giving them a high cure rate if detected early. Effective treatment includes surgery, radiation or both.

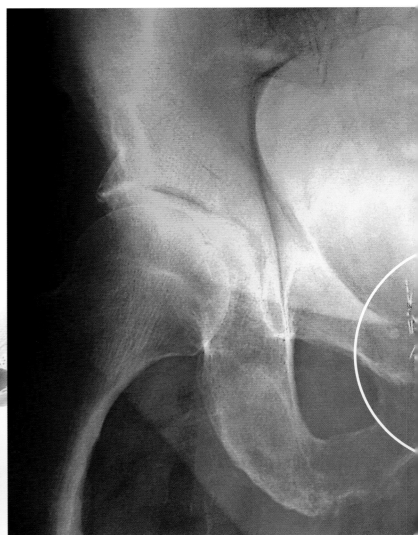

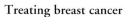

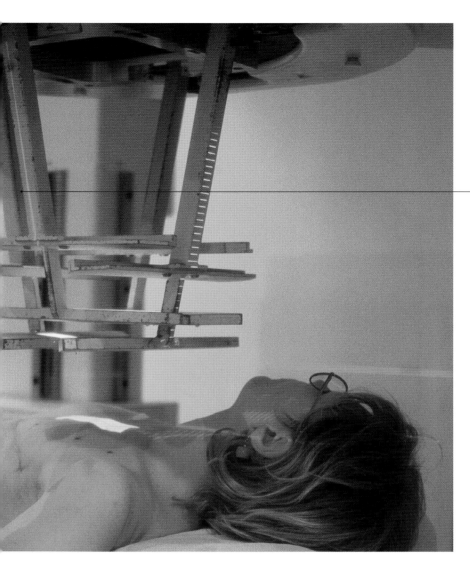

Treating breast cancer

Depending on the cancer's stage and type, breast cancer treatment may involve surgery to remove part or all of the affected breast, radiation (as in the photo on the left, showing radiation treatment after mastectomy) or chemotherapy designed to kill cancer cells, hormone therapy that prevents the cells from multiplying or a combination of these. High-risk patients, generally those with a strong family history of the disease, sometimes opt for prophylactic mastectomy—removal of still-healthy breasts.

Radiation therapy

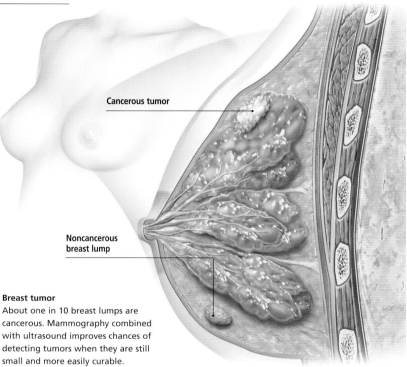

Cancerous tumor

Noncancerous breast lump

Breast tumor
About one in 10 breast lumps are cancerous. Mammography combined with ultrasound improves chances of detecting tumors when they are still small and more easily curable.

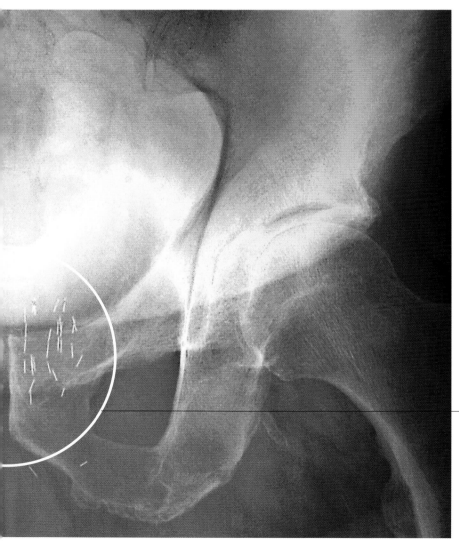

GENES AND BREAST CANCER

Women who carry abnormal copies of either of two genes are at higher risk for developing breast cancer or ovarian cancer. These genes, called BRCA1 and BRCA2, are tumor suppressor genes that usually help repair genetic damage that can transform a normal cell into a cancerous one. Mutated versions are implicated in about five percent of all breast cancers. The mutations are most common in women of Mediterranean or Eastern European Jewish descent. Of those who inherit a faulty BRCA gene, nearly 90 percent develop breast cancer by age 65. Genetic testing can determine if a woman carries mutations of either gene.

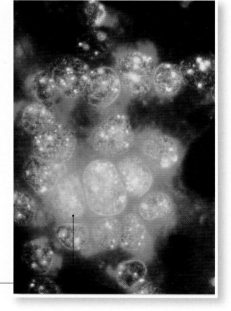

Breast cancer cells

Radioactive rod implants

Prostate cancer

Prostate cancer is one of the most common malignancies in men, second only to lung cancer in many nations. Prostate tumors often develop slowly and may not cause major symptoms, such as blood in the urine or bone pain, until well advanced. No definitive cause is known, although aging, being of African heritage and obesity increase the risk. In some cases, heredity may be a factor. Prostate cancer can be treated with radiation therapy, such as radioactive rods implanted into the gland.

Sexually Transmitted Diseases

Bacteria, viruses and other pathogens that are communicated by sexual activity can trigger a variety of sexually transmitted diseases, or STDs. Untreated, many STDs can lead to infertility or other long-term damage. Syphilis is caused by the bacterium *Treponema pallidum* and is potentially lethal, while nearly all those who become infected with HIV eventually die of an AIDS-related illness. Some STDs are all the more dangerous because they may initially cause few or no symptoms. One of these is chlamydia, a bacterial infection that strikes an estimated 90 million people worldwide each year. It attacks the genital and urinary tract, and for up to 40 percent of infected women, its first outward sign is inflammation of the uterus, ovaries and oviducts. This complication of chlamydia or untreated gonorrhea, called pelvic inflammatory disease (PID), could result in infertility.

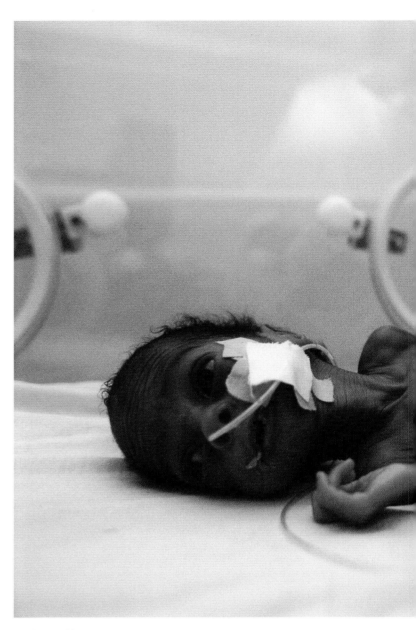

Newborns with AIDS
Newborns can become victims of HIV/AIDS when the virus crosses the placenta and infects a developing fetus. However, HIV-infected mothers can reduce the risk by taking antiretroviral medications during pregnancy and having a cesarean section to decrease delivery time.

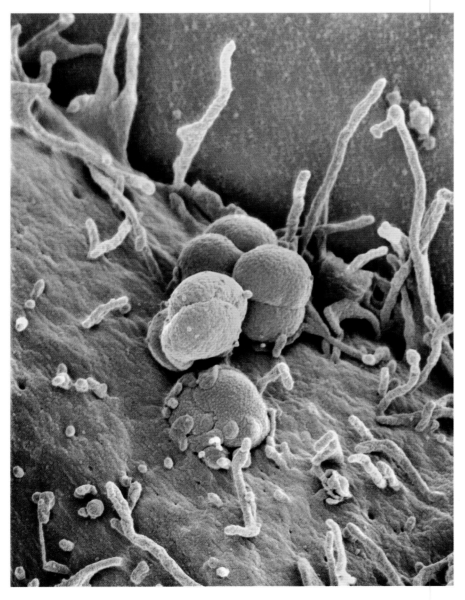

Gonorrhea
This colored micrograph shows yellow bacteria that cause gonorrhea. The microbes are in the process of infecting epithelial cells (brown) in a reproductive tract. Many patients have no symptoms, unwittingly allowing the infection to progress.

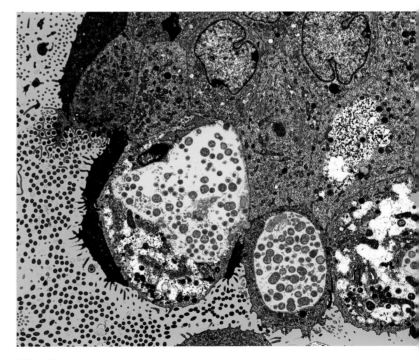

Chlamydia
Here chlamydia bacteria (red dots) are infecting cells in a woman's fallopian tube (gray). This extremely common STD can inflame various tissues of the reproductive tract, such as the cervix, creating scarring that leads to infertility.

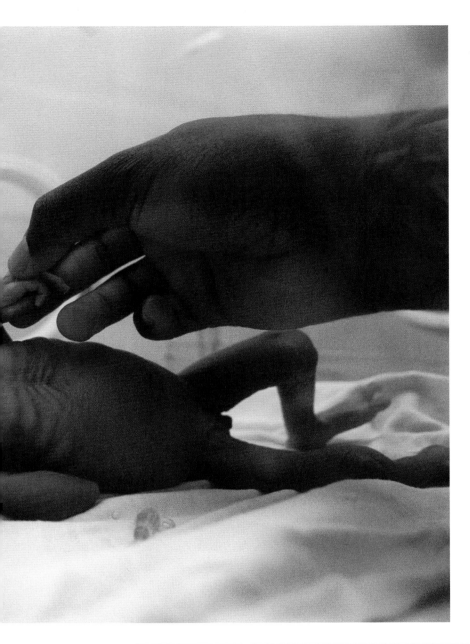

Impact on newborns

A pregnant woman who is infected with an STD may pass on the disease to her fetus or newborn child. Certain STDs, such as syphilis and HIV infection, can cross the placenta during pregnancy. HIV and several other infections, such as chlamydia, genital herpes, gonorrhea and hepatitis B, are transmittible while a newborn is passing through the birth canal during labor. Even the breast milk of an HIV-infected mother can contain the virus. The consequences of an STD infection can range from miscarriage and stillbirth to devastating health problems for affected babies.

SYMPTOMS AND TREATMENTS FOR SEVERAL COMMON STDS

STD	CAUSE	SYMPTOMS	TREATMENT
Chlamydia	*Chlamydia trachomatis* bacterium	Can be asymptomatic. Possible symptoms include painful or frequent urination, vaginal or penile discharge, pain during intercourse and irregular menses.	Tetracycline, an antibiotic
Genital herpes	*Human herpes virus type 2*	Painful lesions on and around the genital area	Acyclovir, an antiviral medication
Genital warts	*Human papillomavirus* (HPV)	Warts around genital area	Warts tend to disappear on their own
Gonorrhea	*Neisseria gonorrhoeae* bacterium	Painful urination and penile discharge in men. Abdominal discomfort, vaginal discharge, abnormal bleeding in women.	Ceftriaxone, an antibiotic
Syphilis	*Treponema pallidum* bacterium	Lesions on the penis or within the vagina are the initial symptom. Secondary symptoms include rash, fever and joint pain.	Penicillin

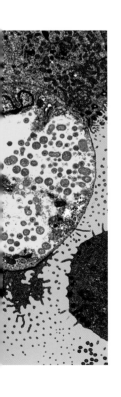

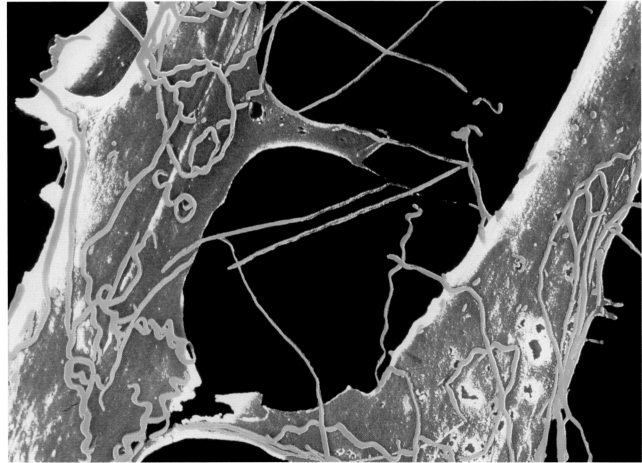

Syphilis
Pale, threadlike spirals on green-tinted cells from a man's testicles show syphilis bacteria. Early treatment with penicillin has long been a reliable cure, but today antibiotic-resistant syphilis is becoming a serious public health threat.

REPRODUCTIVE TECHNOLOGIES

Infertile couples wishing to conceive a child can pursue a variety of technological options. For women with hormonal conditions that prevent normal ovulation, fertility drugs can stimulate the release of one or more eggs. The drugs commonly result in twins, triplets and even larger multiple births. A variety of personal circumstances, including a male partner's low sperm count, may lead a couple to try assisted reproductive technologies, or ARTs. One of the simplest and least costly is artificial insemination, in which donated semen is placed into a woman's vagina or uterus, usually when she is ovulating. Another common option is in vitro fertilization—placing eggs, sperm and stimulating chemicals together in a laboratory dish. If fertilization is successful, one or more of the resulting embryos are transferred to the woman's uterus. Some couples undergo complex surgical procedures that insert eggs and sperm or even a developing zygote, or fertilized egg, into a woman's oviducts in order to reproduce.

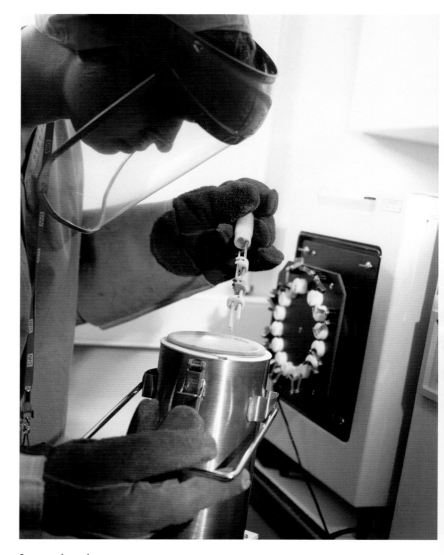

Sperm and egg donors
Women and men both may donate gametes for use by infertile couples. The donated eggs and sperm may be stored frozen in liquid nitrogen, then used later for in vitro fertilization procedures.

Multiple births
Fertility drugs can stimulate the ovulation of several eggs simultaneously, leading to a multiple pregnancy. Often only some of the fetuses survive, but all of these quintuplet boys arrived in good health.

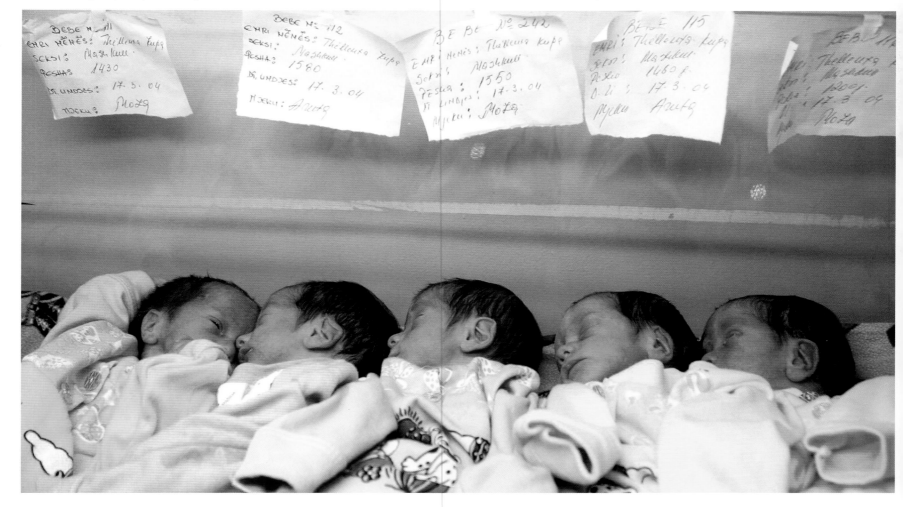

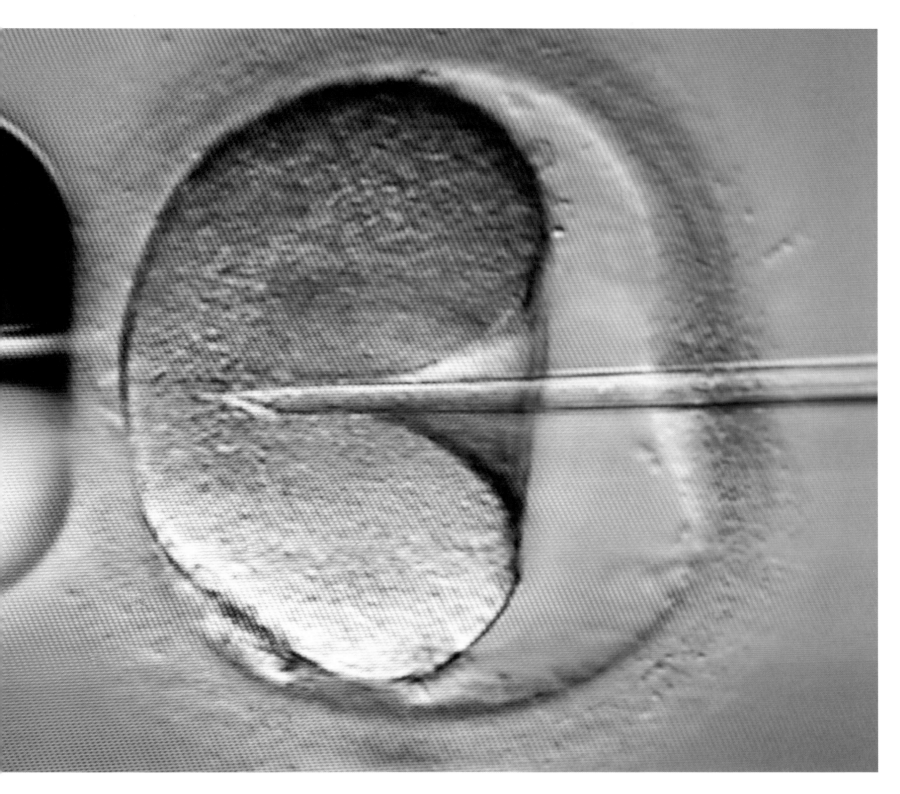

PREIMPLANTATION DIAGNOSIS

It is increasingly common for embryos conceived by in vitro fertilization to be screened for possible genetic defects before being implanted into the prospective mother's uterus. The test usually occurs at the ball-shaped, eight-cell stage (right), when none of the cells has begun to specialize and all are therefore functioning with identical genetic instructions. Doctors remove one cell and analyze it for genetic disorders. If none is discovered, the ball is inserted in the mother's uterus in the hope that it will implant.

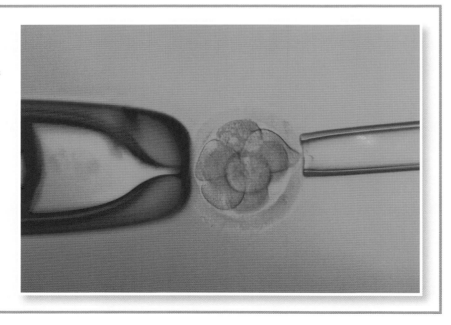

ICSI

In ICSI, short for intracytoplasmic sperm injection, a mature sperm or even a still-developing stage called a spermatid obtained from the male partner is injected into an egg's cytoplasm (above), the jellylike material that surrounds the egg cell's nucleus. If all goes well, the injected sperm nucleus will fuse with that of the egg and fertilization will occur. ICSI is used in cases where the future father's sperm do not swim as usual, or when they fail to develop into mature cells.

DIAGNOSING PRENATAL HEALTH

Medicine now offers many options for evaluating the health status of an unborn child. These techniques give advance information about possible genetic or developmental issues, or even about the baby's sex. They also allow parents and physicians to plan for birth complications, such as a possible breech birth. Ultrasonography is a simple, noninvasive technique that uses sound waves to generate images of a fetus. It provides a general view of the baby's position in the uterus and its developmental progress. Amniocentesis and chorionic villus sampling (CVS) are both invasive techniques that allow a physician to examine fetal cells in amniotic fluid or the fetal portion of the placenta. Samples of the mother's blood may also reveal evidence of several types of abnormalities, such as the neural tube defect spina bifida. In rare cases, physicians may attempt highly specialized surgical procedures before birth to correct potentially life-threatening conditions.

Fetal surgery

Some potentially harmful conditions, such as congenital heart defects or a lower urinary tract obstruction, which can result in kidney damage, may be corrected before birth. The most common, least risky approach is closed-womb intervention, in which a physician uses miniature instruments introduced through a hollow needle inserted into the mother's uterus. Ultrasonography or fetoscopy help guide the operation. In open fetal surgery, the surgeon opens the mother's abdomen and uterus in order to make a surgical repair. Because it involves major risks to mother and child, open surgery is performed at only a few centers and only in extreme circumstances.

AMNIOCENTESIS AND CVS

The amniotic fluid that surrounds a fetus contains sloughed fetal cells that can be analyzed for certain genetic features, including gender and disorders such as Down syndrome and sickle-cell anemia. In amniocentesis, a physician uses a needle to obtain a sample of the cells for analysis. In CVS (chorionic villus sampling), the sample comes from the chorion, the fetal portion of the placenta. Both procedures are associated with risks, including infection and possible injury to the developing baby.

Amniocentesis

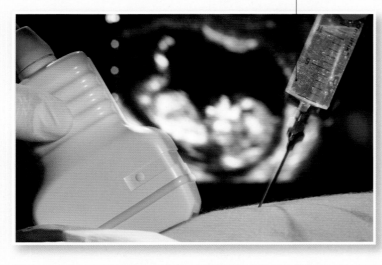

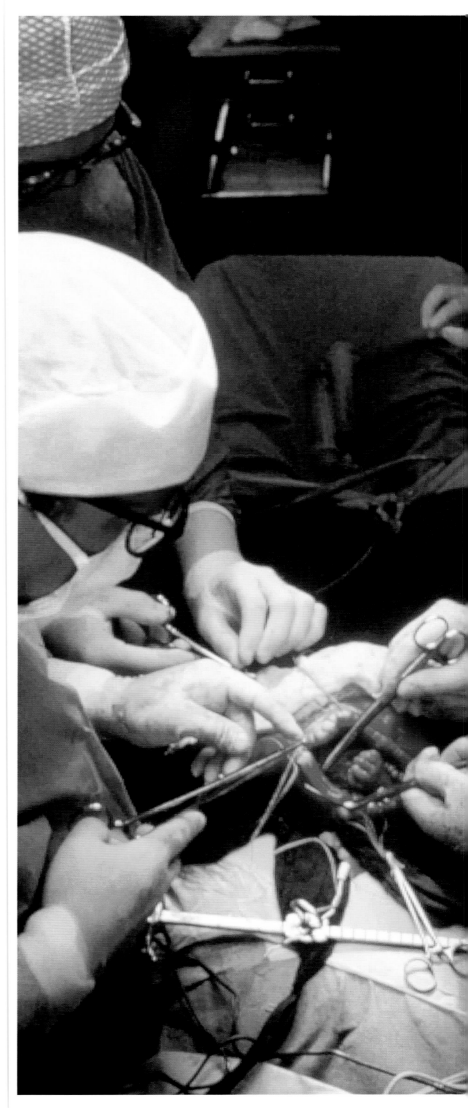

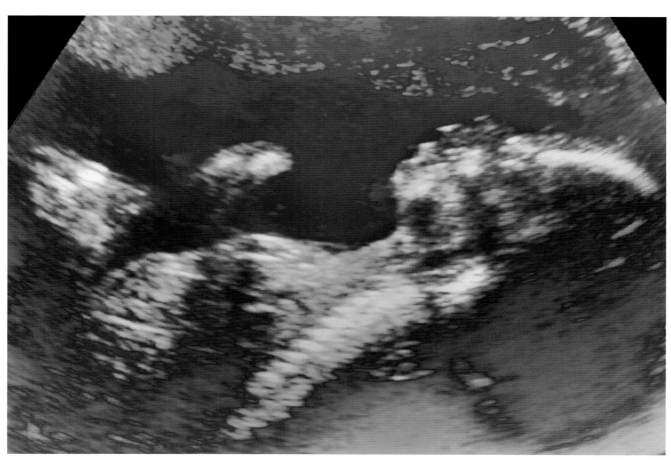

Ultrasound
This colored ultrasound shows a 20-week-old fetus. A hand can be seen above the torso with a leg at the left. Ultrasounds are now routinely used to visualize a pregnancy's progress. In addition to monitoring fetal growth, an ultrasound is valuable for early diagnosis of spinal defects and heart conditions.

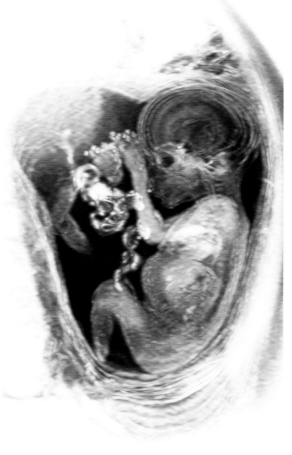

Fetal MRI
Magnetic resonance imaging can provide a detailed view of the developing organs in a fetus, as well as of the mother's tissues. It usually is reserved, however, for cases in which there is a serious health issue suspected, such as defects of the nervous system, which cannot always be seen clearly with an ultrasound.

Correcting a birth defect
This historical photograph shows a child born with spina bifida, a birth defect that today can be prevented with proper maternal nutrition. Sophisticated pre-delivery treatments now allow some abnormalities to be corrected before birth.

HEREDITY AND DISEASE

Biomedical researchers have discovered links between harmful forms of genes and thousands of diseases and disorders, with new ones continually being added to the list. Mutant forms of single genes cause some diseases. Such abnormal genes may arise spontaneously or they may be inherited from parents. If the abnormal gene is dominant, as with Huntington's disease, a person who carries it will inevitably develop the illness. If the faulty gene is recessive, as with cystic fibrosis and phenylketonuria (PKA), an affected child must have inherited a copy of it from each parent. More often the picture is not so simple. Many genetic disorders, like most other human traits, may be multifactorial—they develop only through the interaction of several genes. In cases where an otherwise healthy person simply inherits a predisposition to develop a given disease, environmental events, lifestyle choices or some as-yet unknown factor may tip the balance.

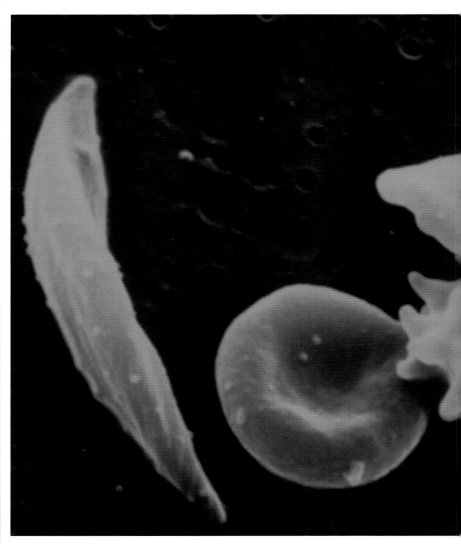

Sickle-cell anemia
Sickle-cell anemia is an example of the genetic phenomenon called pleiotropy, in which one gene has effects on more than one physical or chemical trait. People who develop the full-blown disease have inherited from both parents faulty, recessive genes that are responsible for making the blood protein hemoglobin. Ultimately, however, the resulting damage to red blood cells harms virtually all of the major organs. Individuals who only inherit the defective gene from one parent typically have a much less devastating condition called sickle cell trait.

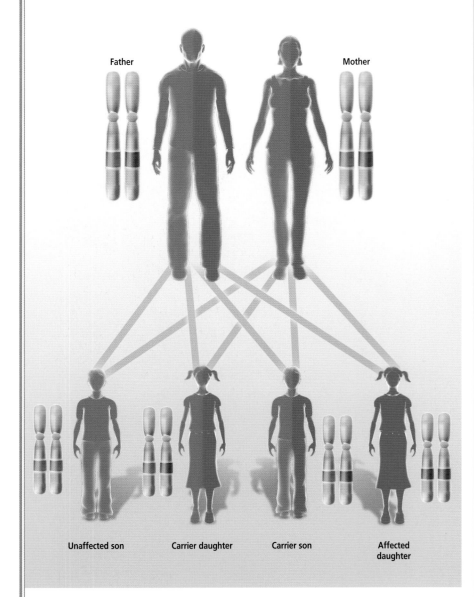

Autosomal recessive disorders
With autosomal recessive disorders, both parents may be carriers of the flawed gene without being affected themselves. Each child has a 25 percent chance of receiving the gene from each parent and developing the disorder.

GENETIC PEDIGREES
Geneticists use pedigree charts to track multiple generations of families in which a particular trait, such as familial breast cancer, is manifest. Pedigree analysis is often used to identify individuals at risk of transmitting or developing the trait in question. In cases where a familial genetic disorder is rare or poorly understood, constructing a pedigree may allow researchers to determine if the disorder is caused by a single dominant or recessive gene, or if it is located on a sex chromosome or an autosome.

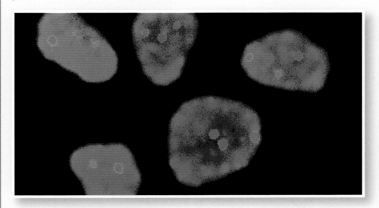

Down's syndrome chromosomes
This micrograph shows Down's syndrome chromosomes (red) in the cell nuclei (blue) of a fetus. Down's syndrome is a genetic disorder caused by an error in cell division and can be tracked by geneticists with the help of pedigree charts.

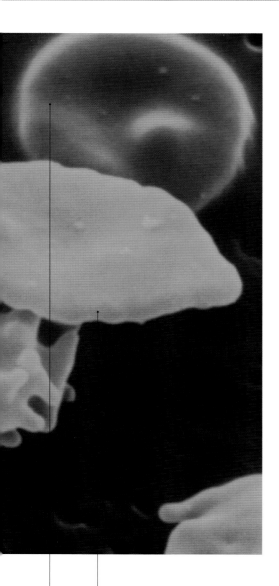

Sickle cell

Normal red blood cell

Hemophilia
The X-linked, genetic blood-clotting disorder hemophilia has several forms. This boy has the rarer type, hemophilia B. Twice each week he must inject a medication that provides the missing clotting factor, called factor IX.

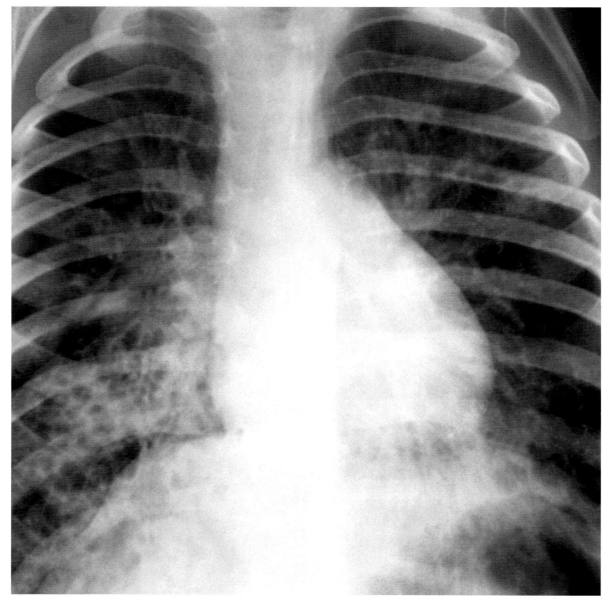

Dominant vs recessive traits

The same gene commonly has slightly different chemical forms. The effect of its dominant form always masks the effect of its recessive form. As a practical matter, a person who inherits a dominant gene form from one parent and a recessive form from the other parent, will have the dominant trait. Genes for long eyelashes, chin dimples and the disease cystic fibrosis, which clogs lung airways with mucus as shown on this X-ray, are all dominant. In order to display a recessive trait, such as attached earlobes or phenylketonuria, a person must inherit the recessive gene form from both parents.

END OF LIFE

Death is an inevitable part of life. Whether due to injury, disease or simple old age, death ultimately comes when the heart and brain cease functioning. When a terminal disease is the cause of death, patients may experience a steady decline, sometimes punctuated with intermittent crises, or they may seem surprisingly healthy until the last month or two. As the course of the disease advances, typical symptoms such as fatigue, loss of appetite, shortness of breath, incontinence and pain may come to the fore. In the last weeks or months before death extremely ill or elderly people often become less able to manage personal hygiene or housekeeping tasks such as preparing meals. Some become increasingly confused or anxious. Despite this onslaught of challenges, caregivers including family, friends and medical personnel can tap a variety of medical and other resources to help make the end of life as dignified and comfortable as possible.

THE EXCEPTIONAL MADAME CALMENT

To date the longest-lived human was Jeanne Calment, a Frenchwoman whose age was documented at 122 years and 164 days at the time of her death in August 1997. Madame Calment exercised regularly well past her 100th birthday. Her birth family included several relatives who lived well into their 80s and 90s, suggesting a genetic component to her extraordinary longevity.

Oldest person on record
Here is Jeanne Calment as she celebrated her 120th birthday.

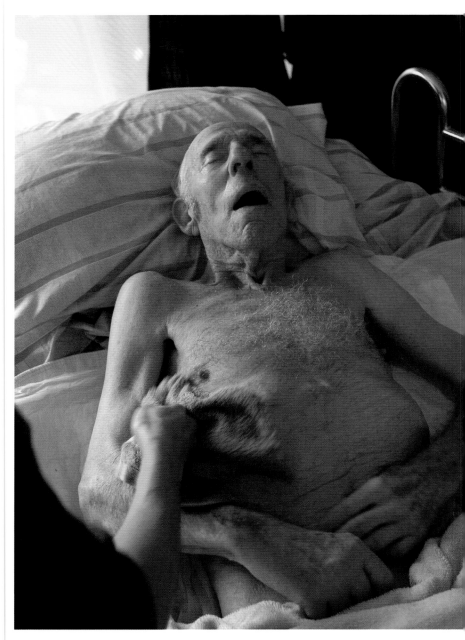

Dying
The loving care of family members and others is a boon to dying patients. This man died only days after his son-in-law took this photograph of his daughter giving him a soothing sponge bath.

Rank	Country	Both sexes	Country	Males	Country	Females
1	Japan	82.6	Iceland	80.2	Japan	86.1
2	Hong Kong	82.2	Hong Kong	79.4	Hong Kong	85.1
3	Iceland	81.8	Japan	79	Spain	84.2
4	Switzerland	81.7	Switzerland	79	Switzerland	84.2
5	Australia	81.2	Australia	78.9	France	84.1
6	Spain	80.9	Sweden	78.7	Australia	83.6
7	Sweden	80.9	Israel	78.6	Italy	83.5
8	Israel	80.8	Macau	78.5	Iceland	83.3
9	Canada	80.7	Canada	78.3	Virgin Islands	83.3
10	France	80.7	New Zealand	78.2	Sweden	83
…						
191	Lesotho	42.6	Zambia	42.1	Zimbabwe	42.7
192	Sierra Leone	42.6	Mozambique	41.7	Zambia	42.5
193	Zambia	42.4	Angola	41.2	Mozambique	42.4
194	Mozambique	42.1	Sierra Leone	41	Lesotho	42.3
195	Swaziland	39.6	Swaziland	39.8	Swaziland	39.4

World life expectancy at birth: top ten and bottom five countries
Life expectancy at birth is an average calculated for a group of people born in the same year. The average is significantly lower in countries with high rates of infant and childhood mortality, poverty and decreased access to health care. Also, the bottom five countries all suffer from high rates of HIV/AIDS. According to the United Nations 2005–2010 figures, the world average life expectancy for men and women combined is 67.2 years.

Limits to the human life span

Cell biologists suspect that one or more internal mechanisms influence the pace of aging. So far as is known, no human being has lived beyond age 122, and other organisms also have a maximum life span. One reason may be that cells are genetically programmed to divide only a certain number of times. For humans that number seems to be 50 to 80 divisions at most. Another theory, "cumulative assaults," proposes that many age-related bodily changes develop due to accumulating free radical damage to DNA.

Hindu rites
A funeral pyre in Bali honors the Hindu tradition of cremating the dead shortly after they pass away. Hindus have observed this tradition for thousands of years.

DNA damage
DNA may be damaged by radiation, including the UVA and UVB wavelengths from sunlight. Intact DNA has two long, connected strands of chemical units called nucleotides (colored bars). This image depicts sunlight-induced breakage of the links between certain bases.

New Orleans farewell
In a traditional New Orleans funeral, family and friends make an emotional public farewell by touching the casket as it is carried to the cemetery.

Funeral money
A Hong Kong cemetery witnesses the somber ritual burning of funeral money, funds the deceased person may require in the afterlife.

FUTURE OF MEDICINE

Tomorrow's physicians will call upon sophisticated medical tools and a deepening understanding of the genetic underpinnings of disease. At a quickening pace, scientific research is being translated into medical advances with real-world applications. Scientists in many nations are striving to develop acceptable ways of using stem cells to grow replacement tissue and organs. An ever more detailed map of the human genome is spurring biomedical researchers to develop new therapeutic drugs for cancers and other diseases while expanding frontiers of gene therapy hold the promise of improving the lives of patients with genetic conditions. Some of medicine's future will be tiny—on a nano scale (one-billionth of a unit) and personal. Scientists envision and are working on "nanobots," robots smaller than a cell that will be able to repair DNA and personalized medicine, treatments tailored to an individual's genetic profile that make medications more effective and safer.

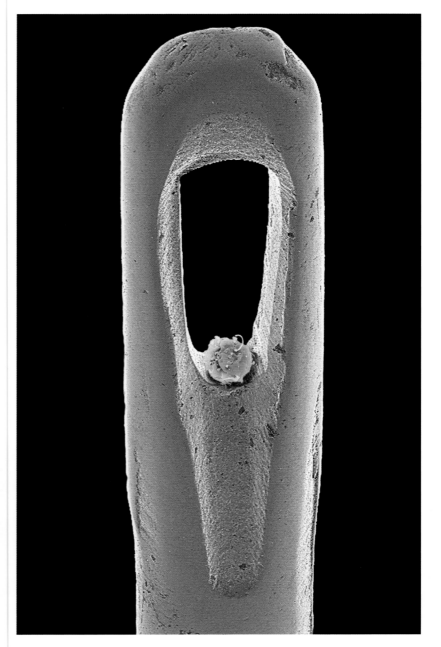

Stem cell technology
This micrograph shows an embryonic stem cell in the eye of a needle. Ethical concerns have slowed efforts to harness embryonic stem cells to replace or repair damaged tissue in diseases such as Parkinson's and Alzheimer's. Researchers are making rapid progress in efforts to obtain viable stem cells in ways that do not destroy an embryo.

Nanobots
Bacteria-sized nanobots—microscopic medical machines already under development, navigate the body to seek out and destroy pathogens and cancer cells and perform miniature surgical operations. This computer art shows a nanobot injecting a drug into an infected T cell in a human body.

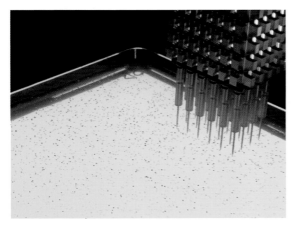

Genetic research
The black spots are bacteria colonies, engineered (cloned) to contain human DNA. These will be used for sequencing—determining the order of the four bases of DNA. DNA sequencing is done to find the exact cause of a genetic disease.

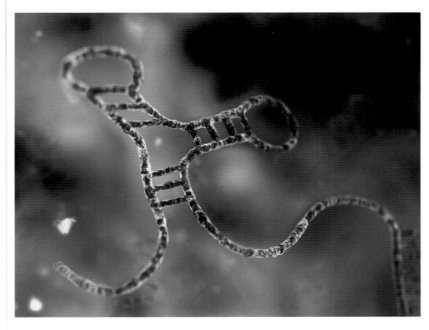

RNA interference
RNA (ribonucleic acid) plays a key role in translating genetic instructions in a cell. A mechanism called RNA interference (RNAi) can prevent some viruses from multiplying by turning off their genes. Researchers are exploring the use of RNAi to disable disease-related genes in humans.

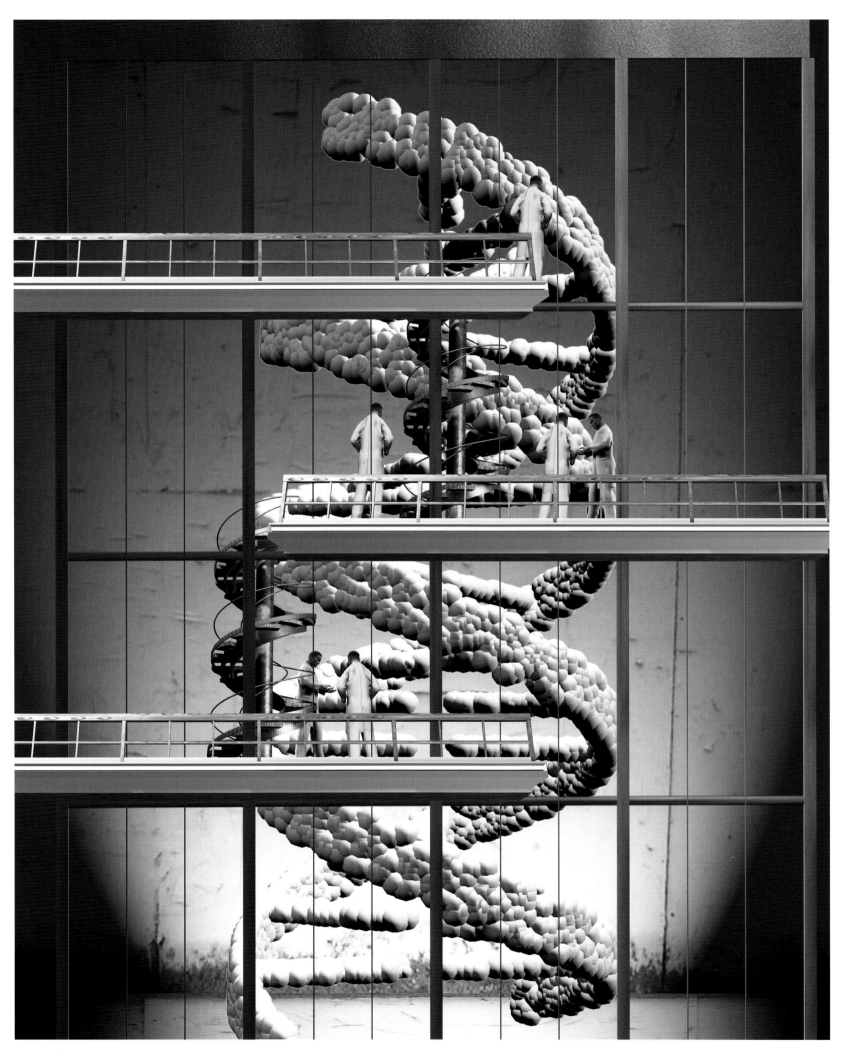

DNA repair
This conceptual artwork of DNA undergoing maintenance and repair could reflect the repair of DNA damaged by genetic disease or environmental factors, the maintenance of healthy DNA to prevent age-related diseases or the modification of DNA, also known as genetic engineering.

REFERENCE

MEDICAL MILESTONES TO 1850

For millennia, humans have been trying to understand and treat every manner of body ailment. Here are a few examples of achievements and medical "firsts" along the way.

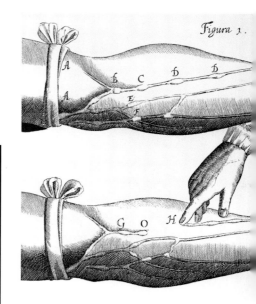

The Edwin Smith Papyrus, written in an ancient Egyptian script about 1900 to 1600 BCE, is the earliest known medical literature.

This Chinese anatomical drawing from about 1030 BCE shows acupuncture points on an arm.

William Harvey's 1628 book on the heart and blood circulation is considered one of the most important contributions to physiology.

Hippocrates, born around 460 BCE, was an early inventor of medical devices such as this one that uses gravity to treat joint dislocations.

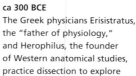

This illustration depicts Edward Jenner vaccinating his young son against smallpox in the late eighteenth century.

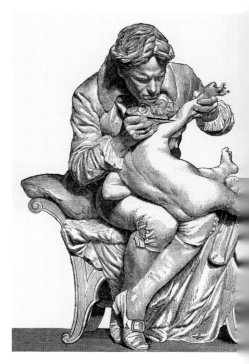

This skull, now at the Archaeological Museum in Cusco, Peru, shows evidence of cranial surgery by the Incas performed in the sixth century.

ca 2650 BCE
Imhotep, one of the first physicians known by name and the "father of Egyptian medicine," is born. Surviving papyri indicate much earlier origins of Egyptian medical knowledge.

ca 1000 BCE
Chinese doctors practice acupuncture, treat patients with herbal medicine and massage and employ a rudimentary form of vaccination to protect against smallpox.

ca 300 BCE
The Greek physicians Erisistratus, the "father of physiology," and Herophilus, the founder of Western anatomical studies, practice dissection to explore the human body indepth.

500
Incas practice trepanation—boring a hole in the skull to treat brain disorders or for mystical reasons. Bone healing shows many patients survived the operation.

1240
Ibn al-Nafis, an Arab physician and surgeon, studies and correctly describes pulmonary circulation, blood flow between the heart and lungs.

ca 1050 BCE
The physician Esagil-kin-apli of Borsippa compiles a book listing a wide range of symptoms, his observations of related factors and recommended techniques for diagnosing ailments.

ca 460 BCE
The renowned Greek physician Hippocrates is born. Hippocrates advocated a rational system of medical thought that ascribed illness to natural causes rather than to supernatural forces.

CE 129
The Greek physician Galen is born. Galen used animal dissections as the basis for detailed writings on human anatomy. Although full of errors, physicians referenced his work for 1,400 years.

1000
At around this time, Persian doctor and scholar Avicenna compiles a vast medical encyclopedia that Europeans used for medical training for centuries.

1543
Belgian physician Andreas Vesalius performs then-illegal dissections of human bodies and publishes a collection of anatomical drawings that corrected errors in Galen's work.

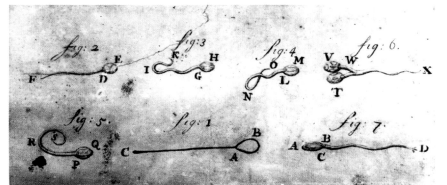

Anton van Leeuwenhoek sent this drawing of human sperm as viewed through a microscope to London's Royal Society (a science society) about 1670.

This is an illustration of the seventeenth century microscope used by Robert Hooke.

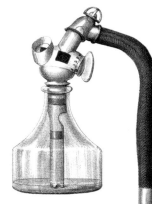

Dr. Laennec uses the stethoscope he invented to help listen to chest sounds and diagnose ailments in 1816.

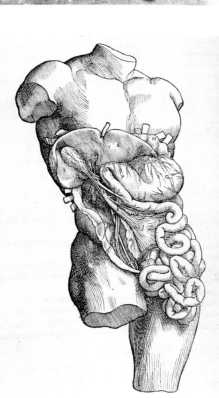

This is a drawing from De humani corporis fabrica (On the Fabric of the Human Body), a series of seven books by Andreas Vesalius in 1543.

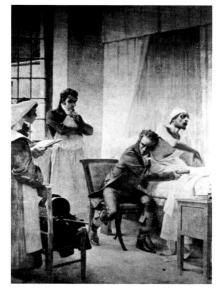

Masks such as this one were used in the mid-nineteenth century to administer ether.

Galen's second-century understanding of internal organs and circulation included the erroneous idea that the heart was a single pump.

1628
English physician William Harvey publishes the first correct description of blood circulation in arteries and veins.

1665
Robert Hooke uses the term "cell" for the basic unit of life after studying plants and insects with a microscope of his own design.

1667
English physician Thomas Sydenham sets forth principles of medical examination and epidemiology (the science of disease spread), recognizes iron deficiency as a cause of anemia and uses quinine to treat malaria.

1677
Dutch shopkeeper and inventor Antoni van Leeuwenhoek, considered the originator of microbiology, develops a microscope powerful enough to observe sperm, red blood cells and microorganisms.

1727
Stephen Hales, an English clergyman with an interest in science, becomes the first to measure blood pressure when he inserts a tube into a blood vessel and observes the blood rise.

1761
Italian physician Giovanni Battista Morgagni lays the foundation for the correlation of symptoms with diagnosis when he ties the autopsy reports of 640 patients to their pre-death symptoms.

1796
English physician Edward Jenner is the first to vaccinate against smallpox by inoculating a boy with fluid from cowpox sores, thereby triggering immunity to the closely related smallpox.

1805
German chemist Friedrich Sertürner extracts morphine from opium, paving the way for its use as a painkiller.

1816
Prompted perhaps by the death of his mother due to tuberculosis, French physician Rene Laennec develops the first stethoscope for amplifying chest sounds for diagnosing disease.

1839
German zoologist Theodor Schwann becomes the first to describe cells in animal tissues as tiny living units and states that all living organisms are composed of cells.

1842
U.S. surgeon Crawford Long pioneers the use of ether gas as an anesthetic, employing it to dull pain while he removes a cyst from a patient's neck.

Medical Milestones
1850 to the Present

Breakthroughs in the late nineteenth century and throughout the twentieth century have scientists poised for more exciting discoveries in the coming years.

Frederick Best and Charles Banting are shown in this 1923 photograph with one of the first mammals whose diabetes was successfully treated with insulin injections.

The pasteurization process, invented by Louis Pasteur (1822–1895), kills human pathogens in food.

Shibasaburo Kitasato is best known for discovering the bacterium that causes bubonic plague in 1894.

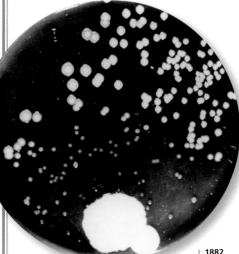

This 1928 photo shows Alexander Fleming's original culture plate in which he observed *Penicillium notatum* destroying colonies of the bacteria *Staphylococcus*.

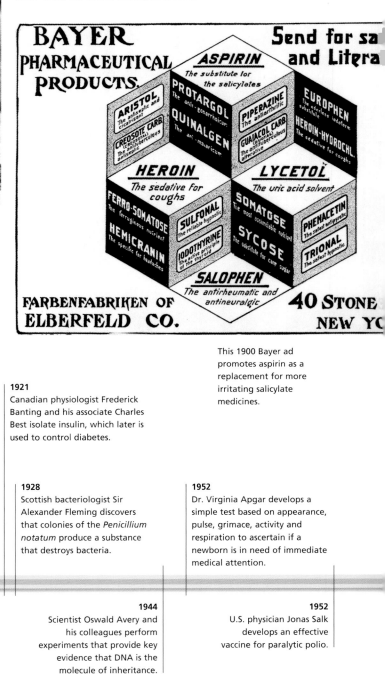

This 1900 Bayer ad promotes aspirin as a replacement for more irritating salicylate medicines.

1882
German researcher Walther Flemming establishes that some material (chromosomes) is passed to daughter cells when a parent cell divides. His work is a foundation for modern cell biology.

1897
German chemist Heinrich Dreser develops aspirin (salicylic acid) from plant extracts.

1921
Canadian physiologist Frederick Banting and his associate Charles Best isolate insulin, which later is used to control diabetes.

1865
English surgeon Joseph Lister begins using carbolic acid as an antiseptic in surgery. His dramatic reduction in death rates leads to the routine use of antiseptics in surgical procedures.

1890
Emil Behring and Kitasato Shibasaburo develop a diphtheria antitoxin and discover antibodies. Almost simultaneously, Elie Metchnikoff puts forth the cellular theory of immunity.

1901
Pathologist Karl Landsteiner discovers the human blood groups A, B and O, and how to differentiate between them, making it possible to safely administer blood transfusions.

1928
Scottish bacteriologist Sir Alexander Fleming discovers that colonies of the *Penicillium notatum* produce a substance that destroys bacteria.

1952
Dr. Virginia Apgar develops a simple test based on appearance, pulse, grimace, activity and respiration to ascertain if a newborn is in need of immediate medical attention.

1870
French scientist Louis Pasteur demonstrates that infectious disease is caused not by "bad air" but by microorganisms—the beginning of the germ theory of disease.

1895
German physicist Wilhelm Roentgen discovers X-rays, laying the foundation for their use as the first medical imaging technology.

1910
German chemist Paul Ehrlich and Japanese bacteriologist Sahachiro Hata chemically modify a toxic compound to create a drug to treat syphilis. Their process is the basis for most modern pharmaceutical research.

1944
Scientist Oswald Avery and his colleagues perform experiments that provide key evidence that DNA is the molecule of inheritance.

1952
U.S. physician Jonas Salk develops an effective vaccine for paralytic polio.

This 1919 photo shows a man receiving treatment using Roentgen Rays, named after the German physicist who first explained the electromagnetic radiation used in X-rays.

Lousie Brown, the first baby born using in vitro fertilization in 1978, with Dr. Pierre Soupart, who led the medical team.

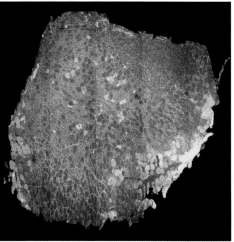
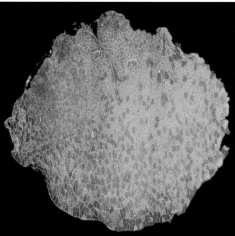

Gene therapy restored normal muscle function (above right) in a research mouse whose original 2006 micrograph (above left) showed a type of muscular dystrophy.

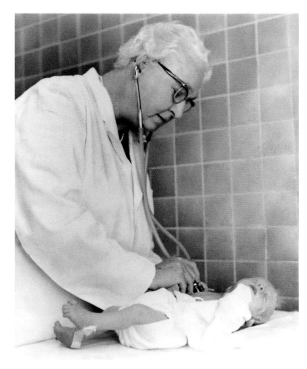

Dr. Virginia Apgar assesses the health of a newborn on October 2, 1966.

This image shows Francis Crick's original 1953 sketch of a DNA strand.

Dolly, the world's first cloned sheep, shown here in 1996 with embryologist Sir Ian Wilmut, who led the experiment.

1953
American James Watson and Briton Francis Crick discover the double-helix structure of DNA and the mechanism by which it can replicate to pass on genetic information to new generations.

1970s
Englishman Sir Godfrey Newbold Hounsfield develops the technology for computer-assisted X-ray imaging, or CT scanning, for imaging internal body parts.

1978
In England, Louise Joy Brown became the first baby to be conceived by way of in vitro fertilization.

1996
Researchers at the Roslin Institute in Edinburgh, Scotland announces the birth of the ewe Dolly, the first animal to be cloned from an adult cell.

2007
Mario Capecchi, Sir Martin Evans and Oliver Smithies win a Nobel Prize for their work in gene targeting in mice, which furthers genetic research.

1950s–1960s
In 1954, U.S. physician Joseph Murray performs the first successful kidney transplant. In 1967, South African surgeon Christian Barnard performs the first human heart transplant.

1973
U.S. biochemists Stanley Cohen and Herbert Boyer successfully insert foreign genes into a bacterial cell, providing the foundation for all future genetic engineering.

1970s–1980s
First used in 1977, magnetic resonance imaging (MRI) revolutionizes diagnostic medicine. In 1987, positron emission tomography (PET) became available, used initially for imaging brain abnormalities.

2003
The Human Genome Project consortium announces the completion of the overall sequence of the human genome, the sum of human genetic information.

2008
Scientists at Advanced Cell Technology mitigate the ethical debate curbing stem cell research by developing human embryonic stem cell lines without the destruction of embryos.

GLOSSARY

ABO blood type

A term used to describe a set of markers on red blood cells. Humans may have A markers, B markers, both A and B, or neither-in which case the blood type is O.

Accommodation

The ability of the eye to adjust its focal length so that light rays are focused properly on the retina.

Acetylcholine

A major neurotransmitter conveying signals between neurons in the central nervous system, and between motor neurons and muscle and gland cells.

Action potential

A nerve impulse.

AIDS

Acquired immune deficiency syndrome, in which infection by HIV (the human immunodeficiency virus) makes a person susceptible to numerous diseases.

Adipose tissue

Tissue containing cells specialized to store fat.

Adrenal cortex

The outer portion of the adrenal gland. It secretes steroid hormones, including the stress hormone cortisol.

Adrenal medulla

The inner core of each adrenal gland. It secretes epinephrine and norepinephrine.

Aldosterone

A steroid hormone from the adrenal cortex that acts (in the kidneys) to help regulate blood pressure.

Allantois

One of the extraembryonic membranes that develops in early pregnancy. It gives rise to the embryo's first blood cells and bladder.

Allergy

An immune response against a substance that is normally harmless to the body.

Alveoli

Tiny air sacs in the lungs where oxygen diffuses from air in the lungs to the blood, and carbon dioxide diffuses from blood to the lungs.

Amino acids

Molecules that are the building blocks of proteins.

Amniocentesis

Procedure in which a sample of amniotic fluid is removed in early pregnancy and analyzed for evidence that a fetus has genetic defects.

Amnion

The protective sac that encloses a developing fetus; it is filled with amniotic fluid.

Androgen

A male sex hormone. Testosterone is the main human androgen.

Anemias

Blood disorders in which red blood cells do not supply sufficient oxygen to body tissues.

Antibiotic

A substance that kills or inhibits the growth of microorganisms.

Antibody

Any of the defensive proteins produced by lymphocytes. An antibody binds to a specific antigen and flags it for destruction by other immune system cells.

Antibody-mediated immunity

Immunity conferred by antibodies produced by B cells and that are present in body fluids, especially blood and lymph.

Antigen

Any substance that stimulates a response by the immune system.

Antioxidant

A substance that can neutralize free radicals before the free radical damages dna or some other cell part.

Aorta

The largest artery in the body, it carries blood from the heart's left ventricle to the rest of the body.

Apoptosis

Genetically programmed cell death; a mechanism that helps shape body parts during development and also destroys abnormal body cells.

Appendicular skeleton

Pectoral girdle, limbs and pelvic girdle.

Apoxia

Lack of oxygen.

Arrhythmia

An abnormal heart rhythm.

Arteriole

A small blood vessel that branches off an artery and connects to capillaries.

Artery

A large blood vessel that carries blood under pressure from the heart to body tissues.

Association areas

Areas of the cerebral cortex that integrate different inputs and then produce responses involving sensory perception, reasoning, memory and other complex cognitive functions.

Astrocytes

Branched glial cells in the brain that help nourish brain neurons and perform other support functions.

Atherosclerotic plaque

An abnormal deposit in artery walls that consists of fatty material, calcium salts and other substances.

Atrioventricular (AV) node

Mass of tissue between the heart's atria and ventricles that receives nerve impulses from the sinoatrial node and transmits them to the ventricles.

Atrioventricular valve

One of two heart valves through which blood flows from the atria to the ventricles; prevents return of blood to the atrium.

Atrium

Either of the two upper heart chambers. The left atrium receives oxygenated blood from the lungs, the right atrium receives deoxygenated blood from tissues.

Aura

A sensation or emotion that is a warning symptom of an impending epileptic seizure or migraine headache.

Autoimmunity

A condition in which the immune system mistakenly attacks the body's own tissues.

Autonomic nerves

Nerves associated with the autonomic nervous system, which regulates involuntary or automatic body functions.

Autosome

A chromosome that does not carry genes for sexual traits.

Axial skeleton

Bones of the head, chest and vertebral column.

Axon

A long extension, with branched endings, from the cell body of a neuron. Nerve impulses travel along axons.

Bare nerve endings

Pain receptors found in the skin.

Basophil

A type of white blood cell that engulfs and destroys microorganisms and also has a role in allergies.

B cell

A type of lymphocyte (white blood cell) that arises in bone marrow and can make antibodies against foreign cells or substances during an immune response.

Benign

Not malignant, as with a noncancerous tumor.

Bilateral symmetry

Having a body with two halves that are basically mirror images of each other.

Bile

A yellowish fluid that assists with fat digestion. Bile is produced in the liver and released from the gallbladder.

Biological clock

A timekeeping mechanism associated with the pineal gland that adjusts cyclical physiological events such as sleeping and waking.

Blastocyst

An early embryonic stage that consists of a small cell mass surrounded by a balloon-like ball of cells.

Blood-brain barrier

Term for the specialized walls of brain capillaries, which prevent some types of harmful molecules from entering the brain from the blood.

Blood clotting

Coagulation of blood into a thick gel.

Blood pressure

The fluid pressure generated by heart contractions; it keeps blood circulating through the cardiovascular system.

Bone marrow

The soft, spongy tissue in the cavities in bones such as the sternum and hip bones; stem cells in bone marrow give rise to red and white blood cells.

Bone tissue

Mineralized connective tissue that forms bones.

Brain lateralization

The assignment of certain brain activities, such as language functions, mainly to one of the two brain hemispheres.

Brain stem

The brain region formed by the pons, medulla oblongata and the midbrain.

Bronchiole

Any of the small, branching airways in the lungs.

Bronchus

One of the two large airways that branch from the windpipe (trachea) and lead to the lungs.

Burn

Tissue damage caused by intense heat, radiation, or chemicals such as certain acids.

Cancer

A disease state in which cells multiply unchecked, forming a malignancy that may spread to other parts of the body.

Capillary

The smallest type of blood vessel. Substances in blood move to and from body cells across the walls of capillaries.

Cardiac cycle

The complete cycle of one heartbeat.

Cardiac muscle

The type of muscle found only in the wall of the heart.

Cardiac pacemaker

A cluster of cells in the heart that regulates the heartbeat.

Cartilage

Firm connective tissue that cushions bones and joints and provides support in areas such as the nose and ears.

Cartilaginous joint

The type of joint in which cartilage fills the space between the linked bones; a cartilaginous joint permits only slight movement.

Cecum

The blind-ended pouch at the beginning of the large intestine (colon).

Cell

The smallest living unit. Individually, a cell's parts are not alive.

Cell-mediated immunity

Immunity conferred by the various kinds of activated T cells, which attack infected or abnormal body cells or cells that have been transplanted and also release chemicals that regulate immune responses.

Central nervous system (CNS)

The brain and spinal cord.

Cerebellum

A region at the rear of the brain where reflexes that maintain posture and adjust limb movements are controlled.

Cerebral cortex

The thin, outer layer of the cerebral hemispheres. Some parts receive input from sensory nerves, others coordinate responses.

Cerebrospinal fluid

A clear fluid that surrounds and cushions the brain and spinal cord.

Cerebrum

The largest and most developed part of the brain, divided into right and left hemispheres. The cerebrum is where cognitive functions such as thought and learning occur.

Chemoreceptor

A sensory cell that responds to chemical stimuli.

Chorion

One of several membranes that develop around an early embryo; it becomes a major part of the placenta.

Chorionic Villus sampling

Sampling procedure in which a tissue sample from the placenta is analyzed during early pregnancy to check for possible genetic defects in a fetus.

Chromosome

A DNA molecule and its associated proteins.

Chyme

The semi-fluid mixture of swallowed food and gastric fluid that passes from the stomach to the small intestine.

Cilia

Delicate, moving hairlike cell structures.

Clone

An organism or cell that is genetically identical to a single parent organism or cell.

Cochlea

Coiled, fluid-filled chamber of the inner ear where pressure waves are translated to signals the brain can interpret as sounds.

Compact bone

The dense bone tissue that makes up the outer part of all bones and the shafts of long bones. It contains channels for blood vessels and nerves.

Complement system

A set of proteins that help target and destroy pathogens (antigens) during immune responses.

Cones

The photoreceptors in the eye that respond to bright light and help provide sharp, color vision.

Congenital

Present at birth.

Connective tissue

Tissue, such as bone, cartilage, ligaments and tendons, that supports body organs and other structures.

Cornea

The clear, outer layer of the eye. Together with the lens, the cornea focuses light on the retina.

Corpus callosum

A band of several hundred million neuron axons that links the right and left cerebral hemispheres.

Corpus luteum

A structure that develops after ovulation and secretes hormones (progesterone and estrogen) that prepare the uterus lining for possible pregnancy.

Corticosteroid

A steroid hormone secreted by the adrenal glands that reduces inflammation in tissues.

Cytokine

A signaling substance that functions in some immune responses.

Cytoplasm

The semifluid portion of a cell that contains all organelles except the nucleus.

Cytoskeleton

A network of protein filaments that provides internal support and structure to a cell and aids in cell movement and division.

Dendrite

A short, branched extension from a neuron that receives nerve impulses from other neurons.

Dendritic cell

A type of defensive cell that assists in launching immune responses by lymphocytes.

Dermis

The inner layer of skin, beneath the epidermis. The dermis contains sensory nerve endings, sebaceous glands, hair follicles, and blood and lymph vessels.

Diaphragm

The dome-shaped skeletal muscle that separates the thoracic (chest) cavity from the abdominal cavity.

Diastole

Period during the cardiac cycle when heart chambers relax and fill with blood.

Digestion

The physical and chemical breakdown of food into small molecules the body can absorb.

Disease

Any deviation from good health.

Disease vector

An agent (such as an insect) that transfers a disease-causing pathogen from contaminated organisms or material to new hosts.

Dislocation

The displacement of a bone from a joint. Dislocation usually results in the tearing of joint ligament, tendons or both.

DNA

Deoxyribonucleic acid, the genetic material. DNA consists of subunits called nucleotides.

DNA fingerprint

The unique sequences of nucleotides in a person's DNA. Except for identical twins, no two individuals have the same DNA sequences.

DNA repair

Natural processes in cells in which enzymes repair defects in strands of DNA.

Dominant gene

A version of a gene that masks another, recessive version of the same gene.

Drug addiction

Severe dependence on a drug, often following a period of increasing use and the development of physiological tolerance to an addictive substance.

Dynamic equilibrium

The balance state that monitors the position of the head in response to movements such as rotation, acceleration and deceleration.

Ectoderm

The outermost tissue layer that forms in an early human embryo. Its cells give rise to the skin and nerve tissue.

Egg cell

A mature female reproductive cell; also called an ovum.

Electrocardiogram (ECG or EKG)

A recording of the heart's electrical activity that can be detected through electrodes placed on the skin.

Embryo

In early development, the term for the stage that begins shortly after conception and lasts until the end of the eighth week of pregnancy.

Endocrine gland

A gland that secretes hormones, which usually are carried in the bloodstream to target cells.

Endoderm

The innermost tissue layer in an early human embryo. It gives rise to many internal organs.

Endometrium

The lining of the uterus.

Endoplasmic reticulum

A system of internal cell membranes that are involved in the synthesis, modification and transport of proteins and other molecules.

Endorphin

A chemical produced by the brain that acts as a natural pain killer.

Endoscopy

The general term for a procedure in which a type of fiber-optic device is inserted into the body through a natural or surgical opening.

Enkephalins

Are a type of endorphin.

Enzyme

A protein that speeds ups (catalyzes) chemical reactions.

Eosinophil

A type of white blood cell that can digest foreign matter and participates in immune responses to parasites, worms and allergens.

Epidermis

The outer layer of the skin.

Epiglottis

A small flap of cartilage in the throat that covers the larynx during swallowing so that food does not enter it.

Epithelium

A tissue composed of a single sheet of closely packed cells. Epithelium lines internal and external body surfaces.

Erythrocyte

A red blood cell.

Erythropoietin

A hormone released by cells in the kidneys that stimulates the production of red blood cells.

Estrogens

Female sex hormones, which are produced by the ovaries.

Eustachian tube

A narrow tube connecting the middle ear to the back of the throat.

Exocrine gland

A gland that releases a product, such as sweat or tears, into ducts that deliver the substance to the skin surface, into a body cavity or into a hollow organ.

Extracellular fluid

All body fluids that are not inside cells, such as blood plasma.

Fertilization

The union of the nuclei of an egg cell and a sperm cell.

Fetoscopy

An endoscopic method used to directly view a developing fetus inside the womb for prenatal diagnosis of possible disease.

Fetus

The term for an embryo after it completes eight weeks of development in the womb.

Fever

A body core temperature that is elevated above the normal range.

Fibrous joint

A joint in which two bones are connected by fibrous connective tissue.

Filtration

In the kidneys, the filtering of substances from blood by nephrons. Filtration is the first step in the formation of urine.

Follicle

In the ovary, the structure where an oocyte (egg cell) develops, along with associated cells that have other reproductive functions.

Foramen magnum

The largest opening in the skull, where the spinal cord connects with the brain stem.

Fovea

A dense area of cone cells in the retina; the part of the eye where vision is sharpest.

FSH

Follicle-stimulating hormone. Produced in the pituitary gland, FSH stimulates the production of eggs in females and sperm in males.

Ganglion

A cluster of nerve cell bodies.

Gastric fluid

The highly acid fluid that begins food digestion in the stomach.

Gastrointestinal tract

The digestive tract.

Gene

A segment of DNA that contains instructions to build a particular protein. Genes are the basic units of heredity.

Gene mutation

A change in the nucleotide sequence in a gene, as when a nucleotide is deleted.

Gene sequence

The order of nucleotides that make up a person's genes.

Gene therapy

Technology in which one or more normal genes are transferred into cells in order to correct a genetic defect.

Genetic code

The chemical correspondence between sequences of nucleotides in genes and amino acids in proteins. Each amino acid is encoded by a sequence of three nucleotides.

Genome

All the DNA in a full set of chromosomes.

Germ cells

The cells in reproductive organs that are specialized to give rise to eggs (in ovaries) and sperm (in testes).

Gestation

The period of pregnancy lasting approximately 280 days.

GH

Growth hormone, also called HGH (human growth hormone) and STH (somatotropin).

Gland

An organ or group of cells that produces and releases one or more substances, such as hormones, digestive juices, sweat and tears.

Glomerulus

A cluster of looping blood capillaries in a kidney nephron where water and dissolved substances are filtered from the blood.

Glottis

The opening between the vocal cords.

Glycogen

The chemical form in which the body stores glucose; glycogen is stored mostly in liver and muscle cells.

Golgi apparatus

A cell organelle specialized to modify, sort and package proteins for export from the cell.

Gray matter

The nerve tissue in the cerebral cortex and spinal cord. Gray matter has nerve cell bodies, white matter does not.

Growth factor

A signaling molecule that can cause cells to divide, leading to growth of tissues and organs.

Gustation

The sense of taste.

Hair cell

A type of mechanoreceptor that can trigger nerve impulses when it is bent or tilted.

Helper T cell

A type of T lymphocyte that facilitates immune system reactions by activating and directing other cells in immune responses.

Hemoglobin

The iron-containing protein in red blood cells that binds oxygen.

Hemostasis

Stopping blood loss, mainly by blood clotting.

Hepatic portal system

A set of blood vessels in the liver that receive nutrient-rich blood from the digestive tract via the hepatic portal vein.

Hippocampus

A structure in the limbic system that functions in the formation of long-term memories.

Histamine

A chemical released by mast cells that promotes inflammation, as in allergies.

Homeostasis

A state of internal balance in the body that is achieved largely by mechanisms that adjust the chemical composition of blood and tissue fluid.

Hormone

A communication molecule, produced by an endocrine gland, that travels through the blood to target cells and tissues.

Hypodermis

The layer of connective tissue just below the skin.

Hypothalamus

A region at the base of the brain that regulates various metabolic processes, such as body temperature and appetite.

Immune response

The body's physiological response to foreign material (antigens).

Immunization

A procedure such as vaccination that provokes a mild immune response and confers immunity to a particular disease.

Immunodeficiency

An abnormal decrease in or total lack of immune responses.

Implantation

The process in which an early embryo becomes embedded in the wall of the uterus.

Inflammation

A general immune system response to infection or irritation, producing redness, heat, swelling and pain.

Inheritance

The transmission of genetic traits from parents to offspring.

Innate immunity

General immune responses including inflammation and the activation of complement proteins.

Inner ear

The innermost portion of the ear; it consists of the cochlea, the organ of hearing and the vestibular apparatus, the organ vital to balance.

Integument

A body covering; in humans, the skin.

Intercostal muscles

Muscles between the ribs that expand the chest cavity during breathing.

Interferons

Family of proteins that help regulate immune responses to viruses and some kinds of cancer cells.

Internal environment

The internal fluid environment that surrounds body cells. It consists of blood and tissue fluid but does not include fluid inside cells.

Interneuron

Neurons in the brain and spinal cord that communicate only with other neurons.

Intervertebral disk

Cartilaginous disk between spinal vertebrae.

Ionizing radiation

Electromagnetic radiation that has enough energy to change the structure of atoms.

Iris

The colored part of the eye that can dilate or contract the size of the pupil to adjust the amount of light that enters the eye.

Karyotype

A complete collection of the chromosomes in a somatic (body) cell. It usually shows all 23 pairs of human chromosomes.

Keratin

A protein found in cells of the skin's epidermis and in hair and nails.

Killer t cell (cytotoxic t cell)

A type of lymphocyte that directly destroys cells infected with particular viruses or bacteria.

Labor

The birth process.

Lactation

The production and secretion of milk from a woman's mammary glands (breasts).

Larynx

The upper part of the windpipe (trachea); it contains the vocal cords.

Lens

The thin, transparent structure in the eye that focuses light on the retina.

Leukocyte

The general term for white blood cells.

LH

Luteinizing hormone. Released from the anterior pituitary, LH triggers ovulation in females and testosterone production in males.

Ligament

A band of strong connective tissue that connects two bones at a joint.

Limbic system

Brain regions that collectively control or influence emotions, motivation and memory.

Lipid

A greasy or oily compound, used in cells for energy or to build parts such as cell membranes.

Lymph

The tissue fluid carried in vessels of the lymphatic system.

Lymph node

A small organ that is usually found in clusters in the armpits, groin, neck, chest and abdomen. White blood cells in lymph nodes collect and destroy foreign matter before it enters the blood.

Lymphocyte

A type of white blood cell, including T cells and B cells, that participates in immune responses.

Lymph vascular system

The vessels of the lymphatic system, which collect and transport lymph.

Lysozyme

An antibacterial enzyme in tears, saliva and sweat.

Macrophage

A type of large white blood cell that functions in tissue. It engulfs and destroys cellular debris and foreign material such as bacteria.

Mast cell

A type of white blood cell in tissues; mast cells release inflammatory chemicals such as histamine.

Mechanoreceptor

A sensory receptor that responds to mechanical pressure.

Meiosis

The type of cell division that produces gametes (sperm and eggs); only cells in the testes (males) and ovaries (females) divide by meiosis.

Meissner's corpuscles

Mechanoreceptors in the skin that are sensitive to low-frequency vibrations and pressure.

Melanin

The pigment that gives color to the skin, hair and eyes.

Melanocyte

A cell specialized to produce the pigment melanin, which may be brown, black or yellowish. Melanocytes help give skin its color.

Memory cells

A subset of t and b cells that remain in the body after an immune response and that later can mount a stronger, more rapid response to the same antigen.

Meninges

Membranes that cover the brain and spinal cord.

Menopause

The gradual cessation of menstruation. Menopause usually occurs when a woman is in her late forties or early fifties.

Menstrual cycle

The cyclic shedding of blood and endometrial tissue from the uterus of a non-pregnant female.

Merkel's disks

Mechanoreceptors in skin that are sensitive to fine touch and pressure.

Metabolism

The sum of chemical reactions in cells by which they obtain and use energy.

Microsurgery

A surgical procedure using miniaturized instruments, generally through a minimal opening.

Microvillus

A hair-like projection from the surface of some epithelial cells, as in the lining of the small intestine; microvilli are specialized to absorb substances.

Middle ear

The central cavity of the ear that conducts sound to the inner ear. It contains the three tiny ear bones and the eardrum (tympanic membrane).

Mitochondrion

A cell organelle where the cellular fuel atp is formed.

Mitosis

The type of cell division by which body tissues grow and body cells replicate.

Monoclonal antibodies

Antibodies produced in the laboratory; made by cells descended from a single parent cell.

Motor neuron

A neuron that carries motor impulses from the central nervous system to muscles and glands.

Motor unit

In muscle tissue, a neuron and all the skeletal muscle fibers it controls.

Mucous membrane

A thin, moist membrane containing mucus glands. Mucous membranes line body cavities that open to the outside.

Muscle fatigue

Reduced tension or force exerted by a contracting muscle, due to prolonged activity by its fibers (muscle cells).

Muscle fiber

A single muscle cell, composed of bundled myofibrils. Muscle tissue tissue that can contract (shorten) when it is stimulated by nerve impulses. The three types of muscle tissue are cardiac, skeletal and smooth muscle.

Muscle tone

A steady state of low-level contraction. Skeletal muscle tone helps stabilize joints.

Mutation

A change in the chemical makeup of a gene. Mutations may occur spontaneously or due to the effects of a virus, ionizing radiation, a chemical or some other factor.

Myelin sheath

A fatty, insulating wrapping around the axons of many motor and sensory nerves. It is formed by the outer membranes of schwann cells.

Myocardium

Heart muscle tissue.

Myofibril

A contractile filament in muscle cells.

Natural killer (NK) cells

Lymphocytes that mount a general attack against foreign material in the body.

Negative feedback

A mechanism of homeostasis in which a change in some condition triggers a response that counteracts the altered condition.

Nephron

A tiny tubule found in the kidney that filters wastes, unneeded substances and fluids from the blood, producing urine.

Nerve

A bundle of neuron axons and supporting cells

Nerve impulse

A brief reversal of electrical voltage across the cell membrane of a neuron. Nerve impulses convey information between nerve cells and other parts of the body; also called an action potential.

Nerve tract

A cablelike bundle of neuron axons in the central nervous system.

Nervous tissue

The category of body tissue that includes neurons and associated support cells.

Neuroendocrine

Control center in the brain, the parts of the hypothalamus and pituitary gland that interact to control many physiological functions.

Neuroglia

Cells that provide physical and metabolic support to neurons; more than half the nerve tissue in the body consists of neuroglia.

Neuromuscular junction

The junction where a motor neuron synapses on a skeletal muscle fiber.

Neuron

A nerve cell.

Neurotransmitter

Any of the signaling chemicals released by nerve cells.

Neutrophil

A type of white blood cell that ingests and destroys foreign material.

Nociceptor

A pain receptor, usually a free nerve ending.

Nuclei

In the brain, neural ganglia (clusters of nerve cell bodies).

Nucleic acid

A long, chain-like molecule composed of nucleotides. Dna and rna are types of nucleic acids.

Nucleus

The cell organelle that contains most of the cell's genetic material, in the form of DNA organized in chromosomes.

Nutrient

A substance not naturally made in the body and that is required for proper body functioning.

Obesity

Having excess body fat, typically 20 percent above the recommended weight for a given height and age.

Olfaction

The sense of smell.

Olfactory receptor

A receptor in the nasal epithelium that is sensitive to odorant molecules.

Oncogene

A gene that causes cancer. Oncogenes generally develop from previously normal genes that have undergone a mutation.

Oocyte

A developing egg.

Organ

A body part, such as the heart, liver, stomach and brain, that consists of one or more tissues that collectively perform a specific function.

Organ of Corti

A region of membrane in the inner ear that contains the sensory hair cells involved in hearing.

Organelle

In cells, a sac or compartment that is enclosed by a membrane and that has a particular function.

Ossicles

The middle ear bones (incus, malleus and stapes).

Osteoblast

A bone-forming cell.

Osmoreceptor

A sensory receptor that detects changes in water volume in a body fluid.

Osteon

The basic structural unit of compact bone.

Otoliths

Calcium carbonate crystals in the inner ear that function in sensing gravity and changes in acceleration.

Ovarian cycle

The monthly cycle in an ovary during which a follicle develops and an egg is ovulated.

Ovulation

The release of an egg from an ovary during a woman's menstrual cycle.

Oxygen debt

A reduced oxygen level in blood when working muscle cells consume energy faster than it is replenished.

Oxytocin

A hormone from the hypothalamus that stimulates uterine contractions during labor and the release of milk from a female's breasts.

Pacinian corpuscle

A pressure-sensitive mechanoreceptor in skin and some internal organs.

Pain

Conscious awareness of an injury to body tissue.

Parasite

An infectious organism that obtains nourishment from the tissues of its host.

Parasympathetic nerves

Nerves involved in physiological processes that maintain normal body functions such as digestion and excretion; part of the autonomic division of the peripheral nervous system.

Pathogen

A disease-causing organism.

Pectoral girdle

The set of bones that connect and support the upper limbs; includes the shoulder blade (scapula) and collarbone (clavicle).

Pelvic girdle

The set of bones that form the pelvis and connect to and help support the lower limbs.

Perception

The process of becoming aware of, understanding and interpreting stimuli from sense organs.

Pericardium

The double-layered membrane that surrounds the heart and lines the pericardial cavity.

Peripheral nervous system

The nerves traveling into and out from the spinal cord and brain.

Peristalsis

Wave-like muscle contractions that move material through the digestive tract.

Ph scale

A scale used to measure the relative acidity of blood and other body fluids; it ranges from 0 (most acid) to 14 (most alkaline). A ph of 7 is considered neutral.

Phagocyte

A cell that can engulf and destroy matter such as foreign cells, dead body cells and other debris.

Pharynx

The throat.

Pheromone

A substance released from an exocrine gland that serves as a social communication signal between members of the same species.

Photoreceptor

A sensory receptor that responds to light energy, such as the rods and cones of the retina.

Pituitary gland

An endocrine gland in the brain that interacts with the hypothalamus to coordinate and control various physiological functions, including other endocrine glands.

Placenta

An organ that delivers nutrients to a developing fetus and carries away wastes. Its structure helps prevent the blood of mother and child from mixing.

Plasma

The fluid portion of the blood.

Plasma cell

A type of B cell that produces antibodies.

Platelets

Cell fragments in blood that function in blood clotting.

Pleural membrane

The double-layered serous membrane that encloses each lung and lines the adjacent surface of the chest cavity.

Polygenic trait

A trait that results from the influence of several genes.

Pons

The portion of the brain stem that links the medulla oblongata with the midbrain.

Positive feedback

A homeostatic mechanism that intensifies a change from an original condition. Intensifying labor contractions during childbirth are an example.

Prion

An infectious particle that consists of only protein.

Progesterone

A female sex hormone released from the ovaries that helps prepare the uterus for pregnancy.

Proprioreceptor

A sensory receptor involved in monitoring the position of body parts. Proprioreceptors are associated with joint, tendons and ligaments.

Prostaglandins communication

Chemicals that influence many body functions, for example smooth muscle contraction and blood pressure.

Prosthetic

An artificial body part, such as a joint or limb.

Puberty

The developmental stage during which a person matures sexually and secondary sex characteristics appear.

Pulmonary circuit

The route of blood circulation leading from the heart to the lungs and back to the heart.

Pulse

The rhythmic expansion and recoil of arteries as the heart pumps blood.

Purkinje fibers

Specialized muscle fibers that transmit contraction signals within the heart.

Reabsorption

In the kidneys, the process in which needed substances filtered from blood are returned to the bloodstream while urine is forming.

Receptor

A protein on or in a cell that is activated by a specific stimulus; sensory receptors are examples.

Recessive gene

A version of a gene that can be masked by a different, dominant version of the same gene. A trait governed by a recessive gene usually is seen only when a person inherits the gene from both parents.

Red marrow

The type of bone marrow in which blood cells form.

Reflex

An automatic response to a stimulus.

Releasing hormone

A hormone from the hypothalamus that signals the anterior pituitary to release one of its hormones.

Respiratory cycle

The automatic cycle of inhaling a breath, then exhaling.

Resting membrane potential

The electrical state (voltage) of a resting neuron's cell membrane.

Retina

The light-sensitive nerve tissue in the eye.

Rna

Ribonucleic acid; in human cells, genetic instructions in dna are converted into RNA, which then directly guides the cell's response.

Rods

Photoreceptors in the retina that respond mainly to dim light; rods contribute to night vision.

Sarcomeres

The contractile units of skeletal muscle fibers.

Sclera

The white, outer coating of the eyeball.

Secondary sexual characteristic

A trait such as beard growth or breast development that is associated with maleness or femaleness but is not directly involved in reproduction.

Secretion

In the kidneys, transport of unwanted substances from filtered blood into the forming urine.

Self marker

Molecules on body cells that identify those cells as a natural part of the body.

Semicircular canals

A set of three, fluid-filled canals in the inner ear that provide the sense of balance.

Semilunar valve

A half-moon-shaped heart valve that prevents blood pumped by the heart's left ventricle from flowing backward as it exits.

Sensation

The conscious awareness of a stimulus.

Senescence

The normal process of aging.

Sensory adaptation

In a sensory system, a process in which the firing of nerve impulses generated by receptors slows or stops even though the stimulus stays constant.

Sensory area

A region of the cerebral cortex that processes sensory information and produces a conscious sensory perception.

Sensory neuron

A neuron in the peripheral nervous system that carries impulses generated by sensory receptors.

Sensory receptor

A sensory cell or structure that can detect a particular stimulus, such as light, pressure or a chemical.

Serous membrane

A membrane lining a closed body cavity, such as a joint capsule. Also called a serosa.

Sex chromosome

An X or Y chromosome, which carries genes that determine an embryo's gender.

Sinoatrial (SA) node

A cluster of cells in the right atrium of the heart that initiates and helps regulate the heartbeat.

Skeletal muscle

The muscle tissue that attaches to bones and generally is under voluntary control.

Smooth muscle

The muscle tissue in the walls of internal organs; smooth muscle is not usually under conscious control.

Somatic senses

The "body" senses of touch, pressure, temperature and pain.

Somatosensory cortex

The brain region that processes signals coming from the skin, muscles and joints.

Spasm

The abrupt, involuntary contraction of one or more muscles.

Special senses

The senses of smell, taste, vision and hearing.

Sphincter

A ring of muscle that can contract and relax to control passage of substances through an opening.

Spleen

Organ that filters old blood cells and debris from the blood, stores excess blood cells, and contains infection-fighting white blood cells.

Static equilibrium

The balance sense that monitors the head's position with respect to gravity (the ground).

Stem cell

An unspecialized cell that can divide repeatedly and give rise to descendants that develop into specialized cells.

Stimulus

A form of energy, such as light or pressure, that activates a sensory receptor.

Suppressor gene

A gene with activity that inhibits other, generally cancer-causing, genes (oncogenes).

Sympathetic nerves

Part of the autonomic nervous system: nerves that operate to spur physiological processes such as heart rate in response to stress or excitement.

Synapse

The gap between nerve cells across which nerve impulses are transmitted (as by neurotransmitters).

Syndrome

A set of symptoms that collectively are characteristic of a disorder or disease.

Synovial joint

A joint with a fluid-filled cavity between the two linked bones. This type of joint allows for the most movement.

Systemic circuit

The cardiovascular circuit running between the heart and body tissues.

Systole

In the cardiac cycle, the period in which the heart chambers contract and pump blood out of the heart.

Tastant

A chemical that is detected by taste buds.

Taste buds

Chemoreceptors on the tongue and palate that provide the sense of taste.

T cell

A type of lymphocyte (white blood cell) that becomes specialized in the thymus and functions in specific immune responses.

Tendon

A strong, fibrous band of connective tissue that attaches skeletal muscle to bone.

Thalamus

The chief coordinating and relay center for sensory signals destined for the cerebral cortex. The thalamus is located in the forebrain.

Thermoreceptor

A sensory receptor that responds to changes in temperature.

Tissue

A combination of two or more types of cells and associated substances that collectively perform a single function.

Trachea

The windpipe.

Triglyceride

The most common form of fat in the blood. Triglycerides are the major form of stored fat in the body and are an important source of energy for metabolism.

Tumor

An abnormal mass of cells that may be benign or cancerous.

Urea

A waste product of protein metabolism that is excreted by the kidneys in urine.

Vasoconstriction

A reduction in the lumen (space) inside a blood vessel when muscle of the vessel wall contracts.

Vasodilation

An increase in the lumen (space) inside a blood vessel when the muscle of the vessel wall relaxes.

Vein

A blood vessel that carries deoxygenated blood from body tissues back to the heart.

Ventricle

Either of the two lower chambers of the heart, both of which pump blood.

Venule

A small vein that connects capillaries to larger veins.

Vestibular apparatus

A system of channels and sacs that form the organ of equilibrium (balance) in the inner ear.

Villus

Any of the tiny, fingerlike folds of mucosa, such as the mucous membrane lining the intestine. Villi absorb substances such as nutrients.

Visual cortex

The brain region that receives signals from the optic nerves.

Visual field

The entire area visible to the eye at a given moment, including peripheral vision.

White matter

Nerve tissue in spinal cord that has many myelinated axons. Unlike gray matter, white matter does not contain nerve cell bodies.

X chromosome

A sex chromosome with genes that cause an embryo to develop into a female, if the embryo receives one X from each parent.

Y chromosome

A sex chromosome with genes that cause an embryo to develop into a male.

Zygote

The first cell of a new individual, produced when a sperm fertilizes an egg.

INDEX

M

N

ACKNOWLEDGMENTS

The publisher would like to thank the following people for their assistance in the production of this book: Alex Bilsky, John Davis, Hunnah Jessup, Kathryn Morgan, Daniel Rausch, Maureen Shepherd, Kevin Sullivan, Juliana Titin.

PHOTOGRAPHS

Key t=top; l=left; r=right; tl=top left; tcl=top center left; tc=top center; tcr=top center right; tr=top right; cl=center left; c=center; cr=center right; b=bottom; bl=bottom left; bcl=bottom center left; bc=bottom center; bcr=bottom center right; br=bottom right

AAP = Australian Associated Press; Aus = Auscape International; BA = Bridgeman Art Library; CBT = Corbis; GI = Getty Images; iS = istockphoto.com; PUB = Public Domain; Reu = Reuters; SH = Shutterstock; SPL = Science Photo Library; PL = photolibrary.com.

5c TPL; 6bl, br, tc, tr TPL; tl CBT; 12bl, brc, lc, trc PL; r SPL; 13br, tr PL; c, tl SPL; bl PL; 18bl SPL; br, tr PL; 19br, tr PL; 20bl PL, tr CBT; 21tl PL, tr SPL; 22bl GI, r PL; 23br, r PL; rc SPL; tr GI; 24trc PL; 25l, tl CBT; tr GI; 26b, c SPL; c PL; 27brc GI; l, tr PL; 28bc, tr SPL; c PL; 30bl PL; br CBT; tr SPL; 31bl, br PL; trc SPL; 32bl, br, tr PL; 33bl PL; tr Reu; 34c CBT; tr SPL; 35bl, br, tl PL; 40blc PL; tr SH; 41tl SPL; 42bl, bl, l PL; 43br PL; 44br, lc, r, tr PL; 45c PL; 46bl, tr PL; 47tl SPL; tr PL; 49tr SPL; 50cr SPL; tl GI; 52bl, c PL; 54br GI; 56tr PL; 57c PL; 58bl GI; c PL; 59tr GI; 60bc GI; bl, tr SPL; 61b, tlc, tr SPL; 62br, tr SPL; lc GI; 63br, trc SPL; lc GI; 72b AAP; trc SPL; 73b PL; tl, tr GI; 74tl PL; 79brc GI; tr SPL; 82rc GI; 83rc SPL; 84bc AAP; 85tr PL; 86c AAP; lc SPL; 88bl, br CBT; lc, tr SH; 89c PL; 92br AAP; rc, tr PL; 93br GI; 94b CBT; 95bl, br, rc, tlc PL; 96bl CBT; br, t PL; 97bc, bl PL; 98bl, tr SPL; br PL; c GI; 101blc SPL; br, t GI; 102lc GI; tr CBT; 103c PL; 104lc CBT; 105bl CBT; 106bl, br, t PL; 107bl, tr CBT; br PL; 110bl PL; br SPL; c CBT; 112c PL; 114bl CBT; 115bl iS; tr SPL; 116bl, br GI; tr CBT; 118 SPL; bc GI; bl, tr PL; br CBT; 119tl GI; 120br SPL; lc CBT; 121bl, t CBT; br SPL; 122b SPL; tr GI; 123bc CBT; br PL; tr SPL; 126bl PL; c Mütter Museum/Robert Clark; lc SPL; 128b, lc PL; c SPL; 130bl, c, tr SPL; 132bc SPL; r GI; 133br, rc SPL; tr CBT; 134tr SPL; 135bl CBT; bl SPL; rc SH; 136bl, br SPL; 137bl CBT; r SPL; tr PL; 138bl PL; 139tr PL; 140bl SPL; br, c CBT; 141c PL; 142bl PL; 144lc PL; 145b, tr, tr CBT; 146br CBT; r SPL; 147bc GI; c SPL; 148b PL; trc SPL; 149bl SPL; trc CBT; 150bl GI; br CBT; c PL; 151c, tr SPL; 153tr SPL; 154bl GI; r SPL; 155br SPL; rc PL; tr CBT; 156bl, brc CBT; trc PL; 157b CBT; 158bc SPL; c CBT; 160br, l SPL; r SH; trc PL; 161bl, br, tl, tr PL; 162bl PL; br CBT; tr SPL; 164bl, brc SPL; tr PL; 165bl, tr SPL; 166tr PL; 167bl, t SPL; br GI; 168bl SPL; tr CBT; 169c PL; 170bl CBT; 171bl, br SPL; t CBT; 174bl, br SPL; tr CBT; 176lc SPL; 176tr PL; 177c SPL; 178bl SPL; 179tl, trc SPL; 180br, tr SPL; 182bl PL; 183br, tr SPL; r AAP; 184bl PL; br, tr SPL; 186bl SPL; r PL; 187blc CBT; br AAP; t SPL; 188blc CBT; 189b, c CBT; 190bl, br SPL; tr CBT; 191b, trc CBT; 192bl GI; 193bl SPL; tl, tr PL; 194c, tr PL; 195brc SPL; 196blc, c SPL; 197bl PL; br, c CBT; 198bl GI; br SPL; tr CBT; 200br Reu; brc SPL; tr PL; 202bl PL; blc, tr SPL; 203br, r SPL; 204b SPL; l PL; 205b GI; tr SPL; 208br, tr SPL; 210bl SPL; br, r PL; 211bl PL; br Aus; 212bl, r CBT; 213br CBT; 214bl SPL; br GI; 216b, tr SH; 217 PL; 218bl SPL; br PL; 219tl Michael Freeman; 220bl, r PL; trc CBT; 222blc CBT; tr SPL; 223br PL; tr GI; 224b CBT; trc SPL; 225br GI; l PL; 226bl AAP; br, c SPL; 227c SPL; 228b PL; trc SPL; 229br, t SPL; 231br PL; tr GI; 232br PL; tr SPL; 234bl, l PL; trc SPL; 235c PL; 237bl, br, tr SPL; 238bl, br SPL; 239br GI; tlc SPL; 240tr PL; 241br CBT; 242br CBT; c GI; 243t GI; 244br CBT; 245br, tr PL; 246tr CBT; 247tl PL; trc CBT; 248bl, tr PL; br SH; c iS; 249bl, br SH; blc iS; tl, tr CBT; 250r CBT; 251blc, t PL; br CBT; 252br CBT; tr PL; 253b SPL; br, trc PL; 254bl, tr PL; 255b, t PL; 256br, l SPL; tr CBT; 257brc SPL; 258bl, br PL; tr CBT; 259b SPL; 260b CBT; tr PL; 261b PL; c SPL; 262bl, r PL; 263bl PL; br, t CBT; 264br SPL; 264tr PL; 265br PL; 265tr GI; 266bl, tr CBT; 267bl, br, c CBT; 268bl SPL; brc, lc, tr PL; 269c PL; 272bc, rc PL; c, tr CBT; lc BA; tlc PUB; 273c CBT; l, lc, r, t PL; 274c, l, trc PL; r, tr CBT; 275c, lc, r PL; t, tl CBT; trc SPL.

ILLUSTRATIONS

Illustrations by **Argosy Publishing, www.argosypublishing.com**, with the exception of some additional illustrations:

Peter Bull Art Studio 50tr, 56b, 66tr, 76tl, 77c, 124bl, 130br, 170r, 173blc, 208bl, 217tlc, tr, 218tr, 226r; **Peter Bull Art Studio/Argosy Publishing** 240bl, br, 241bl, 242bl, blc, c, trc, 243l, br, 244bl, c, tr, 245tl; **Andrew Davies/Creative Communication** 109bl, 113b.

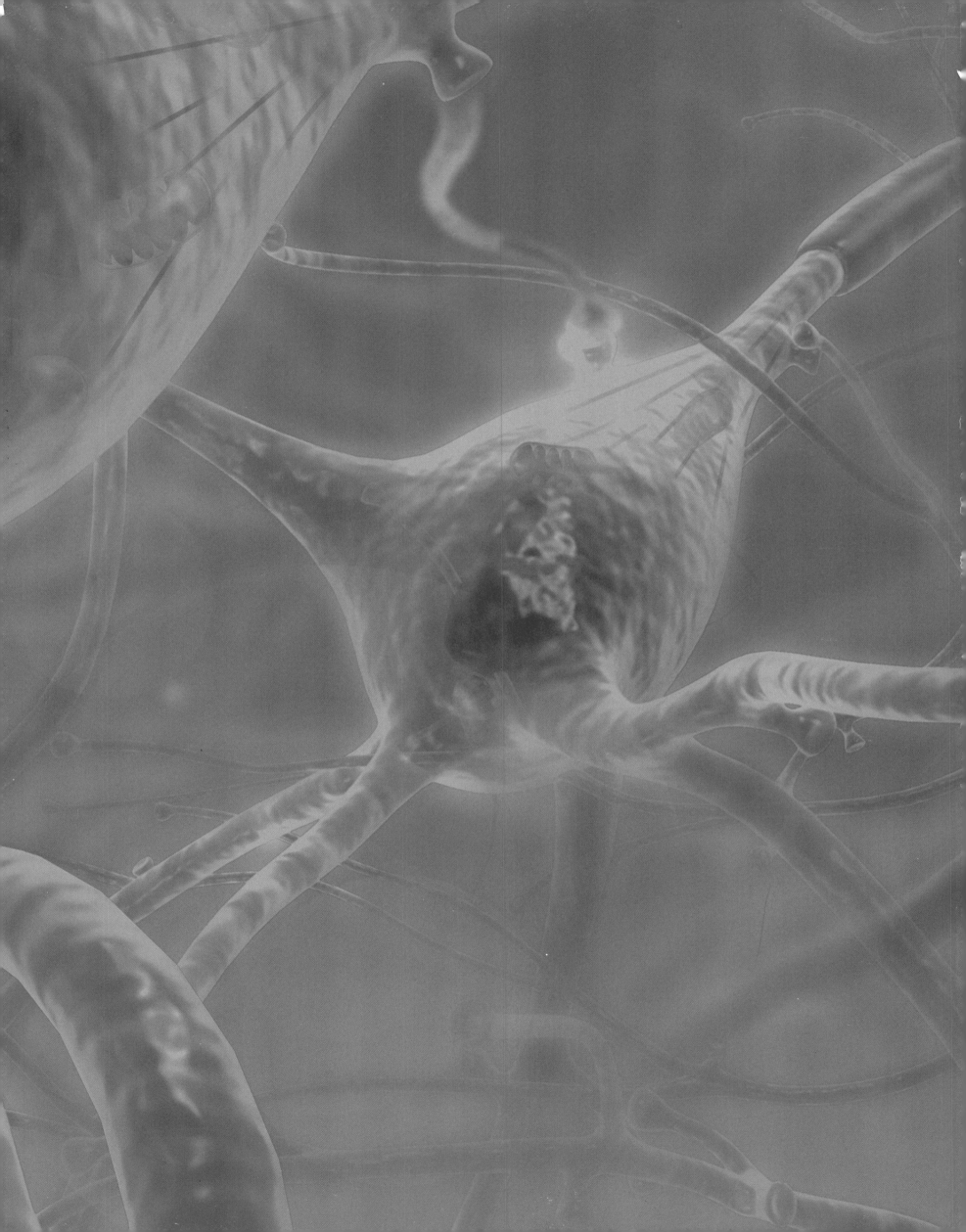